DISCARD

JANET CARRUTHERS

The Forest
is my Kingdom

Illustrated by

P. A. JOBSON

London

OXFORD UNIVERSITY PRESS

Oxford University Press, Ely House, London W. 1

GLASGOW NEW YORK TORONTO MELBOURNE WELLINGTON
CAPE TOWN SALISBURY IBADAN NAIROBI LUSAKA ADDIS ABABA
BOMBAY CALCUTTA MADRAS KARACHI LAHORE DACCA
KUALA LUMPUR SINGAPORE HONG KONG TOKYO

First edition 1952
First issued in this edition 1958
Reprinted 1968

Printed in Great Britain by Richard Clay (The Chaucer Press), Ltd.,
Bungay, Suffolk

The Forest is my Kingdom

Contents

CONTENTS   vii

Chapter 1

SEEGWUN

It was springtime on the Lake of the Woods. Freshets leaped and danced through the forests by its shores.

Bari Bradbrooke loved spring. It brought something delightful to this northland: green-growing things waking from winter's sleep; soft sunshine; pink, blue flower-faces peeping from hooded coats. Bari was only nine, but all the joy and mystery of the forest land was in his blood. Along the cedar hollow he went racing the rivulets that plunged downward to the lake.

Beyond the tree-line a lazy smoke was rising from the cabins cupped between the shores of the distant Point. That was their village. The people who lived in it were half-breed Indians, and so were Bari's folks. But their cabin stood alone on the shoulder of the hill.

Fifty miles away there was a town from which a fish-boat came twice a week in summer bringing mail, groceries, and an odd passenger, and taking back fish and hides; for the Indians made a living mostly by fishing and trapping.

Bari didn't like that way of life. There was something within him kin to the creatures of the woods. When he came to understand that their life had to be taken so that folks might have food and clothes, his spirit rebelled. Tearfully, he questioned his stepfather, who turned to him with a shocked expression in his eyes and said, 'We gotta eat, ain't we? Some day you'll learn, son!'

Faith in his stepfather had to suffice, but clenching his fists Bari had vowed secretly to himself that he would seek a way of living from the lovely things of the woods, a way that would bring no hurt or harm to the creatures he loved.

Over in the village there were other children, but Bari had never been drawn to them. They didn't like the things he liked nor did they join him in his wanderings through the deeper bush.

His mother told him stories of far places and people, but forest life satisfied him. In his heart he dreamed dreams about trees, flowers and fur-folks, and with a burnt stick tried to make pictures of them on scraps of paper. When his mother bought him pencil and scribbler his joy was complete.

Over happy trails he went, whispering sometimes in his own quiet way, 'Woods tell me your stories in pictures', and the woods answered, for Bari had a busy mind and apt fingers.

His stepfather, a big brusque fellow with a rugged frame, lived entirely for money. He wasn't keen on Bari's drawing. 'Idling yer time!' he said crisply, when he caught him. 'Ye're big enough now to be workin'.' So Bari kept his doings to himself and to the woods.

He was heading now for a spruce on the opposite bank. He stopped to listen. The sound of water was everywhere. Then above the eddying swirl at his feet he heard movements, a tiny squeak. Vaulting a rock, he saw a tiny musk-rat caught in a trap. A bound took him over the flooded shore. He released the creature, but a front foot was left in the steel jaws. An eye was injured. It was a silky furry thing. He stroked it as it lay trembling in the palm of his hand. 'You're only a baby rat,' he whispered, eyes wet with tears, 'but I love you an' I won't leave you when you're hurted.'

Ripping a piece of cloth from his shirt he bound the footless leg. Then holding the little creature to his face he added, 'I'll keep you myself. I'll call you Seegwun because it's spring, and I love spring and you too.' He tucked it gently between his shirt and breast.

'Bari! Bari!'

Clutching the rat tight, Bari peered over the rock. Again his father's call, 'Bari! Bari! Where are you?' came over the snow-filled valley. Tucking the rat's head tight beneath his chin Bari crouched lower into his hiding-place. If his father found him he'd have to leave Seegwun, for his father would likely kill her. He could feel the little creature's beating heart as it snuggled, quivering, to the warmth of his breast.

The sharp creak of a sleigh sounded on the snow beyond the ridge. Peeking up, Bari saw his stepfather turning his dog team and sleigh to their cabin door. The dogs were strung out, cowering beneath a lash

Bradbrooke was swinging. Bari could see his mother scurry from the house with blankets and pans.

Then Bari remembered: this was the day his father and mother were going south to another trapping-ground. They were leaving now.

As Bari watched, a man came walking from a fringe of jackpine towards them. Bari knew him. He was Paddy Lindrum, who lived alone at the end of the tamarack valley. He had come sometimes to help his mother draw up her fish catch and to help fix the roof of the house when it leaked. He was a short squat fellow, and he had happy eyes and a gentle voice. Deep lines criss-crossed his face, for he was always smiling.

'Did you see Bari?' Bari could hear his mother asking, as she ran to meet him. Bari didn't hear Lindrum's answer, but they both turned and looked towards the bush.

Bradbrooke's voice rose sharply. 'We ain't waitin' for him. We shoulda bin gone before now. Sleddin' ain't easy when the sun's ahead. The kid knew we were goin'.'

Bari bit his lip. Brad was in one of his tempers. He got that way sometimes when things didn't go well. Between the rocks, Bari could see him walking back and forth, then, pushing his cap back clear of his eyes, he swung his lash. Tut, the lead dog, drew back for the start, his tackle lifted. They were off! Racing back, Bari's mother leaped to the moving sleigh and threw a bundle off to Paddy. The toboggan went whirling across the melting snow.

Bari watched till the sleigh turned the farthest point of jackpine. A sob rose in his throat. His mother had left him! A stab of pain struck at his heart, then he brightened. He knew where Brad and his mother were going. As soon as Seegwun was better he'd follow. It would be fun living in the bush. He had always wanted to do that. A stirring sense of adventure surged through him. He knew every trail, every tree by name, every sag and twist winding the forest's heart.

Holding the rat tight, he rose and went back to the trap. Picking up the foot that lay beside it, he looked at it. The skin was off. The claws were broken, but maybe it could be put back on. He turned it over and over in his hand. Once his mother had sewed a dog's leg, but she wasn't here now. Alone he could do nothing. Tearing another strip from his shirt he wrapped and shoved the foot beneath the bank, then continued his journey to the spruce.

It was a large tree with heavy bark and shelving branches. He liked them because sweeping low they hid him almost completely, yet they afforded a good view of lake and land as he sat, mind and fingers busy with the things that pleased him. In this spruce's arms he kept his secrets—the things he treasured. Every day he came to this hide-away.

From a cleft in one of its branches he took a piece of paper and pencil stub and sat down and began to draw. He pushed the pencil up and down slowly. He had lots of time. He was free! The thought thrilled him.

Suddenly a flock of cawing crows flew from the trees by the shore. Looking up Bari saw a boat nosing up-channel between the ice and land. It was the Mounties'. They came up sometimes at this time of the year to look for poachers. Bari watched till it slid between the Points at the bay's end, then went on with his drawing, stopping now and again to put his hand behind his shirt and touch the rat. It was warm. He could feel the gentle up-and-down movements of its breathing. A strange feeling was beginning to grow inside himself. It wasn't loneliness, nor anxiety about food or where he'd sleep. His stepfather had taught him how to live in the bush. It was an emptiness he couldn't explain.

There was a step and a shadow fell across his shoulder. Shoving pencil and paper into his pocket he clutched the rat and jumped to his feet. Paddy Lindrum was standing on a rock above, looking at him.

With one swift spring Bari cleared the bank, running and leaping water and ice until he reached heavy bush on the far side of the bay. Breathless and shaking he looked back. He could see Lindrum examine the ground around the rat-trap, walk to the spruce and poke amongst the branches. Bari's heart leaped. Was Lindrum going to find his treasures, the drawings and paper and things his mother had given him? A spark of anger kindled in him. That place was his! Leaning against a tree he kept his eyes on Lindrum's every move.

The rat stirred and whimpered. Pulling it from behind his shirt, Bari stroked it. The cloth on its foot was wet with blood. He took it off, ripped another piece from his shirt and re-bound the foot. The rat didn't like it and snatched at him with her teeth. He put her back between his shirt and body where she snuggled quietly down.

He was shivering with cold himself. His trousers soaked with splashing water were hardening like icy boards against his legs. The pieces of cloth he had torn from his shirt-tail let the wind into his side. He walked up and down, keeping an eye across the bay. Finally he lost sight of Lindrum. Likely he had gone home.

Bari wondered if he had found the drawings and papers and things in the tree. The thought sent Bari back across the ice. He walked quickly, watching every fluttering twig or slip of snow. When he reached the path into his hide-away he stopped and looked in every direction before dashing across the bank to his tree.

Lindrum's footmarks were all around; he had walked to the edge of the lake then straight to a point beneath where Bari kept his treasures in the trees. Bari held his breath.

Bounding over, he dived his hand into the cleft between the branches and drew out pieces of paper and bark that he had made drawings on, then some shiny stones and an empty snuff-box. Yes, they were all there, the things he had gathered and kept secret. He was especially glad about the paper. It was part of a calendar. He liked it because it was stiff and easy to draw on. He pushed the things carefully back.

' Bari! '

Paddy Lindrum was at his side.

Pushing the rat well under his arm, Bari edged round the tree. ' Go 'way! Go 'way! I don't want you,' he said, his voice trembling. He wasn't afraid of Lindrum. It was the tiny creature at his breast he was thinking of.

'Your mother said for me to get you an' take you home an' take care of you, Bari.'

Bari's throat tightened. The rat squirmed.

'What happened to the rat you got there in your shirt?' Lindrum went on, bringing his brows together curiously.

'It got hurted in a trap over there.' Bari pointed east, hoping to turn Lindrum's attention.

'Let me see it,' Paddy coaxed, reaching for the animal.

Bari stepped back, bristling with fight.

'Maybe we can fix it up an' help it,' Lindrum continued, rubbing his hands together thoughtfully, 'maybe it ain't so hurt.'

The crinkles in his face seemed to smooth out as he spoke, his voice was gentle.

Pulling the rat from behind his shirt, Bari held it up guardedly.

'It's been trapped all right, but it looks pretty lively,' Paddy said, reaching over and stroking it.

'The foot's off an' it's bleeded a lot.'

'If you took the rag off an' left the foot bare it would heal quicker.' Paddy tapped the tree slowly with his hand before he added, 'Better let it go. Sun and water are good medicine.'

'I call it Seegwun,' Bari said, backing towards the bank. 'I love it, I think it knows me now.' He pushed the rat back within his shirt.

'You come along with me an' bring Seegwun. Me an' you'll look after her. She'll be all right you'll see, but she's got to be fed if you're aimin' to keep her.'

Bari didn't move. Something in the eyes of the man

who was looking at him held him. 'You said she'd get
better, eh?'

Paddy nodded. 'But it's too cold out here for you,
you're shivering now,' Paddy went on, pointing to the
hole in his shirt. 'Your mother said to tell you just to
come and live with me. I figgered you'd like it.
Come on, Bari.' Paddy stepped forward.

For one second Bari stood, then turning, fled the bank
like a shot-at deer, his loud, 'No!' rising above the
splash of his flying feet. He stopped on the first ridge.
Let Seegwun go! Never! That's what Brad would
have wanted him to do too, that is, if he hadn't eaten
her. No. He would stay with her until her feet were
better.

When he looked back Lindrum was hurrying through
the bush. Bari felt relieved. He sat down and tried to
think things out. Take the rag off the rat's foot. No,
he wouldn't do that either. But Paddy said it would
heal quicker if it was bare. Did he mean another foot
might grow?

One thing he would do: he'd move his paper and
pencil and things from the spruce and put them where
Paddy wouldn't know. It didn't take long to find a
pine with knobby arms. A woodpecker had drilled a
cunning hole in the trunk, just big enough to let Bari's
hand in. He could feel the bottom. He brought his
papers and things and put them in.

Then scouting round for a dry spot he sat down.
The air was crisp and there was an icy wind. Drawing
his shirt tight, he huddled close to a tree. The rat was
sleeping. The arm the rat was resting on was growing
numb, and Bari was tired and hungry. He'd stay here

until dark.   But the sun seemed to be taking a long time to move west.

Suddenly he started.   He had been dozing.   There were movements behind.   He jumped to his feet.

It was night.   A baby moon was peeping through the jackpine.   Stars twinkled over the valley.   It was very cold.

His first thought was his pine.   Racing over he stuck his hand in the opening.   His fingers closed on something soft.   He drew it out.   It was a chunk of bannock. Bari loved bannock.   Many times he had helped his mother mix flour, water and baking-powder in a bowl then cut the doughy mass into cakes and bake them over the fire.   He bit swiftly into it till his mouth was full, then he laid it on a branch and poked his hand back into the hole.   He drew out paper and a pencil— a big red one.   It was new.   Bari could scarcely believe his eyes.   He rolled it against his cheek to see if it was real.

' Bari ! '

Bari jumped.

Paddy Lindrum was at his side holding out a pair of socks.   ' Your mother sent these for you to wear, Bari.'

' Brad says I don't need socks when spring comes.'

' Your mother made them, Bari.   They're good an' warm, an' that paper's for you to draw on.   I got it for you from the Mountie—he's back there in the bay.'

Fear clutched Bari.   Why was Lindrum doing this? Was he trying to snare him an' Seegwun?   And the Mountie, what had he to do with it?   He didn't like Mounties.   Tears came to his eyes.

' Come on, Bari, you'll get lots to eat an' I'll get you

more paper an' things. Me an' you'll have a good time.'

Bari looked at him. His twinkling eyes were gentle and the taste of bannock was still in Bari's mouth. Seegwun pushed her head up. ' I ain't leavin' Seegwun.'

' Well, bring her with you. We'll look after her. I guess she's pretty weak or she'd be movin' around a heap more.'

Bari didn't know what to think. Was Paddy bluffing, just saying nice things? The rat was squirming and digging its claws into his chest. Maybe it was hungry.

' I'll help you take care of it,' Paddy went on, holding out his hand.

' Do you like rats? Brad didn't. He'd kill an' eat it an' sell its hide for money.' Bari tried to speak bravely, but a sob came to his throat.

' Sure I like rats. There ain't any around my place.'

' 'Cos you've killed them off, eh? '

Paddy laughed. ' No, it ain't just natural for them to have been there yet.'

Bari kept looking at him. ' You'll let me make pictures if I go? '

Paddy nodded.

Bari hesitated another moment, then reaching for his bannock from the tree he walked over and took Paddy's hand. It closed warm and friendly on his numb fingers.

' I'll carry the rat, so's you can eat your bread,' Paddy offered.

' No, I'll get along all right.' Bari tucked the rat tighter beneath his arm. Every bite of bannock was making him feel better.

They walked without speaking. It was cold, but the sky was clear. At every ridge Bari stopped and looked back. He had felt safe in that spruce's quiet shade; happy in that corner of the forest. Its trees had helped to mother him. With them he had shared his secrets.

'Can I come back here if I want to?' he asked, pushing the last piece of bannock into his mouth.

'Sure, you kin go any place you like, long's you don't get drownded or froze.'

'An' you won't make me go to Brad until the rat's better?' Bari went on, encouraged by Paddy's voice.

'No, you're goin' to stay with me.'

'I know your place; there's nuts back of it there, an' I like the tamaracks. My mother said they were dressed an' was neat like little ladies. You see she teached me to love the trees, to talk to them. She said they were kind and good an' lived just the same's me an' you.'

'That's right and mighty nice livin' they be doin' too.' Paddy's hand closed tighter on his. 'It's a great time me an' you's goin' to be havin' makin' pictures, bakin' bannock, an' raisin' Seegwun.' Paddy's voice was happy.

Bari quickened his pace. He was tired. He could scarcely make the lift of the valley. He was glad when they turned the next corner and saw the light in Paddy's window. It seemed an age before they reached the house.

When Paddy opened the door a rush of warmth met them. The rat struggled and dug into Bari's chest, but he held tight.

'Lie down there.' Paddy pointed to a cot in the

corner. 'I guess you'll have to keep the rat with you for now.'

Bari did as he was told. The rat fought a few minutes then snuggled back against his arm.

Paddy took off Bari's moccasins, rubbed his feet, then threw a blanket over him. He fell asleep at once.

When he opened his eyes it was full daylight. The place was very warm, and he saw Paddy was standing by the stove. Bari felt for his rat. It was still by his side.

Hearing the movements, Paddy swung round. 'You've waked, eh?'

Bari raised himself to a sitting position. 'Can I get up now?'

'Sure, I've eats ready for you. Sit down over here.' Paddy set a mug of coffee and a plate of bannock at the end of the table. 'Bring the rat with you. We'll look after it later.'

Bari got up, pushed a stool over to the table, and began to eat. He was very hungry.

Suddenly he heard a step on the path outside. Bari shot a glance at the window, the door opened and Bradbrooke walked in.

Paddy stepped forward.

Clutching Seegwun tight, Bari dodged behind Paddy.

Bradbrooke glared at him. 'I cum fer you, Bari. Get on your moccasins.'

Chapter II

PADDY

The tone of Bradbrooke's voice meant trouble. He was in one of his tempers. Bari knew it. Slipping in front of Paddy, he stood squarely between them. He wasn't afraid of Bradbrooke, but he didn't want him to go nasty with Paddy.

'The boy's going to stay with me,' Paddy said, laying his hand on Bari's shoulder.

'His mother sent for him!' Bradbrooke's voice rose meaningly.

Bari clutched his rat tighter. There was fire in Bradbrooke's eyes.

'Get your moccasins!' he shouted, taking a step closer. 'Ha! an' you got a musk-rat there, yer allus mussin' around with some critter.'

Bari backed towards the cupboard. 'I don't want to go with you, not just now.' Bradbrooke's jaw set. Bari knew he had said the wrong thing.

Face reddening with anger, Bradbrooke lunged forward and snatched the rat. 'If you come with me you can keep her—if you don't,' he paused threateningly, 'she'll make good stew.'

Paddy wheeled. 'Don't take the boy, Bradbrooke, leave him with me. I'll look after him.' Paddy spoke coaxingly.

Bradbrooke turned, his eyes flashing. 'You mind your own business, Paddy Lindrum. When I need your help I'll ask for it. I cum fer the kid an' I'm takin' him!' Clutching Bari by the shoulder he forced him out through the doorway. 'You get goin'. Don't you know enough to cum when yer told?'

Swift protesting words leaped to Bari's lips, but he didn't speak. Outside, Bradbrooke handed him Seegwun. 'Here, take it, but remember what I tol' you.'

Struggling to keep tears from his eyes, Bari shoved her behind his shirt again. Now his chance for freedom was gone! His chance to stay in the woods and draw! The scowl on Bradbrooke's face didn't invite pleading.

When they reached the bush trail, he picked up courage to say, 'My mother told Paddy Lindrum I could stay with him for a visit.' He had added 'for a visit' his heart pounding with hope.

Lowering a pair of fiery eyes Bradbrooke snapped, 'Yer mother didn't say no such thing! Besides there's work fer you to do; an' looka here,' he added, stopping short on the trail to point a dark quivering finger at Bari's nose, 'there's to be no more of this 'ere scribblin' an' drawin'. Yer old enough now to be doin' somethin' worthwhile, not just a-sittin' around in the bush.'

Bari nodded numbly. He had never seen Bradbrooke quite so cross before. Something inside him rebelled. Now he wouldn't even get back to his tree for his papers and things. They walked quickly, turning up a trail that led back from the shore. Bari swallowed a sob, though the thought of seeing his mother soon cheered him. She'd take care of Seegwun and find a way for him to draw.

The next time he looked up at Bradbrooke he saw that beads of sweat were standing out on his face. His eyes were red. He looked troubled. 'Will you let me keep my rat till it grows up?' he ventured to ask.

Bradbrooke's brows narrowed. 'You know I don't hold with keepin' rats, except fer their hide or to make a pot of stew, but you can if——'

There was a crackling of twigs. Bradbrooke stopped and threw up his head like a startled bear, then grasping Bari by the arm said, 'Hurry! We gotta make the next hill!' Plunging down a snow-filled valley they made for a clearing on the far bank. It was very cold. Bari's moccasins, ripped by sharp ice, let the water in to his feet, but clinging to his rat he hurried forward. Just as they reached the top, two men stepped from a clump of poplars on the hill above.

It was Paddy and another man. Bari's heart leaped with joy. But Bradbrooke stopped, then drawing Bari sharply to the right said, 'Come this way! Them fellah's don't mean no good.'

When they reached denser bush they stopped and listened. There wasn't a sound but the tinkle of water and the drip, drip of the freshening from the poplars behind.

Bradbrooke strode on. Bari could hardly keep up. They were getting deeper and deeper into the forest. Bari couldn't understand. 'Why are we going this way?' he asked, stopping for breath.

'Don't ask, hurry!' Bradbrooke answered, reaching for his hand.

There was a rustling of twigs, branches parted, and Paddy stepped out on to the trail. There was a stranger with him, a white man. He was coatless and hatless, but wore tight breeches and clinking shoes.

Glancing momentarily at Paddy, Bari fixed his eyes on the stranger, who came straight towards him with a smile. 'It was you I came for. I saw your mother last night. She asked me to see that you got to Paddy Lindrum's. She said you were out in the bush when she left.' Drawing a notebook from his hip pocket the stranger went on, 'I've got it down here.' He tapped the book lightly.

A surge of joy swept through Bari. He looked at Bradbrooke, then back at the stranger. 'You mean I can stay with Paddy an'——'

'This boy's mine!' Bradbrooke interrupted, stepping forward. 'It's me that looks after him! Keeps him!'

'I know,' the stranger smiled, 'but you're coming with me. Beaudette's giving her boy into Lindrum's keeping meantime. She'll pick him up later.' The man tapped his book again. 'Better come along.'

Bradbrooke scowled. 'What yer want me for? I ain't done nothin'.'

Pushing the notebook back into his hip pocket, the stranger smiled. 'We'll settle that later.' He turned to

Paddy and added, ' Take the youngster and go on home. Keep him until his mother comes for him or until I tell you different.' Taking Bradbrooke by the arm, he turned back along the trail.

One moment Bari stood trembling, dazed. He was free! Free again! Bounding over he took hold of Paddy's sleeve. ' I'm stayin'—stayin' with you! '

Shaking him off, Paddy started up the trail. ' Wait there a minute, I want to catch up with Hyslop.'

Hyslop! That man must be Hyslop. But who was he? Bari tried to think as his eyes followed Paddy along the trail to the man by Bradbrooke's side.

He was a handsome fellow, with a wind-blown woodsy air. His movements were easy. There was an aliveness about his face and eyes. A glint of sunlight falling through the trees gave a glow to his honey-coloured hair; and his chest, bare between the open fronts of his shirt, was white and fair, much fairer than Bari was accustomed to seeing.

Bari couldn't hear what Paddy said when he caught up with him, but the stranger's answer was plain. ' Bradbrooke's got to keep the law. We've warned him a couple of times about this monkey business with his fish, but he doesn't do what he's told.' With a come-on gesture to Bradbrooke he added, ' He won't be long away. You take care of the youngster! '

Bradbrooke straightened, shrugged his shoulders indifferently, then lifting his hand for good-bye, started off down the trail with Hyslop. But who was Hyslop?

Paddy answered the question when he came back. ' That's Peter Hyslop, the Mountie.'

' Mountie! ' Bari gasped. ' He didn't look like a

Mountie. I don't like Mounties! Brad's tol' me lots of things about them. They don't do no good to us.'

He remembered how a Mountie had come and taken Brad away once or twice before. He had said he was trapping or fishing out of season; likely he had been doing something like that again.

'Brad's bin' robbin' Dave Dakin's traps,' Paddy explained, reaching for his hand. By the time Bari got to the first clearing he had forgotten about the Mountie. The bounding joy of freedom was sweet. He looked up into Paddy's wrinkled face. 'I love livin' with birds an' trees an' things, Paddy. I tol' you already, eh? Well, I'll draw them an' make pictures of them for you now.' He squeezed Paddy's hand to emphasize his promise. Drawing pictures would be his way of saying 'Thank you'.

Paddy's eyes twinkled. 'There'll be lots for me an' you to do when we get goin', Bari.'

The rat stirred and clawed at Bari's breast. It had been sleeping. Taking it out, Bari stroked it. Its eyes were closed. It hardly moved. 'Look Paddy, it's awful quiet,' Bari said anxiously.

'It's hungry. It needs eats an' water. We'll feed it soon's we get home.'

Putting it back in his shirt, Bari took Paddy's outstretched hand. He was very tired. In places the snow was deep, but every step was lightened with hope of the days that were coming.

The sun was well behind the tamaracks when they reached Paddy's cabin. It looked good to Bari, nestling amongst the cedars with the blue shadows of the on-coming night folding about it.

Paddy halted a moment by the shore to strip a piece of bark from a willow. Then he hurried into the house, dropped the bark into a dish of water and handed it to Bari. 'Here, that's for Seegwun. She can eat, can't she?'

Flopping on to the cot Bari drew the rat into his arms, took the dish and held it in front of her. She dived into it, head and shoulders.

'She likes that,' Paddy said, watching, 'an' she knows how to eat all right. Has she et since you got her?'

Bari nodded. 'I fed her flag root, an' teached her.' He added, grinning, 'I'm goin' to draw pictures of her.'

'You're mighty smart to have kept her alive. She don't see so good in that one eye, but it'll come all right.' Paddy stooped and stroked the sleek brown body which was wriggling and struggling to get completely into the dish of water. 'Her scent'll be sharp. She'll smell a heap better than most of them. Critters like that make out if they get a chance.'

Bari smiled. There was something comforting in Paddy's voice and words. Bari was glad that his pet would live. He'd see that it had a chance. He would defend and protect it against all odds.

He was tired now and he could scarcely keep his eyes open. His body was aching. The dish he held quivered in his hand. Dimly he could see Paddy light a lamp, then go over and shake cat-tail fluff from a sack into a pail and set it behind the door. 'That's a bed for her; it'll do for now until she can go outside.'

Bari heard no more. He was vaguely aware of a dish being taken from his hands. His eyes were closing.

He could feel covers being pulled over him and then Paddy's voice trailed off into the distance.

When he awoke it was daylight. He sat up with a start. A trickle of sunlight came through the window and was dancing on the opposite wall. Where was he? Whose place was this? Pushing his hair from his face, he rubbed his eyes. Then he remembered, and in his confused head, yesterday's doings gradually became clear. He was in Paddy Lindrum's house again. Bradbrooke had come and taken him. There had been trouble. Paddy and a Mountie had caught up with them. Yes, a Mountie. A tiny tremor swept him at the thought—but the Mountie had taken Bradbrooke with him, and let Paddy bring him and the rat here. But where was Seegwun?

He looked over at the pail behind the door. He could see her nose sticking up through the fluff. Over in the other corner Paddy was sleeping on a blanket on the floor.

Bari looked round. The place wasn't like Brad's. The logs were smoother, tighter. Daylight didn't come through. The window didn't have holes in the glass. There was a big chair made with deer antlers in the corner, and a table and stove close by the wall. The place was neat and warm. But why was he here?

His thoughts shot to his mother. Where was she? Why had she sent the Mountie to look for him? Where could she be now there was no Brad to look after her?

Bari felt his chest tightening and a hollowness was creeping up into his stomach. His mother would be alone. Why hadn't he thought of that before? He wanted her, wanted to be with her.

He looked over at Paddy. He was lying very still. His hair was tousled over his face and his mouth was open. He was making a strange rickety sound like a frog. Maybe Paddy was very good and maybe he was kind, but that didn't make any difference. He wanted his mother.

Pulling his feet out from beneath the covers, Bari set them quietly on the floor. Easing himself from the bed he moved quietly to the window. Shafts of sunlight were slanting through the pine. There was a glitter of frost on the twigs. Along the valley the trees stood like chiefs with great blankets pulled about them. At the edge of Paddy's clearing the trail forked, one to wind off along the lake shore to the distant houses, the other to lose itself in the green shade of spruce trees flanking the shore. That was the one he would take. He was going now.

He looked at Paddy, then at the door. It was latched. Seegwun's pail was behind it. He could easily lift her and slip out without Paddy hearing. Paddy was all right, but after all there was nobody like his mother. He didn't feel like this yesterday, but to-day was different.

Keeping an eye on the pail, he moved step by step round the wall and reached for the door latch.

Paddy moved. His hand shot up.

Bari leaped to his cot and pulled up the covers. Shaking from head to foot he listened. There wasn't a sound but the gurgle of Paddy's breathing. Bari peeked out guardedly. Paddy was still sleeping. Bari smiled. Why should he be afraid? He wasn't doing anything wrong. If Paddy woke he'd just tell him he

was going to find his mother.   The thought encouraged
him.

Easing back the covers again he slipped across to the
window; the frost-furred twiggery on the bush trail
was waving gently. It was calling just as the wind
called to him when he was lonesome.

His legs shook. He took a couple of steps, then two
more and another, watching every breath Paddy drew.
He reached one hand for the pail and another to the
door latch.

The door shook, the pail clattered to its side and
rolled towards the stove. Seegwun dashed under the
cupboard. Every timber in the place seemed to shake.
One trembling second Bari stood, as if the house was
coming down about him, then scooting beneath the
table he clutched for the rat. He rose bristling with
fear to look at Paddy who had sat up, his eyes startled.

Chapter III

FREEDOM

Holding the rat tightly, Bari backed towards his bed.
'It's too hot in here. I don't like it.' His voice was
tense.

Paddy smiled, pushed a strand of hair from his eyes
then jumped to his feet and opened the window at the
end of his bed. 'Is that better—cooler? Didn't you
sleep good?' There was deep kindliness in his voice
and eyes.

Bari shook his head. 'I don't like sleepin' indoors.
I want to go to my mother now.' He added the last
with a spurt of courage. His first explanation sounded
unreal even to himself.

Paddy's brows came together quizzically. 'Don't you
like it here, Bari? I'm aimin' to make it nice for you.
Get you the things you'd like.' Paddy went on
haltingly, with a hand-wave towards the cupboard, 'I
got lots of eats!'

A touch of shame swept through Bari. Dropping
his eyes to Seegwun, he ran his fingers back and forth
through her fur. What could he say? How could he
make Paddy understand this loneliness that had come
pounding at his heart, the longing to see his mother,
his love of freedom? It was a long minute before he
found words. 'I want to go to my mother, Paddy. I
want to see her, please. Seegwun won't live here inside
a house, Paddy; she'll die. Please let me go, Paddy.'
He put all the longing of his aching heart into his
pleading as he brought his eyes to rest on Paddy's face.

Paddy didn't answer. But lifting Seegwun's pail he
set it at Bari's feet. 'She liked her bed all right last
night, see?' he pointed to the dent her sleeping body
had made in the fluff. 'After we eat we'll take her out
an' put her in the waterhole. I'll fix a place for her.'
He took the rat from Bari's arms and set her in the pail.

Bari's lip quivered. Tears came burning into his
eyes. What did Paddy mean? Was he going to set
Seegwun free?

'You said you'd help me keep her. Seegwun don't
know nothin' yet, nothin' about here. My mother
would let me keep her if you'd just let me go. When
Brad ain't with her it's different. She'd like Seegwun
an'—an'—an'——' Stopping to steady his voice, Bari
wiped his face with his sleeve then added, 'I'll come
back if you want me to later, just let me go now.'
His words died to a sob.

Paddy didn't move. He had taken a stand behind a
chair barring the doorway. He tapped his fingers on
its back as if he wasn't sure what to say. When he
spoke his voice was low and even.

B

'Don't you fret yourself, son, you'll be all right here. You can draw all the pictures you want an' make all the other things you want, too. There ain't nothin' to stop you. Just set on the bed there till I light the fire an' get something to eat, then me an' you'll have a good time.'

Bari slipped back on to his cot. He watched him take the stove lid off, put wood in the fire and light it, then ladle water from a pail into the kettle. Paddy hadn't taken his clothes off during the night. His jacket was crumpled, its collar turned in at the neck. His hair was tousled and long, but there was a hint of laughter in his face as he came back and sat down on the end of the cot.

'I'm goin' to like havin' you, Bari. It's goin' to be great fer me. I won't be so lonesome. Sometimes I got nobody to talk to, just the wood-folks like Seegwun an' the trees an'——'

'But I don't want to stay here just now, not until I've seen my mother, Paddy.'

Paddy moved closer. 'Bari, your mother's gone a different place than she figgered. She was scared you'd follow an' get lost, that's the way she asked Hyslop to look fer you.'

'Hyslop! A Mountie! I don't like him—not yet,' Bari added, seeing the hurt look come to Paddy's face.

'Peter Hyslop's a fine fellah, Bari. I guided, packed for him half-a-dozen winters,' Paddy went on. 'Once when he was a green Mountie he got lost in a blizzard an' nearly froze. I found him an' brought him here.' Paddy's face glowed as if the memory had brought sunshine to his heart. 'Me an' him's good friends. He came across the bay yesterday to tell me about you; I got the pencil an' paper from him, see—I got some left.' He drew some pieces of writing-paper and a couple of pencils from his pocket. 'Here,' and he handed them to Bari.

Bari took them. The pencils were new. The paper was clean and white. Bari was pleased. New pencils and paper had rarely come his way before.

Paddy rose, put water and coffee in a pot and set it on the stove. 'Me an' you's got lots of things to do. You're goin' to make pictures an' we gotta fix a place for Seegwun. Yah, it's great times we'll be havin',' he kept talking as he set dishes out on the table, 'warmin' our feet at the camp-fire, shadowin' fur-folks in the Hunter's Moon.'

Bari felt better. The way Paddy said things sounded good. It gave him a friendly feeling, a reminder of the things he liked.

'Here's somethin' for your feet.' Paddy reached behind the stove and brought out a pair of socks and moccasins. 'They'll be plenty big for you, but they're warm. They'll do for now.'

Bari put them on, then keeping an eye on Paddy, lay back on his cot thinking. His mother had gone. She wouldn't be back maybe till freeze-up. That was a long, long time. It wouldn't be much use trying to find her, and eats might be scarce if Brad was away. That settled it. He felt much better about staying. Besides, Paddy was different from Brad. Paddy liked rats and Mounties. He had a different way of doing things. It was strange. If his mother had been there she could have explained, for she knew everything—at least most things.

Once she had told him that everything living in sunshine had a shadow. Like the poplars; when they laid their dark length across the valley, that was their shadow. Life was like that: bursts of sunshine, with shadows playing along the way so's we'd like the shiny places more. Maybe Brad was the Mountie's shadow, or the Mountie was Brad's sunshine or——

' Come and eat! It's ready! '

Bari sat up.

Paddy was pulling a pan of bannock from the oven. It smelled good and so did the coffee. Bounding from bed Bari pulled a stool up to the table beside Paddy's.

Paddy grinned and put a bowl of porridge and a can of tinned milk in front of him. ' Eat lots, there ain't nothin' better for makin' a man than eatin'.'

Bari didn't need a second bidding. His bowl and spoon were made of wood, but they only held his eye a minute. From the first mouthful of porridge to the last he never looked up. Never had anything tasted quite so good. Then Paddy pushed over a plate of hot bannock with syrup on top. Before Bari finished eating he decided that living with Paddy was going to be all right. Pushing his stool back from the table he drew a deep breath. ' I don't often eat like this, Paddy. I couldn't do it again, not right now.'

Paddy smiled. He had taken off his coat. His red shirt, open at the throat, showed deep seams as if laughter had trickled from his face. His clothes and body had a wood-smoky smell. His knobby fingers touched the things on the table gently.

Bari wanted to say something more, but words wouldn't come. He watched him gather the dishes into a basin, pour water into it and set it on the stove. 'We'll take Seegwun to the lake before we wash them. You put that on,' he added, pointing to a coat hanging on the wall. 'It isn't so hot out. This is the kind of weather musk-rats like.'

Bari didn't move. A terrible fear clutched him. 'I don't want to put Seegwun out; she'll be all right in here. She's just little, she'll get lost if you put her out there.' He glanced at the pail. He would like to have swept Seegwun into his arms, but Paddy was speaking.

'Naw she won't get lost, son. You put on that coat and come.'

Bari got to his feet, but he was still worried. Was this going to be the last of his pet? Paddy had lifted the pail and was going out. There was nothing to do but follow. He grasped the coat and was at Paddy's heels as he turned along the lakeshore towards a flag-flanked pool from which the ice had gone. Bari could see the water gleaming black against the whiteness of the higher snows.

'Paddy, she'll get lost, she'll never come back if we put her in there. Let me keep her please?' Bari grasped Paddy's arm. 'She can't see right, Paddy. Her eye, it's hurted.'

Paddy stopped and looked at him. 'T'ain't by seein' them things lives, Bari. It's by smellin', an' it's right smart they are. She'll scent you 'cause she's lived with you.' There was no doubt in Paddy's voice. 'See, she smells water now.'

Seegwun was pushing her head up over the edge of

the pail. ' She'll die if we keep her in the house,' Paddy
went on. ' She's chewed the wrappin' off her foot see?'
Paddy lifted her out.

Bari looked. There was fluff on the leg stump, but
it looked less sore. The web on the other foot had
come together.

' Someday she'll make a house for herself,' Paddy
continued. ' That's what she gets claws for.'

' But she ain't got all her feet, Paddy.' Bari stroked
his pet. ' She can't be livin' by herself. She can't do
nothin' with three feet.'

' She'll be plenty smart with them, you'll see.'

Still holding the rat, Paddy took a stick and poked
beneath the bank. The ground was hard and brittle.
He moved to the sun side where a touch of greening
showed softer land, and tried again. The soil gave. A
smile came to his face as he straightened. ' This'll be
the place for her. She can't go no farther than the
bay. We'll bring her an' leave her for keeps pretty
soon.'

Bari swallowed hard. Was it possible that Paddy
wanted to get rid of the rat? Forcing his mind away
from the thought, he held tightly to Paddy's arm.

Paddy set the rat on the sand. There was a splash,
a dart, and she was gone! A moment later Bari saw
her sport, duck, then disappear beneath weeds on the
opposite bank.

Clutching the pail, he raced round the bank.
' Seegwun! Seegwun!' There wasn't a sound. Tears
blinded him. He ran back. ' She's gone! I told you
she'd go.'

' She'll come back all right, you wait an' see.'

'No, she won't. Let's go and get her,' Bari cried tugging at Paddy's coat.

Paddy kept looking at the water. There wasn't a worry on his face.

'Paddy! Paddy! why don't you come?' Bari tugged desperately. Paddy didn't move.

Dropping to his knees Bari looked over the bank. He could see the bottom, but farther out the water was deep. He wanted to cry out, to call, to yell, but sobs choked him. Everything he loved was gone—his mother, and now Seegwun!

'Don't feel bad, son. You listen, she'll come back soon. She don't know nothin' else but to come back. She'd scent you anywhere. Listen!'

Paddy sounded so sure. The lopsided grin on his face didn't change. He still kept looking at the water.

There was a gurgle, a swish and a V-shaped ripple came to the water's surface. The rat's head appeared. She swam straight for shore.

Plunging into the water waist-deep, Bari clutched the rat to him and fled to the cabin.

Water dripping from his trousers and shivering with cold he stood in the middle of the floor wondering what Paddy would say.

Paddy came in, Seegwun's pail in his hand. 'You're wetter than the rat,' he said, eyeing the pool of water at Bari's feet. 'Put Seegwun in the pail here, an' get off your cloes. We'll have to get you dried.' There was a hint of concern in his voice.

Bari undressed.

Paddy got a piece of sacking and rubbed his body till it glowed. It made him feel good.

'You'll have to get upon the bed till I fix you some cloes.' Paddy still sounded anxious, but he smiled as he took one of his own shirts from a nail on the wall and slipped it over Bari's head. It only took a minute to slice off a piece from each sleeve and from the tail with his knife. 'I ain't got it figgered why we don't grow feathers, they're plenty warm an' they don't need buttons.' He spoke cheerily as he searched a box for a needle and thread, then proceeded to draw in the neck of the shirt to make it fit. He put a belt of his own round the waist.

Bari was pleased. It was warm soft material and felt good against his body. 'I like this shirt, Paddy. I never had a red one before; maybe you could make me two?'

'Naw! Naw!' Paddy shook his head. 'But I'll fix trousers and moccasins for you. You're about as naked as a worm.'

'I don't need shoes much now, Paddy, the crows are in the valley.'

'They'll have cold feet yet, you'll see.'

Standing by the bed Bari waited while Paddy shortened a pair of his trousers and took in the seams. 'Put these on, they ain't so tidy, but they'll do.' He grinned approvingly.

They were brown stubby things with a baggy seat. But they weren't the first pair of trousers that had been cut down for Bari. His mother did make a better job, but he was wise enough to keep that to himself. In the meantime he was thankful for their warmth.

'You'll have to rest till I get your feet covered,' Paddy went on.

Bari climbed back on the bed.

Paddy brought a deer-hide, put a sock on top for a pattern, and cut out two with extra pieces to cover the toes. He sewed them with thread he had coloured with berry juice. He didn't take long. Nothing seemed like work to Paddy. His fingers moved quickly. Sewing to him looked as easy as falling off a log.

'You know how to do everything, don't you, Paddy?' Bari said as he put his feet into the moccasins. 'I fit them good. See you knowed the right size.'

Paddy smiled. 'You go on out now an' get yourself some sunshine. Take your pencil an' paper with you. Come back in for dinner. It's about noon now. Me an' you's got lots to do.'

Bari wondered if he had heard aright. Paddy was sending him out to draw. No one had ever done that before. He reached for his pencil and paper beneath his quilt, glanced at Seegwun sleeping in her pail and went on out.

Walking wasn't easy in the ill-fitting trousers, but he was free, free! Alone again in the woods! Instinctively he wanted to rush to his spruce and hide his drawing things, but he didn't need to do that any more. It was almost too good to believe.

He made for a rock above the bay and sat down. The sky was blue and warm and kind. Listening to the race of melting snow he thought of many things. The happenings of the morning had crushed the empty feeling he had had completely out of his heart. He had long since learned the value of food, warmth and clothing; learned that the woods were a stern mother. And now he was beginning to recognize the deep

B 2

kindliness of the man he was living with. Paddy seemed so much a part of this forest land, to belong to it, and to understand.

Taking out his pencil Bari began to draw—trees, rocks, water. This was the life. It pleased him.

He was getting hungry. It must be close to dinner time. He got up and went home.

Paddy was putting dinner on the table when he went in. He smiled, and pointing to the stool Bari had sat on in the morning said, ' That's your seat. Pull it in and get yourself filled. Duck and wild rice is good eating.'

Paddy was right. Duck and rice was good eating. Bari ate till he could eat no more, then pulling the drawing from his pocket held it up. ' See I drawed this for you, Paddy.' It was an expression of affection, the only one Bari knew to give.

Face glowing, Paddy took it. If he didn't recognize what or where the picture was he didn't betray himself. A long slow smile crept into his eyes and over his face. ' You're sure a smart one, Bari. You can make pictures all right.' The words went straight to Bari's heart. A little bond of understanding was tied between them. Paddy rose and pinned the drawing on the wall. ' You'll be a picture-makin' man some day if you just keep on. It's not everybody that can do that.' Paddy shrugged meaningly. ' You're sure a smart one.'

Bari was delighted. He jumped up and helped Paddy gather and wash the dishes. The pleased smile stayed on Paddy's face. ' I'm goin' out to hang pails on the birches to catch sap. Would you like to come?'

Bari nodded.

Paddy brought a handful of jam-pails, and they went out across the hollow. Here and there ground-hogs were sunning, squirrels chattered, but Paddy and Bari made straight for a clump of birch on the higher land. There they sat with the afternoon sun warm on their shoulders, Paddy teaching how to whittle spiles and drive them into the tree trunks, then hang pails to catch sap.

'It'll be good flowin', an' frost makes it plenty sweet,' Paddy said, pointing to the brown trickle. 'We'll come back for it in a week. I always boil some for Pete Hyslop. He likes it, an' we'll make some for your mother too.'

That pleased Bari. He frisked ahead of Paddy all the way home. Before supper he had filled the rest of his paper with drawings.

That night when he went to bed he was certain he was going to like Paddy. He wouldn't be afraid to share secrets with him, to tell him the kind of stories his mother liked to hear. Yes, life with Paddy looked good. He was still thinking when Paddy spoke.

'Go to sleep young fellah! I'm goin' to show you how to make a cot for yourself in the morning.'

Peeking over his cover Bari saw him rolling into a blanket on the floor.

Chapter IV

THE MOUNTIE

There was a lean-to behind Paddy's cabin. Next morning after breakfast they went out to it. When Paddy opened the door, Bari's eyes widened. There were saws, axes and hammers hanging on the wall. Board ends and nails were scattered on the floor, just the things Bari had often begged from Brad to make boats with.

'Can't spare 'em!' Brad always said. 'But you couldn't make nothin' but a worm-hole anyway.' Bari didn't like it when he talked like that; the thought of it even now made him clench his fists.

But he looked hopefully at Paddy. 'Maybe, you'd let me in here sometimes to—to build things, canoe or cabin, or—or, that's when I ain't makin' pictures?'

'Sure you can,' Paddy beamed. 'Everybody should know how to make a house for themselves. Birds an'

36

beasts know that much, an' there ain't nobody should be livin' except in the house they make.'

Paddy took an axe from a nail on the wall. ' This,' he said, running his fingers along the blade, ' was Blackhawk's—that's what they called my father—' He stopped, then added slowly, ' You see, us folks called their children the name of the first thing their mammy saw after they were born, so we're kinda kin to the bush.' Laughing lightly he added, ' I don't be knowin' much else.' He kept rubbing his fingers on the axe blade, talking dreamily as if the woods were tangled up with something far back in his memory. ' Yes, there's lots I won't be able to tell you about like readin', writin', an' fancier things you should know, but you'll learn.' He lifted his voice knowingly. ' The bush ain't a bad teacher, and bush folks have a way of their own. It's a mighty fine livin'; I allus figgered there was none better, though there's them that may tell you different, but the scent of the pine an' the singin' o' the wind is hard to beat. Here, take this.' He reached a small hatchet from the wall and laid it over Bari's shoulder. ' That's yours, we'll go out an' cut poplars to make that cot. I'll sharpen my axe at the door here.'

Bari stood while he sharpened his axe blade with a stone, then together they struck across the rising ground to a poplar grove.

There was a glitter of frost on the shrubbery. The earth was crusty beneath their feet. Pussy willows were beginning to sit out along the twigs, and in the hollows there was a smell of buds and growing things.

It didn't take Paddy long to swing his axe through some of the slimmer poplar trees. When he had three or four down he said, ' You snag the branches off with your hatchet, Bari.'

Paddy cut a goodly pile, but with his help the snagging wasn't hard. Then they cut them in short lengths and Paddy hitched a half-dozen over Bari's shoulder, the others over his own, and they toted them home.

' They've got to be peeled and sunned,' Paddy said when they laid them by the door. In half an hour they had a row of glistening white poles leaning against the cabin wall to dry.

Paddy's knowledge amazed Bari. As the days went by their friendship deepened. They walked often in the bush together. Paddy didn't talk overmuch, but his mind was full. Sometimes it was just a fleck of cloud, a fluttering bird, the tracks of a jumper, or the call of a wheeling kildeer he noticed as they took long winding by-ways in their stride.

On these walks Bari felt the urge to do things, nice things. The beauty and friendliness Paddy saw communicated itself to him. To Paddy the forest was a living thing, laughing, singing, cuddling the creatures that lived in it to its warm breast. Bari tried to put these things he saw and felt on paper.

Paddy beamed. ' You'll do it yet, son. You've got it in you.'

But something else was happening. Bari was out of paper. He had used every scrap of wrapping-paper and cardboard Paddy owned. Paddy had allowed him to take the labels from the cans of milk. Now his supply was at an end.

Yesterday he had stripped leaves with the months from the calendar on the wall. Paddy wasn't too happy

about that. 'It's like takin' the moons out of the sky,'
he said, not unkindly, but by the tone of voice, Bari
knew that he would have felt better if he hadn't done
it. All the same he didn't think it really mattered, for
Paddy knew the months by the moon anyway.

Bari tried using bark stripped from a tree. Paddy
didn't like that either. He said the tree would die. In
any case it was no good.

Then Bari had an idea. Granny Mulgrove, who lived
at the end of the vlllage, was getting too old to go
fishing as often as she used. He'd offer to spend half a
day helping her if she'd give him some paper. And
there was Uncle Ted, who got medicine every week.
Bari had seen it come wrapped in white paper. If he
could only get that. Maybe Uncle Ted would let him
cut wood for it. The thought thrilled Bari.

It didn't look far across the bay to where Uncle Ted
and Granny lived, but it was a good four miles by the
shore trail.

That night Bari was at Granny Mulgrove's. As she
listened to his story her face gathered into a deep smile.
'Ye can have it, Bari,' she said in her little crackling
voice, 'all of it, an' you're welcome. When the weather
gets warmer ye can help me fish.'

Bari was delighted.

Uncle Ted wasn't so willing. 'It's a heap better
things ye could be doin' besides scribblin' an drawin','
he said, puckering his face till his eyes looked like
knot-holes in a barky tree. 'But my old back don't
hold up so good now with the wood choppin', an' a
young one like you might sure be helpful.'

That was enough for Bari. Into his busy life came

trips for paper.   He sweated over the wood-cutting and sometimes he swept old Ted's floor and fetched his water, but he felt amply repaid by the sheets of paper Ted kept for him.

Paddy didn't mind.   To him, helping the old folks was a fine thing, and sometimes he sent them a scoop of flour or a making of tea.

Bari never loitered in the village.   But sometimes after his race home he'd stand breathless on the tamarack-rim and look back.   The log cabins hugging the shore looked so tiny, so shy, as if they were hiding from the wind.   And above them he could see the wooden Tender Bird perched high on his pole.   Then he would look away beyond the rugged fringes of the jackpine. That was another world, another Kingdom.   What was it like?   Urgent thoughts and wishes filled him.

Then making believe he was a bird, wings poised for flight, with the lift of the wind on his heels, he'd speed home to tell Paddy all he'd seen and heard and to draw pictures on his precious paper.

He was learning to care for paper now.   One of the pencils Hyslop had sent him had a rubber on the end. It was a long time before Bari discovered what it was for, and it was a discovery.   Now he could draw things, rub them out, and use the paper again!

Seegwun was growing; longer hairs were coming through her fur.   She stayed longer in the water when Bari took her for her dip.

One morning Paddy cut the top, end, and sides for Bari's cot.   Bari helped notch and nail them together. Paddy fitted sturdier pieces on for legs, then Bari and he laced a rope across the bottom to hold the mattress, which Paddy made by filling a sack with cat-tail fluff.

'It's all yours!' Paddy said when they finished. 'We'll take it in. I've a couple of blankets a trapper gave me an' you can have them.'

Bari was thrilled. He had never owned anything before. Having a bed and blankets gave him a feeling of bigness, of consequence. Only men had these.

Every day brought something new.

A couple of nights later Paddy and he were walking the shore. There was a greyness in the sky. Beyond the rugged tips of the cedar came a flash of red. Bari stopped. 'See! See the sky, Paddy, it's being coloured!' He pointed to streamers of orange and red racing south to splatter land and water with sunset fire. 'What does that mean, Paddy? Who makes it pretty?'

Eyes on the flaming beauty, Paddy answered slowly. 'I guess it's a painter, a drawer like you. He comes every night.'

'I've seen him! I've seen him!' Bari cried, clapping his hands. 'I've seen him colour it often. I saw him last night.'

They stepped to a higher knoll and stood watching the colours fade into grey. 'He'll come again, won't he?' Bari asked, eyes shining.

'Every night after supper,' Paddy answered, 'me and you'll come an' watch him.'

'Sunstruck!' The voice came from behind.

Bari wheeled. The glittering buttons of a Mountie's tunic met his eyes. Taking one swift look at the uniformed figure he tore downhill, leaping freshets and waterholes till he reached the opposite bank and dropped to the ground in a stand of pine.

He was scared. His breath was coming in short swift gasps. His heart was racing. He hated Mounties! That must be Hyslop, the one Paddy liked, but he wasn't taking chances. Paddy liked everything.

Wiping the sweat from his brow he slipped along to a clearing where he could get a better view. Paddy and the Mountie were still standing, but they turned and walked towards the cabin. Every little while they stopped and looked across the bay. Likely they were looking for him, but he lay low.

Hours seemed to be passing. Darkness began to streak the sky. Mist rolled up about the jackpine and capered along the shore. Strange shadows came ghosting through the rock. There was a moan in the wind. The night seemed to be alive. He crept close to a tree. Maybe it was the darkness that was making him cold and clammy. An owl hooted and Bari shot to his feet.

There was a light in Paddy's window now. Maybe the Mountie was going to stay there all night. The thought set Bari shivering. He drew his coat tighter and thought of his new cot and warm blankets. Maybe the Mountie was sleeping on them! A convulsive anger and fear swept him; he couldn't stand it. Eyes fixed on Paddy's light he walked slowly round the bay towards it.

When he was close to the cabin he stopped. There wasn't a sound. He felt the ground with his hands for tracks. There wasn't a groove or rut. Wood-smoke came curling from the chimney; he looked up, then back at the window. The lamp-light looked warm and friendly. Dare he go in? How could he find out if the Mountie was there? He stood thinking. Then dropping on his knees, he crept to the window ledge, raised himself and peered in.

Paddy was sitting by the stove, head in his hands. Steam from the kettle was whirling between the lamp and wall. Everything was still. Craning his neck, Bari could see that his own cot and Paddy's were both empty. He drew a sigh of relief. Paddy was alone!

Leaping to the door, Bari lifted the latch. Paddy's hand was on his shoulder. 'I figgered you'd come!'

'Where is he? Where did he go?' Bari asked, flashing anxious eyes around the table.

'You mean Hyslop?'

'Yes, the Mountie. Has he gone?'

'That was Peter Hyslop. Didn't you know him?'

'Not with them clothes on, an' I'm scared of Mounties. Brad says they shoot quick and sure. One nearly got him once.'

'But I tol' you, me an' Hyslop are good friends. Besides your mother trusted him.' Paddy's voice rose meaningly. 'You sit down on the chair there an' get warm.'

Bari hung his head momentarily, for he knew that Paddy was hurt. But drawing the chair closer to the stove he explained, 'I just don't know him, Paddy, an' I wasn't expectin' him. He looks different with them shiny buttons on his clothes.'

Paddy smiled and pushed a parcel across the table. 'He brought you this.'

Bari looked at it. 'What is it? Hyslop doesn't know me!'

'Sure he does. Open it.'

Bari lifted it, untied the string and folded back the wrapping, took the lid from a box and pulled out paints, crayons, pencils and paper. Eyes shining he looked up at Paddy. 'For me? What did he bring them to me for?' He turned the pencils over in his hand. 'I never thought a Mountie would bring me paper an' things.'

'I tol' him you were aimin' to make pictures,' Paddy interrupted. 'I guess he figgers on helpin' you. He says he'll bring more next time he comes. Better get into bed. Here's some berry juice I heated. Drink it!' Paddy handed him a mug. 'It's raspberry!'

Pushing the parcel back on the table Bari drank the juice and went straight to bed.

He couldn't sleep. He kept thinking about the Mountie. Why did he bring him pencils and things? He thought Mounties only came when there was trouble. Peeking over his blanket he saw Paddy wasn't asleep. 'What did that Mountie come here for, Paddy? Will he come back again?' There was a long silence.

'Yes! An' the next time he comes you tell him "Thank you" for the drawin' things.' Paddy's words were crisp. They didn't invite asking more. Still thinking about Hyslop, Bari pulled up his covers and fell asleep.

A week later Peter Hyslop was in on them before they heard his step. Bouncing beneath the table, Bari brought himself up on the other side to fix his eyes on the tall straight figure of Peter Hyslop. His head almost touched the roof. His hair and face and eyes had the same shininess they had had the day Bari saw him in the bush. There was a cleanness, a sureness

about him. His buttons, leggings and shoes glistened.
Bari had never seen anyone so shiny before.

He came over and held out a box. 'Here's a bit of
candy for you this time. There's a couple of pencils in
with it.'

Bari reached for the box with a half-frightened thrill.
But the twinkle in Hyslop's eyes went straight to his
heart. He had to say something. 'I like you a little
bit now, but not the way I like Paddy, you're not so
ordinary.'

Paddy and the Mountie laughed.

'There's some tobacco in the box for you, Paddy.'
Hyslop turned as he walked towards the door, 'but don't
be teaching the young lad to smoke.' He went out as
he was speaking.

'You didn't tell him, "Thank you",' Paddy reminded.

'Oh-h, I'll draw pictures for him, he'll like that. I
won't forget.'

Every night saw Bari and Paddy at the sunset rock.
Bari took the crayons and paper that Hyslop had brought
and, with shaking fingers, tried to follow the master
strokes of the Painter of the Night. That's what Paddy
called him.

When clouds banked the heavens or spring mist wet
their faces, Bari would lift disappointed eyes to Paddy
and ask, 'Where is he? What's he doing?'

'Mixin' his colours.'

Paddy knew, for sure enough next night, purple,
crimson and green would be flung across the rain-washed
sky. Paddy would chuckle, 'See—I tol' you.'

'I'll paint like that some day, I'll make pictures for
you an' Hyslop.' Bari meant it. Welling up within

him was the urge, an indefinable something that made him want to reach to the heavens to clutch the beauty and put it on his paper.

One warm night they gathered their birch sap and boiled it on a fire built by the door. Bari liked the taste of the rich brown syrup. There wasn't much, but it pleased him.

The days were becoming quite warm. A softer whir-r was beginning to play through the cat-tails by Seegwun's pool.

'It's time that rat was in the water,' Paddy said. Bari was satisfied. Paddy made a hole for her beneath the water, pushed some of the fluff from her pail through from the top, then set her free. 'She's on her own now. She'll be plenty happy,' Paddy said, picking up her pail. 'We won't wait.'

Bari didn't feel sad. Her foot was better and she was a good swimmer. Every morning they looked for her tracks. They were easily seen; so was the stroke of her tail on the sand, and the reeds and willow showed her tooth marks. Sometimes on moonlight nights they watched her souse nibblings of flags and roots in the water for her meal.

Frog Moon came. Paddy called it that. The swamp frogs were awake and shouting sp-r-r-ring, sp-r-r-ring!

Paddy made a tiny raft. He put a lighted candle on it, set it on the water in the lily pond, and then they sat down and watched.

Tree toads, or 'peepers' as Paddy called them, came hopping through the flags to gaze with big brown-rimmed eyes at the flickering light. Then ballooning their throats till they almost burst, they'd peep and chirp

the glee of their hearts. These were great nights. Bari loved them, loved to hear Paddy saying in his friendly soft way to the happy little creatures, ' It's mighty smart you are, yah! Plenty spry we gotta be to see you! Changin' your cloes to the colour of the thing you're settin' on.' There was a little bit of mockery in his words. The little creatures looked at him, and maybe they heard him say ' Be kind to them, Bari, they wouldn't harm nothin'.'

The day they had put Seegwun in the water, Bari had had an idea. And now came the first chance he had to get it going, for Paddy was away fishing.

Getting hammer, hatchet, saw, nails and some birch-bark from Paddy's lean-to, Bari cut slim poplars and drove them into the ground by the lake, then bent them into a tent-like frame. Digging, pounding and tugging he worked like a bumble-bee. He must be finished before Paddy came back.

His fingers were cut and his arms ached from stretching the birchbark over the frame. It was hard work. He didn't have time to wipe the sweat from his face or pay attention to the rips he was getting in his clothes. He was puffing and breathless when he saw Paddy coming over the hill. He dropped his axe and stood. What would Paddy say?

' I wondered where you were.' Paddy's voice was anxious as he came at a half-run. He looked at the ' tent' then at Bari, then back at the tent. ' Aimin' to live in that?'

Bari nodded. ' You said everybody should build the house they live in.'

The set of Paddy's jaw relaxed into a smile. ' It ain't

big enough an' it wouldn't stand no storms. I'll help you build a better one. We'll do it right now.'

Bari's heart thumped with excitement.

At night a stout birchbark tent was standing in the lee of the spruce. Bari's dream had come true. He had a place of his own.

Here to this tiny shelter he brought paper, pencils, crayons and a blanket. This was the world he loved. His mother had told him about kings and kingdoms. 'A king was a good person,' she said, 'who lived happily with the folks of his kingdom.'

So the forest would be his kingdom. The trees, flowers, fur-folks and birds would be his people. Yes, and his mother told him there was a god looking after everybody. Paddy would be his god.

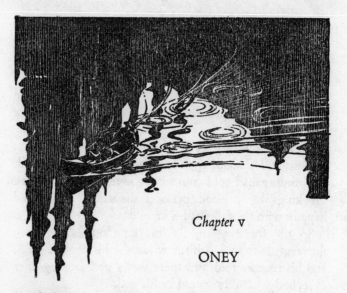

Chapter v

ONEY

Bari's kingdom delighted him. Beyond the shade of
the damp-smelling spruce there was always a stir of
growing things. In the sun-warmed hollows he could
taste sweetness from honey-lipped bells. He loved to
sit on the shoulder of the clearing and watch sunlight
sifting into the blueness of the woods. These were the
things he was going to make pictures of.

To-morrow, after he brought paper from Granny
Mulgrove and Uncle Ted, he'd draw the lake at the
valley's end. It mirrored every twig and cone of the
tree-lined shore. That made it twice beautiful.

But to-morrow, when he reached the Point, he found
Uncle Ted had moved to a fish-camp. So there was
no paper. Granny Mulgrove was mending nets. She
needed help, so Bari worked all afternoon. But at
night she had only a scrap of cardboard to give him.
He was disappointed.

Next morning he sat in his tent trying to think of some way he might raise even wrapping-paper. There were folks in the village he could ask, but he felt a little spirited about begging. Besides he was rather proud of being able to do something no one else did. He wanted to do it alone.

Somewhat disgruntled he spent the morning making drawings with a stick on the sand. He was pleased with his work. But he wanted Paddy to see it; he needed Paddy's praise, his smile. It was part of the answer to the deep longing within him. He was putting the last tree in place when:

'Bari! Bari! Where are you?' Paddy's voice was sharp.

Before Bari could answer, 'Bari! Bari! Come on up here! We got work to do!' Paddy hadn't ever spoken like that before. He threw down his stick and walked up the trail.

As he neared the cabin he saw Peter Hyslop coming over the hill. He was still a bit jittery about the Mountie. It was hard not to connect him with trouble.

He quickened his step to reach the door first. Paddy came out of the lean-to and halted the Mountie. Bari was sitting quietly on his cot when they both came in.

Hyslop was smiling. 'How are you, my boy?' he said friendly like. Bari didn't speak.

Hyslop took off his cap, rolled up his sleeves and washed in the tin basin beside the stove.

Bari never took his eyes from him. He took a comb from his pocket, tidied his hair, then sat down at the table. 'Well how's the drawing going?' He turned a full smile on Bari.

A tremor of awe swept through Bari. He couldn't speak. But reaching beneath his quilt he drew out a number of drawings and handed them over.

Hyslop looked at them, smiled and in a tone of voice Bari liked said, ' This'll be a deer is it ? ' He held one up in his hand.

Bari beamed, nodded and moved to a chair at Hyslop's side.

Paddy had supper on the table. It was baked fish, bannock and wild honey. The Mountie started to eat right away.

Bari kept looking at him. His skin looked soft as a rabbit's ear, but it was brown and weathered. His arms were meaty and strong looking. He moved and ate and did things just like anyone else. His face was smiley and creased round the corners of the eyes the same as Paddy's. Without his coat and shiny buttons and his cap he was just ordinary.

' Eat your supper, Bari.' Paddy's voice turned Bari's attention to his eats.

He ate quickly, an ear on Paddy's and the Mountie's talk. It was about the price of berries and lumber camps.

Suddenly Hyslop turned to him. ' They'll be making a lumberman out of you some day, lad, or maybe it's a trapper you'd rather be ? '

Bari dropped his spoon. Swift protesting words rose to his lips. ' No ! No ! ' he wanted to say. ' I want to draw pictures, don't you know that ? ' But looking into Hyslop's twinkling eyes he felt himself shrivelling like a dried berry. He shook his head. His ' No ' was a whisper.

Paddy spoke. 'I was just aimin' at tellin' him that we got work to do, that he can't be drawin' all the time.'

What did Paddy mean? A little hurt probed Bari.

But Hyslop rose and laying his hand on Bari's head said cheerily, 'You'll be a great fellow yet, my lad! You'll go places!' Feeling his pockets for his mitts he slipped on his coat and turned. 'I didn't bring you anything, paper or scribblers, I came down from the north. S'long!'

Paddy went out with him.

Bari was still sitting when Paddy came back. He looked happy. 'When you've et your dinner, son, I'm aimin' to fix the cabin some. You'll help eh?' There was nothing biting in his voice now.

'Sure!' Bari got to his feet willingly. They spent the afternoon cutting logs. The following days they sawed and fitted them into broken places in the cabin wall.

Paddy called the moon that came peeping through the poplars the Nest-building Moon. Bari saw swallows hovering over the mud-flat with beakfuls of earth, and kildeer building in creases above the rock heads. That was likely the reason Paddy wanted to mend his cabin.

But whenever Bari could, he skipped to his hide-away to draw pictures on the sand. But it wasn't satisfying. His hope was that Hyslop would bring paper next time he came.

At night he played tag with lantern bugs; he liked to think they were stars come to earth. How they got back to the sky was a secret only the moon would know.

Then Berry Moon came. ' Me an' you's goin' berryin',' Paddy said with a grin. Bari had picked berries before, but going with Paddy would be different. The thought made him happy.

They packed blankets and eats into their canoe, and on a gentle night paddled up Sturgeon River.

They chose moss-covered rocks in a hollow on which to sleep, then lit a fire by the water. At sunrise they were scooping berries into pails from the ridges above the river. At sundown they stopped to watch the Night Painter flash mauve shadows across the cleft shoulders of the rocks and turn the blueberry patch to checkered gold. It was then Bari wanted pencil and colours and paper! His being cried for them. At night when they measured their picking and talked about the money they had earned and the things they would buy, Bari cried, ' Put down paper, Paddy— drawin' paper! '

Paddy squinted at him. ' It's a shirt you're much more needin', an' shoes, lad.' Something in Paddy's tone of voice made Bari wonder.

One night, when Paddy and he were sitting by the shore, a tiny figure hove in sight. It was a little girl. Too surprised to speak they watched her come along the rocks. She was walking slowly as if not too sure of herself.

' Who can she be? ' Paddy asked as she skirted the bush towards them, her blue dress breezing about her like laughter. She stood a moment at the end of the path, then running forward shot a shy glance at Paddy before pushing a fistful of raspberries into Bari's hand. ' I bringed these for you,' she said softly.

Bari beamed at her. She was sweetly and roundly made. Her eyes were half frightened, like a fawn's. She was looking straight at him, her face alight with happiness. A flush of joy crept up in Bari. Reaching for her hand he led her to where Paddy was sitting.

Paddy smiled at her. 'Where did you come from, little girl?'

'Over there.' She pointed to a tent lifting its grey wedge against a wall of pine. 'That's my father's, an' he's pickin' berries too. We come from very far.' Then with a roguish squint at Bari she added, 'I see'd you from the rocks. My father said I could come an' visit you.' She dropped her eyes shyly. 'Maybe I can come often? I ain't got nobody to know here except maybe you.' There was pleading in her voice.

Paddy kept looking at her. 'What's the name?'

'Oney Madette. I'se eight. I ain't got no mother. I keeps house for my father.'

'We're tickled to see you, Oney. Me an' Bari likes folks like you.' Paddy spoke gently. 'There ain't so many of them. We'll sure be glad to see you often.'

Bari's heart bounded. He hung on to her hand. Berry juice was dripping through the fingers of his other hand, but he kept his eyes on her. He was going to like her. She was kin to bells and butterflies and lightsome things of the wood.

She wheeled, whisking herself free, and ran down the path.

'She'll come back,' Paddy said, getting to his feet. 'She's a smart one.'

New thoughts came into Bari's head that night. Would this little girl's father be a nice man? Would it be all right to go and visit her? Would she come and see them often?

She did. Every night Oney Madette scampered the shore to join them. Such fun they had building tents, making needle chains, playing Rabbit Run. There was a sparkle about Oney. She was alive, happy!

When Bari got to know her better he told her about his mother. 'Sometime I'll show her to you. You'll like her. She talks about nice things,' he said, glowing with pride. Then he told Oney about Seegwun, and about his kingdom. 'I'm going to make pictures of it, be an artist when I get big. That's what they call a person that paints pictures. My mother told me that,' he added knowingly. 'Other people don't know that.'

Oney listened, eyes wide. 'My mother tol' me to wash my father's shirt an' bake his bannock. She showed me how.' Lifting her voice spiritedly, Oney tossed her head to show she was quite aware of her own qualifications. They both laughed, happily aware of life's promise.

Paddy fussed over them. Sometimes for a treat he crushed blueberries into a can of milk from his precious store. Sometimes it was fish baked in clay or hot cakes and wild honey.

In return Oney wove willow baskets for them; she hunted out their shirts when they weren't looking and washed them by dabbling them in the river.

Paddy patted her and spoke kind words. Bari could see that he too liked little Oney.

Bari told her his troubles: his plan to go back to his mother sometime, and his great need of paper.

Wrinkling her little brow thoughtfully, she said, ' My dad's got paper. I'll bring you some.'

Next night she arrived early. Pulling Bari quickly aside she whispered, ' My dad says drawing's no good, but I brung you this.' She drew a folded paper from the inside of her sweater and opened it.

Paddy's calendar still in mind, Bari looked at it dubiously. It was a map. There were several large crosses marked in ink on it. Realizing he must say something he smiled, ' That's good, but it's got writin' on it.'

' It's got two sides,' she answered, whipping it over quickly.

' Yah, I know.' Bari took it from her hand. ' It'll make a lot of pictures. I'll make one for you.'

She squirmed her little body into a gesture of approval.

Bari tore the map into four pieces and hid it beneath a rock.

It took him several days to get a drawing he considered good enough to give her. At the end of the week he was satisfied: it was a picture much the same as the one Hyslop had praised. Bari was proud of it.

At night he watched for Oney's coming and ran to meet her. ' I made your picture,' he said, hardly able to contain himself as he handed it to her.

She looked at it, then looked at him. Her brown face dimpled from ear to ear. ' I'll keep it, Bari. I'll put it below my bed. My father doesn't know you can draw like that.'

' Show it to him,' Bari said, delighted at her pleasure. ' Maybe he'd like one too.'

c

She squinted at him, tucked the drawing behind the upper part of her dress and said no more.

Bari was very happy.

Next night he was sitting on the rocks alone when he saw a man coming over the trail which Oney used. It must be Oney's father. Bari watched a few minutes, then slid to a dip beneath their camp.

Paddy was sitting higher up sorting blueberries.

Walking swiftly, Madette made straight for him. He was coatless and hatless. His hair was standing on end. When he was close Bari could see that he had a rough face and that his jaw was set.

Bari couldn't hear what he said to Paddy at first, but his voice rose quickly. It was angry. He was saying harsh things. After a while Paddy talked, then Madette didn't talk so loud.

Bari peeked up. Madette was sitting down. He was smiling. Then Bari heard him saying. 'That kid shouldn't be wastin' his time drawin', he should be workin'.' There was silence. 'That map was special and . . .' Bari didn't hear more.

In a little while Madette went home.

Bari rose and went slowly up to where Paddy was sitting. 'Did Oney give you a map?' Paddy asked, looking up with a grin.

Bari nodded.

'It was her father's, special like, I gotta buy him another one.' Paddy kept sorting his blueberries as if thinking what next to say. He chuckled. 'You shouldn't go wheedlin' around wimmin.' He chuckled again. 'It don't pay!'

Biting his lip Bari fought back a tear. He had had

such a good time with Oney. Paddy wasn't angry, however, and he hoped Oney hadn't got into trouble. He wondered about his picture. He really was a little proud of it. Oney would likely talk about it when she came.

She did. She turned up early next night and made straight for him. There was fire in her eye. 'I don't want your picture,' she said, whisking the piece of paper with the drawing from some place within her clothing. Spitting on it she threw it on the ground and jumped on it. 'There!' she said, stopping to catch her breath, 'that's what I think of it. An' my father says drawin's no good, you should be workin'.' She stuck out her tongue, nodded her emphasis and glared at him, before turning and racing back towards home.

Bari stood stunned. He hadn't had a chance to say a word. He looked quickly about to see if Paddy had heard, but Paddy was in the upper bush cutting wood. Swallowing a sob, and clenching his fists, Bari made for the water's edge and sat down.

It was a restful place, where winds stood still and waters were lazy. But nothing was very clear in his head, and his eyes burned. There was a strange feeling at the pit of his stomach. One or two of the frogs sunning and leaping amongst the lily pads stopped and looked up at him. He wished he could be one of them, and dip himself in the cool clear water.

When it began to get dark, he went back to their camp. Paddy was packing the blueberries into sacks. He was in a cheerful mood. 'We're goin' home in the mornin', son. I'd like to get the berries on Tuesday's fish-boat. Besides, you're needin' a shirt an' shoes.'

Bari didn't even add, ' an' paper '. His thoughts were bitter. He rolled into his blanket without a word and fell asleep thinking of the queerness of ' wimmin '.

He was happier next day when they pulled down river. He was going home to his kingdom and to Seegwun.

When he got home he went straight to her pool. There was a tiny push-up amongst the weeds. It was her house—Paddy said so.

The next weeks were busy ones. He helped Paddy boil blueberries and put them in jam-pails. Then they caught and smoked fish, gathered rose hips and made jelly. ' For winter,' Paddy said, his voice meaningful.

One night in the lean-to, Paddy made a chair with antler horns. ' This is for you, Bari,' he said, bringing it into the cabin.

Bari beamed and set it beside his cot. The things Paddy did made him feel important, worthwhile, gave him a new hold on life. He didn't think about Oney now, at least not much. When he did, he felt like clenching his fists and saying to himself, ' I'll show her yet.'

A fish-boat brought some of the things Paddy ordered with the blueberry money. Bari was in bed when they came, but he bounded to Paddy's side when the door opened and the package was thrown in. Quivering with excitement he helped Paddy rip off the string and paper.

There was a shirt—a red one, a pair of socks and shoes all for himself. Smiling from ear to ear, he lifted them on to the table. Then his eyes popped wide. In the bottom of the parcel was a drawing-book and two pencils. He grasped them, looked at them, then looked at Paddy. 'Thanks, Paddy. I like them.' Paddy's eyes twinkled. 'Like the shirt?'

Bari nodded. But it was the paper he liked best.

Chapter VI

FREEZING MOON

The Moon of Falling Leaves came. The forest turned red, gold and kildeer brown. There was a moth-winged greyness in the nights. The leaves seemed bursting with warmth as if they had filled themselves with sunshine and could hold no more. Bari tried to put the colours on paper. There was lure in them.

The air grew crisp. The blue of the summer sky became hard and cold. Snow came. Bari loved snow; it was earth's blanket. Wind cut feathery patterns on it, and it made the writing of fur-folks plain.

His mother had told him how a windegooqua came these nights, soft-footed and silent, and quieted the waters, turning the breath of the flowers into fluffy robes to dress the trees and bushes. Last night she must have come, for the folks of his kingdom were wearing misty white, but the flowers and grass—the gentler folk—were black. Their heads were drooping brokenly.

Could it be that they were dead? The thought struck
grief to Bari's heart. His mother never said what happened then. Paddy would know. Bari went straight
to him.

He was mending nets in the cabin.

'Where do flowers go when they die dead, Paddy?'

Paddy looked at him, wrinkled his brow and tugged
hard on his cord. 'They don't die dead, Bari. They
only sleep.'

'They look awful dead to me, Paddy,' Bari answered.

'Well, they ain't,' Paddy said firmly. 'They're just
sleepin', dreamin' up patterns for pretties to set out in
the spring. You wait an' see.' There was a warmth in
Paddy's eyes.

And he was right. Bari knew it. He had seen spring
and the pretties lots of times.

Next morning Bari found a leaf-roofed nest in a
poplar. In it, tail curled about him for warmth,
Adjiduhmo was sleeping. There was a string of katydid
eggs in the twiggery and a moth-house clung to a
bough. Beneath one of the willows a deer-mouse had
lined a robin's nest with fluff.

It was sleeping-time all right. The folks of his
kingdom were tucked in warm behind the cobwebby
hoar of the 'gooqua's weaving. Winter soon drew her
blanket tight beneath the shoulders of the hill. The
lake froze, and there was a crackle in the snow-bowed
cedars.

Paddy lit the lamp early these days and sat by the
stove with a long needle mending Bari's clothes and
darning socks. 'It's a fall chore,' he said. 'It kinda
belongs to the crackin' of trees an' lamp time.'

Bari roasted hazel nuts, and sometimes fish, the way Paddy taught him, by taking off the stove lids and holding them over the open fire. Paddy called it ' bush supper '.

On clear nights Paddy sometimes took him to a tangle of juniper. ' Now,' he said, ' you just sit here an' watch.'

One, two, three . . . eight, sometimes more rabbits would come hopping, frisking into the starlit clearing. ' Drift Spirits ' Paddy called them, and that's what they looked like, leaping through the glittering pines. But a cracking twig or slip of snow would send the white-coated dancers scurrying. They were safe: Paddy didn't trap nor snare.

Because, ' Once,' he said, ' the evil one was coming to kill the Indians. Knocking down trees, breaking through rocks, they heard him come crashing through the forest. They trembled with fear,' Paddy's voice quivered, ' then the Indians pretended they were rabbits, wheeling, dancing, leaping like their nimble-footed friends. Not recognizing them, the evil one passed by.' Paddy drew a sigh of relief. ' So I like them little rabbits.'

And huddled there in the silence, Paddy told Bari about the stars. ' Up there!' he said, pointing to the Dipper, ' that's the good folks' pipe of peace. It's great times they have up there smokin' an' plannin' things. You can see them, can't you?'

Yes, sure he could. The faces of Tim the grocery man and Daniels, and Rosie, who had gone away a long time ago—he could see them up there amongst the stars. Turning to the Little Dipper, Paddy went on,

'That pipe belongs to the little folks I guess, 'cause they don't smoke.' Paddy chuckled, but his voice was wise. 'That big star at the top,' he pointed, 'that's the Pole Star, don't forget. A good spirit put it there, a pole bright an' shinin' so's bush folks like you an' me can't get lost. Some night I'll show you the trail by the stars, then you'll be safe.' Turning his gaze to the Milky Way, Paddy added, 'That light's from the camp-fires of them that's gone away. They're lightin' the home trail for the rest of us.' Paddy shrugged and smiled. It was some minutes before Paddy took his eyes from the sky. He was at home in the starry heavens.

Bari loved the stories Paddy told here in the forest night; there was something wholly delightful about them. Bari felt that he kind of belonged to the rabbits and the stars and the Milky Way. His mother didn't know these stories, but he would tell them to her; she would be thrilled.

At night he sat in the lamp-light trying to draw the stories, the dancings and the camp-fires. Crude wiggly strokes he made, but over and over he worked on them till they looked true to his anxious eye.

He was thinking of his mother a great deal now. 'When'll my mother come for me?' he asked Paddy.

'It'll likely be in Freezing Moon, son, when the ice gets hard.'

When Freezing Moon came peeping over the tamaracks Bari watched the bush trail. At every sound he raced to the door. But no mother came.

Then something began to happen. A change came over Paddy. He hardly spoke these days. The glint went out of his eye. He sat long spells looking through the window. There was something on his mind. Bari knew it. 'Don't you like livin' with me any more Paddy?' he asked one night after Paddy had eaten supper without speaking.

'Sure I do, there's nothin' I could like better.' Paddy smiled his deep friendly smile. 'It's great times we've had, me an' you, isn't it?'

Bari felt more satisfied.

A week later Peter Hyslop came. He was sitting in the cabin when Bari went in at noon. 'Well, you're looking good, young man,' he said with a big smile, then kept on talking to Paddy.

Bari slid quietly into a corner and busied himself trying on the Mountie's mitts that were lying with his coat and cap on Paddy's bed.

Hyslop and Paddy kept talking low. Now and again Bari caught some of the words. Paddy's face was anxious, as if what he was saying troubled him. Hyslop seemed happy enough. Finally he got up. 'I can't stay for dinner to-day, Paddy. I want to get clear of the bush before dark.'

Paddy rose slowly. He didn't seem to hear Hyslop, but looking him straight in the eye said, 'Last year at this time I had a dozen mink, this year I ain't got nothin'.'

'You'll catch up, Paddy,' Hyslop answered, putting on his coat. Then turning to Bari, he said, 'I'll be seeing you soon. Are you still makin' pictures?' Hyslop's smile was kind. It made Bari feel good.

As soon as Hyslop went out, Paddy said, 'I've got news for you that Hyslop brought from up north. He was talkin' to your mother. You're goin' to see her.'

' Mother ! '   Bari leaped to his feet.   ' Is she coming ? '

' No ! you're goin' to stay with her for a spell.'

' When ?   How ?   Right away ? '

' Hyslop's coming for you soon's the lake's froze. Brad's going logging.   I've got to trap, an' your mother can't come for you.'   Paddy's voice lowered.   ' I'm sure goin' to miss you; it won't seem the same around here.'

Paddy stood looking through the window.   His face was sad.

' I'll come back, Paddy,' Bari said, choking back a sob.   ' I gotta come back.   I'll come often.'

' We'll eat dinner, then we'll bring wood in,' Paddy said, turning to the stove.   ' It's takin' lots of fuel these days.'

Bari couldn't eat dinner, neither did Paddy.

Nor did Bari think of fuel.   Right away he began gathering his treasures: leaves, stones, flowers and last of all his drawings.   He had so many things to tell his mother; so many things to show her.

At night he was ready.   His belongings were piled on the chair.

Paddy looked at them.   There was something sober tucked behind his smile.   ' You're in a hurry, eh? Hyslop won't be here for a while; lake ain't safe yet. When you go I'll send blueberries an' syrup to your mother; an' take your blankets, don't forget.'

The next few days Bari hardly moved from the house. Every morning he raced to the lake to try the ice.   He watched every hour of the clock.   Never had time moved so slowly.   He kept an eye on every movement in bush and lake.   A week passed.

'Maybe Hyslop's forgotten,' Bari said, struggling to keep back tears.

'He's a heap of country to cover, an' travellin' ain't good,' Paddy consoled. 'You go out an' fix a slide for yourself on the far hills.'

That is what Bari was doing when he saw the Mountie's shoulders disappearing over the rocks towards the cabin.

Bari raced home.

When he went in Paddy was standing by the stove. There was a strange look on his face.

'Where's Hyslop an'——?' Bari didn't say any more.

Paddy was looking past him on the wall, his lips quivering. He clutched the back of the chair. 'Hyslop was here, he—he couldn't wait—he asked me to tell you—your mother's dead.'

'Dead! Dead!' Bari slumped on to his cot with a piteous cry. The blood in his body seemed to stand still. He was numb, cold. This couldn't be!

'She took flu.' Bari heard these words before the tide of grief swept over him. He laid his head on the table, his shoulders rose and fell in heartbroken sobs that shook him from head to foot.

Vaguely he felt Paddy's hand on his shoulder. 'Hyslop left this,' Paddy pushed a parcel in front of him. 'There's a letter in it from Brad.'

Bari looked up. He gazed a full minute at the brown-paper package, then, hands shaking, began opening it. There was a letter on top. He lifted it and held it in his trembling fingers. Through tear-wet eyes he could see only faintly the pencil writing. He handed it to Paddy. 'What does it say?'

Paddy cleared his throat and blew his nose, then read haltingly, ' " Dear Bari, your mother she say for me to tell you she—was fine—had lots—to—eat. An' for you to stay—with Paddy Lindrum—for keeps, 'cos I'll not—be—home—no more. I'll be trappin'. The Mountie—he says—he'll help look after you—I made a play-sled for—you. I'm sendin' it." It's outside,' Paddy interjected, nodding towards the door. ' That's all he says.'

Paddy laid the letter on the table, opened up the rest of the parcel, took out a dog-harness, some drawings, a pencil stub, and a handkerchief in which were tied pine cones, half-a-dozen shiny stones, and a snuff-box filled with balsam gum. He laid them on Bari's knee.

Bari ran his fingers over the dog-harness, bringing them to rest on a tiny buckle. ' Brad made this for me, the buckle too, said he'd give me a—a—pup sometime,' Bari's voice broke into violent sobs. He laid his head back on the table.

' Don't cry, son, I'll take care of you. Me an' you'll do lots of things yet . . .' The hand stroked gently over his shoulder and rested on his head. Bari drew three or four whimpering breaths and looked up. ' Where do people go when they die dead, Paddy ? '

Paddy brushed some crumbs from the table with his hand. ' There ain't nothin' ever dies dead, Bari. They just sleep. They come again same's the flowers.' There was assurance in Paddy's voice, a peace that eased the hurt in Bari's heart.

' Who takes care of them when they're sleepin' ? ' Bari rubbed his eyes and looked through the window. Paddy was standing by his side. A spot of sunlight came filtering through the trees, it ran down along the window, throwing rainbow colours across the cot. Paddy hadn't answered.

'Paddy, who'll look after my mother?'

'The Painter of the Night, son.' The words came slowly. 'He does nice things, doesn't he?'

Bari nodded.

Paddy drew his chair to the table and sat down. 'I'll make you snowshoes, son. Hyslop's coming back pretty soon. He had things to see to. But he might even be back to-night.'

Bari knew Paddy was trying to make him happy.

But at night Hyslop did come back. He brought a parcel. Bari watched him open it. There were shoes, shirts, socks and mitts. 'These are for you, Bari.' He spoke quietly. 'They'll keep you warm.'

Bari looked at them. But there was no joy in his heart. He didn't pay any attention to what Paddy and the Mountie were talking about, nor did he look up when Hyslop went out.

Bari went to bed. All was quiet but the ticking of the clock. A glow of fire from the stove flickered across the wall. Through tear-dim eyes he could see his mother again, racing after the toboggan that spring morning as it whirled off across the melting snows. Her streaming dress, the strands of her hair. It was all so clear. His body quivered with sobs. He buried his face in the pillow and clenched his fists tight. Finally his eyes closed. He slept.

When he awoke he felt rested. There was a smell of cooking meat and coffee. A sense of gladness came to him, a feeling of home and security.

Paddy, standing by the stove, looked round. 'Did you have a good sleep? I got breakfast ready, me an' you's got work to do. We're goin' to take down your cabin to-day. In the spring we'll build a better one.' Paddy laughed the same old chuckling laugh.

They took the cabin down. Bari guessed it was work Paddy had thought up to keep him busy, same as fixing the roof and piling firewood.

Then one night, sitting by the fire, Paddy said, ' There's somethin' I bin plannin' to tell you. I gotta go an' get work.'

Bari looked at him. ' Ain't we been workin'? '

Paddy smiled. ' Yes, but there ain't been much money in it. I'm aimin' to go an' work for the K.L. They pay good money.' Paddy turned the stove lifter over several times in his hand before he went on, ' You see I need money, we gotta live, gotta eat, both of us. We'll go in the morning an' see if I can get work at the camp east. Hyslop says the K.L. needs men.'

A little spurt of eagerness swept through Bari. ' I'll like that Paddy. I like seein' things. There'll be horses, won't there? '

Paddy nodded.

Next morning, the minute Paddy heard Bari stirring, he jumped up and dressed. They ate breakfast, packed a lunch in their knapsack, and struck east across the lake.

There was a snarling wind, a flash of red in the low-tailed clouds. It was hard walking for sometimes the snow was deep. A frost-bitten spray struck their faces. Bari got tired. But there was adventure in his going, for was he not like a voyager seeking that farther kingdom? A kingdom with men and horses. He had always wanted to see horses.

About noon the sun cut through the clouds. Paddy cried, 'There it is, see! There's the camp behind the spruce. That's the cook-house on the Point. I know Billy Garson, the cook. His wife lives on the other side of the bay. I figger she'll keep an eye on you, an' Garson'll give us lots to eat.'

Bari felt need of it. Right now there was a hollow in his stomach. 'I don't see nobody around,' Paddy said, turning towards the shore. 'We'll make for that skidway where the walkin's easier.'

Bari was sweating. He could feel his clothes sticking to his back, but bravely he breasted the hill and plodded towards the building.

'The heavy timber's east, that's where the men'll be working,' Paddy said, heading towards one of the shanties.

Bari looked about. There wasn't a sign of life anywhere. A piece of white cardboard was tacked on the door of the largest cabin.

Paddy went forward and read the writing that was on it, 'CLOSED TILL SPRING'. His smile vanished. 'We're out of luck—there's nobody at home.' Taking a step forward he spelled out other words scrawled on the cabin wall. '" Gone with the Wild Geese. Back with the Robins!" We'll see what's here in the cook-house,' he said, turning and looking through the window of another building. 'Yah they're gone! There's a pail and dipper on the table, but there ain't no eats.' Paddy laughed thinly and came back along the trail.

Bari was disappointed. He was hungry. There was

nothing else to do but eat the lunch they had brought and go home.

It was black dark when they got there.

Paddy didn't speak of their trip afterwards, but sometimes Bari caught him looking at him strangely as if he was troubled.

Then one morning, leaning over the corner of the table after breakfast, he said, ' I'll have to go an' trap, Bari. I need money to buy flour an' things. Neither of us can eat if I don't get pelts to sell.'

Bari laid down his spoon, ' You mean——'

' We'll both go hungry!' Paddy interrupted with a wry smile, ' good an' hungry.'

Bari dropped the piece of bannock he was holding. ' Hungry!'

' Yes that's it,' Paddy nodded.

' I know hunger. It hurts!'

' That's the reason I want to get out an' trap.'

Bari bit his lip. ' I don't like trappin', Paddy.' His voice rose spiritedly. ' It ain't right killin' beasts.'

' But, son, we gotta live. We need the money for their hides so we can get flour an' sugar an' cloes for me an' you.'

Tears welled into Bari's eyes. ' Why do we have to get them that way? Won't we be looked after like they are?'

Paddy rubbed his brow and his cheek, then fixed his eye on something outside the window for some time before answering. ' It's the Good Spirit fixes them things for us, Bari. We're kinda partners with Him you see. He aims to provide for us. You see, even when we goes away like your mother we comes back; animals don't do that.' Paddy shook his head meaningly. 'So the Good Spirit gave us them so's we'd get flour an' shoes an' things, that's the way of it.'

'Does He take care of beasts too?'

'He takes care of everything. You see, Bari, we don't look at things the way the Good Spirit does. He just lets us know teeny bits of things an' takes care of the rest. He has it all up here in His own thinkin'-place,' Paddy tapped his forehead. 'It's a mighty fizzle we'd make of things if He didn't.'

Bari looked at him. 'Everything, every place?'

Paddy nodded. 'Sure! The bush, an' every place outside.' Paddy swept his hand round his imaginary world. 'It's all planned. The trail me an' you's goin' to take is all set out for us right down to the eats.'

Bari brought his brows together thoughtfully. His mother had told him about God. That must be the same Good Spirit.

Paddy was speaking. 'Can you see now there ain't no harm in trappin'? It's the way things is fixed. But remember, I never trap nor snare rabbits, 'cos I figger evil spirits might have got us but for them.' Paddy halted a moment, then looking up with a straight queer look added, 'Hyslop wants to take you to a school so's I can get away.' Paddy spoke quickly. 'I figgered on getting work at the camp so's I could keep you with me,' Paddy's voice shook, 'but they'll give you cloes an' eats an' everything, an' teach you to make pictures. It's better for you to go,' Paddy ended with a sorry attempt at laughter.

School! Go! The words thudded into Bari's head like dull blinding blows. His chest, his eyes, his throat filled as if he was choking. He clutched his chair, and through the terrible fear that gripped him, forced himself to say, 'You've teached me everything already, Paddy.'

'Only the writin' of the fur-folks' feet and how to find trail by the stars. You'll learn a better way of livin'—your mother went to school, Bari.'

'Paddy, I don't want to go to school! I don't want to leave you!' Bari clutched Paddy's arm and held it tight. 'Peter Hyslop'll bring us eats an' things.'

'Yes, but maybe Peter Hyslop'll get moved. Besides me an' him'll get old,' Paddy gave a short laugh. 'You'll always be back with me in the Berry Moon.' There was a catch in Paddy's voice. 'Better go, Bari. You'll be all right. I wouldn't let you go if I thought you wouldn't.'

'Paddy! Paddy!' Bari's words rose into wild sobs. Letting go Paddy's arm, he got up from his chair and raced from the cabin.

Chapter VII

SCHOOL

Bari didn't stop until he reached the valley's end. But the words 'school', 'hunger', 'school', 'hunger' were still ringing in his ear. He stood a moment looking across the bay. It was silent, ice locked.

Drawing a half sob he turned and walked to Seegwun's pool. It too was strangely silent. Everybody, everywhere was sleeping. Why had they to be resting when he so wanted to talk to them, tell them his troubles.

A breath of wind came up-valley, warming his face and hair. He listened to it singing through the spruce's boughs. Twigs danced to its touch, sunshine fluttered in its trail. It had heard him, it was talking to him. He felt better. Sharing his hurt with the forest made him feel he was not alone.

Into his bewildered head came reasoning. Paddy never cried, never minded doing hard things, and what

Paddy had said had always come out right. Paddy was kind, so was Hyslop. He couldn't let them go hungry. The very thought made him worried.

This business of working and eating seemed to go together. Paddy had to work to get food. Surely there was a way of life where people could do nice things and get food, like making pictures or doing the things they felt like doing, happy things.

Maybe it would be all right to go to school. Paddy had said they'd teach him to make pictures, and maybe they'd teach him how to make a house and build bridges so's he could make money to buy clothes and have a home first. Yes, going to school might be all right. He wiped his face with his sleeve and turned back towards the cabin.

When he went in Paddy was standing by the table. He had a queer look on his face, but his eyes sparkled when he spoke. 'I figgered you'd come back soon.' Paddy always said that.

Running forward, Bari threw his arms about Paddy's shoulders. 'I'll go, Paddy—go to school so's I can learn things. Then I'll keep you! Keep both of you—Hyslop an' you—when you're old.' He stopped short, burying his face in Paddy's arm to keep back sobs.

Paddy eased him to a chair. ' I washed yer cloes, see? ' He pointed to socks and underwear hanging behind the stove. Over in the corner Bari saw a couple of shirts wrapped around a pole. That was the way Paddy ironed them after washing.

Bari smiled.

' Hyslop said he'd come an' get you soon's he could,'

Paddy went on. 'He figgered he wouldn't be long. Let's have something to eat.'

Paddy made coffee and hot cakes. They tasted good. After that they didn't talk any more about it. Bari didn't even think. It was too big, too dreadful a thing for him even to imagine what might be coming.

Paddy worked all afternoon sewing on buttons and making another pair of moccasins. At night Bari's clothes were folded in a pile on the table.

Paddy and he went to bed early. Bari tried to sleep. He tossed and turned. Every little while he wiped tears from his eyes and pulled up his blankets so that Paddy wouldn't hear his sniffle.

When he woke next morning it was snowing. Paddy looked worried. Neither of them ate breakfast. Bari could feel a strange fear growing on him, as if something unreal and terrible was going to happen. He stayed indoors.

He kept wondering about school. What would it be like? Would there be other boys like him? Would there be any girls? And the teachers, would there be men teachers or women? He hoped they would be men. What would the colour of their skin be? His mother had told him that Indians were different from white folks, a different kind of people. 'I'm pale-face, half-breed they call me,' she'd say, stroking her cheek laughingly. 'You see my father was a Frenchman.'

Brad said Injuns an' whites didn't mix, but that couldn't be right. Brad was Injun. He had married his mother, and Peter Hyslop was just as white as could be. He was always friendly. Bari rose, walked over and peeked into the mirror hanging on the wall. He was pleased with the reflection. He ran his fingers over his face. It was soft and light. He was pretty nearly a pale-face. If he washed often he'd maybe get white like Hyslop.

It was getting on towards noon. He went and looked through the window. He wished Hyslop would come; it would be better to get it over, this strange, cruel happening.

Hyslop's step was at the door. He came in, batted the snow from his sleeves and shoulders. 'Well, I'm here, Paddy!' he said. 'It's a rough day. Have you got it all fixed up with the young lad? I came to get him.'

Paddy didn't move nor speak.

Bari clutched the table. Slowly the cabin walls became a blur; everything seemed to grow dark. This must be the end of the world. Blindly he pushed his arms into a coat Paddy was holding out to him.

Paddy was saying something. Hyslop was answering. Bari didn't hear; he pulled on his mitts. Hyslop reached for his hand and they went out together.

'I don't want to keep the dogs waiting, an' it'll take some doing to make the school by dark.' Hyslop's voice was happy.

At the top of the hill they stopped and looked back. Paddy was standing by the door; he raised his hand. Hyslop waved, then taking Bari by the arm turned and raced to the waiting sled.

One of the dogs whimpered, but Bari didn't look up. Hyslop set him on the toboggan and tucked a fur cover round his knees. The team leaped forward. They were gone.

They faced squarely into the storm with snow lashing

their faces. Bari cowered beneath his covering. The dogs kept up their pace. Hyslop didn't speak, except in a coaxing voice to the team. Now and again Bari glimpsed rocks and trees, but he had no idea which way they were going. It didn't matter, nothing mattered. The lope, lope, lope of the dogs and the swirling drift only added to his daze.

It was getting dark. The storm didn't let up. Hyslop talked intermittently. 'We'll soon be there. We shoulda stopped for something to eat, but I wanted to make it in daylight. You'll be all right. You're goin' to be glad you came. You'll like it, Bari.'

It wasn't all right. He wasn't going to like it. He didn't even like riding this way. He pushed his covering back to try and look around. His body was aching and his legs were cramped. He was hungry.

Darkness was closing about them. Suddenly Hyslop said, ' There's the school, see?'

Through a blur of snow, Bari could see it sitting like a bird's nest in a clump of trees. It was very big, very dark. A feeling of homesickness swept through Bari. His knees began to shake.

The dogs stopped. Hyslop got out and lifted him from the sled. He was stiff and cold. Hyslop walked him towards a door and into a building.

There were lots of lights. It was difficult to see. Some big people came. Bari kept looking at the floor. Hyslop talked a lot to a man. Bari wanted to cry, but he choked back his tears and hung on tightly to Hyslop. Then Hyslop said, ' I'm leaving you now. You're going to be all right. You'll have a good time here. I'll come back for you in the spring.'

For one desperate fighting moment Bari held Hyslop.
It was no use. He was going. His steps were dying
along the floor. Tears blinding him, Bari stood bewildered. Someone patted his shoulder. Two big boys
were beside him; they were smiling. 'Your name's
Bari?' one of them said. He was a big fellow with
laughing eyes.

Bari nodded.

'We're to look after you and see you get along all
right,' he went on. 'I'm Jim and he's Fred,' he nodded
towards the other boy, who kept saying 'Don't cry,
you'll be all right.'

They both helped him take his coat off and then took
him to a table where a plate of eats was waiting. They
sat, one on each side of him.

Bari tried hard to keep from crying. He couldn't
eat. The aching hollow in his stomach seemed to have
a lump in it. The boys didn't say anything for a while,
then Jim said, 'Come on, we'll show you where you
bath and then where you sleep.' They took him to a
room where there was a row of white tubs. They ran
water into one of them, then took off his clothes while
he tried to stop them. He didn't like being naked, but
they said he had to have 'a bath'.

They put him in one of the white tubs. He hated it.
They washed and scrubbed him with a cloth and hot
soapy water. It made his skin glow. He felt better.
He put on his clothes again.

After that they took him up a lot of steps to a room
where there were beds and beds and beds. Boys were
sleeping in some of them. 'That's yours,' Jim said,
pointing to one by the window. 'Your pyjamas are

under the pillow. Sleep good. You'll be all right.
To-morrow morning we'll come for you, you gotta be
checked by the nurse.' They went away.

Bari stood a moment. He was still in a daze. They
had said there was something under the pillow! He
lifted it and looked: it was a pair of trousers and a
coat. He wondered about them. They must be to
wear. Likely to keep the bed clean. He looked at the
clothes he had on, then back at the ones in the bed.
Yes, they were cleaner. Quick as a flash he pulled them
on over his own suit. The jacket tangled with his own.
It was really too small. He had to take his own off.
He worked quickly; he didn't want anyone to see. He
hopped into bed and pulled the covers up tight. Even
with the ache at his head and heart, sleep came quickly.

When he opened his eyes it was morning. The boy
in the next bed was raised on his elbow looking at him.
He was a kinky-haired fellow with a very dark skin.
' You cum last night?' he said grinning. ' What's your
name?'

' Bari!'

' Ha, you won't like it here, I don't!' he rolled the
whites of his eyes knowingly. ' My name's Joe. You'd
better get up.'

Bari was glad to have someone talk to him. The
other boys were getting up and dressing. They didn't
pay much attention to him. Joe lay down and pulled
his covers up.

Before Bari had his clothes on, the boys who had
looked after him the night before came along. ' We'll
look after you for a while. You've got to see the nurse
and barber after breakfast.'

Bari didn't want breakfast, he didn't want to see anybody. He wanted to go home. He was afraid. He walked to the dining-room with them, his whole body aquiver. When he sat down the grief of his stricken spirit broke into a flood of tears.

The boy spoke gently, soothingly. 'Eat something, you'll feel better then,' the biggest fellow coaxed. It was no use, the spoonful of porridge choked him. The tears welling over his cheeks made little rivers on the table where he laid his head.

The boys took him by the hand, one on each side, and led him to a room where a woman dressed in white looked at his teeth, his throat, his neck, his arms. He saw her vaguely through his tears, but he was aware only of a terrible pounding ache at the pit of his stomach. Why had this to happen to him? What was it all about?

Fred and Jim took him then to a place where he got new clothes and shoes. The clothes didn't thrill him like the ones Paddy had given him, nor did the shoes. But he shut his thoughts tight. It made him feel better.

After that a boy cut his hair. Nothing mattered now. He wasn't himself any more. He didn't even feel like himself. His arms, his feet and hands were in the same places, but that was about all.

They took him to a large room with seats and desks. They called it a classroom. Bari could hardly see for tears. But there were boys and girls in every seat. They were all looking at him. They were dark skinned like himself. He felt relieved.

Fred showed him to a seat at the back. Joe was

sitting next to him.   Bari was glad, for Joe's eyes kept
laughing in a friendly sort of way.

The teacher was a tall woman.   She was white.   Her
name was Miss Morton.   The boys and girls called her
Windigo.   That's what Joe said.   She talked a great
deal.   Bari sat numbly with a mistiness in his head;
nothing was quite clear.   He didn't see nor hear; all he
felt was a jumble of pain inside him.

He was glad when night came.   He went to bed tired,
hungry and unhappy.   But he slept well.

As days passed he felt better.   He got used to things,
his new clothes and shoes.   He learned how to wear his
pyjamas and he liked the eats.   Joe talked to him a lot.
Joe's friendliness was cheering.   He showed him lots of
things and places.   There didn't seem to be much to
school.   There was nothing different round the end of
one corridor except another corridor (that's what the
boys called them).   It wasn't like the bush where there
was something alive and lovely everywhere you went.

But at the far end of the school there was a room
called the carpenter's shop.   It was like the lean-to at
Paddy's only smarter looking.   There were saws,
hammers, and a lot of tools Bari had never seen before
hanging on the wall and benches along the sides where
the boys made things like cupboards, steps and different
kinds of boxes.

The cupboards were a lot fancier than the ones Paddy
made.   They had drawers with shining handles and
bright painted knobs.

The boys weren't sent to get shop learning until they
were older.   But Bari and Joe liked peering through the
window, watching them work.   Joe said he'd make a

piano when his turn came. 'Of course,' he added brightly, 'it's really houses an' boats we'll be makin' before we finish.' Bari didn't say anything. But in his mind he knew that he would make something for Paddy.

The teacher was a short man with sandy hair and a laughing face. He always worked without his coat and with a white apron folded up at the bottom to hold nails and rulers. The boys liked him. He played football with them and showed them the right way to play hockey. His name was Mr Millen. The boys never called him anything else.

Bari and Joe always joined in the games when he played. Then they showed him how to play one of their own games they called 'crap' with pieces of wood. They had to jiggle their arms, legs and bodies back and forth as they sat, and sing and yodel in a weird sort of way. Teaching Mr Millen delighted them. Afterwards they'd always build a little bonfire and roast potatoes and nuts. They'd eat them with melted butter, which Mr Millen got specially for the occasion.

Bari liked all the eats they had at the table, especially the bread and milk, and he liked playing with the other boys. He was beginning to know their names, and slowly from the flatness of his bewilderment other things were beginning to stand out, the order, the busyness and the staff (that was the other teachers and big people who were around). They were all white.

He wasn't afraid to go into the classroom now. He liked Miss Morton, especially when she wore her red dress and red sparkling things on her ears. Little spasms of delight swept through him when she showed him

how to write and how to make flowers with cardboard.

Sometimes she stood and talked a great deal, then
put twos and threes and ones on the board. That they
had anything to do with him, Bari never dreamed. It
was one of these times his eye fell on a pile of paper
on a nearby desk. He had never seen so much paper
before, and beside it there were pencils and crayons. His
heart beat a tattoo of joy. Here were the things he
craved, the needs of his desires and his dreams.

Then on an empty desk next to him there was a book.
It looked new. Drawing it quietly over, he opened it.
There were two clear white shining pages at the front.
The loveliness of them! Their very whiteness thrilled
him.

Digging a stub of pencil from his pocket he filled the
first page with drawings of trees, then held it up to Joe.

Joe's eyes sparkled. He grinned approvingly.

Encouraged, Bari put his head down and drew for
dear life. He would surprise his teacher, show her he
could draw pictures, do something different from other
children.

He didn't see or hear what the teacher was saying nor
did he hear her tip-toeing to his side.

'What's this you're doing, Bari?' she said, lifting the
book. There wasn't a smile on her face. 'Why did
you do it?' she went on. 'And what is it supposed to
be?' She tapped the desk with a ruler and looked at
him as if she was angry.

Bari sat shaking. He tried to speak, but he felt like
a tiny worm shrinking into a nothingness beneath the
falling heel of a real windigo. Every boy and girl was

looking at him. He grit his teeth and looked helplessly at Joe.

Joe's saucer-like eyes were wide with wonder.

Teacher walked back to the front of the room and held up the book. ' Now, children, pay attention. No one must put a single pencil mark on any reader.' Her voice was stern. ' You will all get a drawing-period later.' She looked straight at Bari.

He winced and looked again at Joe.

' Gee you can draw, Bari!' Joe whispered, black eyes asparkle. ' Don't pay no attention to her. She's just a bumble-bee makin' a lot of noise.' Joe leaned closer as he whispered the last.

Bari's head dropped. His spirit was bruised. His quivering hands sought the desk. He toyed with his pencil. Quietly from under cover of his own desk Joe slipped over another brand-new book.

Bari looked at him. There was roguery in his eye. It lifted Bari's spirits. He sat up with a sense of relief; he had a friend, a champion. The thought gave him confidence, and stirred a spirit of mutiny in him. The clean new book lying in front of him was a challenge.

The teacher was writing on the board, but she was keeping an eye on him.

Still smarting from his disappointment Bari sat in cold indifference, hoping for a chance to open the book and put just the tiniest pencil mark on every one of its white pages. But the chance didn't come. Miss Morton saw to that, and she gathered and piled all the other books on a shelf and watched them like a bear guarding a bees' nest.

In the days following, Joe managed to push scribblers.

books and paper into Bari's hands, saying 'There, draw on them. Let's see you make pictures.' Every time Joe said 'Let's see you make pictures', Bari started on another book. Never had he wallowed in such plenty of paper. He had a tiny suspicion that there might be a reckoning with Miss Morton, for if she ever caught him drawing on anything she'd swoop down on him like a hawk on a tit-mouse and scoop it from his hands.

But there were the real drawing-periods, and Bari loved them. Miss Morton seemed to be a different person then. She gave him pencil and paper, showed him how to hold his work, how to make shades and lines and colour flowers and make them big or small.

Bari worked faster than the other boys and could do better.

Then there were the times after school when Joe and he would race to the woods, when the wind, pine-scented and sharp, would set the snow acrackle. It was then that Bari taught Joe the writing of the fur-folks' feet. Even when the moon was full they loved to wander through the deeper bush; for then, on the clean white snow, paw-prints of the forest folks were plain. Bari knew where to look. And Joe knew so little!

By a crevice in the rocks or sometimes by a wood-chuck's hole they'd find skunk tracks. 'See!' Bari would say jubilantly, 'they make a mark like a cat's only longer an' they track in pairs, two feet together like.' Whipping out pencil and paper from his pocket he'd draw as best he could the double-spaced markings of the skunks' feet.

Up on the high ridges they would find a fox's trail. 'He goes where he gets a good view,' Bari explained,

D

pointing to tiny dog-like footprints winding from the roots of an old stump. 'Three footmarks almost in line, one off to one side, that's them,' Bari added knowingly, getting the fox's trail on to his paper.

Then there was the musk-rat's with the stroke of the tail between, which they found along the sandy shore when spring came. 'I lived with a musk-rat one time,' said Bari confidingly. 'I learned lots from it.' Joe rolled the whites of his eyes dubiously and in a voice none too believing said, 'Musta bin muddy, eh?' But Bari was busy drawing.

All through the jackpine they found squirrels' foot-writing. 'Squirrel's right clever,' Bari stopped to explain. 'He washes his face an' holds his eats in his front paws just like hands. The tracks he makes ain't like anything else's. He's got five toes on his hind feet an' they come first.' And so they would find them leading from a little gathering of cone and nut shells, that gave squirrel's hiding-place away.

Then there was deer-mouse's tiny zig-zagging runways under the snow. They were easy to find. 'He makes a big track for his size.' Bari grinned, pulling back twiggery to show finger-like markings of feet that had darted hither and yon to lose themselves beneath ledges of stone.

There were other things Bari showed Joe; 'pills' owls had coughed up, little pellets of undigested food Ko-ko-ko had cast out of his stomach. Bari always found them beneath their roosting-places. The dents in the snow where sleeping rabbits had huddled for warmth, and sometimes scraps of fur and a jumble of footmarks showing where a fox had caught him unawares.

Sometimes Bari wondered about Joe. He never owned up to being a partner in trouble. Racing through snow-drifts in answer to the bell that called them home, Joe always said, ' You'll be late ', or when things got lost or broken in Joe's hands, Joe would say, ' You'll catch it, Bari! '

Bari's opinion of him was halted between admiration and suspicion, but although Joe never entirely got away with it, he lived cheerfully in the sunshine of his own thoughts.

It was after one of these dashes home that Miss Morton was waiting. ' Come with me, Bari Bradbrooke,' she said in a voice far from endearing. He followed her to the classroom where, pointing to a pile of new scribblers and readers, she asked, ' Was it you who did the scribbling on all these books? ' Her face was like a thundercloud.

Bari looked at the books and then at her, and nodded.

Walking to the front of the room she came back with a strap. He took punishment like a hero, but his heart was breaking. Groping strickenly through tears, he walked from the room. He had a feeling that somewhere in this blackness Joe should have been near. That night he cried himself to sleep.

After that nothing was very clear to Bari inside the school. He liked Joe a little less, his teacher a little more. Often now she said to him, ' You're the best drawer we have, Bari ', or ' You are wonderful with a pencil. I think you must have drawn lots before you came.'

He would like to have told her about the Night Painter and how he watched him, or taken her into the bush before supper and shown him setting golden wedges through the jackpine, but every time he thought of home or Paddy a lump came into his throat.

Everybody seemed to get busier and busier.

'It's comin' Christmas,' Joe said. 'Didn't you never hear of Christmas?'

Bari shook his head.

'You doan' know nothin'. It's a man's birthday, a white man's, but he's dead.'

'Dead!' Bari repeated. 'There ain't nothin' dies dead.'

'There ain't!' Joe's eyes brightened into pools of fire. 'You go an' take a look at the chicken you're goin' to eat for dinner!'

'I don't believe you,' Bari retorted. 'Paddy said they don't.'

'He doan' know nothin' neither,' Joe answered scornfully.

Irked at the jibe at Paddy, Bari threw off his coat and leaped for Joe's throat. There was a wild scuffle, Joe fought desperately, but in fury of anger Bari beat and pounded him.

A crowd of boys gathered. They cheered. One or two tried to grasp Bari, others egged him on. With the plaudits of the gang and old sores rankling Bari plunged into the battle with renewed wrath. He didn't stop until Joe was flattened out in the snow.

The boys cheered and carried Bari into school. He was a hero. The older boys gave him candies and tit-bits of eats, some of them shared the bear grease with which they smoothed their hair. Bari was pleased; he had made a name for himself.

He didn't feel so happy about it next day when Joe faced him with a black eye and a cut nose. But time healed the hurt; and after a while Joe forgot about it, though they weren't as friendly as they had been.

Christmas turned out to be a tree-time. Spruce was brought in from the woods. Red, blue and green lights and sparkling things were put on them. Everyone seemed to be happy.

'I tol' you!' Joe said. 'You get a better birthday when you're dead than when you're livin'. I don't have a birthday, neither do you—not till we're growed up or died dead.'

Bari squinted at him and clenched his fist. Did Joe want another licking?

'Aw, you don't know nothin',' Joe went on, nose puckered disgustedly. 'Do you know people get wings, I bet you don't?'

'Paddy said if we'd feathers we wouldn't need clothes.' Bari lowered his voice dangerously.

'Paddy ain't been to school!'

Bari listened only a moment, then walked away. He was not changing his mind about anything, not for Joe. The things Paddy had told him he was going to keep straight.

Chapter VIII

FLOWER MOON

After Christmas, Bari was never quite happy. The
break with Joe never really healed. There were many
things Bari didn't understand. At night he lay in bed
listening to the wind calling for snow, but he dreamed of
lapping water. Great Spirit Moon had come and gone.
Sucker Moon was just about out. Daylight was growing
longer, he wanted to live outdoors.

Spring came to the woods. There was a gurgle and
murmur beneath the snow. Bari helped the boys make
ditches. Freshets leaped and bounded through the
bush. It was spring!

It coursed into his blood. He tried to fight it, but
it must have been there before he was born.

The classroom was dull. Teacher wanted him to
draw boxes and wooden things. He wanted to draw
birds and butterflies and flowers, the lovely living things
that came to the woods in the spring. As sunbeams came
frolicking along the classroom walls, Bari's eyes followed

94

them. Seegwun would be sunning now on the lake-shore. Life was young in the bush. Picking up his pencil Bari tried to forget it.

Unease was growing on him, something apart from dislike of walls and people and school. It was something that was missing, pine-smelling trails, greening grass. He wanted to see violets, the white star flower of the strawberry and Seegwun. What was she doing? It was an urge, a something that kept pulsing its way into his head and heart.

He tried to quiet it with the thought that next moon the term would soon end. School would close. Hyslop would come for him.

But at night the Flower Moon looked through the dormitory window, a great yellow mocking face, and wind tapped the pane. Bari pulled up his quilts and closed his eyes. It was no use; he saw the dogwoods' bursting bloom, and smelt burning leaves by Paddy's door. All the old longing rushed over him.

The night was long. He turned and tossed. He heard the breathing of the sleeping boys and felt cramped and hemmed in on every side. He threw out his arms, then rose and opened the window. The freshness of night filled him. The moon seemed to laugh and nod as if he understood.

North in the sky Bari could see the Pole Star. It was faint and tiny to-night. Somewhere straight south of it was Paddy's cabin, and his own place, his kingdom. He could see the flags and trees that were his people. They were calling.

In a minute he was into his clothes. He took a quick look at Joe in the next bed and saw that he was asleep.

He didn't even stir when Bari put his head close to him.

Bari grasped his boots, tiptoed to the door, opened it with one hand and sneaked downstairs. Outside he put his boots on. He was gone! Gone! Free! The joy of it! Feet scarcely touching ground, he scudded towards the road.

In a mile he was into bush. He was wary, for it was coming day. Tracking him would be easy in the damp grass. What if they followed and took him back to school? What would he say? It would be safer to travel at night and rest in the daytime.

He turned into a hollow and found shrubbery where a ray of sunrise was warming the moss. He crawled in. Pulling dead leaves over his feet he closed his eyes.

When he woke the air was chill. The sky was grey. Day had gone. He had a gaunt feeling in his stomach. Looking dazedly around he saw water some distance ahead, so he made for it and dropping on his knees scooped handfuls to his mouth. He felt better.

It wasn't dark enough for stars, but keeping tight to the bush he struck towards a rim of spruce. There were snags, windfalls and tangled shrubbery. It was a strange world of trees. Sideways and forward he plunged till darkness seemed to shut him between dark walls. He couldn't go forward.

He sat down. Up the hollow came the bark of a timber wolf. Its clear sharp yelp echoed through the forest behind. Bari tried to tell himself he was not afraid. He got up and stumbled forward. He craned and twisted his head to try and see the Pole Star. Clouds were massing northward; it was a black night. He was lost.

Helplessly, he slumped to the ground. He was hungry. His feet were aching, so was his body. Why did he leave the school?

Huddling into a tree he tried to think. Tears came to his eyes, though he wanted to be brave. The sharp wind of the spring night was making his body shiver. He drew his coat tighter. He was drowsy, but he must keep awake.

Paddy was in his mind. Nobody knew how much he loved Paddy. Paddy, with his wrinkled eyes and knobby hands. He'd have so many things to tell him. Paddy would give him duck and wild rice, lots of it!

Bari would tell him that they killed and ate pigs and cows at the school, and made him bath in a tub in winter and rang bells for everything. Yes, and he'd tell him about Miss Morton too, the things she had taught him about drawing, the flowers she had taught him to make with paper, and then about Joe. No, he wouldn't mention Joe, nor the dead chicken!

Bari's lip quivered. Paddy had needed money to buy eats and clothes. Maybe he wouldn't like him leaving school, maybe Paddy wouldn't have eats enough yet. Hyslop might be cross.

The wolves yelped. There were noises everywhere. Bari shuddered and lay close to the ground.

His thoughts went back to the school. After all he should learn things so's he could make money to buy paper and pencils and crayons. Then he'd be able to make pictures and keep Paddy if he was hungry.

Yes, he'd go back!

He could hardly wait for daylight. He dozed, but at the first streak of sun he was up. His own tracks were easy to follow. His feet hurt and almost refused to walk. But when he came in sight of the school he was happy. There was a song in the poplars as he climbed the rise. As he got close to the school gate, a bell rang. Boys and girls were running from every direction towards the building.

Suddenly three or four boys broke from the others and came racing to meet him. Eyes sparkling, they patted his shoulder and took his arm and ran ahead with him. They were glad to see him!

Bari was delighted. He wasn't frightened when they were with him. It sure felt good to be back.

When he went into the school Miss Morton was standing at the classroom door. 'You're back, Bari,' she said beaming. 'We missed you.' She wasn't angry. 'And I certainly missed you from drawing-class. You know we don't have anyone who draws quite so well as you!' If the sun had fallen into Bari's hands he couldn't have been more surprised.

The principal had come forward; he was talking to Miss Morton. 'I didn't think he'd go far. The boys tracked him east a bit; better see he gets something to eat and fresh clothes.'

It was him they were talking about! Bari was pleased. He felt a little ashamed when the clothes-lady pointed to his torn trousers and ragged socks, but he was really too happy to grieve.

The boys were all pleased to see him back. Joe was the only one who asked questions. 'What did you run away for?' he quizzed with a roguish eye.

Bari shrugged. 'I don't know. Something inside of me made me go.'

'I'd have gone with you if you'd tol' me,' Joe went on happily, 'but you'd have catched it. It ain't right to run away. Didn't nobody ever tell you that?'

Bari nodded.

Joe's wisdom was always a trifle mixed, but he felt a little friendlier to Joe now—indeed he felt a little better about everything and everybody.

Together Bari and Joe watched for the Strawberry Moon. It came at last, a tiny sliver into the summer sky.

'Indian can hang his powder-horn on it,' Joe said knowingly. 'It's sure goin' to rain.'

Rain or sun didn't interest Bari. With the help of the calendar on the classroom wall he calculated that when the moon was full Hyslop would come for him. It would be holidays.

Joe, less sky-minded, kept track of time by breaking a tooth each day from his comb. 'When I don't need to comb my hair any more I go home, see,' he said proudly.

So they watched and waited. Time seemed endless, even with the bustling and hustling of getting new clothes and shoes. There were examinations: Bari didn't like them. He put the weighty things of the classroom from his mind—all except drawing, and Miss Morton said there was no examination in that.

The moon passed the first quarter; Joe's comb was getting slim. Excitement of going home was in the air.

At last the night came. Everything was ready. To-morrow school closed. Any time now the children's folks might come for them. Every boy and girl kept their eyes glued to the window.

Bari went to bed with boots and clothes on. So did the other boys. No one slept. Before daylight, everyone was out of bed, even Joe.

Never had Bari been so happy. He couldn't eat breakfast. Already some of the children were leaving. Why didn't Hyslop come? What if he didn't come at all? By noon Bari's fear had reached exploding point.

Half an hour later Hyslop strode into the hall. The boys gathered round, looking him up and down with admiring eyes. Bari was proud of him, proud to be the one whom he had come to take home.

But Bari didn't know anything else. He was aware of a bundle of clothes being pushed into one hand, a parcel of books into another. Hyslop was taking him by the arm. They were out of the school. They were getting into Hyslop's boat. The motor had started. It was holidays. He was going home!

Chapter IX

RICE MOON

Paddy was watching for them. As soon as they swung into the home bay Bari and Hyslop saw him running along the shore to meet them. The minute they docked Bari, bundle in hand, sprang to his arms. The smell of his wood-smoked clothes was good.

Paddy gave him a rough hug, then holding him at arm's length looked at him. 'It's sure great to see you! It sure is!' There was a ring of happiness in Paddy's voice.

Leaving his bundle in Paddy's hand, Bari raced to the cabin. He was home! Home! Rushing through the door, he tore around the table and out again, kicking and frisking like a young thing in the spring sun.

The putt-putt of Hyslop's motor brought him to a halt. He stood while Hyslop swung his outboard round and waved good-bye, then he ran to Seegwun's pool.

Dropping on his knees, he peered through the flags.

The grass had grown lush and heavy. There were tooth marks on the willow and gnawings of bark on the shore. That was all he wanted to know.

Paddy had put up the birchbark cabin. It was bigger than the year before. Its roof widened over an open doorway facing the hollow. It looked like a tiny porch. There was a table in it and a small chair. Bari was thrilled. The delight of it set his heart throbbing with joy. Again he had his kingdom in the woods.

He ran to the wind-flower dip. White star-bloom of strawberry studded the slope. Roses were sending sweetness through the spruce shade. Yes, his people were out and smiling. He wished he had brought Joe to show him, or Miss Morton. Joe, of course, could never understand. He'd likely grin and say, ' You'll catch it for takin' things that ain't yours.'

When Bari got back to the cabin, Paddy had a fire built, fish baked and bannock toasted. ' We're goin' to eat right now,' he said, with the same old chuckle in his voice.

Such a meal it was! Bari couldn't tell him about the school fast enough. ' You see, Paddy,' he kept repeating, ' it isn't like here. They don't know the things you know, don't know nothin' about the bush. But I can draw now, they teached me. I'll show you how to make a picture, Paddy.'

Paddy smiled. There was a twinkle in his eye.

Next day Bari moved his belongings and his drawing-things to his own cabin. There he felt a supremacy, a nearness to the forest folks he loved.

Every spare minute he spent drawing them, colouring them on paper. He knew every track and trail, every twig and bower of his kingdom. He could take firmer hold of his pencil now. Teacher had shown him how to keep a tree from looking like a bush, and a bush from looking like a tree; had told him about distance and the way to look at things you were drawing.

Sometimes, at night, Paddy and he would sit alone with the scents and sounds of the forest about them, watching the 'gooqua in the shadows. Neither Paddy nor he would speak, but they were very close to each other. Bari could feel it. There was love in their silence. He wanted to live always just like this.

But one night Paddy said, 'We gotta do some work, you an' me. We're goin' to pick rice. I gotta get some money!'

'Money!' Bari didn't need money, so he thought. 'Livin' like this is all right, Paddy.'

'Yah,' Paddy nodded, 'but we need flour an' sugar an' cloes. We'll fix up some sacks an' rogans an' when it comes the golden time,' Paddy said happily, 'we'll go up-lake an' gather rice.'

Bari wasn't too enthusiastic. Back in his memory was his experience with Oney when berry-picking. Bari hated to think about it. Besides, he loved leisure to roam the woods and draw. Such a good time they'd have if Paddy didn't have to work. But he helped Paddy willingly to patch grain sacks and fix rogans to shake rice in.

Rice Moon came. Sumacs were flaming red. Poplars were spouts of showering gold. There were glints of yellow in the breeze. This was the golden time—Paddy said so.

One night, Paddy and he were mending the canoe

when they heard music coming from the bush. 'That's Keego,' Paddy said, without looking up. 'He plays a mouth-organ.'

'Who's Keego?' Bari asked, eyes fixed on a figure coming through the shrubbery.

It was some minutes before Paddy answered. 'He's just Keego, a fellah who lives in the bush. He's different; not just right.' Paddy spoke slowly as if he'd rather not speak at all. 'The Indians say he's got an evil spirit in him. They're scared of him. He's got to live alone. He's about fourteen.'

'Are you scared of him too, Paddy?' Bari asked, eyes still on the oncoming figure.

'Naw, Keego's smart, smart as a cricket.'

'Why don't people like him then?'

Paddy shaved down a pin with his jack-knife before answering. 'They say he brings trouble an' there's no tellin' what'll happen when he's round.'

Keego, skirting the shore, came handspringing across the rocks, poised a moment, toes skyward, before vaulting to the path in front.

He was hatless and coatless. His shirt was patched with many colours, his dark trousers, greening with age, made him almost one with the restless foliage.

He straightened and came forward, hand outstretched. 'I bin workin' over there,' he nodded towards the bush, 'pickin' mushrooms.'

'Get any?' Paddy asked.

'Naw. There ain't any,' he answered, stepping forward and linking his arm through Bari's. 'Can I stay with you? I like you.' He looked straight into Bari's eyes. There was a wildness about him; his hair,

tousling in the wind, was long and brown. His shifty
eyes sparkled, a smile played about his thin mouth as
he repeated pleadingly, 'Can I stay with you please?'
A burst of affection swept through Bari. He looked at
Paddy. Paddy's face was sober.

'Let him stay, Paddy. I like him.'

Paddy rubbed his chin thoughtfully. It seemed ages
before he spoke. 'He can stay a while.'

Bari knew by his voice he wasn't keen about it.

Keego slipped his hand into Bari's. 'Let's go to the
bush.'

Together they tore over the rocks. Keego's hand-
springs breaking into the music of his flying mouth-
organ. Bari had never seen anyone so nimble nor so
filled with laughter. They raced and scampered until
Paddy called them home.

But Keego vanished into the bush just as quickly as
he had come from it. Bari walked back to the cabin
alone.

'I like Keego, Paddy. I wish he would come often!
He knows lots, he can catch fish with his feet, make
fire with a stone,' Bari went on with admiration, 'at
least he says he can.'

Paddy didn't say anything. He didn't seem to want
to talk about Keego.

After they had eaten supper Paddy said, 'We'll start
for rice in the morning. We'll put everything ready in
the canoe to-night.'

Bari began to get excited. Rice-picking was going
to be a thrill, and likely Paddy would give some money
to him. Bari had used the very last piece of drawing-
paper he had brought from school and every shred of

wrapping-paper he could find around the cabin. With money he would buy more and pencils and crayons, everything he needed!

Running back and forth to the canoe with bedding and eats made him forget Keego. He went to bed tired, and was awakened by a thunderous knock on the door. It was still dark. He sat up.

Paddy rose, lit a candle and lifted the latch. Keego bounded in. 'I'm goin' rice-pickin' with you!'

Bari saw Paddy blink as he asked, 'How do you know we're goin'?'

'Saw you loadin' the canoe.'

'You can't go, Keego. It's too far.'

'I know. I bin there lots of times.' Keego nodded agreeably, but there was no backing down in his voice.

Bari shot out of bed and took hold of Paddy's arm. 'Let him come, Paddy. I told him he could. He knows how to make rice, an' me an' him'll have a good time.'

Paddy's brows came together thoughtfully. Bari saw that he didn't want Keego. 'Aren't you going to let him come?' coaxed Bari, tugging Paddy's sleeve.

Paddy looked at him, then at Keego. There was a silence. 'All right if you want him.'

Bari bounded to his cot and began dressing.

Keego had no doubt about going. Already he was clearing eats off the cupboard into a box to carry to the canoe.

'We'll eat before we start,' Paddy said, putting wood in the fire and drawing the coffee-pot on to the stove.

They ate quickly. When night rolled up her blankets they were well up-lake, Keego plying a deft paddle. He was a gay companion. He hailed south-going geese and mimicked chattering squirrels along the tree-lined channels. He was at home on the water. He ran the rapids dangerously, the canoe righting only with his swift back-stroke, and mocking laugh.

Paddy didn't talk much. Once pointing to Keego's ragged moccasins, he said, ' You need shoes, Keego.'

Keego nodded. ' An' shirts ! '

Paddy laughed. ' You'll make enough money rice-pickin' to buy them.'

' You'll pay us ? ' Keego said, eyes glittering.

' Sure, I'll give Bari and you quarter of what we make when we sell our rice.'

' Maybe it not sell.' Keego said dubiously.

' It's sold now. Ted Odzell's promised to buy all we can get in to him by the twentieth. He's got a store out here by the water-line.'

Bari was listening. They were going to get money! He felt like whooping with joy. Now he could buy drawing things.

They were a happy trio. They glided into Mikado Bay at dusk. Choosing a high-timbered poplar, they stacked branches around it tent fashion, then covered them with cedar. They threw balsam on the floor to sleep on. ' The tent'll be good when the nights are cool,' Paddy said. The boys liked it.

Keego built a fire, then, with his slingshot, got two ducks. He mixed clay and water and covered them, popped them on the hot coals and baked them for supper, showing Bari how, and including a bar of music from his mouth-organ with his patter.

When they unloaded the canoe, Bari clutched a pencil he had rolled in his blanket. ' See,' he said, holding it up to Keego, ' this is mine. I draw all the time, except when I'm working.'

Keego looked at it. ' I draw, too,' he said grinning. ' See.' He dropped to the ground, and taking a stick drew figures on the sand. Bari joined him. It was getting dark, and when Paddy called, ' It's bedtime, boys ,' they scampered in.

Paddy was rolling into his blanket. Bari took his and lay down beside him. Keego stretched on the floor behind.

Bari couldn't sleep. He could hear Paddy moving as his balsam bed creaked. Strange shadows capered along the roof of their twigged-in shelter. Through the doorway Bari could see cat-tails quivering in the glow of a fire moon. He was afraid. It must be the wind that was making the night so alive. Over in the corner Keego was sleeping, a streak of light falling over his face.

Suddenly Paddy rose, walked out, and threw a sprinkling of tobacco on the water. Bari knew what that was for. It was to please the Good Spirit, so that no harm would come to them. Paddy must be feeling the spookiness too.

Easing on his elbow, Bari watched him light a fire and sit down beside it. He'd like to have run out and talked to him, but his blanket felt warm and he was getting sleepy. He closed his eyes.

When he awoke Keego was up. Paddy had dug honey from a bees' nest and was melting it over hot water. Keego was fixing fish as he'd done the ducks. Coffee was brewing.

' You gotta eat lots,' Paddy said, bringing bannock

and canned milk from their store. ' There's work to do and plenty hard,' he said, chuckling.

They slid their canoe into the water. The boys took the paddles. Farther out the wild rice-stalks stood blue and hedge-like against the yellow sky. Duck rose with whirring wings from their morning meal as the canoe pushed forward.

' It's a great crop,' Paddy said, pointing to where heavy heads of grain had fallen and lay in tangled masses on the water. ' We'll begin here.' They pulled the canoe to a spot where wind had driven the crop into tiny piles. With a long pole Paddy began lifting it into the canoe.

It was tricky work separating the blades and heads from the yellow roots matted beneath the water. Only Paddy's skill kept the boat from tipping. The morning was warm so Keego and Bari took off their coats and shirts. With spray stinging their eyes they worked until sweat came glistening on their shoulders. Load after load they rowed ashore and spread to dry. They were weary at noon; but they didn't stop, for the grain was ripe and every load meant money.

At night, with sockless feet, they flailed, trenched and trampled the rice heads until the husks fell off, Paddy vying with the boys, who leaped and danced to Keego's ringing mouth-organ. Then they winnowed and shook the rice in their rogans and put it in sacks.

Supper always tasted good: fried rice, rice and duck, or rice with wild honey which Keego and Bari took time to dig from nearby stumps.

These were great nights, sitting by the camp-fire listening to Paddy. He knew everything about

'gooquas who lived in the wind and people who lived
in the sky. The moon came laughing through the trees
as if he'd like to live with forest folks and eat rice and
honey. The glimmering trail he laid across the water,
Paddy said, was dust from spirits' feet who had come
scattering good things on the earth.

Bari wanted to draw these, put these stories on paper,
but he had no paper. Paddy had thought his last packet
of tea had burst, for he didn't know Bari had used it
for a drawing of a boat.

One night Paddy rowed them up-lake to Odzell's
store. It was about three miles. There were a number
of cabins on the Point, but the store stood alone. It
was small and built of logs.

When they went in Odzell was packing eggs into a
box. He was a big easy-looking man with a full-moon
face. Hailing them cheerily, he pushed the eggs aside,
beckoned Paddy to a seat and sat down beside him.

There was another fellow in the store, a tall lean chap
with snappy eyes. He was younger than Odzell. Bari
and Keego turned towards him.

Pushing a mop of tousled hair back from his eyes he
grinned and pointed to a case filled with belts and
hunting-knives. 'Ain't these swell? They're on sale;
the boss is selling them dirt-cheap,' he went on in a
companionable voice. 'Maybe the old man'll buy you
one like this,' he drew out a beaded belt and handed it
to Keego.

Bari's eyes rested on it momentarily, then ran along
a shelf to a pile of writing-pads and scribblers. There
they stayed. He wasn't interested in belts and hunting-
knives. He moved back to Paddy, who had got to his

feet and was ordering groceries. He stood until Paddy tucked the last packet of coffee into his knapsack, then nudged him and pointed to the paper.

Paddy nodded.

'I'll take some of these scribblin'-books. This fellah likes to draw,' he nodded towards Bari.

That was all Bari heard, all he wanted. The joy of getting paper filled him and he went home happy.

The next days were busy ones, but at every opportunity he was out amongst the trees. He made pictures of ferns, tiger lilies and rugged corners with moss-covered rocks. Sometimes he sketched Keego; Keego laughing, Keego dancing. Once he caught a glint of Keego's angry face: a scowl that wasn't good to look at. He showed it to Paddy.

'Don't let Keego see it!' Paddy warned. 'He'll be mighty mad.'

But Keego found it. He liked it. 'That's me ain't it?' he cried. 'Draw it again! I feel like that often.'

Leaning over Bari's shoulder, he'd often point to bird drawings and say, 'That feather ain't lying right; that eye ain't seein' nothin'. It should be here.' Or dancing with eddying leaves or gale-swept reeds he'd cry, 'Draw it! Draw it! Bari, what makes them dance?'

Bari liked it when he told him things. It made him draw better. 'You know lots about birds, Keego, don't you?' Bari said one night.

Keego grinned. 'I'm one of them. I talk to them. Listen!' Cupping hands about his mouth he sent a long quivering laugh lakeward. The mocking laugh of a loon came back across the water. 'See, I tol' you, an' I can pretty nearly fly. Once I nearly did.'

'What happened?' Bari asked, wide-eyed with wonder.

'I ain't tried yet,' Keego answered soberly. But Bari knew that Keego believed in his winged dream.

Maybe he had reason, for Keego was smart. With a sling shot he could drop a twig or split a falling leaf. He taught Bari the kind of pebbles to use, the swift hand-trick that sent them to their mark. Keego never killed small birds or squirrels; he said it wasn't right, because they couldn't shoot back. He made Bari a sling shot and together they practised, Bari throwing twigs in the air for marks.

Bari was an apt pupil. The boys at school couldn't do that. He would show them how when he got back. He didn't know that before Rice Moon waned his skill would be useful.

Chapter X

KEEGO

By the fifteenth of the month Paddy and the boys had
twenty sacks of rice gathered. Paddy stacked them
round a tree. Bari and Keego counted them. Then
Paddy scattered the grain out once more in the sun.
'That'll make it crisp,' he said knowingly. 'There ain't
nothin' like the sun for makin' things right!'

Keego jigged and frolicked, his sturdy limbs had
taken the brunt of the work, but he never seemed to
grow weary.

But Bari was glad when Paddy said, 'Let's have a
holiday! What'll we do?'

'Go paddling where there ain't no rice,' Keego
answered like a shot. So out on the lake they went,
Paddy at the paddles. It was a still day. The water
was as clear as glass. It was hard to see where their
world of reality ended and its shadows on the lake
began. Everywhere there was a smell of maturity and

ripening things, as if the earth had mixed her forests and flowers and was sending forth their sweetness.

'Once,' Keego said, with a burst of confidence, 'I was pretty nearly a fish. The Good Spirit asked me if I'd like to be one, but I said No, because a man can live on land an' swim in water, but a fish can only live in water, and can't swim on land. Being man is one times better.'

Bari stopped trailing his hands in the water and laughed. Suddenly a sob came into the wind and they looked up. The sky was darkening; clouds were racing east.

'We'll go home,' Paddy said, bending to his paddles, but as he spoke they knew it was too late. The clouds fringed, fluffed and broke in torrential rain.

'The rice'll be soaked,' Paddy said, as they tied up the boat.

Keego sprang ashore. He stamped his feet and glowered angrily.

'Never mind,' Paddy said, 'the sun's comin' out an' it says it's goin' to be good weather.'

'I don't talk to the sun,' Keego gloomed, 'it's too far away.'

'We'll turn the rice, it'll soon dry,' Paddy said cheerfully; 'next time we'll put it under cover.'

Keego smiled. Running to a poplar he hung his mouth-organ on a branch. 'I'm giving that to the bad spirit so he won't send no more rain on us,' he said to Bari when he came racing back.

Bari laughed.

Before supper he saw Keego playing his mouth-organ again. Maybe he had just loaned it to the spirit.

Next day was warm. Wind came, and their world of amber and gold mingled again with the blue of rain-washed sky.

Paddy found a place to store the rice, a hide-away between rocks with a stone floor. They roofed it with branches then carried the grain along. Fifteen bags was all it would hold.

' There's a place on the far side of the Point that'll hold the other five bags,' Paddy said, looking over the situation. ' You tote them along there an' we'll tuck them in. It'll be dry an' they'll be easy to load from the water. These five bags can be yours,' he went on cheerfully. ' We'll gather some more yet an' put it with them. You'll get a bit of money for yourselves,' he added with a wink.

The boys looked at each other. Keego's eyes glittered. ' I'll buy cloes an' shoes an' lots of things!' His voice rose happily.

Next day they gathered two more bags, then swept up their gleanings and put them on the boys' side.

' To-morrow I'll go an' tell Odzell to come an' get the rice,' Paddy said smiling.

That night they sat by their camp-fire talking about the things they were going to buy. For Keego, it was clothes. For Paddy, eats, but for Bari, it was paper and pencils and colours. Something was singing inside him; his dreams and his desires were beginning to come real.

When the boys awoke next morning Paddy was out. They looked along the shore, but he wasn't in sight.

' He's gone to see about the rice,' Keego said, blasting away at his mouth-organ.

Soon they saw Paddy coming. They ran to meet him.

'I don't like that music,' Paddy said, his voice strangely hard.

Keego took the mouth-organ from his lips and blinked. 'Why?'

'It tells everybody we're here makin' rice. Maybe it makes trouble.'

'Well, ain't we here makin' rice?' Keego asked, holding the mouth-organ in his hand.

'Give me that mouth-organ,' Paddy said crossly.

Bari looked at Paddy. He had never heard him speak like that before. But Paddy went on in a gentler voice, 'Maybe I too can make music. Once I could play on leaves. Sometime I'll show you,' he added, slipping the mouth-organ into his pocket.

Keego smiled.

But Paddy kept standing as if he wasn't quite sure whether to go on or turn back. There were deep furrows in his brow. Suddenly he said, 'Somebody's stolen our rice.'

'Stolen our rice!' Bari's eyes popped wide. 'You mean——?'

'Yah!' Paddy interrupted, 'about half of it.'

Bari looked at Keego. He was locking his long sinewy fingers together. His face was white with anger.

'Come, we'll go an' see it,' Paddy said, turning round.

No one spoke as they walked along the shore. When they reached the cache, Bari saw that some of the branches had been thrown from the roof.

'We'll scout around. It's somebody that knows about

the rice that's done this.' Paddy's voice was low and even. Bari knew that he, too, was very angry.

Bari stepped inside the cache. It was some seconds before his eyes were accustomed to the gloom, then slowly the bags became clear against the wall. He counted: One, two, three, five, yes—six were gone. One was lying on its side. It had been used for a step. Rice was spilled from it over the floor. Bari went outside. Keego was still standing.

' Come in an' see,' Bari said.

Keego shook his head. His face was sullen.

Paddy was running his fingers along the crevices in the wall. Bari examined the doorway. There wasn't a mark or scar, but some freshly chipped rock was scattered on the stones. Dropping on his knees Paddy crept to the water's edge feeling every bit of ground with his hand. Bari followed. There wasn't a kernel of rice anywhere.

Keego stood wringing a willow twig in his hand as if the wildness in him was stunned into silence.

Paddy straightened. ' The bags must have been taken away by boat,' he said, looking across the water. ' I don't see no other way.' He turned and looked at Keego. ' You boys seen anybody around? '

Keego's face darkened. He shifted from one foot to the other, but didn't speak.

A fear shot through Bari. Could Keego be mixed up with this? He met Paddy's look squarely. ' I ain't seen nobody, Paddy, but see,' he pointed across the bay, ' there's smoke at Cameron Point.'

Paddy nodded. ' There was a fire by the Mission this morning, but that don't mean nothin'; them that took the rice ain't makin' fires, Bari.' Paddy turned on his heel. 'Let's go an' see if your rice is all right.'

They could hardly keep up with Keego as he raced to their cache. But their rice was undisturbed. Not one of their bags had been moved and there were no footprints to be seen except their own.

Paddy stood stroking his cheek thoughtfully. 'There ain't much we can do. Rice has been stolen before. We'll go an' eat, then——' He didn't finish; he sounded as if he didn't know what to do.

There were ugly lights in Keego's eyes, the kind that came when he was very mad. He didn't say a word as they walked back to camp.

Paddy lit a fire and made a meal. No one ate. This thing had killed their happiness. Every now and again Keego rose, walked to the shore and looked across the bay as if looking for something.

Face troubled, Paddy toyed with his spoon. Why didn't he speak, say something, tell them what he was thinking?

Suddenly he looked up. 'We'll break camp an' pack.' His voice was cold and jerky. 'I figger the thief ain't far away. Rice was sneaked out like this last year, quite a bit of it. I'm goin' for the Mountie. You fellows can stay an' watch. I won't be long. I'd hate to lose the rest of the rice.'

The thought of staying without Paddy sent a shiver through Bari.

Keego jumped to his feet. 'We'll get them, Paddy! We'll catch them! They ain't gettin' away with it!' Keego's jaws came together like a clamp. There was anger in the set of his thin mouth.

Bari wasn't so sure of himself. There was a helplessness about it all. What could they do?

They bundled their belongings together, then saw Paddy into his canoe and off. They watched till it grew into a tiny speck on the water's rim. Bari couldn't speak. Fear of staying alone all night was haunting him. He fought a choking sensation in his throat. He mustn't be a coward.

But he didn't feel any better when Keego said, ' When it gets right dark we'll go an' sit by the rice, Paddy's rice. Sometimes I'll slip over an' look at our rice. Maybe the thief find it, an' maybe I catch him.' There was a chuckle in Keego's voice that wasn't sweet. ' Lots of times I've seen cheebuy—talked to them. They tell me things,' he added with a shrug of importance.

Bari blinked. He could feel himself shaking. He didn't like Keego's ideas or plans, but he mustn't let him know he was afraid. He'd try to be brave. What was there to be afraid of anyway?

Keego cooked a wild duck and baked bannock for supper, but Bari's teeth chattered all the time he tried to eat. He wished Paddy hadn't gone away. Keego moved about with a flourish of bravado until it got dark.

It was a breathless, starless night. They sat down together by the side of the water until the outline of the shore was drawn into the blackness of the forest. Then hand in hand they sneaked to the rice rock and crept into the opening. Keego struck a match, and by its spluttering light they could see the sacks were just the same as they had been in the morning.

Coming out again, Keego pointed to a ledge high on

the outer rocks. ' You go up there an' squeeze yourself in; it's a good place to watch from. Sit quiet, I'll go this way.' He pointed toward the heavy timber.

It was too dark to see Keego's face, but Bari took one swift look upwards and hesitated a moment. He wished Keego had stayed with him, but grasping a branch he swung to the first level, then step by step scaled the rock. The shelf was narrow, but it was hidden by spruce, and by mouse-footing along the face he could reach ground again.

He could hear Keego tucking himself into the shrubbery at the opposite side. It wasn't so dark now. There was warmth in the rock. He felt braver. Doubling his feet under he kept his body tight to the stone. He was not too uncomfortable. He settled himself warily; there was animal alertness in the eye he fixed on the ground.

He felt braver now and even thought he might catch the thief. There was a flutter in the leaves behind. The wind whined, but he sat firm.

The Pole Star came out, then a sprinkling of other stars. It must be past midnight. Suddenly there was a swish in the shrubbery. Bari clutched the rock. His body was shaking. Maybe it was Keego. It must be! Yes, he could hear his footsteps padding off along the shore.

Bari settled back and his body began to go numb. Life seemed to be leaving it. He wriggled and knocked his feet together until slithering shale warned him to keep still.

Again he heard movements. He sat up, ear windward. An owl hooted. Bari clutched the rock and held his

E

breath. The night seemed to be getting darker. He hadn't heard Keego come back; could it be he wasn't there? Bari thrust the thought from him. Mist came capering up the gully and rolled about the trees. The foliage hung limp and it seemed as if the world of the living was standing still.

Bari shivered. He was cold. Why had he come! He was a fool. He wanted to cry out, to leap to Keego. Silence hung like a weight everywhere. A streak of light came into the east—day was coming. Bari drew a thankful breath.

A twig snapped. Something was moving in the hollow. Holding tight to the ledge he leaned forward and peered through the spruce. A figure appeared. It was a man. Bari could see him faintly. He seemed to be walking in mist, like a ghost something from another world. He was making for the cache.

Bari held his breath, every nerve in his body quivering. He wriggled along the ledge to see more clearly. The man had disappeared. He must have dropped between rocks. Bari listened and soon heard a rustling in the branches. The man was in the cache!

Shaking from head to foot Bari kept his eyes on the doorway. A sack was pushed slowly through the roof. Then a man's shoulders appeared and gradually the rest of his body. He hopped sideways and straightened. Bari couldn't see him clearly. Long hair blew about his face and his shoulders seemed to stoop.

Bari could hardly contain himself. What should he do? Where was Keego?

The man was hoisting the partly filled sack to his shoulder, and then he strode off into the shrubbery.

Half rolling, half tumbling to the ground, Bari leaped one way, then another in a desperate dash to follow. He stumbled, and when he got to his feet, the man was out of sight. Bari stood, stunned at the ease of the man's get-away. But he could hear him moving up the opposite side of the gully.

Breaking into a run, stumbling through tangled shrubbery, Bari sighted him. He didn't seem to know he was being followed. His lope was easy, but fast. He was gaining.

Head reeling, Bari plunged forward. Again and again he tripped. He stopped, put his hand to his mouth to call, 'Help! Keego!' No, he wouldn't. The fellow might have someone waiting for him.

As Bari hesitated the man came up the bank and hurried into dense shrubbery. It was minutes before Bari saw him again. Then he came clear into the open. One breathless moment Bari stood, then quick as a flash drew his sling and a pebble from his pocket. He aimed, and the stone sped to its mark.

The man disappeared into heavy timber.

Plunging through the gully, Bari came to where the stone had cut the bag. He found a sprinkling of rice, then another and another.

Breathless with excitement, he raced along its trail. He came to a windfall and over it he saw the man's head. He swung right quickly as if he had heard his pursuer. Afraid of being seen, Bari dropped to the ground. From where he lay he could see three or four sacks beneath the shrubbery. What could he do? Where was Keego? Why didn't he come?

A cold sweat broke over Bari. The man was making

for the lake.   As fear unmanned Bari, so it directed him. Jumping to his feet, he followed.   There was something familiar about the figure.

The man halted, then wheeled and faced him.

Bari stepped back.   It was Odzell's helper, the fellow who'd wanted them to buy the belt.   His face was different now.   It was sullen, and there was an ugly droop in his jaw.

'That's our rice,' Bari said, pointing to the sacks. 'I saw you in our cache.'

A leer came into the man's eyes.   'You're the kid that was in with Lindrum.   Where's your friend?'

'That's our rice!' Bari repeated, unheeding his laugh.

Leaning forward the man caught him by the neck, dealing a wallop between his shoulders.   'Don't call me a thief, you sneakin' kid!'

Bari fell, but quick as lightning got to his feet and dived for the rice.

Reckless with rage his adversary tripped him, sending him down again, then set his foot on his stomach and stood laughing.   'You can lie there, smartie, till I let you go!'

A sickening ache went through Bari's head.   His body went limp.

The man took a pipe from his pocket, stuck it in his mouth, struck a match and lit it.

Bari tried to ease up, but the pressure of the man's foot made him feel sick.   He flopped back.

The man laughed.

Out from the shrubbery came a wild 'Halloo!'   It was Keego.   He came leaping towards them, stood a

moment, and then eyes flaming fire swooped like a
demon on the stranger. 'I'll kill you! I'll kill you dead.'
The man cowered, then darted to the bush with
Keego, all the primitive fury of his nature let loose,
after him.

Bari eased up on his shoulder. 'I'll kill you! I'll
kill you!' He could hear Keego's screams rising louder
and louder.

The man turned and came racing back to Bari.
'Don't let him, don't let him touch me!' he cried, eyes
wide with fear.

Keego, a branch of tree in hand, was at his heels.

Bari scrambled to his feet. 'Don't touch him, Keego,
leave him alone!'

Whooping wildly, Keego swung his stick. It just
cleared the man's head.

There was a shout. Paddy raced from the shrubbery.

Breathless, the man leaned against a tree. He was
shaking and his brow was wet with sweat.

'What's this?' Paddy stood looking down on them.

'I'll pay for the rice. I've paid that guy already for
what he sold me.' He pointed to Keego. Then pulling
some bills from his pocket he held them out, his hand
trembling. 'Take these, take these!'

Paddy looked at the money, then at Keego.

With a maniacal yell, Keego swooped again on his
victim. The man fled.

Keego grinned. 'I scare him all right, eh! the old
fox-face. I got evil enough to scare him all right,
Paddy!' Keego repeated gleefully. The fire had gone
from his eyes. He kept opening and shutting his hands
nervously.

Paddy looked at him. 'That fellow says you sold him rice, Keego!'

Dropping the stick, Keego darted into the shrubbery. Paddy and Bari stood. It was a good ten minutes before Keego came back carrying a parcel under his arm. Flushed with excitement, he pulled off the wrapping and handing a box to Paddy said, 'I buyed this with the rice money,' and squinting sheepishly at Bari he added, 'Bari doan' know nothin' about it. I took a bit of rice over to that fellow at Odzells' an' sold it. He asked me where we kep' our rice an' I tol' him,' Keego added, his voice low with concern.

Lifting the lid from the cardboard box, Paddy took out a number of scribblers, pencils and crayons.

'Them's for Bari, a present I buyed with the rice money,' Keego said, tears coming to his eyes. 'I didn't tell that guy to steal, Paddy! I didn't do nothin' wrong did I? Bari needed things to draw with an' I got them for him. I—I guess I got evil spirit or somethin' all right,' Keego sniffed. 'But it sure scared him,' he added, brushing his eyes with his sleeve.

Paddy laid the pencils and scribblers back in the box. 'There isn't such a thing, Keego, as a' evil spirit, or evil in you. You're just different, like the pine is from the poplar, an' there ain't no evil in them.' Paddy smiled a long slow smile. His eyes seemed dreamy and very far away.

'You mean I'm just the same as everybody else?' Keego asked, lifting his head happily.

Paddy nodded. 'We're all the same, Keego! Some day the hawk may nest with the kildeer, an' the stoat cross the water to the rabbit dance, some day maybe?'

Paddy's voice was dreamy like his eyes. 'Here's your drawin' things, Bari.' Paddy handed him the box. 'Better tell Keego " Thank you ". It's plenty smart he was to think about you. Let's go and eat.'

Standing a moment, Bari took the lid off the box and counted, ' One, two, three, four new scribblers ! ' What could he say? The most precious thought of all was that he had paper, crayons and pencils. Now he would be able to draw. Keego was looking at him.

' I'll make pictures of you, Keego, an' the leaves an' rice and things.' That was the best thanks Bari knew.

Keego grinned.

' What about the Mountie? ' Bari asked, when they caught up with Paddy.

' Oh! Hyslop was away north, the other fellows were out, so I came right back,' Paddy said happily. ' Figgered I couldn't leave you an' Keego alone. But I saw Odzell. He's comin' for the rice at noon. We'll get him to pick up that by the windfall when he comes.'

Drawing Keego's mouth-organ from his pocket, Paddy handed it back. ' I thought this was what maybe let folks know where there was rice. Guess it wasn't, an' I can't play it, Keego,' Paddy shrugged happily, ' not like you.'

Keego put it to his mouth and, handspringing across the rocks to its rollicking music, reached camp first.

Odzell came for the rice after dinner and paid Paddy the money.

Bari and Keego were thrilled for they each got a share.

They helped Paddy pack their canoe and glided out of Mikado in the dusk of the autumn night.

Chapter XI

ONEY RETURNS

A lazy smoke was drifting over the tamarack-rim,
katydids were whirring, and Bari's kingdom lay mellow
in the light of the ripening moon when they tied their
boat to Paddy's dock.

Bari was glad to get home. He had so many things
to show Keego. He loved Keego; there was something
inspiring in him, something that pushed him along the
road he wanted to go. Keego understood. And there
was always something new popping up in Keego's
thoughts.

Bari found Keego had an accomplishment that he
hadn't time to demonstrate while rice-picking: he
could climb trees. It was an art with him. He went
up poplars like a squirrel and wove his way through
cedars like a spring breeze.

He tried to teach Bari. 'It's great pictures you can
make from up a tree, Bari,' he said with a knowing

air. 'You get a better view, a different one. There ain't nobody drawed pictures from a tree before.'

Bari was thrilled.

The idea was good, but in action it was different. It didn't work—Bari wasn't built for climbing trees.

Surveying the wreckage after their first experiment, Paddy was stern. 'Two fish-boats wouldn't bring cloes enough to keep you goin'.'

Bari protested mildly, 'I was goin' to draw pictures. They'd be better.'

'You keep your feet on the ground, an' you'll go places.' Paddy might have said more had he seen the bleeding scratches and bruised flesh beneath.

Bari thought he detected relief in Paddy's next words: 'Hyslop's comin' to take you to school on Monday. I'll get your things ready.'

Monday, that was only two days away! Bari took off one moccasin, shook sand out of it and did the same with the other before speaking. 'You'll be lonesome, Paddy, without me.'

'Lonesome!' Paddy laughed. 'With the wind singin' an' the 'gooquas fixin' their finery? Besides,' Paddy added, with a twinkle in his eye, 'Keego says he's going to stay with——'

Keego looked up. He was sitting on a rock untangling a snare. 'Sure, I'll stay with you, Paddy, an' with Granny Mulgrove an' everybody too.'

Paddy laughed. 'You'll be far from Granny Mulgrove's before snow flies, Keego!'

Bari didn't sleep that night. His body ached, and a cold hand kept clutching at him. He pulled the covers up tight, but it was still there.

E 2

When he got up next morning, Paddy was washing his underwear and socks. He watched him wind them on a pole to dry, then fold his trousers on a board and push it beneath the mattress.

A cold lump settled in the pit of Bari's stomach.

Right after breakfast Keego and he hied to the bush, but no matter what they did the shadow of school lay on Bari's thoughts. Finally he said to Keego, 'I don't want to go to school, I want to stay with you. School's no good.'

'Naw, it ain't,' Keego agreed, shaking a sympathetic head. 'I never went to school, Paddy never went to school, an' me an' him knows plenty.'

'I want to stay here in the bush an' make pictures,' Bari went on, drawing Keego to a seat at his side.

'That's plenty learning. Just tell Paddy you ain't goin'. Gee, the sun in your hair an' the smell o' the wind feels good, doesn't it?' Keego added encouragingly, 'They won't never miss you; you don't do nothin' to help them anyway. Tell Paddy that.'

Much as Bari loved Keego, he had doubts. But they got up and went home.

As they walked up the trail to the cabin door they heard singing. They stopped and listened. 'There's somebody in the cabin that ain't Paddy,' Keego said, nodding towards the door. 'Let's go this way.'

Slipping round the side, they tried to peer through the window. They couldn't see anything, but they could hear voices.

Lifting the door-latch quietly, Bari and Keego tip-toed in.

Paddy was shaking flour into a bowl on the table

and, kneeling on a chair behind him, a girl was watching. Their backs were to the door. ' I can cook now, Paddy, and do lots of other things too. Mrs Carson has showed me,' the girl was saying. It was Oney Madette!

She swung round. ' Oh, Bari, I didn't see you!' There was gladness in her voice. ' My, you have grown!'

' Hullo, Oney, I didn't know you at first,' Bari said. ' You've grown too. This is Keego.'

Keego slipped on to a stool half-hidden by the cupboard.

' Hullo,' Oney said shyly, and turned back to Paddy. ' If you get me something to roll them, I'll help you. I've baked biscuits lots of times.'

Paddy poured some grease into the flour then handed her a bottle. Bari watched her mix the dough, roll and pat the cakes into shape and put them in the pan. When she finished she turned. ' I go to school now, Bari. My father's come to live down here on the bay. He got me a place to stay in town so's I'd get to school every day. I like it.' Her face was kindled with happiness.

Bari looked at her. He didn't know whether he was glad about her father coming to live near or not. He hadn't forgotten the night he had visited them when they were berry-picking on the Sturgeon, the time he had said, ' Drawin's no good. That kid should be workin'.'

A rush of resentment swept through him. He didn't know whether he even wanted Oney around helping Paddy. He could learn to cook and help Paddy. He remembered the time she had trampled the picture he had drawn for her into the sand.

Then he relented. He moved closer to the table. She sure looked smarter now than she used to. Her dress was fancier. When she had come to dabble their shirts in the Sturgeon puddles to wash them her feet had been bare, but now she had nice shoes on.

Oney's eyes followed Bari's. 'Mrs Carson—that's the woman I live with—buys my clothes. She gets me lots of other things too and shows me how to do things the right way. There's so much to learn. My father wants me to know everything.' She spoke quietly.

Bari backed to Keego's side. He kept looking at her and smiling. There was something different about her. It wasn't her clothes nor the tilt of her head; it was something knowing, something shining from within.

Paddy had put the biscuits in the oven and sat down on a chair. 'I allus said Oney was a smart one. She'll go places.' There was a purr in his voice.

Oney was on her feet putting on her coat.

'Sing for us again, Oney. The boys didn't hear you.' Paddy looked up at her coaxingly.

'I can't, Paddy. I don't like to.' There was a little quiver in her laugh.

'It was sure good to hear you,' Paddy went on. 'I never knowed you could sing.'

She turned her face to the window. Her voice rose softly beneath her breath; deepening, swelling it spilled like sunlight through the cabin. In a moment everything was beautiful: sunshine, laughter and the soft trailing scent of roses seemed to fill the air that they breathed.

Bari could see Keego's sinewy hands locking themselves till the knuckles showed white.

The singing stopped. 'Mrs Carson's going to send me for singing lessons so's I can learn to sing good.' Oney reached for her coat.

'Learnin' the swallow to fly,' Paddy said laughingly.

'But my dad wants me to know how to do things right. I must go now. I'll come and see you often; I get home for week-ends.'

Flashing a glance at the boys she was gone like a winged creature darting to the sun.

Bari looked at Keego. He was sitting glooming, the corners of his mouth turned down. 'We doan' know nothin', me an' you,' he said drearily, jerking a thumb towards the door. 'Her, she knows everythin'!'

Paddy was taking the biscuits from the oven, but he looked up. 'She's a smart one all right, Oney. She ain't ordinary an' she's got things pretty slick now. Jake's sure pullin' for her.'

Bari rose and went over to his cot. He felt as if a sudden wind had touched him, whisking his thoughts to the girl's sparkling trail. His clothes were piled ready for school, and he looked at Keego still twiddling his thumbs. 'I'm going to school, Keego!'

'So am I,' Keego said brightening, 'but not till I get older, then I won't have so much to learn.' Keego rose, put on his coat and said, 'Good-bye.'

Paddy smiled. 'There's no knowin' where he'll be before spring, but he's been a heap better since you an' him's been together.'

Bari was ready to go back to school when Hyslop came.

But school was different. He was put in another classroom, and he had another teacher, a short sharp-voiced woman with straw-like hair. The boys called her Lynx, because she saw everything.

Bari was happy going into a new room. It was larger, and there were flowers in the window. He was given new readers and a pen and ink to write with. And oh! His heart went pit-a-pat when he saw the paints—water-colours the teacher called them. Now he'd do things.

But now there was more and harder work: 'rithmetic, with figures that were hard and got mixed up in his head, grammar, and heaps of other things. But his mind was alert and he picked up knowledge readily, faster than some of the other children.

He still didn't connect the things he was learning with his future, for they weren't part of the life he wanted to live. It was drawing—art, the teacher called it now. That was his Pole Star, off in the sky of his dreams.

Whenever he had a chance he took his pencil and made good use of any paper within reach, hoping Lynx wouldn't get so cross as Windigo. He covered the fly-leaves of his reader with butterflies, trees, musk-rats, flowers and, to the pictures already there, he added Seegwun and Paddy.

The seat next to him was occupied by a little girl with an impish frown and a turned-up nose. Her real name was Keewatin-nabeton, which means 'north wind blowing cold'. In front sat Ka-ke-way-we-tung (ever-lasting noise). They were just called Mary and Annie. Bari wondered why, when their real names suited them so well. North Wind froze him out with her stare. Everlasting Noise managed in some mysterious way to convey knowledge of his sketching to Lynx. It always ended the same way. ' Come up here, Bari! '

When he got to Lynx's desk, eyes snapping fire she would say, ' Haven't I told you not to scribble on those books,' and reach for her strap.

Bari took punishment manfully. It didn't hurt, not even his pride, but deep in his being there was a fixed unchangeable idea that he wasn't doing wrong. It wasn't for recognition or boastfulness that Bari drew pictures in the leaves of his books; it was a push that came from within, something he couldn't fight, something that made him happy even when punishment was sure.

That October, Bari was promoted to the workshop. He was very happy. Five other boys and his friend Joe were beginning with him. Mr Millen looked very solemn when they marched in. Bari expected he'd give them each a hammer and saw and start them making a book-case or a desk right away. But there was more to it than that.

Mr Millen spent the first lesson explaining about tools, their uses and about different kinds of wood. ' This craft, a carpenter's,' he said in a very quiet voice, ' is a noble work. Remember the Man of Galilee was a carpenter. You must do your work well. It must be true, exact. It can't be any other way.' He said it in a way that made the boys feel good.

Bari felt that Mr Millen must be a very fine man.

Next day he started Joe and two of the others making a box to hold firewood, and Bari and the rest making stools. Everything had to be measured just right. Bari didn't like that. Paddy had always put things together without rule or counting. This getting things down to a fraction of an inch irked Bari. It was too slow. His hands fumbled, and he was awkward with boards and wood.

When his stool was finished each leg was a different length. Mr Millen would have altered it, but Bari didn't want him to see. He proceeded, with much sweating and puffing, to put it right. When he finished, the stool had hardly any legs left.

Joe came and looked at it, rolled the whites of his eyes into an astounded squint, and said, ' You'll catch it.' The other boys eyed it gravely.

The sequel was a talk from Mr Millen. ' Bari,' he said in a voice different from his usual one, ' a carpenter must be particular, very particular. If he cut the place for a window or hung a door without measuring correctly it just wouldn't do. A quarter of an inch will make a difference. You must pay attention to what you are doing.'

Bari persevered. He studied hard, took time with measurements and was careful with marking. His fingers grew deft and stronger. He handled tools with more confidence. But deep down in his heart he didn't like the work. It was too stiff, too straight. He wanted to work where his hands could swing freely, where he could put sunshine and wind-blown shadows in with the stroke of a brush.

Mr Millen was patient. He was pleased with Bari's progress. Later on, Bari made a tool-chest for Paddy, fitting each compartment with care. It was harder work than Bari had ever done before. Every now and again he'd have to unfasten his shirt-neck and wipe the perspiration from his brow. But he knew how pleased Paddy would be with the chest.

At the end of the lesson, his marks were not high, but Mr Millen was kindly. ' Remember, Bari,' he said, ' this may be the one thing that you will be able to make a living by when you get out into the world.' He emphasized ' the one ', but it was, ' when you get out into the world ', that kept ringing in Bari's ears. Of course Mr Millen didn't know that he was really going to be an artist.

Many times during the winter, Bari found himself thinking of Oney. The girls in his classroom were mostly shy young things who chewed paper and giggled roguishly at him. They weren't like Oney. They didn't shine.

Of course, there were the boys. There was Wilfred, who sat in the front seat, whom the boys called Wildfire. He had a stub nose and smoky eyes, and he was always ready to fight. His clothes were untidy and often bore evidence of his last battle. When he first came to school, he ate everything : wax crayons in the classroom, tooth paste, and even bulbs that teacher had bought to grow flowers. ' Highsents ', or something, she called them. Wilfred sure got a licking for that. Bari smiled when he thought of it.

Then there was Pinesse at the back of the room, with the chirpy voice and bird-like face. Everybody called him Chick. He was quiet. He kept his hair plastered down with grease. After school he always played with little children, who were no company for Bari.

Moons passed much more quickly now. Teacher

allowed him to draw and colour two Christmas cards. That delighted him. He sent one to Hyslop and one to Paddy.

One evening when Joe and he were whittling out a boat from a piece of wood, teacher came with a letter. 'It's for you, Bari,' she said, holding it out. 'Would you like me to read it for you?'

Bari sprang to his feet excitedly. He had never had a letter before. Taking it in his shaking hands, he tore the envelope open and held the sheet of paper in front of teacher. He followed the words as she read: 'Dere Bari, that rat she ain't no more. She got ketched in ice. I never set no traps near her case her feet would get tangled up again. Now I kin set traps, there's plenty rats there. I'll keep the money I get for their hides for you. That's all. Paddy.'

The words were big and crooked, but they brought tears to Bari's eyes. 'That's my rat, Seegwun,' he said, turning to Joe.

'She's dead, eh?'

'Nothin's dead, Joe. I tol' you that! She's up there.' Bari pointed to the sky.

Joe's eyes widened. 'That's what you think.' Joe stuck out his chin knowingly. 'What you think's goin' to happen them childrun of hers? They're headin' for fur coats. Did you ever see a fur coat? Paddy says he's goin' to trap them for their hides. It's mighty cold they'll be if they ain't dead.' There was a nasty lift in Joe's voice, but Bari didn't say anything. His eyes were still wet.

His teacher pushed the letter back into its envelope. 'Don't feel badly, Bari. You'll always remember your pet. If you like, you can come and write a letter to Paddy. I'll help you.'

Bari was grateful. He followed his teacher in. She got him pen and paper, and then slowly, with her help, he wrote down his thoughts. He had practised writing his name. Proudly he put it at the end of the letter, ' Bari Bradbrooke '. He felt better : writing the letter had eased the hurt.

That was the start of Bari's letter-writing. It brought something new into his life. To be able to write to Paddy was wonderful. But many of the things Bari wanted to say he drew in pictures. Paddy would understand the flowers and winged things coming between the words. Besides, it was easier to draw his teacher than to spell ' teacher '. If she wasn't flattered with the mop of hair he put on her head or the strap he put in her hand, when she read out-going mail she didn't betray herself. Bari was really beginning to like Lynx now.

And there was Seegwun. Bari never tired of drawing pictures of her. That was his tribute to her memory. He kept them beneath his pillow. It was Seegwun who had brought him Paddy, Seegwun who had started him on his new life.

He could hardly wait for Berry Moon, the time when he would go home. But at last it came.

When he got back to his kingdom he went straight to the place where Paddy had buried his pet. It was a quiet hollow facing the lake, flanked by a growth of willow. That night and every night after, Bari carried water and strips of bark to lay on the tiny mound, so that Seegwun's spirit would know that she was not forgotten.

That summer Oney came often to see them. She was different now, not like the child she had been at their first berry-picking. She was older and easier to get on with. She had learned so many things, and she was interested in what he was doing now. He was beginning to like her again.

One day when Paddy and he were paddling across-lake, Paddy looked up and pointed to a figure skirting the shrubbery. ' There's Jake Madette ! '

As they reached the shore Jake's voice came through the bluff, ' Boozoo ! Boozoo ! Paddy ! Great day for doin' nothin'.' When he reached lake-edge he sat down on a rock, took out his pipe, stuck it in his mouth, struck a match, and lit it with the air of the leisurely. When Bari leaped to land, Madette glared hard at him, but he didn't smile.

His clothes were neater than they had been before, and he looked well kept. There was a scattering of grey in his raven hair. His face was wolfish and thin, but there was laughter in his eyes, which narrowed into pin-points of curiosity as he turned to Paddy. ' Are you makin' that kid work ? It's time he was doin' somethin' to help keep you.'

For a brief second Bari thought he was going to be happy with Oney's father, but quicker than a lightning's flash he disliked him. A slow-burning hatred seeped into his spirit.

' Where are you goin', Paddy ? ' Madette went on as Bari and Paddy shouldered axes and hied up the bank.

' Across the Point for willow. Me an' Bari's goin' to make baskets.' Jake threw back his head and laughed a deep shaking laugh.

'You'll die workin', Paddy, an' that kid,' he took his pipe from his mouth and spat contemptuously on the sand, 'ain't goin' to make many baskets for ye.'

Bari shook with anger. Why had Madette to be like that? He resented his laugh, his mean words and the ugly look on his face. 'Does Oney's father work?' he asked, as Paddy and he turned into the bush.

'He does a bit of huntin' an' wood choppin'. Oh! Jake ain't a bad fellah, he's a mighty good neighbour. He's got high-falutin' notions about Oney, but she's doin' pretty good. It's proud of her we'll be yet.'

'We'. The word struck Bari. Even Paddy's tone of voice told him that he too was proud of Oney.

Bari could not keep Madette out of his thoughts. Every time they met, Jake would say, 'You should be able to do some real work now', or, 'Don't you ever get tired doin' nothin'?' Sometimes his voice was soft and friendly; sometimes he even gave him a handful of nuts. But Bari had no friendship in his heart for him. He hid his drawings when he saw him coming, and counselled Paddy, 'Don't tell Oney's father that I'm going to be an artist when I grow up.'

Paddy laughed.

Time went on. School was teaching Bari many things, but nothing had changed his mind. He was still going to be an artist.

His needs grew and he got choosey. 'I need a felt hat' or 'I haven't got a white shirt,' he wrote to Paddy. 'All the boys have hockey skates except me.' Letter-writing was easier now; maybe it was because he was sure of an answer. It always came promptly, with one, two, or sometimes a five-dollar bill tucked in an envelope with a piece of paper, and Paddy's wiggley 'O.K.' scrawled on it. There was never stint of clothes when Bari needed them.

Once did he err. Seeing some of the older boys put cold cream on their faces, he wrote: 'My face is broken, I need money to fix it.'

The answer was Paddy himself, eyes distraught and sweating from his fifty-mile tramp through snow. 'You ain't hurt, eh?'

Bari shook his head, and both were too happy to talk about Bari's message.

Holidays came again. Nothing was more delightful to Bari than the carefree hours he spent in the woods.

Oney was home now. She watched him draw and brought him pictures to copy. 'I keep telling Mrs Carson about you, Bari. She says you should keep right on an' study, an' then you'll be a great artist.'

Bari looked at her. 'What does your father say about it?'

'He doesn't say anything. I don't talk to him about your drawing.'

Bari was well aware of what Madette would say, but he was happy that Oney did not feel like her father did.

They didn't talk about her singing, but there was no need. Out over the lake in the summer twilights her songs came clear and sweet. It was something she couldn't keep to herself.

Keego was often with them. Bari tried to teach him drawing, writing and some of the things he learnt at school. But the Great Teacher of the Woods had schooled Keego and he knew it.

Into Bari's growing mind came an awareness of the

rhythm of things. A steady doling out of the real things of life. Spring, summer, autumn and winter came as unfailingly as suns and moons marched across the sky.

Once when tiny buds came peeping through spring sleet, Bari said to Joe, ' It would be too bad if we didn't get summer, wouldn't it? '

Lifting startled eyes, Joe answered, ' We wouldn't get holidays! Somebody would catch it, and it wouldn't be me.'

Bari smiled, but the face that was looking at him was concerned.

But it didn't take from Bari the sense of security and recognition of a supreme planning above and beyond the kingdom he saw.

Since Paddy had explained things he saw the need for trapping. But the way the Indians lived was hard: making rice, setting traps, hewing timber. In that kingdom beyond the forest rim there must be other ways of living. He felt that somehow there would be a niche for him. Paddy would help him; Paddy was still his god.

So the swift-wheeling cycles of moons carried him over two, four, six years, berry, rice-time and trapping. There were hunger moons too but these Paddy never mentioned. Soon Bari would be leaving school.

Chapter XII

MADETTE

Bari counted off the last months of school life just as he had done the first ones the winter he began. To-night he lay in bed watching the Berry Moon creep over the jackpines, a wholly delightful thrill racing through him. To-morrow he was going home. But he knew learning would not be over.

All through the last week, sitting behind his desk he had been filled with clamouring urgent thoughts and plans. There were so many things he was going to do, so much that should be done, but above and over all he knew that he was going to make pictures. There was a vagueness about how he would do it, but the goal stood out as clearly in his mind as the Pole Star stood in the northern sky. And Paddy and he were going to have such good times. Besides the foster-love that bound them they had one thing in common: love of home and of the woods. And hadn't he a kingdom of his own right in the valley by Paddy's shore?

Bari hadn't disliked school. He was an apt pupil, popular and 'a good guy'. He liked sport and played the game. In art he picked prizes as easily as he would spring flowers. School had sheltered and guided him, and food and clothing had come without effort.

The years had been kind to his body as a look in the mirror told him, for he was handsome, a fine upstanding fellow with a keen eye. Yes, school had been good. He liked it, every minute of it, but the love of freedom was in his blood. To-morrow he was going home!

He rolled over in his bed and pulled up the covers. It was hard to sleep with his heart pounding like a trip-hammer and his feet itching for the trail.

When he awoke it was raining. He leaped out of bed and looked through the window. Shrubs and trees were drenched; flowers and grass dripped water. The earth was washing itself for the occasion! That's how he liked it: clean, rain-washed, with fresh-stilled wood scents filling the air.

He dressed quickly, for he was looking forward eagerly to the coming day. And it wasn't long before Hyslop came for him. By the time their outboard had swung into the boat channel the sun came out and leaves were tossing themselves dry in a capering wind. Already Bari felt the wings of his freedom. It was in the air, in the spray, in the waves that flung themselves gleefully in their racing wake.

When they came in sight of Paddy's cabin they could see him standing at the end of a tiny dock he had built.

He looked a small spare figure as he paced back and forth in the sunlight, but his face was knotted into a big smile as they pulled alongside.

Pitching his books ashore Bari sprang towards him. 'I'm done with these! I'm through! Home for keeps! Gee, it's great to be free! I've had enough!' Tightening his hold on Paddy's arm he added, 'Except what you'll be teaching me and,' he went on, nodding towards the woods, 'the forest here.'

Paddy pushed him back, eyes glowing. 'They've made a good job of you. You're right smart lookin'.'

Hyslop laughed. 'I told you, Paddy. He's got his education up to where you take over. See you finish it good! He's going to keep you and me when we get old. Remember he promised? And see here,' he added, turning to Bari, 'you make it more than tobacco-money. Paddy and I are used to luxuries.'

Bari laughed. 'Paddy'll show me how, Corporal Hyslop. He's kept me seven years and liked it.'

'Well, I've got to go. Go on up and see what Paddy's got ready for you.' He hopped into his boat. 'I'll be seeing you.'

Picking up his books, Bari turned. From where he stood he could see that a piece had been built on to the west side of the cabin. Eyes widening, he gazed. 'You made the house bigger!'

Paddy grinned. 'For you. Just finished it.'

Bari bounded up the path and through the newly made door. Nails and shavings were still lying around, hammer and saws stood in the corner, but the room was filled with the homey sweetness of freshly sawn cedar. There was warmth, a friendliness in it.

A peep of the lake came through the window; there the beauty of birches and pine doubled itself on the bay's clear water.

There was a new-made table with shelves above, and a couple of chairs in the corner with hide-covered cushions.

'Oney made them,' Paddy said, coming through the door, 'an' them, too.' He pointed to strings of cones curtaining the wide window. 'She liked fixin' things.'

'Oh, is Oney home?'

'No, she's down east. Mrs Carson took her for singin' lessons. Jake don't expect her back this summer. She's sure going places, is Oney!'

'Where's Jake?'

'Up north. He'll be back for berryin'.'

Bari untied the strap from his books and began arranging them in the shelves. The place delighted him. 'You must have known I needed more space, Paddy.'

'I figgered you'd like a corner of your own. We'll eat and then——'

Keego came racing through the door, shirt flying, hair on end. 'You're home for keeps!' he cried, grasping Bari's hand. 'An' they got things pretty soft for you, pretty slick,' he waved his arm round the room, 'but you gotta live outside. It's the sun an' wind you need; look at me.' Keego thrust out his arms and chest proudly.

Bari looked at the weathered face crinkling with laughter and ran his hand over the iron-hard muscles of the sturdy arm. 'I'll be with you, Keego, don't you worry about me. I've had enough indoors to last me a life.'

'What you goin' to do?' Keego asked.

Bari drew a deep breath. He couldn't think fast enough.

'He's goin' to make pictures, that's what he's aimin' to do,' Paddy spoke up with a chuckle.

Keego grinned. 'Well, I just come to tell you, Good-day.' He went out as quickly as he came.

Paddy put a meal on the table, duck stuffed with rice, fresh bannock and berries. He had saved the duck for the occasion.

Bari ate with gusto, but there was lots to talk about. He told Paddy about things he had done, people he had met and the things he was going to do after a while.

That was the beginning. Every day and every hour of the day was filled with happiness. Paddy and he were as busy as bumble-bees, fishing, chopping wood and berrying. Keego spent most of his time with them.

Then there were restful nights when Paddy and he sat silently by the fire, saying nothing. But there was love in the silence, and it was sweet.

In on them one of these nights walked Jake Madette, face beaming. He held out his hand. 'So you're home, big boy! It's great to see you, an' you ain't a bad looker either.' He slapped Bari's shoulder. 'You're sixteen now, eh? When I was your age I was cuttin' a couple of cords of wood a day.' He laughed proudly and sat down between them with an air of complete satisfaction. 'My Oney,' he went on, pulling out his pipe, 'Paddy'll have tol' you likely, she's doin' awful good. That woman she works for,' he continued, striking a match on the sole of his shoe, 'says she's sure goin' to surprise us.'

Bari looked at him sideways. He had grown stouter. His face was flabbier, and he had an air of importance, self-assurance that irked. But he was likeable and friendly, and after that he came often to yarn and drink coffee, and mostly to talk about Oney. That's what Bari thought.

One night it rained so Bari stayed in, drew out his paints and began to work on a water-colour. Jake came in. Seating himself on a chair he began talking to Paddy, but he kept an eye on Bari. When talk lulled he turned, grinned and asked, 'What you aimin' to do with yourself, young fellah?'

Bari tapped the table with his hand and kept looking at his work.

'He's plannin' to be an artist, Jake,' Paddy spoke up.

'A artist, what's that?'

'That's makin' pictures—paintin' them. Ever since he was a young sap he's painted an' drawed.' Paddy's voice was warm, confident.

Bari saw Jake's brows come together darkly. 'There won't be much money in that, I'm thinkin', an' pictures'll be pretty tough chewin' if yer hungry.' He laughed a deep hilarious laugh.

It wasn't what Madette said that hurt, it was the way he said it. His jest, his laughter, did something to Bari and, like a bud stricken by a wintry blast, he wilted. After this, he found himself watching and leaving the cabin when Jake hove in sight.

When he had been home a couple of months Bari had a letter from Oney. A dainty little note saying she was glad that he was home and hoped he'd find lots of work and asking what he was going to be.

Bari answered, telling her his plans and how happy he was.

It was almost rice time when he ran into Jake again. He came in one noon, smiling. Sitting down he took out a cigarette, stuck it in his mouth and lit it, and then talked quite a while before saying, ' I gotta fix my cabin roof, Paddy. It's leakin'. Thought maybe you an' the boys would help. It's a job a man can't do hisself, an' you fellahs got the tools.'

' We'll be there in the mornin',' Paddy said promptly. ' If you get everything ready, we'll do it in a day. Keego'll be round an' he'll help.'

Jake looked pleased. Bari expected him to say something about Oney, but he didn't. When he got to the door he called back, ' I'll have things ready. Come as soon's you can.'

Keego came at night. He was pleased with the prospect of helping and went to get the tools ready. Bari wasn't keen on going, but he knew Jake wouldn't like it if he stayed away and would think he was lazy.

They were at Madette's soon after sunrise next morning. The only preparation Jake had made was to sit and wait. The leak in the roof wasn't new, nor was there only one. He had piled logs, hay and sods on them for successive years until the ridge pole snapped and was threatening to pour the roof in on the floor.

Paddy tackled the work with a will. Bari stayed close and worked hard, while Keego tore into it with glee. He threw down earth and hay, ripped off the rafters, and hoisted timber with the agility of a cat.

Jake made the eats and dodged the heavier work, but he was grateful and said so at night when they gathered round the camp-fire to chat. 'Yah, you done a good job. My cabin's snug now. Keego ain't so dumb: he can handle tools all right. When I was his age,' Jake went on, 'I had my own cabin built, cut, sawed, an' chinked the logs and niver thunk a thing about it.'

'Ha, I could build a dozen cabin,' Keego answered with a sniff of contempt, 'but I ain't goin' to—an' so could Bari,' he added loyally.

'Yah,' Jake conceded, 'Bari's all right, but he's aimin' for too sissy a job.'

Bari could feel the blood mounting to his face. Why did Madette say things like that? Why did he always talk that way?

All the way home Bari thought of them, and they hurt. Why couldn't Madette understand that he wanted to do things, big things, but how could he out here in the bush? When he was at school, Paddy had supplied him with money. Now Paddy didn't give him a cent. Bari kept turning the situation over in his mind. It grew, gnawing and tormenting him. He tried to think of a solution. There didn't seem to be one. He seemed to be a prisoner, hedged by a barrier through which he could not even see light.

Every time he thought of Madette, he clenched his fists. His dislike for the man was growing into more than hatred, but he'd show him that he could paint pictures, make money, and go places same as Oney. Bari threw up his head spiritedly.

On the way home he said to Keego, 'I'm sick of that Madette. He thinks I'm no good, can't do anything! I'll show him! I can't even draw in peace—he comes

pokin' around laughing at me. There's a hide-away
beneath the birch on the Point. I'm goin' to move my
things there; I'll keep it for a place for myself where
I can draw an' paint when I like. Will you help me
move?'

'Sure.' Keego grinned.

That night he helped Bari clear a hollow beneath
the birch and move in Bari's books, paints and drawing-
things.

'My kingdom again!' Bari said wistfully when they
finished. 'Maybe some day I'll build a house here. I'd
like to, just to show Madette that I can, that he doesn't
know everything!'

Bari felt more cheerful, but next night Paddy said,
'We're goin' rice-pickin' Monday. We'll have to get
ready.'

Bari's spirits fell. He didn't want to go. 'I'm not
much good at it any more, Paddy. Couldn't I stay at
home?'

'Stay at home!' Paddy repeated. 'We gotta make
money, gotta live.'

Bari went. The work irked him, his steps lagged.
Rice harvest had lost its savour.

'Come on, Bari, get a move on!' Paddy spoke
sharply, in a tone of voice he had never used before.

Bari sulked. Neither Keego's banter nor the flying
music of his mouth-organ lifted Bari from his
lethargy.

When rice harvest was finished, Paddy sold it as
always and sent for clothes. Bari didn't like that; he
wanted to choose his own clothes. Besides, there were
other things he wanted to buy, and how could Paddy

know the kind of ties and shirts he liked? Bari swallowed his chagrin.

When they got home he spent most of his time with Keego in the bush and in the place he called his own. Sometimes he would stand looking away beyond the jackpine rim and wonder about the kingdom there. But he wasn't idle, for back in his mind was Madette. The resolve he had made to show Madette that he could make good was probing him on, keeping him alone, for he couldn't stand the scoffings of Oney's father.

The corners of landscapes, animals and flowers coming into being on paper were proof of Bari's work. He was an artist at heart, and the knowledge of symmetry, distance and shading that he had gained at school gave fidelity to his touch.

Paddy did fall work, chopping wood and mending nets.

But something strained was creeping into their life, an aloofness Bari couldn't understand. Paddy was changing. Jake Madette was the cause. Bari sensed it. He was always sneering at him, always bragging about Oney. Now, Paddy was praising her. 'That Oney's sure gettin' places, an' Jake can be right proud of her, an' I'm thinkin' she's right smart, myself,' he said one day. Then he seemed quite cross and abrupt. He never stopped working. Out of a clear sky he'd say, 'Better get a hustle on an' get in some wood', or ask sharply, 'Where have you been?' Bari would like to have told him, but he wanted to keep his secret. Besides, Paddy never asked about his drawing any more. Although one night he said, 'You sure waste a lot of time.'

F

Bari was stung to retaliation. 'You know I like drawing, Paddy!'

'That was all right when you were a youngster, but now you're grown up.'

Bari was cut to the core. Paddy wasn't interested any more. All their old camaraderie had gone. He stood a moment looking beseechingly at Paddy, then broken, frustrated, he groped blindly towards the door.

There was a step and Madette came roystering in. Pulling a snapshot from his pocket he held it up. 'See what come to-day.'

Paddy reached for it, looked, then his smile deepening, he handed it to Bari who had halted. 'It's Oney, she's sure pretty nice.' There was a warm note of admiration in his voice.

Bari rested his eyes on it a moment. Yes, it was Oney, sparkling, vivacious Oney! Her eyes, her hair, her whole being, even the traily dress she wore seemed to be alive with laughter.

'She looks like me, don't she?' Jake said, beaming.

Bari squinted at him, handed back the picture, and walked out, a wild bewildering hurt battering at his heart.

He made straight for a rock beside Seegwun's pool and sat down. Alone in the darkness he tried to think things out. Oney hadn't answered his letter. Likely Jake had written and told her he was no good. Maybe if he went away he could find something to do, something worth while, but he couldn't go without money. And he couldn't go back to school.

Here where he sat had been his kingdom. Part of one of the uprights of what had once been his castle lay in the shadow of the bank. Beyond was the sand Seegwun's feet had tracked.

Now the 'gooquas and his kingdom were gone. Only the water looked up at him, cold, black and unfriendly. He laughed a short bitter laugh. Paddy had been his god. Now he too was failing him. A pain of unutterable loneliness swept through him. Surely there must be a way. Surely the God of the big world must see him, must know about this thing that was beating him. Clutching a branch from the side of the pool, he wrung its twigs in his hands until the bitterness of his spirit broke into a sob.

A star came twinkling on to the pool. Bari looked up. The moon, slipping from clouds, silhouetted trees and lake into beauty. The pine on the opposite Point were lifting heads trusting and serene to the starry heavens. A sense of well-being came to Bari, a reminder that there was another Kingdom beyond. Out there, there must be a chance for him. There must be a way...

He heard the cabin door opening, Madette came out and turned towards home. Bari rose and walked back to the cabin. When he went in Paddy was putting wood on the stove. He looked up sharply. 'You shouldn't have gone out, Bari. Madette ain't such a bad fellah!' Paddy's voice was kindlier.

Bari smiled. He went to bed right away.

Next morning Paddy was a lot cheerier. Bari felt better. When he finished breakfast he said, 'I'm going to look for Keego to-day. Haven't seen him for a while, and maybe I'd better take some eats.'

Paddy looked at him queerly. 'You're not aimin' to go far are you?'

Bari shook his head. 'Just north a bit.'

Paddy wrapped a couple of bannocks and a piece of cheese in a paper and handed it to him.

Bari took it, put on a heavy coat and hurried out. It was a rimey morning and heavy under foot. He made for a hollow where there was a good stand of cedar. Staying only long enough to take in the stoutness of its growth, he headed north. Soon he heard music.

He caught up with Keego who was mending a canoe. Keego greeted him with a hand-wave and looked pleased when Bari said, 'I been looking for you all morning.' Bari sat down on a stump before continuing, 'I've got an idea for us to do something, Keego.'

'Me?' Keego said, dropping his hammer. 'Me too?'

'Could we get the makin's of a house?'

'A bird can do that,' Keego answered, unenthusiastically.

'Could we two build a cabin?'

'I could build a cabin myself, but I ain't goin' to.' Keego's eyes came together suspiciously. 'What's wrong with the one you got—Paddy's?'

'Paddy says everybody should know how to build a cabin; should build the house they live in. I'd love to do something, something that would please Paddy. I learned a bit about building at school.'

'What's wrong with your picture-makin'?' Keego quizzed, in a still not too enthusiastic voice.

'Jake Madette laughs at it an' says it's sissy.'

Keego snorted, 'That wa-wa doesn't know enough to know he doesn't know nothin'. I ain't buildin' no house, Bari, that's work! If I did, it would be up with the eagles so's I could talk to the stars an' spit on Jake

Madette!' Keego's lip curled contemptuously. 'Don't pay no attention to that coot. Nobody can draw pictures like you! Besides, workin' ain't no good. Look at me!' Keego shrugged, 'I don't do nothin' an'——'

'I thought we could build a cabin on the quiet,' Bari interrupted, 'where nobody would see.'

Keego's eyes widened. 'Can't build a cabin where nobody'll see. Folks can see a house without lookin'— besides it's goin' to snow.' Keego belted his coat tighter and nodded skyward. 'An' snow tells everythin'.' Keego went on in an assured voice, 'You keep on drawin'; your pictures are great! Just like as if they were livin'.'

There was sincerity in Keego's eyes, a loyalty in his voice that made Bari feel good. He didn't tell him that all night he had tossed and turned trying to think of some way to reinstate himself in Paddy's regard, and through all his troubled thoughts was a hope that Keego would help.

They spent the day together. At night as Bari made for home there was a scud of snow, and wind came whistling about his ears. Keego was right. Winter was coming!

Hastening his steps, Bari kept tight to the shore. The storm lulled. And as he skirted the rise to the cabin he heard voices. Hyslop's boat was in the dock. Looking between the rocks he could see Hyslop and Paddy standing. He kept low so that they couldn't see him. He heard his name. He stopped and listened. They were talking about him.

'It's too bad he didn't get the brunt of the world,' Hyslop was saying. Bari could see him in the lamp-light from the window; he was standing, feet parted, arms folded, a serious thinking look on his face.

'I don't know where he goes or what he does. He's away most of the time, an' it looks as if he didn't care for the house or the place I fixed for him no more.' Paddy's voice was sad.

'These young fellows are hard to handle at that age, Paddy. What he needs is good hard work! Send him to one of the lumber camps; they can use him.' Hyslop took a couple of steps towards the boat and turned. 'They'll pay him good wages.'

Each single word they said struck like a knife-thrust into Bari's being. He crouched lower; he mustn't betray his presence.

Paddy stepped forward, and although snow was falling again his face showed clearly in the glow from the window. It was troubled. 'Pretty tough goin' in them lumber camps, ain't it? An' Bari's got it in him to be an artist. You said so yourself.' There was challenge in Paddy's voice.

'There's better men than him at lumber camps, an' nobody'll stop him being an artist.' Hyslop spoke crisply. 'There'll be moonlight on the timber and the frost'll fancy up the shrubbery for him. He can cool his heels painting it.'

Bari winced. Hyslop was angry.

'I've got a bit of money of his, Peter, that I got for rat pelts. It's his by rights.' Paddy continued, 'It might help him, surprise him!'

Swinging himself into the boat, Hyslop called over his shoulder, 'He'll get two surprises if I get hold of him and they won't any of them be in cash. Don't you dare give him money. Let him earn it. You've done enough for him.' Hyslop's motor hummed and swung out to the bay.

Bari looked up. Paddy was going into the cabin.

Conscious only of a deep agonizing hurt, Bari slipped up to the cabin and in. Paddy was standing by the table; his shoulders sagged, his face looked haggard. The furrows about his eyes deepened. 'D'you find Keego?'

Bari nodded.

'Want supper?'

Bari was vaguely aware of the question. He shook his head. A gust of snow hurled against the window.

'It's a rough night,' Paddy went on. 'It's goin' on to winter so I gotta get fuel in an' fix the lean-to. There's a couple of weeks' work to do.'

Bari undressed and went to bed. He couldn't bring himself to speak.

Pulling up the covers Bari lay numb and confused. He couldn't sleep. One thought kept hurtling through his bewildered head: nobody wants me! Nobody wants me! The world is against me. Again he could hear Hyslop's words, 'What he wants is good hard work.'

Then flashingly an idea came. He could work. That was the very thing he wanted. He didn't have to stay with Paddy. He was a man now. The thought gave him courage, and he could feel an easing of the tension that had held him tight. He lay motionless, his mind busy. Before he slept he had made his plan.

He woke early and saw that Paddy was up making breakfast. He was bending over a pan on the stove.

He swung round and, with something of the old friend-liness in his voice, said, ' It's snowed all night. Wish I'd had more firewood in, an' the lean-to fixed.'

' We'll go get firewood right away, an' then I'll help you fill that sag in the lean-to.'

Paddy looked at him.

They ate breakfast cheerfully. The wind had fallen and the storm was settling into a low drift. As soon as they finished eating, Paddy drew on an extra sweater. ' If you stay an' keep the fire goin', I'll go chop some of the nearby balsam.'

' I'm goin' with you,' Bari answered, without looking up.

So side by side they cut and toted fuel to the cabin, and then they fixed the lean-to.

Paddy seemed happier. Something of the old camara-derie came back, the understanding they had known and loved, even though hours passed in silence.

The work was hard. Winter had swooped down, blanketing their world with snow and locking the lake with ice.

Bari was glad when Paddy said, ' The lake's sure froze solid; no risk walkin' it now!'

That's what Bari had been waiting for. Five nights ago he had made plans. To-morrow he would put them into action.

Chapter XIII

THE LUMBER CAMP

Bari went to bed early, but he didn't sleep.

He rose before dawn, dressed, packed a knapsack, rolled his blankets and lit the fire. When he heard Paddy stirring he went over to his cot and said, 'I'm goin' away to-day, Paddy. I'm goin' to work.'

Paddy shot up, looked at him, rubbed his eyes and looked again. It was some seconds before he spoke. 'Maybe that would be better, Bari. I ain't got much for you here.' He waved his hand around the cabin meaningly. 'Maybe you get yerself a chance. There ain't much in the bush for you.'

'It's lonesome here,' Bari answered evenly.

Paddy's face shadowed. A queer strained look came into his eyes.

'Don't worry, Paddy, it's just like I'm goin' away to school again, only I'll be makin' somethin', earnin' money. I'm a man now,' Bari added with a short laugh. It was hard to keep a lump from rising in his throat.

Paddy sat some minutes staring at the wall as if his mind was fixed on some far-distant thought, then getting up he dressed, crossed to the corner cupboard and took out a parcel. 'I sent for some cloes for you; they come last week.' He undid the wrapping, pulled out a couple of shirts, three pairs of socks and a pair of mitts, and pushed them across the table. 'They should be plenty warm.'

Bari looked at them a moment, then lifting one of the shirts ran his fingers along its soft red folds. 'Gee, they're swell, Paddy, just what I need. That'll save me buying them when I get a pay.' Bari hesitated, a strangling feeling was coming back to his throat. 'I'm goin' east to a lumber camp. They say they need men.' He turned quickly and pushed the clothes into his knapsack.

They ate breakfast without speaking. Once or twice their eyes met. There was a sadness, a hollowness in Paddy's face that Bari hadn't seen before. His own lip quivered, but the talk he had overheard between Hyslop and Paddy hardened him. He rose as soon as he had finished eating and put on his coat. It was Paddy who spoke: 'If you don't make out, or—or—or don't like it, you'll come back, eh? It ain't so easy in them camps.' There was a catch in his voice.

It brought a lump back to Bari's throat. He must get going. He nodded vaguely, donned heavy coat and overshoes, shouldered his blankets and stepped through the doorway, with a briefly flung, 'I'll be seein' you— in the spring.'

He drew a freer breath when he got out. The hard feeling at the pit of his stomach left. He headed north into a stiff wind. This was what he wanted, to go places, do things.

He knew every tree landmarking the shores, every by-way threading the bush. He never looked back, nor did his thoughts rest a moment on the man whose eyes (had he only known) were following him to the snow's farthest rim.

It was a long tramp, but the confidence of youth sustained him. Daylight still dallied on the drifts when he skirted Drybury to K.L. Camp Sixty. He had heard lots about camp life, loggers, fallers and riggers. Now he would be one of them. He breasted the last hill to the buildings buoyantly.

Turning to a widening trail he saw half-a-dozen men straggling in from the bush. A team of horses and sleigh swung from a side road.

Bari slackened pace. Heading for the first building he ran full tilt into a little fellow coming from the road. The man stopped and looked at him curiously. ' Are you lookin' for somebody ? '

' The boss,' Bari answered, easing up his blanket-strap.

' He's over there in that building behind where the team's standing.' The man pointed to a hut at the ebb of land.

Bari made for it. The word ' Office ' was painted on the door. Before Bari could knock a voice called ' Come in '.

Drawing a deep breath Bari pushed open the door. A man sitting behind a desk looked up. He was stockily built, with greying hair and a pleasant face, but his

stare was cool and steady. ' Are you looking for work ? '
he asked curtly.

Bari wanted to say ' Yes ', but words wouldn't come.
He fumbled with his mitts.

' What's your name ? ' The man took up a letter
and began reading as he asked.

' Bari Bradbrooke.'

' How old are you ? '

' Seventeen.' Bari's head went up as he said it. He
wasn't seventeen for nine months, but the thought gave
him a good feeling.

There was a silence colder than the snow over which
Bari had travelled. A slow twinkle came into the man's
eyes. ' You don't look too husky, but I can use you.
You can help the cook.'

Burning disappointment swept over Bari. He could
feel it flaming into his face as he turned towards the
door. The man was speaking.

' My name's Marnett, Ted Marnett. You go over
there and have supper.' He rose and pointed through
the window. ' That's the cook-house with the light by
the door. Shorty the cook'll show you your bunk. I'll
see you later.'

Resentfully Bari turned towards the cook-house.
Wash dishes ! Peel potatoes ! That's what he'd have
to do !

' Hi there, big bhoy ! '

The voice startled him. It was Shorty's. It couldn't
be anybody else's. He was standing in the doorway,
white aproned, his smile glistening. ' Wash there, me
lad,' he pointed to a water-bucket sitting by a basin on
a tree stump. ' Then come right in. There's a sate for

ye at the end of the table.' His voice was as happy as his smile.

Slipping his bundle to the ground, Bari took off his coat and washed. He hesitated a few minutes, but the smell of beef stew and coffee coming through the door-way was sure good. He stepped in.

The place was steamy and warm. A table ran up the centre. Every seat beside it was filled, except the one at the end. As Bari slipped into it, twenty pairs of eyes lifted and looked at him. No one spoke.

It was some minutes before he had courage to look up and run his eye round the table. There were big men and little men, with whiskered, happy-go-lucky faces.

The fellow next to him was big and heavy jowled, with sooty eyes. He nodded and winked, but kept on eating with the gusto of a bear. The chap sitting opposite was the one he had spoken to coming in. He smiled when their eyes met. He had scads of rusty hair and a thin laughing face; but it was friendly, and his smile was quick. Bari liked him.

During the meal he pushed bread, salt and pepper Bari's way with an understanding nod. As soon as the meal was finished everybody rose and went out. He came straight to Bari. 'I'm Jim Wilkens, the stable boss. I hope Marnett sends you to me. I need an extra.' He put his hand on Bari's shoulder. 'You'd like working in the barn.'

Bari smiled. He didn't know what to say, so he was glad when the cook called, 'Hi, this way, me lad. I gotta show you where you slape.'

Bari picked up his bundle and followed.

The bunkhouse was a large low building tucked in a stand of spruce. 'This is a great place fer ye, me lad; an' it's roight glad I am to be gettin' ye,' Shorty said, opening the door and switching on a light. 'That's yours,' he pointed to an end cot. 'It's close to the door so's ye can get out aisy. Slape good and good-noight, me bhoy.' The half-chuckle in his voice warmed Bari's heart.

He slid his blankets to the bunk, spread them out and sat down. The place was warm and cosy, and the cots were all neatly made. He couldn't see how many, for they dwindled into darkness at the far end.

He folded back his blanket and began taking off his shoes. The door opened and Marnett's head popped in. 'Making out O.K.? Sleep good an' be on the job in the morning. Shorty'll call you. We'll try you for a couple of weeks and see how you get along. Cheerio!'

Bari straightened. So Marnett was just trying him out, even at peeling potatoes and washing dishes and that sissy stuff!

He finished unlacing his shoes, kicked them into the corner took off his clothes and got into bed with a bang. He'd show these camp fellows what he could do. He'd peel potatoes too if he had to, and he'd do other things. He was no kid. He'd show them that. He bristled.

Outside the wind had whipped up to a blizzard. He pulled the blankets up and they gave him a good feeling, for his body was tired.

The men came straggling in and went quietly to bed. He didn't look up at them. No one had come into the bed next to him when he closed his eyes. He fell asleep.

When he awoke, a lantern had been lit and was dangling from a rafter at the far end. Bari saw it was ten minutes to five. No one was stirring.

He rose, washed, dressed and went to the cook-house. He met Shorty at the door, a pan in his hand. 'Didn't ye slape good?' he asked, bringing his brows together quizzically.

'Dandy, but I wanted to get to work.'

'It's the good Lord that's sent ye to me Hisself,' Shorty said, turning back in and laying down his pan.

'Drink this.' He poured out a mug of coffee and pushed it across the table. 'We'll ate after the men's aitin'. It's mostly aitin' and work here.' Shorty wiped his face with a towel. 'But oi don't mind s'long's oi gits a bit of a rest between toimes.' He gulped a mug of coffee and handed Bari an apron. 'Put this on. We gotta get movin'.'

Shorty must have been up some time, for the stove was going full blast, porridge was cooking and bacon was sliced ready for the pan. Doughnuts were simmering in a kettle of grease.

The cook-house wasn't large. It was painted white and was clean; the towels were fresh, and sealers and tins were shining and neatly labelled. There was a feeling of wholesomeness, of things well done, about the place.

'Get the porridge out, the men's comin',' Shorty said, scooping it on to plates and pushing them into Bari's hand. 'Set them round the table.'

Bari worked fast. The men were filing in. There was no time to look round, but he nodded to Wilkens who was sitting in the same seat as last night. Once or twice a voice said, 'Bring me milk, kiddo,' or 'Kiddo, get me bread.' The men spoke quietly and they had kindly eyes. Bari's name was fixed—he knew it. He was 'kiddo'. There was no backing away from it.

Before a week passed Bari learnt that the joy of working in a lumber camp was the joy one put into it. It was the cheery heart-warming things Shorty and the men did in the everyday grind that made life worth while. The men were hearty and rugged, with spirits geared to the work. Bari liked them and their rollicking banter, and he liked Shorty. The round-faced little Irishman was no slacker.

Bari washed dishes, peeled vegetables and cleared tables at a pace at which he had never done any- thing before. Shorty taught him how to make pie, mix doughnuts, and let him in on the secrets of his specials—the dishes the men liked. Shorty fed them well.

But there was something missing in Bari's life. Even after Marnett came along and said, 'You're a great worker, kiddo; Shorty says he can't do without you,' the feeling was still there.

Sometimes when chores were done and pies and doughnuts stacked well ahead, Shorty and he would stroll out to take a peek at the men. Bari liked the loggers and teamsters. They hailed him cheerily.

The high-riggers, belted to what seemed the forest's very tip, made him think of Keego in his eyrie talking to the stars. The log-laden sleds on glistening trails, the smell of freshly cut wood, and the axemen's

' Timber-r-r ' on the frosty wind fired a spark in Bari's imagination and sent it flaming through his blood.

In his father, and his father's father, and in *his* father's father before that, yes farther back than he could ever think, there had been love of living close to the forest's heart. Maybe that was why it was calling him now.

Surging above the dish-washing and pot-splashing there was an urge to answer. He'd race to the bunk-house, grasp pencil and paper and begin to sketch. It wasn't hard to make these clear crisp pictures of the woods look real. They sprang from within his being.

But one night Shorty discovered him drawing. It was then Bari found that Shorty was a gentleman of moods. ' Don't let me catch ye wastin' toime, me bhoy! It's no slackers we keep around here. When we ain't busy there's work to do!' He jerked out the words without even a glimpse at Bari's picture.

Laying down his pencil, Bari slid his sketch beneath his mattress. Shorty maybe saw the look of defeat seeping into Bari's eyes, but he went on, ' There ain't nobody ever the worse off workin', Bari! Work's good for ye. It's a foine lumberman ye'll make if ye only set yer moind to it, me bhoy.' Shorty's conciliatory words weren't very cheering.

After supper they were washing dishes again—after all, it was a chore that palled. But maybe Shorty was right. There was a quality in this busy urgent life, a worth-whileness that gave zest to labour. The thought sent Bari's head up and his shoulders back. He'd show them he could work!

But there was that eternal inner urge; it popped

up when trees cast shadows on the sunlit drifts and the forest stood blue and mysterious beneath the Spirit Moon.

It was now that Bari began to get better acquainted with Wilkens, the stable boss. He was a friendly glib-tongued fellow with a quick eye. Bari went often to the barn to chat with him. At night they sat in a lantern-lit corner, Wilkens cutting birds, ink-wells, candle-holders, tricky things from wood with his jack-knife. Bari, too, liked doing that. This bond of making things drew them together. It encouraged Bari to pull his drawings from beneath his mattress and show them to him.

Wilkens' face kindled. 'By jiminy! You can draw, Bari! Anybody ever tell you that?' he added, holding the sketches at arm's length. 'You've got something there, an' to think you never mentioned it. You shouldn't be washin' dishes, sloppin' with pots an' pans. Why, you're an artist!' he added, with an exclamation of enthusiasm. 'Keep on, kiddo, you'll go places with this. You'll be the Tom Thomson of our camp!'

'Who's he?'

'A guy that painted pictures, real pictures! He lived amongst the woods an' rocks, painting. He made a name for himself. Did you never read about him?' Wilkens went on, admiration in his lowering voice. 'Thomson was a brother of wild things, for he lived with them. He was chosen as one of seven to paint pictures of this northland.' Wilkens spread his hands towards the bush. 'He saw beauty there, a wildness that other folks couldn't see. He put it in pictures.

You've got something, too, Bari, if you only stay with it. Don't let anyone tell you different.'

Bari was thrilled. Scooping his drawings into his arms he turned to go out, then hesitated. 'I've got to wash dishes, work, you know. Shorty doesn't think much of this stuff.' He looked down at his pictures. 'He says it's a waste of time.'

'Waste of time!' Wilkens focused his bird-like eyes on Bari's face. 'You bring your drawin' things over here to the barn an' I'll fix a light so's you can do a bit now and again if you want to.'

Bari was gone. Five minutes later his drawing-things were in a horse-stall behind bales of hay. The old bogey of keeping his work hidden was still dogging him. But why should it? It wasn't a crime to draw and paint.

Then, as if the God of big things was taking a hand, a parcel came one night for Bari. One of the teamsters brought it from the Narrows. Bari could hardly believe his eyes. It bore many postmarks, and clearly typed on the label was 'Bari Bradbrooke'. What could it be? He had never had a parcel by mail before.

Excitedly he ripped the wrapping off, took out a box of oil paints, a palette and bottles of linseed oil. Then there was a small canvas, with a letter tucked in the corner. Bari grasped the letter, tore it open and read, 'Dear Bari, My father says you've gone to a lumber camp, so hope this gets to you all right. The canvas and paints are for you to paint a real picture. I'm not sending brushes, as I know you have them. Mrs Carson hopes you'll keep on with your art.' Blurring, the words danced and faded before his astounded eyes, but at the end, 'Oney' stood out clearly.

Bari raced with the parcel to Wilkens. ' See! See what I got! A friend sent it. She—she knows I paint.' Bari felt himself reddening. ' She wants me to paint a real picture ! '

Wilkens grinned and nodded. ' No excuse now for you not goin' ahead.'

' She didn't send brushes, but I'll get some, somehow,' Bari said, fingering the paint-tubes. ' I'll keep everything here in the barn.'

That night, in their corner, Bari with Wilkens' help devised two brushes, one from the hairs of a squirrel's tail, the other from a snip of a horse's mane. ' They ain't fancy, but they'll do ! ' Wilkens said when they had finished glueing them, ' an' good luck to you.'

Each day Bari rose early. He got through his morning chores quickly, saw to it that Shorty had no kick about lagging, and when his rest-time came—which Shorty conceded was really necessary—and every other time he had the chance, he was behind the bales of hay in the barn painting.

One day a couple of the men stumbled in on him. They looked, blinked and looked again, then turned to look into the stern face of the stable boss. ' Mum's the word, boys, don't say anythin' to anybody. The cookie's cookin' up a surprise, not for eatin' though.'

They seemed to be delighted to be in on the secret and went off talking with Wilkens in undertones.

Next night, when Bari went to bed, there were three brushes below his pillow—a camel, a hog's-hair and a whitewash brush. Bari lifted them, ran his hand over the wide wall-brush and smilingly carried them to the barn.

Wilkens laughed. 'You can paint the world now, Bari! We got great guys in this camp.'

Bari's picture was more than brush strokes. It was the tamarack valley he had set himself to paint, because it was home and his kingdom. His heart was there. And hadn't Oney sent him the 'tools' and told him to go ahead. He smiled when he thought of her father; what would he say if he saw him now?

Wilkens' praise of Bari sent his hopes and dreams sky-rocketing. Then there were tales of money and places, things Wilkens owned and the opportunities of the big world. His words thrilled Bari. 'Drawin' here in the bush is no good, Bari. You've got to get out. You can't go back to live in the forest. It would be a crime to let you. I won't do it. I tell you what, I'm buildin' up a place that'll be just right for you. It's for tourists. You'll meet the right people, folks with money. You can work for me and paint between times. I'll pay you good wages, an' you can make a bit on the side with tips.' Wilkens' voice was eager, and there was expectancy in his face as if he saw a future glow. 'It's a chance for you, Bari. I'll be startin' west right away. If you don't go I'll have to get another man to drive the team back. You see I just come here in winter because I send horses. I like horses.' Wilkens shrugged. 'Like looking after them.' He brushed some straw from his trousers as he went on, 'That picture you're painting will be worth a bit of dough if you can only get it in the right place,' Wilkens lifted his voice coaxingly, 'and——'

'Do you mean it? Do you want me?' Bari jumped to his feet excitedly. 'I—I—I want to go! I'll go

anywhere with you! Wait till I run an' tell Shorty.'
Bari dashed out of the barn.

'I'm goin' with Wilkens at break-up—he's givin' me
a job!' The words tumbled from his lips as he raced
into the cook-house.

Shorty, standing slicing bacon by the table, halted
his knife momentarily and looked up.

'Wilkens is a pretty good fellow, isn't he?' Bari
went on. 'It's—it's good of him to want me to go,
don't you think so?'

Shorty put the sliced bacon into the frying-pan and
leaned casually against the wood-box. 'Yes, he's a livil-
headed fellah all right, is Wilkens, but don't lit him be
turnin' yer head, me bhoy. Don't forgit what oi tould
ye.' Shorty stopped and wagged a finger significantly.
'It's work that counts, an' ye, yerself, what ye put into
it, not what the other fellah does.'

'It's the chance I've been wantin', waitin' for, Shorty.
I can hardly believe I'm goin'!' Bari's voice shook with
expectancy.

'That's all roight, but ye'll have to work hard just
the same, me bhoy,' Shorty continued, turning to his
bacon.

'Shorty, did you never have a hobby?'

'What's that?'

'Somethin' you do just because you like it.'

'Oi work, my bhoy.'

'Well I'm sure awful glad about goin',' Bari said
smiling. 'I'll tell the boss when he comes in.'

When the drip of freshening came to the woods Bari
sat down and wrote to Paddy. 'I've got a job for the
spring with a man who's going west. He's going to

pay me good wages. I'm sure tickled to get the chance. Don't worry about me, I'll be back in summer, same as usual!' Bari lifted his pen and looked a long time at the words. Would he be back in summer? Ever since Oney had sent the parcel of paints he had been filled with urgent thoughts and wishes. Now he was hoping they would turn into something more than dreams. No, he wouldn't write anything more to Paddy. He signed his letter off simply, ' Bari '.

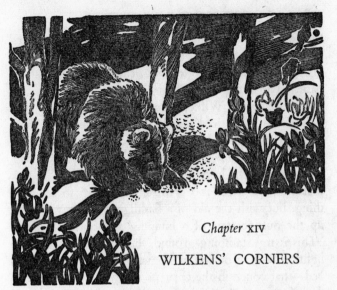

Chapter XIV

WILKENS' CORNERS

Bari took the road west with Wilkens on a March morning. They each drove a team with a sleigh-load of wood. Wilkens was on the lead.

Bari was proud to be trusted with horses. Wilkens had taught him how to groom and care for them. Driving gave him a feeling of power and he was fired with the spirit of adventure.

They travelled leisurely, stopping to rest and feed. At night they bedded down at places Wilkens knew. By noon next day they were clear of bush and into flat country with a sprinkling of bluffs and buildings. The journey seemed endless. The sun on the snow hurt Bari's eyes, the whistling skid of the sleigh grated on his ears, but the road was good. He walked by spells to straighten his cramped limbs and to chat with Wilkens, who rode less and less as the miles went by.

It was their fourth day out. Bari was losing sense of

time and direction, but after sundown the horses picked up speed and after another couple of hours' travel a group of buildings ghosted out of the night across their path. The horses stopped.

' We're here!' Wilkens shouted gaily.

Bari was more tired than he had ever been.

Wilkens came to him at once and said, ' I'll take you right in, and you get to bed. It's been quite a trip. I'll look after the horses.'

It was too dark, too confusing for Bari to see anything, but with the aid of a flashlight, Wilkens led him up the outside stair of a building and opened a door. ' This is my stamping-ground,' he said, switching on a light. ' Make yourself at home. Better get right into bed—that couch in the corner's ready for you. A man does for me. He an' I sleep in this other room.' He pointed to a door beside the one they had come through.

The room was large and there was a huge desk and swivel chair at one end. A safe stood in the corner with table and cupboard between. The other part of the room seemed to be the living end. It had two easy chairs and a table, shelves with books and pictures on the wall and there was a rug on the floor. The couch was made up ready for sleeping. The place looked homey and it was warm.

Bari went straight to bed. He heard Wilkens come upstairs later and go to his room. That was all.

When Bari awoke next morning he felt rested. It was daylight, so he rose and looked through the window. All he could see was flat land, with snow and sky greying with clouds. Where they met was hard to define.

He crossed to the other window; the view wasn't much different. There wasn't a shrub or tree in sight, but right in front of the house there were crossroads and a number of buildings straggled back to what looked like a village. Lumber was piled in a yard across the corner, and behind it the skeleton of a building rose black and fire-charred against the sky. Here and there patches of bare ground were showing through the sooty snow. Bari had never seen anything so unlovely. For a moment he felt that he had been deceived. Something inside him recoiled.

He was still looking through the window when Wilkens came in. 'Great country, eh?' he said, slapping Bari's shoulder boisterously. 'There was a fire over there last fall,' he went on, nodding towards the blackened uprights. 'Pretty nearly got the lumber yard. But——'

Bari looked at him. His face must have expressed his thoughts.

'Don't you like it? What's wrong with it? Why, out there's the best country in the world. It doesn't look very pretty right now, but believe me it's dandy!' Wilkens' voice rang with enthusiasm. 'These two highways out there go through the best grain country in the North American continent.'

Bari smiled. He knew he should say something nice. 'I—I—I just didn't think there was a country any place without trees.'

'Without trees!' Wilkens repeated. 'Why, we got trees, lots of them. Come an' see.' He drew Bari to the door and pointed to what looked like a poplar grove half a mile away. 'Just look at that! Besides this is

the prairie.   Didn't they teach you geography in school?
You've been bushed, my boy, that's what's wrong with
you.'

From anyone else the words might have hurt.   But it
wasn't easy to be cross with Wilkens.   He was so happy.
' Come on an' eat.   That's what I came to get you for.'

Following him down the unpainted stairway Bari felt
a strange hollowness at heart that he found hard to keep
from showing when Wilkens opened a door into a lower
part of the building and asked, ' What do you think of
this ? '

It was a cold barn-looking place with a couple of
large windows coming together to form a corner.

' It's all right.   What's it for ? '

' I'm turnin' it into a store—a gift shop for tourists.
You an' I'll put shelves in.   The goods are on the way.
That'll be your job, lookin' after it.   You've a knack for
that sort of stuff.   You'll have lots of time for paintin'.
Your pictures'll sell like hot cakes.   You see I've a filling-
station, car an' repair shop.   This is a dandy corner.
They're layin' a sidewalk to it.   It's a prize, an' I just got
it by the skin of my teeth.   There's a real fortune here ! '

Wilkens was so confident.

They went into a tiny room at the back.   ' We eat
here ; it saves us mussin' with a stove upstairs.'

Breakfast was set ready.   A man who was stooping
over an oil-burner turned round, smiling.

' This is Dan, the fellow I told you about,' Wilkens
said, waving Bari to a chair.

Dan was a wheezy little fellow with sagging shoulders
and a pair of sharp eyes that Bari felt were looking right
through him.   But Bari liked him.   It was a happy meal.

As soon as they had eaten, Wilkens got up. 'Danny'll look after you. Make yourself at home! Look around and get your bearings. I'm going out to the barn. You can come out after a while and help unload the wood. When the snow's gone we'll have lots to do.'

When the door closed, Danny stretched his legs comfortably and started to talk in a friendly sort of way. 'He's a great fellow, Wilkens. You'll get along with him all right. You're an artist, eh?'

Bari's head went up. To be called an artist made him feel important. He looked appreciatively at Dan, who continued with an extra big wheeze, 'There's some young fellows around you can pal with, but you stick to Jim Wilkens, he's got more ideas about makin' money than there's hairs in a dawg. He's a go-getter, an' soon's spring comes you'll see!'

But spring didn't come quickly. Winter was in a frisky mood. She flung snow into the wind that tore madly across the flats, piling drifts and swirling it into their faces till they could scarcely stagger to the barn.

'It's a blizzard,' Dan said casually. 'We get lots of them this month. Sign of a good crop.'

Up in the confines of Wilkens' room Bari felt like a trapped creature. He paced the floor. He tried to peer through the window. A day, a night, and another day. He had never seen a storm like it.

Then above the spume of drift the stars came out. The Big Dipper swung clear and bright. Thin moonlight again lit the sky into familiar beauty.

Bari stood at the top of the steps and looked at it. He could see the Pole Star, the Hunter and his Dogs; and somewhere beneath the lead dog was Paddy's cabin. Bari felt better to know it was there, for it gave him a sense of security. He hadn't thought a great deal about Paddy lately, but to-night he felt the need of something to steady him. It was there in the little cabin beneath the starlit heavens.

Before a month had passed Bari found that all Dan had said about Wilkens was true, and more.

He was a go-getter. There wasn't anything within a score of miles that he wasn't into, or interested in, especially if there was money in it. He kept the place alive. Everything he touched seemed to buzz into action. Nothing stood still. He expected the people around him to work, and he never spared himself. But he was likeable. His enthusiasm and good spirits burst and bubbled like sunshine through the grey dirty days of the outgoing winter, and he was kind.

'Work!' he said happily, 'I go and look for it; I don't wait for it to come to me.'

Wilkens made him an easel, bought paints, brushes, and encouraged him. 'If you work as hard here at your painting as you did at the camp, you'll go places, Bari.'

Bari set the easel up in his room and tried to paint. But it was no use. Maybe it was the excitement, the whirling pace Wilkens kept up, for if he wasn't outdoors hammering and spading, he was indoors whistling and whittling. He was never at rest for a minute.

Bari realized that it took more than paints and brushes to produce a picture: something he couldn't put in words, peace of mind, quietness of the inner self. Beauty came from within. His brush needed its touch.

Sometimes he caught it out in the poplar grove when

the wind hummed through the sweet-smelling saplings, sometimes in the blue-grey twilights or the sunset.

Then he thought of Paddy, till the quick painful beating of his homesick heart scurried him home to dream about the cabin in the woods, to see in his sleeping thoughts a brown wrinkled face bending over his cot and feel knobby hands tucking the covers on to his shoulders. Then he was rested. When he awoke he smiled. Life was strange. It played pranks with people's thoughts and plans. He realized that living with Paddy had sometimes irked him. Madette had scoffed at him, making him hide his dreams and his desires. Now he was free and opportunity was at his door. He had everything he needed. Life was stirring and exciting, but he couldn't paint.

Again and again he tried, but it was no use. He put his paints away. It was like putting a comrade in a cupboard and locking the door. Without them he was lost and lonely.

He got to know lads of his own age, happy carefree fellows whose life had been different from his. True, they were friendly, but their friendship lacked warmth. They could not be companionable, for to them the woods and trees and springing life meant nothing. They made him welcome in their homes, but they looked casually at his art, guardedly at his dark skin. That's what he felt. To them he was ' the Indian! '—something apart.

Sometimes at night he sat alone behind the barn listening for a singing bird, watching for the companioning whisk of a snowshoe. Then covered up in bed later he fought tears, for something inside him kept urging him to go home. Go home! At heart he was still a child.

But how could he leave Wilkens, who had been so good to him, who had helped, boosted him and given him a chance he'd never otherwise have had? And there was Danny, who had shared his books and magazines with him, wheezed upstairs with hot drinks and nice things for him. How could he say to them, 'I want to go home. I don't like it here. I don't belong'?

It was April. Freshets were dividing the snow, but they didn't sing or scamper like the frolicking ice-freed waters in the bush. Bari felt he had lived a hundred winters since leaving camp.

At last, spring came bursting into full tide of beauty. Baby leaves were peeping out on the poplars. The flats were growing green and warm. There was a smell of buds and, on the far-travelled wind, there was a whiff of smoke.

Into Bari's blood the urge to go home came like a torrent. He couldn't fight it. It was bigger and stronger than he was. His spirit battled for justice for the man who had helped him. He knew that Wilkens had given him opportunity: a chance that might never come again. And wasn't this the land he had wanted to see, the country beyond the forest rim of which he had dreamed? But there was a peacefulness in the forest's deep shade and in the clean clear waters of the lake that this prairie land would never know. It was no use. He had boasted to Paddy that he was a man. Now he knew that he had spoken impetuously. The raging rioting flood of homesickness swept reasoning away.

It was night now. There was a half-moon. Through

the window he could see the dark outline of the buildings silhouetted against a darker sky. There was nothing stirring. Life seemed to have gone out of the world.

Bari rose, dressed and wrote on a piece of paper: 'I had to go. Thanks for everything.' He laid it on the pillow, then slipped downstairs to the kitchen. Going to the cupboard he tucked some pieces of bread and a couple of slices of meat into his pocket then, tiptoeing out, raced for the east-going road.

When he was out of sight of the buildings he stopped, drew a long deep breath of night air into his lungs, then started off again with a long swinging stride. The road was good. Where it broke into cross-trails through sparsely settled stretches he recognized landmarks he had seen on his journey west.

When the sun rose he was miles from Wilkens' Corners. Teams of horses and men began moving towards the fields to plough. He saw cows being taken in from pasture. He stopped and wondered about going on.

News of his disappearance might be spreading. Wilkens might even be following him. No, he wouldn't take a chance travelling by day—night would be safer. Besides, rest was necessary, for the going might be tough. Instinct made him seek cover. He ate a piece of his bread, then made for a haystack that stood well away from any buildings. Then, looking round to see that no one was in sight, he hollowed out enough hay to make a good opening and crept in, covering himself lightly. The hay felt good to his body; it was sweet with a newly mown smell. He curled up and closed his eyes.

A rooster crowed, and a calf bawling in a nearby pasture kept him awake for a while. He slept, but was aroused by a wild snort in his ear. Jerking himself to a sitting position he looked squarely into the face of a huge pig. She snorted, grunted, blinked and snorted again. That she had every intention of rooting him out of his bed was clear, for there was vengeance in her eye. Bari sat stock-still until a litter of scampering squealing little pigs gathered to fix him with a dozen curious stares. Bari was not afraid of pigs, but there was danger of them betraying his presence. He lunged at the mother. She wheeled and, family at her heels, tore across the field in a cloud of dust.

Bari saw by the sun it was just noon. He settled back to rest. He was startled from his next sleep by the sound of wheels. He sat up and peered out. A team of horses with a wagon and hay-rack was coming rattling over the field towards the stack. As it came closer he saw there were hay-forks and ropes in the rack. A young man was driving, and they were coming straight for the stack.

Bari looked swiftly around. There was no time to escape. A tremor of fear swept through him. What would he say? What would he tell the man? He floundered in his mind for words. The wagon was just on him. He drew tightly into the stack and held his breath. The wheels passing within a couple of yards, skirted the end and rattled off into the distance. Bari drew a relieved breath and sat still a good many minutes before creeping out.

It was grey dark. He looked round. Everything was quiet. He ate a piece of his bread and meat. Sleep had refreshed him, but he was very thirsty. He looked about for some likely place for water. Off in the east he could see farm buildings with a windmill. There would be a well there. He hung around the stack till darkness gave cover, then started out.

It seemed a good two-mile walk. There was a large house and barn and smaller buildings, between which he could see a windmill and water-trough in the centre of the yard. There were cows lying by a pasture gate, but he slipped quietly past. As he crept under a fence a light appeared in an upper window of the house. He could hear faint moving of the windmill and a trickle of water seeping into the trough. He walked forward with a spirit of bravado.

Like a flash a dog streaked from somewhere behind the house. A volley of barks blasted the silence, seeming to bang and re-echo through every board in the nearby buildings. The cows rose to their feet.

Bari stopped dead. He knew there was danger in running. He stood, hardly knowing what to do. The dog was coming right for where he was. Diving his hand into his pocket, he tore off a piece of his meat and threw it. The dog halted, snapped at it and came on. Bari threw a second and a third piece, then his bread, backing as swiftly as he could towards the road. The house door opened and a man stepped into the yard. For a second Bari thought it was all up. The dog, gulping the eats, was making a rush for him. There was a sound of horses' feet. Down the road from the opposite direction came a couple of men on horseback. They were cantering briskly. The dog turned and raced to meet them. Turning on his heels Bari sped across the field, not daring to look back. He kept on, hardly knowing which way he was going. That was the end of his thirst. And he had lost his eats.

When he was out a safe distance he stopped to take stock of the sky. There were scudding clouds and a blurred moon. It didn't take long to find the Pole Star. It hung low and seemed less bright than usual. The Hunter and his Dogs were surely too far east. From that, Bari realized that he was heading south. Turning, he walked in the opposite direction, ignoring road and trail until the lead-dog fell in line with the Pole.

He had bearings now. His spirits rose, for he was at home in the starry heavens, and every step was carrying him back to his forest kingdom. Already in the dim distance, bluffs and clumps of evergreens were dotting the land.

His feet were weary, but he walked quickly. On and on; would morning never come? His thirst came back and he was hungry. Once or twice he stopped where land dipped low and put his ear to the ground, hoping to catch the sound of trickling water. There was nothing but silence and the occasional whirr of a night bird's wings.

At last the foreglow came into the east. Nearer and nearer it came, reaching its friendly warmth out to him. It seemed to be calling him home. Body bent towards it, the joy of its beckoning gave push to his hurrying feet.

When daylight came he had no thought of rest. How long it was now since he left Wilkens' Corners he didn't know. Days and nights were becoming only a blur in his memory. But he kept on. Soon he was in bush country. The rustlings of birds, scents and sounds of the forest gave him new life. Then, as if in answer to his need, he spied a tiny stream. Throwing off his coat he raced forward, and dropping flat, dipped and re-dipped his face in its cool water, then drank his fill. Afterwards he stripped to the waist and washed, and dried himself with his shirt. As he climbed the rise of the opposite bank he came on a growth of wild strawberries. He sat down and ate. Truly this was his country! Yes, he knew every landmark now, and every trail led home. Heart bounding he pushed forward.

It was about mid-afternoon, for the shadows were angling east, and Bari was heading for a fringe of jack-pine above the tamarack-rim. Suddenly a crow cawed and there was a flutter of wings. It was a warning. Bari stopped and listened. There was something coming. He could hear movements; see the longer grass in the hollow swaying gently. The shrubs parted, and Bari stepped behind a tree.

A bear cub came trotting into the open. He was a plump woolly little fellow and seemed in no hurry. He stood looking round leisurely, then nosing the ground and sniffing the air began running in circles. Then racing to a stump he poked around and dived into an opening in the side.

There was a howl, a terrified squeal. Turning head over heels he tried to regain his feet while crowds of bees swarmed over him. Squealing and yelling he tried to beat them off with his paws, but they kept buzzing angrily around his head and eyes. He rubbed his face on the ground and whined piteously.

Bari leaped forward. The bees scattered. He swept the cub into his arms. There was a snapping of branches and a thunderous growl. Bari turned and found himself looking into a bear's flaming eyes a leap and a half away. His peril was imminent. He was aware of the body-smell and the warm breath of the enraged beast as it lunged towards him. He dropped the cub and sprang sideways.

The bear's claws tore through his trousers and down through the calf of his leg as he clutched a branch and swung clear, scarcely aware of pain.

When he looked round the bees were back. The bear turned to her squealing cub, and Bari could see her stamping and cuffing. Her fierce eyes looked red as she lurched awkwardly at the stinging swarm. The cub ran up a tree.

There wasn't a minute to lose. The battle between bear and bees couldn't last long. Shaking with fright, his face stinging, Bari slipped from the tree and stumbled towards water. His leg hurt and blood was through his trousers and over his boot-top. But his face was worse. It was burning, and he could feel swelling round the eyes.

He made for a group of dandelions, picked, split the stems and rubbed them into the stings. He had seen Paddy do that. When he got to the water, he washed his leg wound, tied a piece of sapling bark over it and bound it with a strip off his shirt.

It wasn't easy to walk now, but he hurried as best he could, fearful that the trail of blood might be a lead for the bear. He could make home by midnight with luck. But gradually his pace slackened, for every step he took hurt; his body was tired, and there was a hollowness in his stomach.

When night came it was very warm and still. For a short time the moon lit the forest into the clearness of day, then slid behind clouds. There was something ominous in the hush. The earth seemed to be holding its breath, waiting for something to happen. Far up the lake Bari saw lightning, and there was thunder; low along the forest wall it rolled.

Bari couldn't hurry, he couldn't think, he couldn't breathe. At times he could feel a lightness in his head; it must be the fright over the bear. But the coming storm gave him a sense of cover.

Clouds massed overhead. They seemed to be boiling and whirling over the tree-tops. It grew very dark; there was sharper lightning, thunder rattled and seemed to thud along the ground at his feet.

He must seek cover. Making for a clump of willow, he dropped to the ground and crept well under the foliage.

The sky opened, and rivers of water poured on earth and woods. Bari was thankful for the cool freshness of the rain. It damped his face and eased his cracking lips and throat.

He lay till the storm cleared, then got up and struggled forward. It was easier going now, but his clothes were wet and clung to his body.

The stars came out. He sighted the bay. It lay calm and untroubled in the light of the summer moon. And beyond, in the lap of the valley, he saw Paddy's cabin. Home! Home! Injury, storm and weariness were no more. Every muscle of his body strained to breaking point, he took the last stretch of trail at a swinging lope.

Chapter xv

DECISION

Before he reached the door it opened. One half-second
Bari stood, then he was scooped into Paddy's arms.
' I'm home! Home!' All the longing of his homesick
heart was in his voice.

' I bin lookin' for you,' Paddy said happily.

Bari followed him in, glad that the darkness hid his
torn clothes.

Paddy lit the lamp, turned and looked squarely at
him. ' Your face! What happened? An' your
cloes?'

' Oh, I got into a bees' nest, but I didn't get any
honey,' Bari laughed shakily. ' I tore my clothes running.' He didn't have the heart to tell more.

Paddy's brows came together quizzically. ' Didn't you
know there can be a pile o' trouble in a bees' nest?
Better get your cloes off an' into bed. I'll fix you up.'

' Get me somethin' to eat first. I'm awful hungry.'

Paddy scurried about, put paper and wood into the stove, lit it and put on the kettle.

' I was up west,' Bari felt it was necessary to say something, ' but I got fed up. It's a longer walk home than I figured.' He hoped Paddy wouldn't ask any questions, not just yet.

Paddy didn't. He was rummaging in a box in the corner. He turned and said, ' Here, there's a dry shirt and socks and a sweater.'

Bari put them on and lay down on his cot. His eyes would hardly keep open. It was good to be home. This was what he had longed for: the homey warmth of friendly things.

Paddy pushed a mug of hot berry juice into his hands. He drank it, and before Paddy could bring more, he was asleep.

When he awoke the sun was shining through the window. Paddy was up, and there was a smell of frying meat and baking bannock.

' Better stay in bed,' Paddy said.

' No, I'll get up. I feel better, but I still got a big hole in my stomach.'

Paddy grunted knowingly.

Bari dressed, feeling shaky; but little thrills of happiness kept bursting over him.

' Sit in an' eat. You look as if you needed it,' Paddy said, pointing to a plate at the end of the table.

Bari tackled the bannock greedily. He felt as if the hole in his stomach would never be filled. He saw Paddy watching him. ' It ain't possible for a fellow to eat too much is it?' he asked, laughing.

' It's your face I'm lookin' at, it's—it's——'

'I know,' Bari interrupted. 'It ain't purty, but you'll fix it, eh?'

Paddy nodded.

When Bari finished he went back to his cot and lay down. Next thing he knew was Paddy bathing his face with cold tea. It made him feel better. He could touch his eyes now, and the swelling was going down.

Paddy looked haggard and troubled. His shoulders seemed to be sagging more. His hand trembled and shook as he smoothed wet cloths over the bites, but he didn't say anything.

Bari was glad. He couldn't tell him about Wilkens or the camp yet.

Next day his face and leg felt much better. He rose early and made breakfast. Paddy seemed more like his old self again. They ate leisurely. Paddy was tickled at little commonplaces. Then he said, 'It's great times me an' you'll be havin' again if you ain't going back to where you was.'

Bari saw his brows come together anxiously.

'No, I'm not. I like it here best. I know that now.' He hesitated, hardly knowing what more to say. 'I—I—'

A soft 'Hullo' came up the path.

Paddy jumped to his feet.

There was a note of music; it hung a moment, swelling, deepening, then burst into song.

'It's Oney, she's at home now,' Paddy said, beaming.

Springing forward Bari opened the door. There was a flash of blue, a swish of dress. 'Bari!' His name died into her laughter.

Making for Paddy, she took his arm affectionately,

then turned, eyes twinkling. 'I didn't know you were home, Bari. Paddy's missed you!' Then lowering her voice, half reproachfully said, 'You're thinner, your hair, your face look different. What have you done to yourself? Suppose you've done lots of painting?' Her face rippled happily. There was no doubt in her voice.

'Yes, yes, Oney. I did,' Bari answered, clutching the chair to steady himself. How could he tell her he'd left her picture and everything else and walked out? He hadn't even told Paddy.

'Mrs Carson thinks your work is good. She knows quite a bit about art. Were the things I sent a help?'

Bari drew a deep breath. He was thankful she didn't wait for his answer.

'It'll be like old times again,' she went on. 'I have a long holiday this year. We're not going east again till late in the fall.' There was laughter in her voice, her whole being seemed filled with sunshine. She was gone before Bari could say anything. She turned at the bottom of the path and waved.

'She's just the same old Oney,' Paddy said, as they watched her trip along the shore. 'She kep' askin' for you an' I kep' tellin' her you were comin'.' There was triumph in Paddy's voice, as if he was well pleased that his expectations had been fulfilled.

Bari smiled; it was so wonderful to be home again.

The day was a happy one. Bari went everywhere; to the nesting-places, Seegwun's pool, to the squirrels' haunts and the flower-filled valley. He filled himself with the joys of his kingdom. 'Everything is just in the same place,' he said when Paddy and he sat down to dinner.

'Did you think they'd move?'

Bari laughed.

Keego came in.   Dropping his knapsack on the floor, he leaped forward and grasped Bari's arm.   'If it ain't the Bari himself.   I sure missed you, so did Paddy; but Oney,' he nodded confidentially, 'she come every day to see him, not to see me,' he went on, shrugging solemnly. 'I ain't anythin' to look at.   I bet you done lots of things, painted pictures an' built houses, an'——' Keego thrust his head forward expectantly.

'No! No! Nothing like that.'

'Well, I got yours figgered out.   The one you're aimin' to build.'

'Oh, I'd forgotten about that.   Did you tell Paddy?' Bari asked laughingly.

'Naw.   I didn't told nobody, you said not to.'

Paddy was standing in the corner grinning.   Bari knew he wasn't taking Keego's talk seriously, as the boy chattered on.   'Me an' you's goin' to build a house. But we ain't puttin' any roofin' on.   I don't hold with roofin'.   It keeps out the sky.   That's what's wrong with Jake Madette, too much roof.'

Bari and Paddy laughed.

But Keego's face was grave as he turned to go.   'I'm goin' to tell Granny Mulgrove that you're home.   I'll be seein' you!'

When the door closed, Paddy laughed again.   'He's always agin' Jake.   Never liked him.'

'I used to feel that way myself, but I don't any more,' Bari spoke truthfully.   Camp life and rubbing shoulders with men had taught him much.   He was even looking forward to seeing Oney's father.

So when he saw Jake coming up the path at night he went to meet him.   Hand outstretched, Jake grinned from ear to ear. ' So you're back, big boy! You don't look so hot, but it's great to be seein' you.'   Tilting his head importantly Jake went on in his same old blustery voice, ' I allus said it was work you needed, that's what gets you places, not paintin' pictures,' he added with a scornful curl of his nose.

Bari smiled.   He tried to speak, but didn't know what to say.   He hoped Jake wouldn't begin to ask questions.

Jake's next words were proud.   ' They'll have tol' you about my Oney.   She's a great singer !   She's going to be singin' fer concerts an' big folks,' he went on.   ' It's a mystery—a—a *maestro*—that teached her.   It's a great singer she is all right.'   Jake ended with an assuring nod that brought a smile to Bari's lips.

He couldn't help but be happy with the man whose face was glowing with enthusiasm over his daughter's achievement.

Paddy came from the cabin and joined them.   Jake turned to him. ' You ain't never heard nobody sing like Oney, did ye, Paddy ? '

Paddy shook his head.   ' None but the hermit thrush.'

That pleased Jake.   He went into the cabin with them. The rest of the evening was happy.

When he rose to go home, his invitation was cordial. ' You come over an' see us, young fellah.   Me an' Oney likes company.   She'll be catchin' up with some nice fellah one of these days.'

Bari rose and put wood on the stove. Madette's words were still in his mind. 'Jake hasn't much use for painting pictures, eh?'

Paddy was still smiling. 'It ain't his line.'

'I don't know what his line is, except Oney, an' if it hadn't been for Mrs Carson, she'd——'

'Oney's got it in her, Bari,' Paddy interrupted. 'She'll go places, nothing'll stop her.'

Bari bit his lip. 'It was Jake that made me mad, Paddy. He kept saying that painting was sissy.' Bari sat down, cupping his hands about his knees. He went on, 'He seemed to think the only worth-while things for a man to do is to handle an axe, chop wood or build a cabin. Keego an' I would have liked to,' Bari laughed, 'but snow came. That's what Keego was talking about. When you kept asking me where I was and what I was doing, I was drawing and painting, off by myself. I wanted to get away from Jake Madette.'

Paddy tapped the table with his brown fingers and kept his eyes on the stove.

Bari wanted to tell him everything. 'At school it was bells, bells, bells. I got enough of that, telling you when to go out an' when to come in. I was glad to get away, to be free.'

Paddy looked round. The deep lines in his face smoothed into a shallow smile. 'I wasn't aimin' to be hard on you. I didn't know what you were doin'.'

'I didn't think of that. I wanted to be a tough guy, a kind of Tarzan, I guess.' Bari shrugged. 'But I liked the camp. The boys were swell, so was Wilkens. I liked the west in a kind of a way, but I just couldn't stay. It isn't in me to like sidewalks and hard buildings and hard land. Wilkens worked and worked—all he ever thought about was making money, but I liked him just the same. Wish I could like Jake Madette in the same way.'

Bari said the last hastily; he wanted to bring the subject back home. He couldn't tell Paddy he ran away from Wilkens, nor about the picture he was painting, or the things the men had done for him. Paddy mustn't know that. He wouldn't like it. He would be hurt. Besides he wasn't fussy about Bari's drawing now.

'I wish Oney's father would realize everybody isn't alike. I don't want to get sore at him again,' he said after a long silence.

'Don't worry about Madette. You'll make out all right with him. We figgered you'd be back for the summer.'

'I didn't bring any money with me. I spent most of my wages on clothes an' shoes an' things, an' I came away without them.' He said the last in a self-accusing voice, without adding that he had a month's wages coming, still in Wilkens' hands.

Bari saw now where he had made a mistake walking out and leaving clothes, wages and even Oney's picture and his paints. The very thought made him angry with himself. But the night he left Wilkens' Corners there wasn't a thing in his head but the whirling giddy idea of getting away.

The money he had left would have been a help to Paddy, but what could he say? He hoped Paddy would never know how foolish he had been. As for Oney and her picture, well, things sure had a way of tangling themselves up on him.

'It's good to have you home again. It's been lonesome without you. Jake and Oney come pretty often, but it ain't like anybody stayin' with you.' Paddy's words were reassuring, but there seemed to be a yearning in his eyes.

It gave Bari a strange feeling. He felt small, a flop. He was deceiving Paddy not telling him everything, but he didn't have the courage, the strength to face the situation. He felt a little glad that he had explained his reason for going to the lumber camp. Maybe later he would tell Paddy the rest.

Bari went to bed early, but he didn't sleep. It was Oney's picture that was troubling him. It was the bitterest thought of all. What he was going to tell her, he didn't know.

The feeling of frustration and failure got him up in the morning with the desire to work harder than he had ever worked before, to do things for Paddy, prove that he was not a slacker.

It was mid-summer. Paddy was getting out logs to repair his cabin. 'I should build a new one,' he said, looking wistfully at his sagging gable, 'but I ain't so spry as I once was.'

Bari looked at him. He was thinner, his shoulders had lost their breadth and something of his old zest had gone. Yes, Paddy was failing. The thought strengthened Bari's will to work. He spoke glibly, 'We'll do it, Paddy, you an' me together, at least we can begin, an' Keego'll maybe help.'

Paddy smiled.

So the warm days found them in a stand of cedar, chopping, trimming, measuring logs, Bari using the knowledge he had gained at school. Keego helped willingly at times. He worked hard and so did Bari, for Paddy still wielded a vigorous axe.

Madette visited them frequently, giving advice. It was always the same: 'When you go buildin', Paddy, get that young Bari workin'' or 'Don't go buildin' a bigger place than ye need, let that big boy shift for himself now.'

The words made Bari swing a swifter axe, but neither by look nor flicker of an eye did he show what he felt. Keego usually stuck out his tongue at Madette from behind a covering branch.

Oney came often in the evenings to see them. She sang, and baked the odd pan of biscuits. And always she asked about her picture. At first it sent a flush of shame to the roots of Bari's hair. Then, with a quickness born of desperation, he answered, 'I'll surprise you some day with that picture.'

That pleased Oney, but Bari himself didn't know what the surprise would be other than him summoning courage to tell her the truth.

Sometimes Oney spoke of her singing lessons and her teacher. 'I like him—he's taught me many things, and I'm lucky to have had the chance to go to a *maestro*. I often wonder how it happened to me. I don't think I deserve it.'

Bari listened. Oney was so kind, so unboastful. He envied her. Once he had been filled with wishes and ideas: thoughts he'd meant to turn into something worth while.

H

But now, when he had had his chance, he had spoiled it. He was a failure. He couldn't even go back and begin again. He couldn't face Wilkens or the camp. He had lost the opportunity that had been laid at his feet. Worse still, he could see no opening path into the future, not now. His thoughts were bitter and nagging.

Then above the blackness of it all rose his spirited fighting self. He would go back to Wilkens, tell him he was sorry for what he had done and get his clothes and his picture. Wilkens and Danny too would understand. It was almost six weeks since he had left. Just as soon as they had all the logs cut that Paddy needed, he would start off. He would tell Paddy that he was going for his clothes. It didn't seem so hard now that his mind was made up.

One night Paddy walked over to Madette's. Bari made supper and was waiting for him. He seemed to have been away a long time.

Suddenly the door opened and Paddy came in. He walked to the corner of the room and threw down a bundle of twine before speaking. 'Oney's goin' away to-morrow. Mrs Carson's been called east sooner than she figgered, an' she's takin' Oney with her.' Paddy drew his chair into the table and sat down. 'Jake says she may be away quite a while. Some fellah wants her to go singin', a—a tour he calls it.' Paddy ended with a smirk of pride.

Bari was slicing bread and he didn't look up. A bitterness, a something he couldn't explain flamed through him. Oney's doings had always been a challenge. To-night the news of her going away hurt.

' She said to tell you to go over an' see her in the mornin'.
She's busy gettin' her cloes ready,' Paddy went on.
' Real purty ones they are.'

Bari bit his lip. He liked it better when Oney came
to see them. ' That means I'll have to listen to Jake. I
wish somebody would take him singing or on a tour.'

Paddy laughed.

They ate supper quietly. Once or twice Bari thought
he saw a flicker of pleasure on Paddy's face, because of
Oney likely, but neither of them mentioned her name.
Bari couldn't help thinking about her. Likely she would
want her picture or ask about it. Had she told her father
about sending paints and canvas to him? If Jake ever
found out about him running away from Wilkens it
would be a sad day. Bari was still thinking when the
hum of a motor came up-lake.

' It's Hyslop!' Paddy said, jumping to his feet.

Bari rose and followed him to the door. He hadn't
seen Hyslop since the night in the beginning of winter
when he had overheard them discussing him. He wasn't
too sure what the Mountie would say now.

There wasn't a boat in sight, but Paddy's ear, tuned
to Hyslop's engine, wasn't deceived. By the time Paddy
and he reached the water's edge an outboard had rounded
the Point and was coursing towards their wharf.

' Hullo! Hullo, you fellows!' Hyslop hailed them
cheerily as he swung alongside and leaped ashore. ' I've
got a bundle for you,' he went on, reaching for a parcel
from the boat. ' It's for you, young fellow. Next
time you go travelling bring your luggage back with
you and tell folks where you're going before you leave.'
Hyslop spoke sharply.

Bari looked at him, then at Paddy. He could feel his face reddening. 'It's my clothes and things from the west.' There was enthusiasm in his voice as he took the parcel. 'Where did you get them?' He could have leaped with joy, but now he would be found out!

'How did I get them?' Hyslop repeated with scorn. 'The man you worked for sent them; said you walked out on him. He was scared something might happen to you and put one of our men on your track.'

'I left a letter,' Bari said, looking confusedly at Paddy.

'Did you put an address on it?' Hyslop interrupted.

'No-o.' Bari winced at the sharpness of Hyslop's voice.

'Wilkens felt responsible. You're only a youngster,' Hyslop went on, 'and here, he sent this,' he drew an envelope from his pocket. 'It's your wages. Good job somebody looks after you.' The look on Hyslop's face was more disturbing than his words.

Bari met his eyes squarely. 'I guess I've made a fizzle of things, Corporal Hyslop. I—meant to go back for my clothes soon's we got our logs out. Thanks for this.' Bari took the letter and tucked it in his pocket. 'I had to come home. It was somethin' I couldn't help or——'

'You'll learn the hard way,' Hyslop interrupted. 'Wilkens said you were a good worker and everybody liked you.'

Paddy hadn't spoken. He was walking ahead of them up towards the cabin. Bari tried to see his face. What he would say now that he knew the truth Bari couldn't guess.

Hyslop's voice mellowed. 'Wilkens said you were

working on a picture. He seemed to think it was good.'

'Did he say that?' Bari brightened. 'Maybe it's in here,' he tapped the parcel. 'I'll open it and see.'

Inside the cabin, while Hyslop and Paddy watched, he ripped off the wrapping and pulled out shirts, underwear, socks and, 'Here it is!' He held up the picture, heart pounding with excitement. 'Oney sent me the canvas and paints.' He looked up into Paddy's narrowing eyes.

It was Hyslop who spoke. 'I like it. It looks good. You've got something there, I think. Why didn't you give yourself a chance? What's wrong with you?'

Bari was pleased. He waited for Paddy to say something. Was he going to acknowledge the picture was worthwhile? Bari watched a wry smile come creeping round his mouth. 'Oney must think you can paint.' There was a chuckle in his words, but they didn't convey the idea that Paddy was going to consider painting pictures a useful occupation.

Bari was glad Hyslop spoke. 'Yes, I like your picture,' he said. 'All you need is push, Bari. That thing that gets folks places—like Oney Madette.'

The words stung. Why had he mentioned Oney? Bari's head went up. He squared his shoulders, lifted the picture and leaned it against the clock.

'What are you planning to do with yourself and the picture now?'

Was there sarcasm in Hyslop's voice?

Bari fumbled with the string that had tied the parcel. 'I don't know. Do you think it's good enough to do anything with?'

Hyslop looked at him. 'Haven't you spunk enough to try? I don't know a thing about art myself, but there's those who do.' Hyslop shrugged. 'It's your picture!' He walked to the door.

Bari followed.

Half-way down the path Hyslop turned, stood a moment thinking, then called, 'Mrs Wingate has an artist friend coming to visit her next week—Tuesday, I think. If he saw your work he might tell you how to go about things. I don't know anything about pictures.'

'Do you think Mrs Wingate would see me?'

'I'm sure she will. She won't, of course, if you don't go.'

Why did Hyslop have to add that barb?

But he smiled. 'Think it over. I'm in a hurry. Want to make Frenchman's Portage before it's too dark.' He turned and ran down the path with a curtly flung, 'Good-bye! It's up to you', over his shoulder.

'It's up to you' rang in Bari's ears as he stood, a dozen confusing thoughts milling through his head. He couldn't go back into the cabin and face Paddy, not just now. There were so many things to say, too many things for which he couldn't find words.

He turned and walked towards the bush. His biggest regret was that he hadn't made a clean breast of everything when he came home. He had let Paddy down.

Bari didn't walk far. The woods felt close and friendly, and they gave him a sense of security and peace. But flashingly it came to him that it wasn't peace he wanted, it was action. He must do something. 'It's up to you'—Hyslop was right. There was no progress here, nothing that would push him forward. This was a battle he was fighting with himself. It was on his action, on what he did that his future depended. This thing that was holding him back he must conquer. His mind was made up. It didn't take long to think out his plan.

It would be hard leaving Paddy; it always had been. It wasn't easier now. Paddy was failing. He needed him. He needed help. Bari had learned the depths of Paddy's kindness, his tolerance and what he had been to him. Now it should be Paddy's turn to get care. There must be some way. As things had a way of tangling themselves so there must be a way of straightening. Bari braced himself and went back to the cabin.

Paddy was sitting mending a shirt. He looked up.

'I should have told you everything when I came back, Paddy. I'm sorry. I wanted to keep my picture-painting a secret. I guess I made a mess of things all right.'

The furrow in Paddy's brow deepened, but there was no reproach in his eyes. 'I figgered you'd come back home. I wouldn't want you goin' too far away just yet.' He stopped to thread a needle.

'I'm goin' again, Paddy. I want to try out my picture. I've got to go! Hyslop says it's good. I'll come back when I've done something worthwhile with it.' Bari hesitated. Why didn't Paddy speak? 'We'll have our logs out on Saturday, I'll go then,' Bari went on.

Paddy cut a piece of cloth from the patch he was sewing, turned in the edges and drew his needle through it. 'Don't forget an' go an' see Oney in the mornin'. She's comin' back to say good-bye to Jake, but you mightn't see her.'

'I'll be there,' Bari spoke quietly. He wondered if

Paddy was going to say any more. It was a long minute before he spoke.

'If you're aimin' on goin' places, I guess you gotta hustle.'

'You'll get along, will you?' Bari couldn't help but see the sparkle in Paddy's eye, his answer came quickly. 'I bin gettin' along a long time. There ain't been many snags I ain't got by; t'won't be no harder now, Bari.'

When Bari got to Madette's next morning the fish-boat was already in their dock. Oney's bags were aboard. She stood waiting. She was wearing a red dress, and a rose was tucked in her hair. 'You're late,' she said, half reproachfully, but in a minute she was herself again, alive with the joy of living and doing.

Bari could only look at her. There were so many things he wanted to say, to tell her. 'Your picture, it's—it's——'

'Yes, what about it?'

'It's almost finished. If I'd known you were going I'd have hurried.'

'It must be wonderful!' she said mockingly.

The boat whistled, Madette was at her side.

With a swift-flung 'I'll be seeing you', she stepped aboard.

Bari watched the boat swing clear and go out into the channel, but it was the figure in the red dress, who stood waving with all the gaiety of a seasoned traveller, on which his eyes rested. Oney loved to go.

Bari caught something of the infectiousness of her sparkle, and took the home trail painfully aware of his own lack. He didn't even hear Madette saying, 'You'll sure be hearin' about that Oney of mine. She's no man's fool, not yet!' It was fortunate, for there was a smirk in it.

As Bari neared home, Keego came out of the cabin and walked towards the bush. Bari hurried. If he caught up with him he might help with the logs.

Paddy was piling brush in the back hollow.

Bari ran to the house to throw off his coat. When he opened the door he stood dumbfounded. His picture was hanging on the wall, but with a nail driven through the canvas. Strokes of red, purple and yellow oil paint covered it. His palette and tubes lay on the floor. Keego had been painting.

Anger swept through Bari. Making straight for the picture, he ran his fingers over the daubed canvas, then brightened. His palette knife and a rag would clean it. But the nail driven through the top had made a three-cornered rip. Easing the picture off, Bari examined it. It would mend with tape or cloth. The first flush of anger passed, but he would have to be careful where he left his painting-things in future.

While he was still looking at the canvas, Keego came in, face glowing. ' I made a picture, it's good, eh?'

' You sure did! but you're better at chinking logs than painting.' Bari didn't have the heart to say more.

Keego smiled all over his face. ' Yah, I can build houses an' paint pictures, too.'

' Stick to the house-building, Keego. Nobody can beat you!'

In the evening Bari cleaned and repaired the picture. He did it carefully and he was pleased with his work.

Working hard with Keego's help, they finished logging

H 2

at the end of the week. At night Bari put finishing touches on his masterpiece: strokes that brought trees and water to his satisfaction.

He got ready for his trip to town. He wasn't enthusiastic about calling on Mrs Wingate. He'd just as soon face a trapped fox as a strange woman, but he must shake off these bogeys, these trivial biting things that held him back. They took the zest out of life.

Carefully he lined up his assets. He had a cheque for sixty dollars, health, a picture and an urge that only the God of the great spaces knew, to paint the stories of his people. Bari threw up his head when he thought of it. He was going forward.

Chapter XVI

ACHIEVEMENT

Two days later, Bari walked into Hyslop's office.

Hyslop, sitting by his desk, looked up with a shade of surprise in his face. 'Hullo, Bari! I wasn't expecting you.'

'I'm going to look for work. Thought I'd bring that picture in,' he tapped the packet he was carrying, 'and show it to Mr Wingate—is that what you called him? But I don't know where to go.' He tried to speak casually, but already the thought of talking to someone he'd never seen before was sending spasms of he didn't know what careering through him.

'Oh yes, that's a good idea, Bari. The man's name is Van Dousan. He really is a somebody in the art world.' Hyslop rose, and coming to Bari's side, continued in a friendlier voice than usual, 'I think he's a relation of Mrs Wingate. She's interested in that sort of thing too.' Hyslop tapped the back of a chair meditatively. ' I think the best thing to do is to go up and see her.'

' I hate buttin' in on folks,' shifting his parcel to the other arm.

' That isn't butting in. Tell Mrs Wingate I sent you. She'll be glad to know you; maybe be able to help you herself.'

Bari moved towards the door.

Hyslop's eyes were on his shoes. ' You walked in, eh? Anybody who walks that distance can go farther.' Hyslop laughed lightly. ' Better have something to eat first.'

' No, I'll go see the lady right away, if you'll tell me where she lives.'

Hyslop followed him to the door and pointed. ' See that white house on the hill facing the bay? That's it. Go this way, round by the fish-dock. Her house is the last on the street. There's about a dozen in a row. Hers has green shutters—you can't go wrong.'

' Thanks. I'll tell you how I make out. I'll come back this way.'

Bari turned along the street. He wasn't too sure of himself, but he kept going. The houses were large; each stood in a trim square lawn. He didn't like the look of them.

But this was that other world, the world that held his future and into which he must go. These hard-looking houses, straight sidewalks and even lawns were part of it. He must get to know how people lived here. That was part of the learning that would lead him to his goal.

He took firmer hold of his parcel and counted the houses, one, two, four, six. Now he was at ten. He could see the last house. It was larger than the others. By the time he stopped in front of it a quiver was running up and down his spine.

He looked at the cement walk running from the gate to the door. It didn't look as if anyone ever travelled on it. The blinds on the front windows were drawn. They were white. Between the green shutters they gave a sealed-up appearance to the house.

Bari stood looking around. There wasn't a soul in sight. He looked back along the street. He hadn't seen a sign of a soul since he came into it. He looked again at the house and then moved slowly towards the gate. A dog started to bark somewhere in the rear. He straightened his tie, looked around again to see if anyone was watching, lifted the gate latch and hurried in. If a bear had popped over the back fence he'd have been thankful. Drawing a deep breath he stepped up to the door and pushed the bell.

It shrilled through the house and came clanging back with a double echo that froze him to a standstill. Before he regained equilibrium the door opened and a young woman stood facing him. She had on a black dress and white apron. Her face was like a thundercloud. Half closing her eyes, she focused them on a point somewhere above Bari's head, and said, 'What do you want?' Her voice wasn't a bit like her looks; it had a hint of roses in it.

'I'd like to see Mrs Wingate,' Bari said as politely as he could.

'She's not in.'

'I'd like to talk to her,' Bari went on, too confused to be aware of her answer.

'She's not here. You can't!' The girl snapped sharply. She sniffed and was about to close the door when a man appeared.

Taking a cigar from his mouth he came forward smiling. 'I'm Jack Wingate. What can I do for you?' His voice was pleasant. His greying hair brushed smoothly to his head made his face seem large, but it was friendly and there was a gleam of laughter in his eyes.

'I wanted to talk to Mrs Wingate,' Bari repeated with a trifle more confidence. 'Peter Hyslop, the Mountie, told me to come and ask you about a painter who was coming here.'

'Painter who was coming here!' Wingate repeated, stroking his chin thoughtfully. 'Never heard of him.' He turned to the girl at his elbow. 'Have you?'

The girl shrugged and glared at Bari again. 'No, the man who was painting the downstairs cupboard's finished.' She sniffed and faded into the rear.

The man stood as if not knowing what to say.

Bari moved uneasily from one foot to the other. 'I wanted to see Mrs Wingate about a picture I have—I—' Bari wavered, 'I——'

'Mrs Wingate's out of town. Don't know when she'll be back,' Wingate interrupted, tapping a slippered foot on the stair. 'Come back some time next week.'

The door shut. Bari was back on the sidewalk. It was all over. Drawing a sigh of relief, he mopped his brow and stood quivering from the ordeal. It hadn't been too difficult, but he was glad it was over. He was

sorry he'd promised to go back, but he retraced his steps
quickly for he had other things in mind.

Hyslop met him at the door. 'No luck, eh?'

Bari nodded and told his story. 'Seems funny they
don't know anything?'

'Oh, that's Wingate's cousin. He's just come back
from overseas the other day, an' the maid, she's not
been so long there either, she wouldn't know anything.'

'Wingate said to go back next week, so I'll try again.
Thanks for giving me the tip about this fellow—this
artist. I'll keep my fingers crossed.'

Relief at getting the ordeal over offset the first pang
of disappointment. Bari went straight from Hyslop's
to a store on the outskirts of town. It was owned by a
man called Rogers. He was a kindly but shrewd fellow,
who sometimes put work in Paddy's way.

When Bari went in Rogers was alone. He held out
a welcoming hand. 'Hullo, stranger! How are you?'

'O.K., Mr Rogers. I've something here I'd like to
trade.' Bari drew his cheque from his pocket. 'I want
to send some clothes an' eats to Paddy. Can you help
me? You know about what he usually gets in clothes.'

'I think I know his sizes,' Rogers answered, reaching
for the cheque. 'What would you like?'

'Suit, shirts, mackinaw, shoes an' things!'

'I'm afraid you'll have to forget about the suit.
Money doesn't stretch too far, you know.' Rogers
grinned good-naturedly. 'I'll fix you up with the rest.'

Bari picked out mackinaw, shirts and socks and laid
them on the counter. It was the first time he'd ever
bought anything for Paddy. It thrilled him and gave
him a feeling he'd never had before.

'There isn't going to be anything left out of this cheque, Bari, if that's what you figured,' Rogers looked up from totalling the items. 'Indeed, you're going to owe me something.'

Bari stood a moment, hardly knowing what to say. 'Paddy's got to have clothes an' things. I'm going to go to work just right away.' Rogers tapped the counter with his fingers and kept gazing at the account.

Bari fingered his picture. Would he offer it or sell it? He couldn't do that. He knew Rogers was a close dealer. Bari moved restlessly from one end of the counter to the other. Paddy needed the things; Bari could see his threadbare coat, his patched underwear, hear him saying, 'I gotta get cloes.'

Yes, Paddy had to get clothes. Bari didn't hesitate. 'I've got a picture I thought I might sell, I could——'

Rogers smiled. 'I'll keep it, maybe I can get rid of it for you, but I'm not interested in it myself.'

The words fell on Bari like a dash of cold water. How could Rogers be so casual, so indifferent? Bari clutched his picture tighter. It was part of him. Could he let it go, just like this? He didn't want Rogers to sell it! Didn't want anyone to buy it! It was Oney's! It would always be something more than paint and canvas and a picture. He looked down at Rogers pencilling figures on a scrap of paper. 'How much do I owe you?'

'Thirty dollars.'

Bari hesitated. 'I'll give you the picture to keep. You won't sell it, eh?' Bari handed his parcel over reluctantly. 'Soon's I earn some money I'll pay you. I want Paddy to get the clothes an' things. There's paints an' brushes in the parcel, too; I'll be back for them.' Bari smiled grimly. He had a strange sinking feeling at his heart as he turned slowly from the counter. 'You'll send these things right out?'

'Sure, first fish-boat. You said you were looking for work?'

Bari nodded. 'I need it.'

'There's a road-gang out on the highway. The fore-man was here last night looking for men. You might have a chance yet! It's three miles north.'

'Thanks a lot. I'll go right out.'

Bari headed straight north. He was tired and hungry, but he must get work. The road-gang vacancy wouldn't last. And prodding him on was the fear that Rogers might do something with his picture.

He had no difficulty in finding the road-workers. They were gathered round a steam-shovel listening to a snappy little fellow who looked like their boss. When Bari walked up every eye turned on him. It was the little fellow who spoke. 'Goin' far?'

'Not if I can help it,' Bari said, forcing a smile. 'I'm looking for work.'

'If you can handle a pick and shovel, you've got it, chum. You'll have to find your own bunk though. We'll feed you. I'm Gus Wheeler, the foreman.'

'When do I start?'

'In the morning. We eat at seven.'

Bari didn't wait to hear more. Every bone aching with tiredness, he walked a quarter of a mile back to a bluff, threw his knapsack into the shrubbery, took a drink of water from a nearby pool and rolled up in his blanket. He slept the sleep of exhaustion.

He woke early, but he felt rested.   He was thankful to have work.   As long as weather was fine other sleeping-quarters wouldn't be a necessity.

He joined the road-gang at breakfast.   Then shouldering pick and shovel he followed Wheeler to the part of road he was to work.

The foreman was a man of few words.   Pointing to rock rising on both sides, he said, ' Get this moved and levelled.   We gotta get this contract done by freeze-up. You'll work alone.'

Bari started.   The work was new to him.   It was back-breaking.   His hardest day's work seemed so little against the mountain of rock he had to clear.   Hands blistered, and nagged by thought of losing his picture, he forced himself on.

Wheeler fed them well.   At night the men scattered to sleeping-places.   Bari didn't get to know them as he did the lumber-camp boys, nor did he rest one minute while it was possible to add a dollar to his pay.   But he knew he couldn't keep up the work.   If only he had money to redeem his picture and buy shoes, he would be satisfied.   He lay awake at night thinking about it and of all the things that Rogers' dollars might do with his painting.   In two more days he'd have thirty dollars.

But storm came racing out of the north.   The weather broke, and rain came soaking and sending them shivering to shelter.

Bari set out to seek lodgings.

Up and down the streets he went.   Occupants of large houses looked askance at him.   Owners of smaller homes had no room.   He thought of Hyslop and Oney.

But independence asserted itself; he wouldn't ask for help if he could get along without.

'Still sleeping outside?' Wheeler asked two days later as rain gusted against their cook-car.

Bari nodded.

'Better come home with me. We haven't much room, but the missus'll fix you up.'

'Thanks!' Bari said gratefully. He didn't add that he was much more worried about getting money enough to redeem his picture than about getting a place to sleep. Even rivulets racing past his sodden bed in the shrubbery gave him little concern.

But that night he gathered together his belongings and went with Wheeler. Wheeler's missus was a big woman with a big heart. She took him up to their attic and said apologetically, 'It's not much of a place. We keep just junk an' odds an' ends here.' She pointed to boxes, clothes and magazines lying in the corner.

Bari smiled. The place looked heavenly to him. There was a table at the far end and a faded sofa against the wall. A window in the roof gave lots of light. While Bari was looking things over Mrs Wheeler disappeared, then came lumbering upstairs with a chair and a mirror. 'There,' she said in a motherly voice, 'I'll have to look after you. It's terrible to be sleeping outside in weather like this.'

Bari was grateful to her. As soon as she had gone he ran a string across the corner and hung his clothes on it to dry. In a day or two he felt quite at home.

But it kept on raining. Work outdoors was impossible. When Bari stood alone in the tiny bedroom above the eaves, with the window flung open to the dreary sky, the old trapped feeling he had at Wilkens' Corners came back, and with it the biting thought that now he had a room to pay for and no work.

A sense of disillusionment and disappointment swept through him. He thought of Paddy and home. There was only one way out. Pulling on his coat he ran from the room, downstairs and out into the falling rain. His thoughts were not happy, but his mind was made up.

It was work he needed, something to do. Along the street he went, rain falling gently on the sidewalk breaking the silence and sending a cold quivering hopelessness through him. Maybe the God of big things might take a hand. With the thought a streak of westering sunlight broke through the clouds. Wind tossed the rain aside.

Nearing the main part of town, Bari saw a man nailing boards on what looked to be a temporary building. He was a frail little fellow with a limp. The wind almost swung the boards from his hands.

Bari crossed the road, watched him a moment, then took hold of a board and held it. A look of gratitude came to the old man's eyes. ' Thanks, young fellah. It ain't so easy workin' agin the wind.'

Bari smiled. ' I don't mind helping you. I'd like a couple of days' work.'

The old fellow shook his head. ' I'm doin' this for wages myself. The Fair Board might hire you though; the wet weather's held them up. They've to be ready for Friday.' The man turned again to his nailing.

' What kind of a fair is it? '

' Oh, cattle, horses, garden truck, sewin', bakin',

pictures—showin' them for prizes.' The builder spoke matter-of-factly without looking round.

'Think I could get work?' Bari asked with a touch of excitement. 'Where would I go to ask?'

'Round the corner there; there's a fellow in the office.'

In five minutes Bari had his bargain made. Two days' building stalls in the inner part of the building. The work came easily to him, thanks to Mr Millen's teaching, and he worked with a will. By the time he finished he knew all about 'The Fair'. That's what he thought.

When he got his pay, he tore back to Wheeler's for his road money, then out to Rogers to collect his picture, every step buoyed with thought of what he was going to do with it. But his spirits rose and fell like a wave in the wind in fear that Rogers might have disposed of it.

Rogers had kept his word. It was still in the wrapping in which Bari had handed it over. Rogers' words were terse. 'I'm not interested in pictures; don't know anybody that is.' It was the first time Bari felt happy over such a remark.

Next morning the weather was fine. Bari worked on the road, but at five o'clock he was at the Fair door with his picture.

The place looked different from the day before. The fragrance of flowers oozed through the dankness coming from the sawdusted floor. There was no one in sight but one or two men with ribboned lapels. Two women were tacking a quilt on a wall. They didn't even see Bari, who stood fumbling with his picture, not knowing which way to go or what to do. Then he saw a woman

arranging flowers.   As he made for her a man came in
and began unwrapping a parcel on a nearby table.   Bari
stopped and looked.   It was a picture.

Turning it over several times, the man studied it,
looked at the wall, measured the space, then stepped back,
drew hammer and nails from somewhere and began
driving a nail into the wall.

Aware only of his own urge, Bari vaulted a rail to
the man's side.   'Are you going to hang that picture
up?'

The man swung round, looked hard at Bari, took a
nail from his mouth and drove it into a beam before
answering.   'Yes, it's an exhibit.   Looks to be in the
money, too, but it's not mine.'   The man's voice lowered
to a casual, disinterested tone.

'I've got a picture I'd like to put up, too,' Bari went
on, pulling the wrapping from his canvas.   'Could I
use your hammer?'

The man fixed a pair of cool eyes on his.   'Is your
picture entered?'

'Entered!   Sure, I've got it here.'

'Yes, but it's got to be entered,' the fellow said,
without changing his tone.   'If it isn't, it's too late.
Go on over and ask Slade—that chap standing by the
door.'

Laying his picture down, Bari bounded over and
tapped Slade's shoulder.   'I want to put a picture up on
the wall beside that one,' he said, pointing to the one
being hung.

'Have you an entry?'

'You mean—what is it I've got to have?'   Bari
grasped Slade's arm impatiently.

'An entry,' Slade answered brusquely. 'If you haven't you're too late, time's up. You'll have to go!'

'I want to put up my picture,' Bari answered spiritedly. 'There's room up there.' He pointed to a vacant wall.

'My boy, you've got to pay an entry fee. The time's up!' Bari felt himself being pushed towards the door. Resisting as best he could, he pleaded, 'Please let me stay. I'll put the picture up myself.'

'The picture isn't tagged. We're closed.' Slade's voice rose ominously. 'Here's one of the head men coming. Go this way, quick!'

Bari was out. The bolt shot in the door. One bewildered moment he stood, then wheeling, he pounded on the panels. He must get his picture; it was in on the shelf. He pounded again. There was no answer.

He went round to a side entrance. It was padlocked. There was a notice tacked above, saying, 'Door Open To-morrow 10 A.M.' Bari felt crushed, beaten.

He was glad neither of the Wheelers were in sight when he went back to the house. He had told them nothing of his picture or plan, but he knew Mrs Wheeler would be quick to detect the shadow he couldn't keep from his face. He mounted the stairs quietly.

The house was silent. From the upper landing he glimpsed the rugged outline of forest against the sky. His eyes came back to the drab fields and houses straggling into the distance.

This was not his world! His whole being cried out against it. It crushed him, struck at the roots of his spirit, killing his soul. Back over the years memory went as he stood.

This urge, this nameless thing that was within him

had been so futile, so helpless. Brad hadn't liked it.
He had got into trouble at school for drawing—scribbling
they called it—on their books. Jake Madette, Bari
winced when he thought of him, had scoffed and sneered
at picture-making. Hyslop and Paddy hadn't thought
too kindly of it lately, and to-night was that tussle with
Slade. Nobody wanted him or his pictures. Was it a
phantom he was chasing, something unreal, built and
coloured with the deep, glowing shades of his dreams?

He didn't like road work. The artist in him rebelled.
The lumber camp and Wilkens' Corners hadn't
answered his need. Then he thought of Oney, sparkling
spirited Oney! His head went up. The picture was
hers. He'd go in the morning and get it. At night
he'd take it to the Wingates.

After he went to bed he thought over the words he'd
say to Mrs Wingate. They didn't come easily, for Bari
was still shy at heart.

Next morning he asked for time from work to go to
the fairground.

At ten o'clock he was in the Fair building. It didn't
look like the same place. There were flowers, balloons
and streamers in a blaze of light. It took Bari a minute
or two to spot the place where he had laid his picture.
When he reached the table he saw it was covered with
fancy-work.

He looked sharply about. People were milling back
and forth, but he couldn't see any of the men who'd
been in the night before. He walked the length of the
building and back, scanning every recess and stall. But
there wasn't a sign of his picture. Where could it be?

Suddenly he saw Slade. Racing over he tapped his

shoulder. 'Did you see the picture I left in here last night?'

'It was over there last night.' Slade pointed towards the side door and hurried off.

Up and down the shelves on both sides of the door Bari looked, but there was no picture. Could it have been thrown away? The thought set Bari quivering with apprehension. Why had he been so foolish? Why? Why? Why had he come at all? Hurrying towards the exit he ran full tilt into a man with pencil and notebook in hand.

'Did you see a picture? I left it here last night?' Bari asked, heedless of whom he was speaking to.

'There's one in the ante-room,' the fellow said, jerking his thumb towards the rear.

With a bound, Bari was into it. A man was standing by the table. He had Bari's picture in his hand.

Bari's impulse was to leap forward; but he hesitated, while the man held the canvas at varying distances, then laid it down.

Bari stepped up. 'That's my picture. I brought it in here yesterday.' The man didn't seem to hear; he kept looking at the painting as if fascinated. Then without lifting his head he asked, 'Who painted it?'

'I did.'

The man turned quickly and looked at him, then propping the canvas against the wall gazed at it again.

Bari moved uneasily. The man was a stranger; what business had he with the picture. Why didn't he say something? Bari stepped closer to get a good look at his face. It was good humoured; his eyes were searching as he lifted them again to Bari's face. 'I'm scouting for talent.' His voice was low and even. ' I guess I've got it. I paint a bit myself sometimes. My name's Van Dousan.'

' Van Dousan!' Bari gasped. ' You mean you're——' words came trembling from Bari's lips without order or meaning.

' Where do you come from?'

Bari hardly heard Van Dousan's question. Something in his whirling head kept him from saying what he wanted.

' If your folks can send you east with me, I'll keep you and help you to study. It won't take you very long.'

' I'll go! I'll go! I'll go and tell them now.' Bari backed towards the door. ' I'll leave my picture with you.'

' Be at the hotel on Monday morning, if your folks agree. I can't wait longer.'

Bari cleared the building, conscious of nothing but that he had reached his goal.

There was no one at home at the Wheelers', but scribbling a note, he left it on the table and started for Paddy's cabin.

By the time he covered a dozen miles, the first flush of excitement flagged. The staggering reality of what was happening took its place. The dreams he had had through all the long years were coming true.

But he would need money. He hadn't thought of that. It took the edge off his enthusiasm now, but didn't dampen his spirits. He would work, make money to pay his fare. It would keep him back a couple of months or so, but he would go back on Monday morning to Van Dousan and explain.

He hurried on.

When night came he was too tired to continue. He crept beneath shrubbery and slept. He rose refreshed.

The sun was just up when he bounded into Paddy's cabin. Paddy was standing by the stove. He swung round, eyes alight.

'Paddy! Paddy, I've made good!' Bari rushed forward and gripped Paddy by the shoulder. 'My picture's all right—you know, the one I painted for Oney,' he added, voice hoarse with excitement. 'An artist, a real artist, is going to help me to study, keep me, pay for it.' Bari's voice rose quiveringly, as he flopped on to a chair.

Paddy looked at him with guarded eyes. Paddy never spoke much and he didn't say much now. He kept looking through the window at the trees as if he might learn from them what it was all about.

Bari rattled on, 'It's great, isn't it? I'll go places, see things, do the things I've wanted to do, and——'

Something in Paddy's face stopped him.

'Oh, I won't be going just yet, Paddy. I haven't got the money for my railway ticket. I'll have to work for it. It'll take a couple of months.'

A smile chased the shadow from Paddy's eyes. He turned, put some wood on the fire and drew on the lid, then crossed to the cupboard, the laughing lines in his face deepening. 'You want to go, eh?'

'I sure do, Paddy.'

Paddy opened a drawer and took out a leather bag. It was filled with notes. Scattering them on the table, he said, 'That's the pelt money from Seegwun's rats. It's yours. I kep' it for you!'

'Paddy!' Their eyes met. A look of understanding passed between them.

'Oney's at home,' Paddy said quietly. 'She cum back to say good-bye.'

Bari jumped to his feet. 'I'll go tell her! I'll go now.'

Out of the cabin he went and, with feet scarcely touching the ground, he sped to Madette's. As he breasted the hill, he saw Oney coming on the run. They met on the tamarack-rim.

Eyes shining, she listened to Bari's story. 'Bari! And it's my picture,' she exclaimed, her face kindled. 'I'm so happy for you.' She seemed to dance with joy. 'Let's go an' tell Dad.'

Taking Bari's hand she raced with him across the sunlit valley. Jake was walking towards the lake. He turned when he saw them. Bari retold what had happened.

Jake squinted dubiously, then, face brightening, exclaimed, 'I allus said you had the makin's of somethin' in you, young fellah! It's Jake Madette that ain't never far mistaken!' Then, with a boisterous wallop on Bari's shoulder, he added, 'You'll build a cabin for yerself yet!'

Bari prepared for his journey. He had many anxious thoughts during the busy day. He knew that, in spite of Paddy's evident pleasure at his prospects, Paddy needed him, needed him now as he had never done before. The logs lay ready for the cabin they were going to build.

'Keego trimmed an' edged them,' Paddy said, when he came on Bari looking at them. And, as if in answer

to Bari's unspoken worry, added, ' He's helpin' me ! '
Music came from the bush trail as he spoke. Keego came
in sight, an axe over his shoulder.

He quickened pace when he saw Bari ; a minute later
they were shaking hands. ' They tell me you're goin'
to paint pictures, eh ? ' Keego said in a voice not too
weighted with admiration. ' Well me, I'm goin' to
build a house ! An' it's me that can do it. Can't I,
Paddy ? '

Bari laughed. He felt glad to know that Keego would
be helping Paddy.

It seemed right that Peter Hyslop should come the
morning Bari was leaving, bringing a shirt and pair of
socks. ' I was glad to hear of your luck, Bari. You'll
keep right on from here. Don't let anything stop you,'
Hyslop said, as he walked from the house with Bari to
his waiting boat.

At the turn of the trail they halted. Bari could see
Keego raising the first upright for Paddy's cabin. Then
his eyes rested on the woods. There he had shadowed
secret trails and dawn flights. The music of the water,
even the spume lashing Paddy's sanded doorway was
tuned to his spirit. The very surge of its freedom bound
him to the forest that lost itself in the lonely winds of
the north.

It wasn't hard to wave good-bye to the figure standing
on the rise, for deep in Bari's heart was the
knowledge that in the Nest-building Moon of another
spring he would come again, for the forest was his
kingdom.

The Indian Background

This story of a half-breed Indian boy has been written in the forest lands of northern Canada, and some of the expressions and names for birds, animals, and seasons are Indian. Here is an explanation of them:

Adjiduhmo . . .	*Squirrel*
Cheebuy . . .	*Ghost*
Keego . . .	*Fish*
Ko-ko-ko . .	*Owl*
Onemik (Oney) .	*Bud*
Seegwun . . .	*Spring*
Windigo . . .	*Giant*
Windegooqua ('gooqua) .	*Fairy*
Rogan . . .	*Basket*
Wa-wa . . .	*Goose*

The Ojibway Indians' Moon Calendar

Great Spirit Moon . .	*January*
Sucker Moon . . .	*February*
Frog Moon . . .	*March*
Nest-building Moon . .	*April*
Flower Moon . . .	*May*
Strawberry (Berry) Moon .	*June*
Red Raspberry Moon . .	*July*
Huckleberry Moon . .	*August*
Rice Moon (Moon of Fading Leaves)	*September*
Moon of Falling Leaves .	*October*
Freezing Moon . . .	*November*
Spirit Moon . . .	*December*

Snowshoe. A rabbit.

Tender Bird. A bird cut out of a piece of spruce, painted, blessed, and mounted on a high pole above Ojibway villages by the medicine-man to keep evil spirits away.

▪ FIGURES DU PASSÉ ▪

■

MARCEL REINHARD

LE GRAND
CARNOT

★ ★

L'ORGANISATEUR DE LA VICTOIRE

1792 - 1823

· FIGURES DU PASSÉ ·

HACHETTE

OUVRAGE DU MÊME AUTEUR

La Légende de Henri IV, Hachette, éditeur *(épuisé)*.

Le Département de la Sarthe sous le régime directorial, Presses bretonnes, éditeur (couronné par l'Académie française).

Henri IV ou la France sauvée, Hachette, éditeur (couronné par l'Académie française).

Avec Bonaparte en Italie, Hachette, éditeur (couronné par l'Académie française).

Histoire de la population mondiale de 1700 a 1948, Domat-Montchrestien, éditeur.

Le Grand Carnot, T. I : De l'ingénieur au conventionnel, 1753-1792, Hachette, éditeur.

La France de la Révolution, Hachette *(en préparation)*.

AVANT-PROPOS

L A PÉRIODE *fulgurante, celle des efforts héroïques et des violences terribles, celle des dangers, des responsabilités écrasantes et des succès décisifs, s'ouvrit avec la Convention et surtout avec le Grand Comité de Salut public. Ce fut le temps de l'Organisation de la Victoire.*

L'Histoire en a attribué le mérite à Carnot.

Mais une opposition acharnée, tantôt agressive, tantôt sarcastique, lui a disputé — depuis ce temps jusqu'à nos jours — une gloire, disait-on, usurpée. Ce courant s'est opposé au culte familial qui exaltait le héros national et républicain dont les descendants suivaient l'exemple en fournissant un ministre à la Seconde République et un président à la Troisième.

Heureuse fortune pour un biographe qu'un sujet si âprement débattu ! Quel stimulant pour suivre les traces de l'action, remonter aux auteurs et tenter de surprendre leurs intentions ; surtout lorsque les ressources documentaires n'ont pas été méthodiquement exploitées. Du coup le cadre biographique éclate, toute la défense nationale est en jeu : les comités, la Convention, les généraux et les armées.

Et c'est aussi la guerre. Cette guerre nationale, dont nous avons vécu les terribles développements, est alors apparue. Menée par la nation armée, animée par le patriotisme, conduisant à l'héroïsme certes, mais au chauvinisme, à la haine inexpiable et à la frénésie de la destruction. Chemin de la guerre totale ! Chemin méconnu par ceux qui attribuent à l'évolution de la technique le rôle décisif, alors que, si des techniques aveugles et barbares sont adoptées, c'est bien consciemment et volontairement : la guerre totale est dans l'esprit avant que la technique la réalise. De fait, les hommes de la Révolution ont hésité, aux frontières de la barbarie, devant la mise à mort des prisonniers, le recours à des armes nouvelles et le sacrifice massif des jeunes générations.

Histoire-bataille ! Pourquoi revenir à ce genre dédaigné et même proscrit ? Nous savons le poids de l'épée jetée dans la balance et le sort d'un peuple au lendemain d'une campagne perdue. Il importe donc de comprendre pourquoi ces batailles furent livrées et comment elles furent gagnées ou perdues.

De plus la vie militaire, l'armée, tinrent une place croissante dans la vie de la France à cette époque. Il faut faire revivre cette étonnante société qu'était une armée de la Révolution, avec ses soldats de métier et ses volontaires, ses généraux improvisés, sa discipline flottante, son élan prodigieux, ses paniques soudaines, ses trafiquants et ses héros. Carnot fut amené à les voir de très près, d'abord en qualité de commissaire, sinon même de chef, à Furnes et à Wattignies, puis comme chef de la section de la Guerre au Comité de Salut public, comme Directeur et comme ministre de la Guerre.

Plus encore les incidences de la guerre sur la vie d'une nation apparaissent comme l'une des données les plus importantes, notamment au temps des guerres nationales. La liaison entre l'activité militaire et les activités civiles, dans l'économie, les transports, les finances et dans la politique, forme l'un des traits les plus propres à expliquer une époque et une situation. Les exigences de la guerre ont conduit Carnot à participer à une sorte de dictature collective.

Car il fut aussi mêlé à l'action politique, cet organisateur de la victoire. Dans quelle mesure ? C'est toute la question, aussi passionnément discutée que celle de l'organisation de la victoire. Carnot fut-il terroriste ? On ne peut éluder cette difficulté qui fait pénétrer au sein du gouvernement révolutionnaire, entre Robespierre et Saint-Just, entre Prieur et Lindet, pour tenter de définir le partage des tâches et des responsabilités.

En somme, après avoir recherché comment Carnot était devenu révolutionnaire, il s'agissait de savoir quel révolutionnaire il avait été, quelle révolution il avait faite, ou tenté de faire.

L'homme qui fit Bonaparte, puis qui se dressa devant l'Empereur, tel fut Carnot,... du moins on l'a prétendu. Dans cette étonnante période, si pleine et si complexe, qui va de 1795 à 1815, le général de l'armée d'Italie est devenu le maître de l'Europe pour laisser enfin la France envahie et la Révolution vaincue. Or Carnot a patronné le général de l'armée d'Italie ; Carnot était alors l'un des présidents de cette république à cinq têtes, le Directoire. Si Bonaparte a grandi, si la République a été renversée, ce ne fut pas sans relations avec la politique de Carnot. Et le césarisme eut un moment Carnot pour ministre, il se fût même bien volontiers contenté d'être ensuite sénateur, alors qu'il condamnait le césarisme et l'Empire. Cette période, pour être moins classique et moins souvent évoquée, n'est pas moins importante dans la carrière de Carnot. Elle permet aussi de mieux pénétrer la vie politique au temps du Directoire, du Consulat, de l'Empire.

Enfin les démêlés avec Louis XVIII ne sont pas les moins curieux. Décoré de l'ordre du Lys, Carnot propose au roi une politique qui indigne les royalistes et lui vaut une réplique de Chateaubriand, puis l'exil.

**

Comment remercier tant de chercheurs, d'érudits, d'archivistes et de bibliothécaires qui ont bien voulu s'intéresser à la lente préparation de ce travail ? Tels MM. G. Lefebvre, Godechot, Gaston-Martin, L. Jacob, Fabre, les commandants Chalmin, Petitjean, MM. Cambier, Lacroix, le capitaine de vaisseau Hamel, G. Bouchard. Nous avons une dette particulière à l'égard de certains archivistes, notamment MM. de Prat, Herzog, Estienne, Bongard, Davillé, Leussat, et de certains bibliothécaires, notamment MM. Eygun, de Poitiers ; Gagnebin, de Genève, Mlle Dupic, de Rouen ; Batey, d'Oxford, et aussi M. le chanoine Coolen.

Les archives familiales ont fourni, comme pour la période précédente, un apport considérable. Nous remercions les membres de la famille Carnot qui les ont si aimablement mises à notre disposition, Mlle L. Carnot, MM. François, Pierre-Sadi et Lazare Carnot. Nous remercions aussi M. le professeur P. Carnot des renseignements qu'il nous a aimablement communiqués.

D'autres archives privées nous ont aussi, grâce à l'obligeance de leurs détenteurs, apporté diverses pièces, notamment les archives de la famille Murat, celles de M. de Chasseloup-Laubat, de Mlles Coyreau des Loges et Arbelet, et de M. Séhet.

Enfin nous avons tiré parti de la correspondance rassemblée par le regretté Mautouchet en vue d'une publication non poursuivie.

LE GRAND CARNOT

DE L'ORGANISATEUR DE LA VICTOIRE
A L'EXILE

PREMIÈRE PARTIE

LA PATRIE EN DANGER

CHAPITRE PREMIER

LA CRÉATION D'UNE ARMÉE

« Depuis le 10 août il y a des Pyrénées. » Ce mot de Lacuée à Pache correspondait à la situation créée par l'hostilité croissante de la République envers Louis XVI, les Bourbons et tous les rois. Hostilité où se mêlaient la forfanterie, le patriotisme et l'appréhension ; les cris d'alarme se confondaient avec les appels belliqueux.

Le ministre des Affaires étrangères, Lebrun, exposant la situation européenne le 26 septembre, annonçait que l'Espagne prendrait part à la guerre. Les journaux brissotins, le *Patriote français*, le *Courrier* de Gorsas, menaient campagne pour la propagande, l'extermination des « satellites de l'Inquisition »; ils publiaient aussi les lettres de frontaliers apeurés dénonçant des préparatifs militaires espagnols.

Tout le Sud-Ouest, fief girondin, réclamait des troupes, voire une guerre; il manifestait sa volonté à la Nation, à l'Assemblée, au ministre de la Guerre, Servan. La Convention était sommée de détacher trois de ses membres, pour être commissaires aux Pyrénées, et assurer, en accord avec le ministre, la défense de la frontière et la préparation d'une force armée [1].

Servan accueillit volontiers ces demandes et pressa la Convention. Il était alors en mauvaise posture. Inquiet et

instable par tempérament, malade à cette époque, il était en
outre alors vivement attaqué par la presse et par certains
Conventionnels à cause des marchés onéreux qu'il passait
avec les fournisseurs de guerre. On s'étonnait qu'il eût envoyé
en Angleterre, sous couleur d'y acheter des fusils, un de
ses cousins, qui était aussi son filleul, et qu'il lui eût fait
remettre cinquante mille livres par le fameux trafiquant
d'Espagnac ; et le filleul s'attardait à l'étranger. Grand ami
de Roland, et plus encore de Mme Roland, Servan était
attaqué par les ennemis de ce ménage ministériel. Il résolut,
le 25 septembre, de démissionner pour raison de santé. La
création d'une armée aux Pyrénées pouvait lui permettre
de caser des amis et de se réserver une place. Il fit donc
décréter que l'aile droite de l'armée du Midi deviendrait
armée des Pyrénées, qu'elle recevrait un état-major, et
que lui, Servan, la commanderait en chef [2].

La Convention et les autres ministres avaient favorisé
cette combinaison qui fournissait à la Gironde une armée
installée dans sa région, commandée par un ami dévoué,
capable de lutter contre l'Espagne et, le cas échéant, de
combattre les Montagnards. Fabre d'Églantine dénonçait
déjà l'ébauche d'une légion, dans cette contrée, où l'on
recrutait un état-major de hobereaux et de fils de famille [3].

Pour préparer l'organisation de la nouvelle armée, pendant qu'il prendrait quelque repos, Servan nomma son
ami Lacuée, adjudant général chef de brigade, commissaire
du pouvoir exécutif aux Pyrénées. Ce Lacuée était le type
même du Girondin. D'origine noble, possédant des terres
dans son pays natal, près d'Agen, il avait collaboré à l'*Ency-
clopédie* et pris part à la phase libérale de la Révolution,
mais il n'était nullement démocrate. « Militaire philosophe »
sous l'Ancien Régime, il avait été conseiller du Comité militaire de la Constituante, il était entré à la Législative,
au Comité militaire de laquelle il avait connu Feulint ;
Servan l'avait enfin pris pour second dans l'administration
de la Guerre. Il excellait aux travaux administratifs et ne
manquait pas d'ambition ; Vergniaud tenta même d'en faire
le successeur de Servan, mais la Gironde crut tenir mieux
le département de la Guerre en lui préférant Pache. Servan
fut amené, par sa mission aux Pyrénées, à se lier avec
Carnot [4].

En effet, la Convention avait décidé, le 23 septembre,
d'envoyer aux Pyrénées deux missions de trois représentants,

l'une à Perpignan, l'autre à Bayonne, pour « préparer des moyens assurés de défense » et « rétablir l'ordre public partout où il serait troublé ». Carnot avait été nommé membre de la mission des Pyrénées occidentales.

Jusqu'alors il n'avait fait qu'assister en silence aux séances de la Convention, ce qui ne l'avait pas empêché d'être porté, le premier, au Comité de la Guerre et, un peu plus tard, d'être élu au Comité diplomatique. Sa notoriété le soutenait[5].

La mission était complétée par deux parlementaires de la région, le robin Lamarque et l'avocat Garrau. Celui-ci allait devenir l'ami de Carnot, s'attachant à lui de toute la force de son patriotisme et de sa cordialité, qui étaient immenses.

Lacuée accompagna les commissaires de la Convention. Il fut bientôt rejoint par un ingénieur, détaché des Ponts et Chaussées dans le Génie militaire, Lomet. Lui aussi allait se lier à Carnot avec un enthousiasme exclusif qui se manifeste cocassement dans ses souvenirs, toujours passionnés et souvent sujets à caution [6].

Ainsi s'achemina un petit groupe dont Carnot était et resta longtemps le chef. Pourtant les éléments étaient disparates par leurs origines et leur politique, Garrau se montra encore plus Montagnard que Lacuée n'était Girondin. Carnot, sans se lier, inclinait toujours vers la Gironde.

La tâche des commissaires était accablante, à cause de Servan. Celui-ci, pour faire adopter son projet, l'avait dangereusement simplifié : détacher l'aile droite de l'armée du Midi, au nord des Pyrénées, et la doter d'un état-major. On découvrit que l'armée du Midi n'avait pas d'aile droite aux Pyrénées, ou presque pas, cependant que l'état-major, à commencer par Servan, n'apparaissait pas. Tout le travail retomba sur les commissaires, principalement sur Carnot, le seul qui fût militaire.

Le mardi 2 octobre ils étaient arrivés à Bordeaux, capitale des Girondins. Ils y séjournèrent jusqu'au 7. Carnot s'y lia avec la famille du Conventionnel Ducos.

Reçus avec éclat par le conseil général, la municipalité et le Club des Amis de la Liberté et de l'Égalité, les commissaires firent une enquête « sur la position militaire du département,... sur l'état de ses routes, celui de ses subsistances ». Ils décidèrent d'organiser une armée de quarante mille hommes, moitié levés immédiatement, moitié laissés chez eux jusqu'au jour où les opérations — l'offensive — les rendraient nécessaires. Ce projet, vanté par Gorsas, porte-parole des Girondins [7], fut retenu par Servan et par Dubois-Crancé.

Il fallait donc lever des volontaires, les encadrer, les équiper, les armer, les exercer et subvenir à leurs besoins. Tâche nouvelle pour Carnot, mais qui le préparait à l'orga-nisation des armées de la République. Il s'y livra avec promptitude et décision, efficacement secondé par Lacuée.

Élargissant son champ d'action, Carnot fit imprimer une circulaire réquisitionnant les hommes dans les dix-sept départements des Pyrénées occidentales et orientales. Les administrations devaient indiquer le nombre des hommes déjà mobilisés, avec une liste nominative à l'appui. Ils devaient faire connaître le nombre des hommes de seize à cinquante ans, en état de porter les armes, et non mariés ni fonctionnaires. D'après ces données, les commissaires répartiraient les bataillons à lever entre les départements [8].

Au dire des commissaires, les résultats furent aussi bril-lants que prompts : en huit jours la Gironde rassembla un bataillon, le Lot-et-Garonne en offrit deux de plus qu'on ne lui demandait. Mais ils avaient tort de généraliser : ces beaux résultats étaient exceptionnels.

Les administrations départementales répartissaient à l'aveuglette les contingents à fournir entre les districts, ceux-ci se tournaient vers les communes qui devaient trou-ver le nombre prescrit de volontaires. Or les hommes dis-posés à servir s'étaient engagés en 1791. Depuis, en dépit de l'envoi de commissaires, il avait été si malaisé de former des bataillons, qu'on en était venu à la contrainte, ou à l'achat Dans le Tarn, les volontaires étaient désignés d'office par le scrutin, le choix tombait parfois sur des fonctionnaires, sur des malades, sur des infirmes, et même sur des vieillards. Singuliers volontaires ! Ou bien il fallait se cotiser et soudoyer des mercenaires, tantôt cent cinquante livres, tantôt deux cents, tantôt trois cents. Par ces procédés, et à grand-peine, on obtint des unités. Dans le Lot, le premier bataillon se réunit le 7 novembre, il lui manquait une centaine d'hommes, le second se rassembla le 31 janvier, il comptait cinq cent quarante-cinq présents sur un effectif théorique de huit cents. Dans les Basses-Pyrénées, le 26 décembre, le premier batail-lon était incomplet de deux cents hommes et de la compagnie de canonniers. Il y eut pourtant quelques exceptions, comme le district de Figeac qui fournit trois cent quarante-cinq hommes au lieu de deux cent quarante-six qu'on lui avait demandés [9].

Dévoilant leurs arrière-pensées, les Girondins voulurent appeler à Paris des bataillons du Sud-Ouest, notamment de Libourne. Les commissaires s'y refusèrent et envoyèrent ces troupes à Bayonne. Ainsi Carnot déçut-il la Gironde [10], mais sans rompre avec elle.

Avant de quitter Bordeaux les commissaires avaient proposé la démolition du Château-Trompette, bastille menaçant la liberté de la ville, selon une idée chère à Carnot, qui l'avait naguère énoncée à la Législative, non sans causer de scandale. De Bordeaux les commissaires se rendirent à La Réole, Marmande, Agen, Montauban, Auch, Tarbes et Pau, pour atteindre enfin Bayonne, le 12 octobre, et s'y fixer jusqu'à la fin du mois.

La levée des hommes se poursuivait. Carnot y ajouta une idée de son cru — ou plutôt empruntée à son cher Vauban : l'utilisation des frontaliers, spécialement précieux dans un pays difficile, aux passages rares et peu accessibles. Il voulut lever ces « montagnards connus sous le nom de *miquelets*,... accoutumés à gravir les rochers, et seuls instruits des sentiers et des défilés ». Le 22 octobre, il décida de former deux compagnies, dont Lacuée désignerait les sous-officiers et les officiers. Grave entorse au principe électif auquel Carnot s'était jusqu'alors montré si attaché. Concession à Lacuée, qui flétrissait les officiers des volontaires, officiers élus par « l'intrigue, l'or et le cabaret ». Mais cette concession demeura exceptionnelle.

En vain Lacuée stigmatisa les vices des volontaires — si peu volontaires. « Vous avez vu, écrivait-il à Carnot, quel esprit de cupidité anime la plupart de ces hommes qui ne devraient être guidés que par le civisme ; quel esprit de licence parmi des hommes qui, au nom de la loi, devraient être immobiles et muets. Il faut absolument, vous l'avez bien senti, une manière d'éloigner de l'armée tous ceux qui la déshonoreraient par leur insubordination, leur cupidité, ou par l'esprit agitateur dont ils seraient animés. Permettez-moi, citoyen, de recommander cet objet à votre sollicitude. »

Carnot préféra demeurer fidèle à la discipline spontanée qu'il avait célébrée avec éclat sous la Législative. Et pourtant ! Une insurrection avait éclaté à Saint-Jean-Pied-de

Port, où des officiers frappés de proscription, menacés de mort, avaient réclamé le secours des commissaires. Ceux-ci, loin de sévir contre les soldats, mirent en congé trois de leurs officiers. Le soldat s'insurge, professait Carnot, là où l'officier n'est pas patriote : « Il n'y a de bonne et de véritable subordination que celle qui est inspirée par la confiance. » Aussi le maréchal de camp Gestas, qui avait réclamé un « exemple sévère » contre les mutins de Saint-Jean-Pied-de-Port, fut puni. Servan avait d'ailleurs reçu des dénonciations contre lui. Gestas, ci-devant comte, périt sur l'échafaud.

En revanche, les commissaires n'accueillirent pas à la légère les dénonciations lancées par les Jacobins contre certains officiers. Le club de Bayonne avait demandé la destitution du commandant de la place, des officiers du Génie et d'Artillerie. Carnot fut clément. A propos du colonel directeur des fortifications de Bayonne, il exposa sa ligne de conduite :

« Informés que le citoyen Foulhiac... n'a pas réussi à se concilier entièrement la confiance des citoyens de Bayonne, déclarons que, loin de vouloir partager aucune prévention défavorable à cet officier, nous pensons au contraire que ses longs et bons services méritent une récompense honorable,... mais *persuadés qu'il est toujours dangereux de contrarier l'opinion publique* (sic) et connaissant le mauvais état de santé du citoyen Foulhiac, nous autorisons l'adjudant général Lacuée... à lui accorder un congé provisoire.... »

Foulhiac fut donc mis à la retraite grâce à l'indulgence de Carnot, ce qui n'empêcha pas sa veuve, sous Louis XVIII, de réclamer une pension parce que son mari avait démissionné « dès que le roi légitime [avait] été dépouillé de son trône » !

Des mesures analogues furent prises à Blaye et à Tarbes. C'était assez bénin, mais toujours des officiers étaient frappés et non des soldats ; Carnot restait fidèle à ses principes et savait résister à Lacuée. La principale force des armées était alors le civisme, pour la ménager, il fallait laisser les hommes renvoyer les officiers suspects de tiédeur [10].

* *

« Ce n'est pas tout d'avoir des hommes, écrivait aux commissaires le conseil général du Gers, il faut des armes, il faut des habits.... »

Carnot et les commissaires réquisitionnèrent l'habillement et l'équipement. Les départements devaient faire le nécessaire. Des négociants firent des dons, des citoyennes se mirent à tailler et à coudre des draps, des fournisseurs renoncèrent à leur bénéfice. Mais il fallait de l'argent. Carnot ordonna au payeur général des Basses-Pyrénées de fournir des fonds, ailleurs il fit employer la caisse ecclésiastique. Il allait de l'avant, convaincu qu'on lui saurait gré de créer l'armée, même s'il devait entamer les fonds publics, qu'il ménageait le plus possible.

La même méthode lui servit pour le gros armement. Il acheta du cuivre à Cabarrus — Cabarrus, le père de la future Mme Tallien — et l'envoya au fondeur. Il faisait construire affûts et caissons, il préparait l'établissement d'une École d'Artillerie.

Ce zèle pour l'Artillerie ne lui était pas coutumier. Carnot subissait ici l'influence de Lacuée. Celui-ci, ancien aspirant d'Artillerie, avait conservé une grande admiration pour les bouches à feu. Il voulait une « artillerie formidable,... sans cet agent puissant on ne doit rien entreprendre ».

Or Lacuée voulait entreprendre. La Convention avait prescrit de préparer la défense, Lacuée proposait l'attaque et, pour une part, il fit admettre ses vues par Carnot : l'effectif de quarante mille hommes avait été calculé pour l'offensive ; Carnot écrivit bientôt qu'il espérait que l'armée pourrait entrer en Catalogne en mars ou en avril. Il exalta une politique de prestige, celle d'une république naissante, fière et victorieuse.

Pourtant il espérait et il voulait la paix. Il répudiait la propagande, contrairement aux Brissotins [11]. A propos d'un incident, les commissaires déclarèrent que, si la nation française voulait que tous les peuples fussent libres, elle « savait néanmoins respecter le gouvernement et l'indépendance des autres nations ». Dans une lettre ils s'avancèrent plus loin : « Nous préférons, nous désirons la paix, sans laquelle aucun peuple ne saurait être heureux, et nous la voulons surtout avec les Espagnols nos anciens alliés.... Tant qu'une nation voisine respectera notre indépendance, loin d'attaquer la sienne, nous nous ferons un devoir de la secourir, et nous nous empresserons de resserrer les liens d'amitié et de fraternité qui doivent unir tous les peuples. »

Toutefois Carnot n'acceptait le maintien ni des frontières franco-espagnoles, ni des conditions qui régissaient le commerce entre les deux nations : « Il faut nécessairement ou la guerre ou un autre traité... qui affranchisse notre commerce des entraves honteuses qu'il éprouve. » C'était là une revendication étrangère aux considérations militaires et politiques, liée au contraire aux idées économiques de Carnot, et dont nous aurons à dire l'importance. Notons seulement qu'on ne saurait dégager une politique nette de ces déclarations contradictoires.

Pour lors, Carnot et ses collègues visitaient précisément la frontière : Saint-Jean-Pied-de-Port, Saint-Palais, Mauléon, Navarrenx, Oloron, Pau, Lourdes, Bagnères-de-Bigorre, Tarbes.

Ils admiraient les « âpres beautés que la nature déploie, les monts sourcilleux, les cascades qui s'y précipitent de leurs sommets, et les vallées solitaires qui rappellent l'homme à lui-même et au bonheur de la vie pastorale ». Carnot n'avait pas oublié les prestiges de Rousseau.

Enfin, le 19 novembre, ils arrivèrent à Toulouse qu'ils s'étaient assignée comme centre de séjour, pour tirer les conclusions de leurs observations, les confronter avec celles de leurs collègues des Pyrénées-Orientales et s'accorder avec l'état-major de l'armée des Pyrénées.

A Toulouse on trouvait, à défaut du général en chef, le chef d'état-major, Choderlos de Laclos, le romancier fameux, mais aussi l'ennemi de Vauban et des ingénieurs, l'adversaire personnel de Carnot. Il se dépensait alors pour quitter la place. Il allait être nommé gouverneur général des établissements français dans l'Inde. En attendant il se gardait de tout zèle inutile, mais il voulait attribuer un rôle glorieux à l'armée des Pyrénées : « Il importe à la gloire, à la tranquillité et même à la sécurité de la République française, de déclarer la guerre au gouvernement espagnol. » Cette guerre porterait l'armée en territoire ennemi, car, déclarait encore Laclos, « il n'existe de guerre défensive efficace que par des opérations offensives [12] ».

Au même moment Servan donnait enfin signe de vie : « Une infinité de causes ont concouru jusqu'à présent [22 novembre] à m'empêcher de me rendre à Toulouse », écrivait-il à Pache, son successeur au ministère. Cette explication flottante dissimulait les déboires de Servan qui avait espéré un commandement à Genève, mais le général Montes-

quiou n'avait pas voulu attaquer cette ville ; la situation se modifiant assez pour ne plus lui laisser d'espoir, il
jugeait donc à propos de songer à son armée, mais sans hâte,
préférant lui laisser prendre corps.

Or les difficultés s'accumulaient. Les commissaires envoyés
aux Pyrénées-Orientales étaient partis pour la Provence,
laissant à Carnot et à ses collègues le soin d'étudier l'ensemble du front pyrénéen. Au même moment Carnot apprit
que tout pouvoir financier était refusé à la mission des
Pyrénées : la Convention en avait ainsi décidé, le 15 novembre, sur la demande de Cambon. Ainsi les moyens
disparaissaient quand la tâche s'élargissait !

Par la plume de Carnot, les commissaires s'en prirent à
la Convention : plus qu'une justification, c'était une contre-
attaque.

« Loin d'outrepasser nos pouvoirs, si nous avons dérogé à
ce que prescrit la loi, ce n'a été que pour en restreindre
l'absurde prodigalité.... Nous devons le dire hautement,
malgré la sagesse de vos vues, pour obtenir aujourd'hui le
paiement de la créance la plus modique et la plus légitime,
il faut plus de démarches, de dépenses, d'entregent, qu'il n'en
fallait autrefois pour obtenir des pensions extravagantes. »
Une telle situation expliquait « la misère profonde du peuple,...
les chemins impraticables, les hôpitaux sans moyens, les
municipalités écrasées de dettes,... l'instruction publique
abandonnée ».

Plus directement, la mesure qui les frappait ruinait l'œuvre
des commissaires : « L'ensemble de nos mesures est rompu,
nos opérations sont coupées.... Nous remettons les choses
dans leur état actuel, entre les mains du ministre de la Guerre
qui fera mieux apparemment [13].... »

Le mot de la fin annonçait le rebondissement de l'affaire :
les commissaires frappés par la Convention s'en prirent au
ministre. En effet, lui seul pouvait désormais accorder les
moyens financiers indispensables ; il eut l'imprudence de les
promettre, et ne les procura pas. Dès lors l'armée créée
par les commissaires, et qui comptait — disaient-ils — plus
de vingt mille hommes, se désagrégea. Les uns désertaient,
d'autres étaient licenciés faute de vivres, de vêtements et
de soins.

Servan, qui se rendait enfin à son poste, déclarait en passant que tout manquait, et que le ministre ne répondait pas
aux lettres les plus importantes [14].

Lacuée surenchérissait : « Ce n'est pas ainsi qu'on a sauvé la France du 10 août au 20 septembre », écrivait-il à Laclos. C'était là grief des ministres anciens — ou futurs — contre l'homme en place. C'était aussi l'attaque de Girondins contre Pache qui devenait Montagnard.

Carnot lui-même intervint avec cette violence passagère qui stupéfiait de la part d'un homme habituellement si pondéré. Il écrivit le 4 décembre, à la Convention :

« Je vous envoie, chers collègues, diverses pièces qui prouvent évidemment la malveillance du ministre de la Guerre, ou son impéritie absolue, ou qu'il ne veut point d'armée des Pyrénées. Je pourrais vous en envoyer beaucoup d'autres qui prouvent, ou son ignorance, ou son mépris profond pour les lois dont l'exécution lui est confiée. Je me borne, quant à présent, à vous faire part de celles qui mettent à couvert la responsabilité morale des commissaires de la Convention, et je lui annonce cet envoi. »

Cette dénonciation arrivait à point. Montagnards et Girondins luttaient farouchement à propos du procès du roi, du rôle de Paris, des finances, de la politique générale. Tout leur était bon pour s'accuser réciproquement. La région du Sud-Ouest jouait son rôle dans ce conflit perfide et tonitruant. Des adresses s'envolaient contre Marat, contre Robespierre, contre l'anarchie, contre la dictature parisienne. On parlait d'envoyer contre la capitale — dénomination contraire à l'égalité — des bataillons de Méridionaux. Pache, qui était passé au service des Montagnards, était le plus haï.

Quand on lut à la Convention la lettre de Carnot, Buzot attaqua Pache, l'homme de la Montagne, et l'on voulut arracher sa démission. L'entreprise ne réussit pas ce jour-là.

Il est remarquable que Carnot — et lui seul, Lamarque ni Garrau ne signèrent sa lettre — ait ainsi soutenu les Girondins et Dumouriez qui avaient déclenché contre le ministre une lutte à mort. Sans aucun doute les bureaux de la Guerre agissaient avec une lenteur désastreuse — telle réclamation des commissaires, en date du 16 octobre, n'obtint une réponse dilatoire qu'à la fin de novembre. Mais Carnot pouvait savoir par son frère Feulint que le ministre avait de plus graves soucis sur le théâtre des opérations.

Feulint, en effet, avait été envoyé à l'armée de la Moselle pour y presser l'action de Kellermann, puis à l'armée du Rhin pour décider Biron à servir sous Custine, et pour activer les opérations. Feulint avait pu constater que les besoins des armées combattantes étaient immenses et que Pache se dépensait de son mieux. Ne devinrent-ils pas collaborateurs directs ? Le 7 décembre, Pache chargeait Feulint de « prendre une connaissance générale de toute l'administration personnelle du département ; de recevoir communication de toutes pièces envoyées au chef de cette administration, avant leur répartition dans les divers bureaux, ainsi que de tous rapports ou dépêches proposés par ceux-ci à la signature ministérielle [15] ».

Quand la lettre de Carnot eut été lue à la Convention, cette collaboration devint impossible : le 20 décembre, Feulint était nommé lieutenant-colonel directeur du dépôt des Fortifications. Dans ce nouveau poste, il se montra plutôt malveillant à l'égard du ministre [16].

Le conflit se prolongea. Le 29 janvier 1793, une délégation de la Haute-Garonne, conduite par un ami de Laclos et des Girondins, répéta devant la Convention les attaques de Carnot, de Lacuée et de Laclos. Aussitôt après ce réquisitoire, Barère ajouta que, la veille, au Comité de défense générale, Carnot avait accusé le ministre de n'avoir rien fait pour organiser l'armée des Pyrénées et d'avoir tout fait pour la désorganiser. Après Barère, les commissaires lurent leur rapport, qui incriminait aussi le ministre. Cette manœuvre aboutit enfin le 2 février. Carnot avait tout fait pour provoquer la chute de Pache [17].

A cette date, l'œuvre des commissaires était interrompue depuis plus d'un mois. L'armée des Pyrénées n'était pas prête, elle ne devait pas l'être davantage le 7 mars, quand la guerre fut déclarée à l'Espagne. Mais Carnot avait beaucoup appris. Il avait monté et manié les rouages d'une armée, il s'était intéressé à toutes les armes et à tous les services, il avait été initié par Lacuée à l'administration militaire, il avait étudié les possibilités de lever des hommes, des chevaux, du ravitaillement et de fabriquer du matériel. Il avait même rédigé une « Instruction aux troupes composant l'armée des Pyrénées », malheureusement cette publication est aujourd'hui introuvable. Enfin Carnot avait découvert la région du Sud-Ouest, ses moyens militaires, mais aussi ses populations, son esprit public, son économie.

LA RAISON D'ÉTAT

ADRESSANT son rapport sur la mission aux Pyrénées à son ami d'Arras, Buissart, Carnot remarquait : « Je ne m'y suis pas borné à la partie militaire, j'ai un peu voyagé en moraliste et en administrateur[1]. » Carnot s'était intéressé à l'esprit public, aux hommes et à l'économie, ce qui nous informe sur ses idées dans ces divers domaines.

La remarque initiale que provoque son analyse de l'esprit public, c'est qu'elle ignore ce qui passionnait alors tous les esprits : le procès du roi.

Il déclarait que la « nouvelle révolution », celle du 10 août, avait réuni tous les esprits, que la Convention jouissait d'une « confiance sans bornes, que les [esprits] étaient parfaitement à la hauteur des circonstances », parfaitement républicanisés ; il vantait le patriotisme « sage » des Bordelais, l'esprit de sacrifice des populations, mais il ne disait rien des sentiments que suscitait le sort du roi.

Après ces déclarations et ce silence optimistes, Carnot abordait les grands problèmes politiques.

La critique était impitoyable : « Nous sommes obligés de dire que, presque partout, nous avons trouvé les pouvoirs constitués sans force, la hiérarchie des autorités totalement bouleversée,... les plus lâches passions se faire accueillir à force d'imposture, le mérite modeste exclu de toutes les places par l'impudence et les plus viles intrigues, le saint nom de Liberté servir aux violences et aux brigandages, l'hypocrisie du civisme écraser le civisme lui-même. »

Pourtant Carnot et ses collègues n'avaient suspendu que bien peu d'administrateurs, ils n'en avaient fait arrêter aucun. C'est que, pour eux, le mal tenait plus aux circonstances et aux institutions qu'aux hommes. Pour y remédier, il importait d'éduquer le peuple et de fortifier les autorités.

Le peuple, surtout dans le Béarn et le Pays Basque, avait

fait son admiration : « Il était républicain avant nous, il ne connaissait ni privilèges, ni seigneurs, ni droits féodaux, isolé par son langage particulier autant que par le site de son territoire, il a toujours conservé le type de la nature,... l'égalité naturelle. »

Ainsi, par les yeux de Rousseau, Carnot avait curieusement observé !

Mais ce peuple était « fanatisé »....

Carnot ne voulait lui arracher ni ses prêtres, ni ses églises, ni même ses cloches. Sa philosophie, dédaigneuse des superstitions et ennemie du fanatisme, comptait avec le temps et avec les passions humaines. Il apportait une rare discrétion dans ce domaine. Chargé d'assurer l'ordre public, quand il adressait un questionnaire à une administration, il s'informait de tout, hormis des questions religieuses. Il laissait faire, à la condition qu'il n'y ait ni violence, ni discorde, sinon, il s'en prenait aux prêtres réfractaires « fauteurs d'anarchie », et de soulèvements populaires. Le départ des violents et des religieuses l'enchantait, pourvu qu'on leur coupât le chemin du retour. Pour le reste, que chacun agît à sa guise et payât des ministres du culte, s'il en voulait, ce n'était pas affaire de gouvernement.

Pourtant, aux armées, c'était le gouvernement qui aurait dû s'occuper du culte, traditionnellement, au moyen des aumôniers militaires. Carnot n'aborda pas la question, il laissa Lacuée en entretenir Pache :

« Plusieurs des régiments que j'ai vus n'ont point d'aumôniers, d'autres en ont et ne savent comment les payer. Il serait nécessaire de déterminer la Convention à se prononcer. » En attendant, Lacuée proposait d'autoriser les soldats à se rendre aux offices paroissiaux, s'ils le souhaitaient, et ne voulait conserver que « quelques aumôniers » pour les armées en campagne. Quant aux « chapelles », on en prévoyait cinquante et une, mais il estimait que les seize qui existaient, de Bayonne à Perpignan, étaient plus que suffisantes [2].

Moins tranchant que Lacuée, Carnot ne voulait rien brusquer, mais tolérer, pour supplanter, le jour où on aurait suffisamment agi sur les populations. C'est dire le rôle fondamental qu'il attribuait à l'éducation nationale.

Prolongeant le travail qu'il avait amorcé au Comité d'Instruction publique de la Législative — et ses réflexions plus anciennes sur le pouvoir de l'habitude et de l'éducation —, il insistait sur la nécessité d'organiser promptement des institutions où se développerait la vertu, ressort des républiques.

Certes, il n'énonçait pas les réformes à accomplir, mais il précisait les risques que l'on courait en les ajournant. Visiblement, certaines conséquences de la Révolution l'inquiétaient, et tous les abus qu'il condamnait lui paraissaient venir du manque d'éducation. Il prévoyait même un risque mortel : l'échec de la Révolution, ruinée par la Terreur. « Une génération nous suit, écrivait-il, dont l'éducation est abandonnée depuis trois ans ; pour peu qu'elle tarde encore, elle ne sera plus en état de jouir de la liberté. Déjà, de nouveaux préjugés semblent prendre la place de ceux qu'on a détruits, on voit des citoyens de bonne foi... considérer l'intolérance et la dureté comme le caractère distinctif d'un vrai républicain, qui s'étudient à devenir farouches, et instruisent leurs enfants à ne juger du degré de patriotisme des autres citoyens que par celui de la terreur qu'ils inspirent ».

Cet idéal spartiate répugnait à Carnot : s'engager dans une telle voie conduirait à transformer la nation française en « une horde de sauvages ». Pourquoi ne pas cultiver les vertus qui étaient le charme et l'honneur de la vieille tradition, celle qu'il avait tant aimé chez les Basques : la piété filiale, le goût de la simplicité, le sentiment de la bienveillance et le respect pour les mœurs ? On y joindrait certes l'amour ardent de la patrie, « amour ardent mais éclairé ».

On saisit là tout ce qui séparait Carnot de Saint-Just, par exemple, cette sagesse, cette mesure, et l'attachement d'un homme de quarante ans au passé. L'un et l'autre voulaient la justice et l'honnêteté, la régénération de la nation, mais non pas par les mêmes moyens, ni avec la même tension. L'un et l'autre avaient le même mépris pour les profiteurs de la Révolution, les hypocrites et les bureaucrates. Carnot, s'il qualifiait d'absurde le projet de partage des biens, la « loi agraire », souhaitait pourtant porter « sur tous les points de la République une distribution égale de la force et de la richesse communes ». Mais, surtout, il soupirait après l'ordre : « Il est temps que l'ordre renaisse. »

Le plus urgent était de remédier à l'indépendance et à la rivalité des pouvoirs politiques qui avaient vicié la constitution de 1791. Le pouvoir serait puissamment concentré et n'aurait pour frein que la collégialité et la brièveté des mandats. Le gouvernement serait entre les mains de comités, les ministères seraient supprimés, selon le vœu de Bourdon de l'Oise. De plus, dans les communes, les municipalités inefficaces seraient groupées par cantons en municipalités cantonales, comme le préconisaient Condorcet et Gensonné.

Ces propos furent associés à une action pratique qui montre aussi le souci de faire aboutir la Révolution. Le principal ressort se trouvait dans les clubs, chez les amis de la Constitution — ou plutôt de la Liberté et de l'Égalité, — puisqu'il n'y avait plus de constitution. Carnot, naguère hostile à ces clubs, avait commencé d'y fréquenter lors de ses premières missions. Cette fois il y prit la parole, il s'y fit inscrire comme membre, il les utilisa comme « moyens de persuasion, toujours si puissants chez une nation libre ». Mieux encore, avec les autres commissaires, il en créa là où ils n'existaient pas. C'est là un aspect de son activité que l'on a d'ordinaire négligé. D'autre part, le rapport s'intéressait aux questions économiques et financières, qui exerçaient une si puissante action sur l'opinion publique.

Carnot s'indignait que l'État fût si mauvais débiteur, qu'il s'acquittât si mal des pensions dues aux meilleurs défenseurs de la Révolution. Il s'élevait contre la répartition « inégale et arbitraire des contributions », alors qu'il eût fallu exonérer le pauvre qui n'avait que « le nécessaire le plus resserré pour exister avec sa famille », et frapper le superflu. Il était patriote et démocrate à cet égard.

Il souhaitait le développement des ports, des canaux et des routes, artères du commerce et de la civilisation, parce qu'ils formaient les liens entre les diverses populations ; ils permettaient d'éveiller la solidarité, l'intérêt pour les affaires générales de la République, d'unifier les langages et les mœurs, et de diffuser l'instruction.

Grâce à l'ordre, à la bonne monnaie, aux communications, la prospérité renaîtrait, et avec elle s'accroîtrait l'attachement des populations au régime. Des ressources nouvelles pourraient être créées par l'État pour employer les démobilisés lorsque la guerre serait terminée, par exemple le reboisement des montagnes et le défrichement des landes.

Carnot rêvait même de rationaliser la vie économique, sous la direction d'un état-major de techniciens et de savants : « Il faudrait qu'un état annuel de la France fût rédigé par des savants et des artistes [ce qui signifiait alors des techniciens] qui seraient envoyés partout, sur les lieux mêmes, pour faire des expériences, discuter et approfondir chacun des objets ; que cet état contînt, dans un ordre méthodique, tout ce que ces savants ou artistes auraient pu recueillir sur l'état de la population, sur l'agriculture, les mines, les manufactures, les communications, la production, le commerce et généralement sur tout ce qui est du ressort de l'économie politique ; en y joignant les observations, réflexions et projets qui seraient jugés par eux pouvoir contribuer à la plus grande prospérité de l'État. Ces tableaux, dont les Anglais connaissent l'importance depuis si longtemps, devraient être présentés chaque année, à époque fixe, au Corps législatif, et c'est là qu'il trouverait les bases mathématiques (sic) sans lesquelles il est impossible de parvenir jamais à un système raisonné d'administration. »

Ainsi le point de vue de l'homme d'État, exigeant une puissante autorité, exactement informée, et résolue à trancher les problèmes concrets, l'emportait sur le souci du moraliste et du théoricien. La mission aux Pyrénées apportait donc beaucoup plus que celles qui l'avaient précédée, beaucoup plus que ne fournirent les commissaires envoyés à Perpignan, beaucoup plus que la Convention n'avait demandé. Carnot avait établi l'ossature d'une armée, il avait rassemblé un matériel documentaire abondant, varié, choisi. Il avait enfin proposé des principes et des méthodes pour accomplir la Révolution, en redresser les abus, en garantir la durée. Son rapport était une manière de discours-ministre, de candidature à de plus hautes fonctions.

Toutefois les chances de Carnot dépendaient de sa politique. Il était alors fort lié avec les Girondins, allait-il se fixer dans leur camp ? Quelle attitude comptait-il observer lors des votes qui devaient conclure le procès du roi ?

**

Lorsque Carnot reparut à la Convention, les discussions sur Louis XVI étaient closes, il s'agissait d'en tirer les conclusions. Ce fut l'objet des votes fameux [3].

« Louis Capet est-il coupable de conspiration contre la Nation et d'attentats contre la sûreté générale de l'État ? » L'Assemblée répondit affirmativement presque à l'unanimité. Carnot, Lamarque et Garrau s'associèrent à ce verdict. Quand il fallut fixer la peine, les divisions reparurent, les passions se heurtèrent. La Gironde avait proposé un referendum ; Carnot, Lamarque, Garrau, Ducos s'y refusèrent. Aux modérés, qui se plaignaient de délibérer sous les poi-

gnards, Garrau et Lamarque ripostèrent violemment :
« Voilà comme parlaient les Ramond, les Vaublanc, les
Dumas, lorsqu'ils voulaient faire transporter l'Assemblée
législative à Rouen », s'écria le premier. « Je viens de parcourir beaucoup de départements, ajouta le second, j'ai vu
des audacieux dire que la Convention délibère le couteau sous
la gorge,... je l'ai lu dans les journaux,... et j'ai vu des hommes
honnêtes qui le croyaient de bonne foi. Arrivés à Paris,
nous avons observé que jamais il n'avait été dans un état
de calme plus parfait. » Carnot n'intervint pas. Il s'associait
par son silence aux déclarations de ses compagnons.

L'appel nominal commença par les députés des départements que les commissaires venaient de parcourir : Haute-
Garonne, Gers, Gironde. La plupart de ces députés, Vergniaud, Guadet, Gensonné, Ducos, votèrent la mort. Les
anciens commissaires furent appelés à leur tour. Garrau et
Lamarque motivèrent leur arrêt de mort par le délit et par
le code, l'égalité voulait que le roi fût frappé comme tout
autre coupable. Ce fut aussi l'opinion d'un ami de Carnot,
le Bourguignon Guyton-Morveau.

Carnot s'expliqua brièvement :

« Dans mon opinion la justice veut que Louis meure, et
la politique le veut également. Jamais, je l'avoue, devoir
ne pesa davantage sur mon cœur, que celui qui m'est imposé,
mais je pense que pour prouver votre attachement aux lois
de l'égalité, pour prouver que les ambitieux ne vous effraient
point, vous devez frapper de mort le tyran. Je vote pour la
mort. »

A côté des principes et de la justice, intervenaient donc
dans la décision de Carnot la politique, les circonstances,
la raison d'État, le salut public, tout ce qui préoccupait les
Montagnards [4].

Dès lors et à jamais Carnot était régicide. Au cours des
trente années qu'il vécut encore, il revint à diverses reprises
sur ce point, ses biographes après lui, et les historiens ont
prolongé le débat passionné que soulevèrent les régicides.

D'abord, en 1798, Carnot fugitif se justifia en évoquant
le procès du roi, du grief qu'on lui faisait d'avoir protégé
les rois et les empereurs : « J'ai voté la mort d'un roi »,
répliqua-t-il [5]. Seize ans plus tard, au milieu des conflits
de la Restauration, Carnot rejeta sur les émigrés la responsabilité de la mort de Louis XVI : leurs trahisons avaient
dressé contre le roi la nation tout entière.

C'était, dans les deux cas, déclaration de polémiste.

Vint le dernier exil. Dans la solitude, Carnot méditait, écrivait et documentait ses biographes, notamment Körte. Il ne leur dit rien sur le régicide, mais il le commenta dans des notes intimes. A plusieurs reprises, il en fit la justification au nom du patriotisme, parce que le roi avait fait appel à l'étranger ; les événements récents donnaient une résonance nouvelle à cet argument : « Il y a des devoirs inflexibles en politique comme en révolution, et le premier de tous, c'est de ne jamais livrer son pays aux étrangers, lors même qu'ils s'offrent pour appuyer avec leurs armées le système qu'on regarde le meilleur [6]. »

Carnot évoquait aussi la thèse du contrat entre le monarque et la nation, que rajeunissaient les discussions sur la Charte.

Rien de tout cela n'était neuf ni original, Carnot ne s'en tint pas à ces banalités. Il évoqua les passions, les forces respectives : « La France s'est trouvée partagée en patricides et régicides. Tant que ces derniers ont été les plus forts, ils ont tué leurs adversaires ; quand les patricides sont devenus les plus forts, ils ont tué les régicides. »

Cette pensée sacrifiait un peu à la littérature, Carnot lui donna plus de vigueur : « Les choses en étaient venues au point qu'il fallait nécessairement que le roi pérît, ou la Convention, et il serait absurde de recevoir le coup quand on peut le faire tomber sur son ennemi. » Dans ce raccourci à la Tacite, le moraliste s'efface, le politique est implacable et ramène tout à une situation. Ce trait lui parut-il insoutenable ? Il l'atténua par une adjonction, « que le roi pérît ou la Convention et la France avec elle [7] ».

Après ces mots, peu importent tant de déclarations publiques ou inédites, qui brodent sur le thème et montrent en Carnot le complexe du régicide. Un seul point est curieux : jamais Carnot n'a invoqué la volonté des soldats. C'est Reubell qui écrivit : « Les soldats qui nous environnent ne conçoivent pas comment le tyran, au nom duquel on les égorge tous les jours, peut encore exister [8]. »

⁎⁎

Plongé dans les luttes parlementaires, mêlé aux mouvements parisiens, ressaisi par les questions urgentes, Carnot voulut tout à la fois tirer les conclusions de sa mission aux

Pyrénées et travailler à résoudre les problèmes qui commandaient l'avenir. Sa pensée se durcit, sa volonté tendue lui fit oublier les charmes du Pays Basque et les projets lointains d'action post-révolutionnaire. Peu à peu il fut dominé par la nécessité d'assurer le salut de la Révolution, le salut public, et il devint l'homme de la raison d'État. N'est-ce pas elle qui lui avait dicté l'arrêt de mort contre Louis XVI ?

Au Comité de Défense générale, ébauche incertaine et récente d'un Comité de Salut public, Carnot fit admettre diverses décisions pour régler les affaires pyrénéennes; il les défendit parfois à la Convention — crédits pour les fortifications, discussions sur la guerre éventuelle avec l'Espagne. Il veilla aussi à l'avenir du Génie, faisant accroître le nombre des élèves à l'École de Mézières. Il reçut enfin diverses missions secondaires concernant la défense des colonies, l'examen des plans de campagne du général Dillon, l'évaluation des renforts nécessaires aux troupes de Belgique [9].

Soudain, le 19 février, il émit une proposition révolutionnaire. On discutait alors les modalités du recrutement militaire. Carnot proposa le vote d'une décision radicale : « Tous les citoyens âgés de vingt à vingt-cinq ans sont tenus de partir pour les frontières [10]. » C'était l'aboutissement d'une pensée qui se dessinait depuis longtemps chez lui, et qui correspondait au principe qu'il formula quelques semaines plus tard : « Tout citoyen est né soldat. »

Cet axiome appartient au projet de « déclaration des droits des citoyens » que Carnot soumit à l'Assemblée [11]. Le premier article en exprime tout l'esprit : « Le salut du peuple est la suprême loi. » Carnot en tirait une série de droits de la société sur le citoyen : service militaire, financier, économique. La société pouvait aussi imposer « un mode d'éducation nationale ». En échange, elle devait « répandre le plus uniformément possible le bonheur et les jouissances ». Cette subordination de la personne à la collectivité était tempérée par le droit, bien théorique, pour chacun « de se rendre indépendant de toute la société », et aussi par celui « de vie et de mort sur lui-même [12] ».

Sans doute les conflits entre le citoyen et la société devaient-ils s'effacer pour faire place à un appui, à un amour mutuels. Les lois, l'éducation, l'habitude réaliseraient cette transformation, sinon pour la génération présente, du moins pour les autres, car la Révolution travaille au « bonheur des générations qui nous suivent ». Mais présentement, pendant la lutte révolutionnaire, il fallait affirmer et faire entrer dans la réalité ce mot d'ordre : « Les droits de la cité vont avant ceux du citoyen. »

Cette règle inflexible, Carnot allait l'appliquer tour à tour en politique extérieure et en politique intérieure, avec une énergie de plus en plus farouche.

**

Coup sur coup, du 14 février au 8 mars, Carnot fit décréter l'annexion à la République française des territoires de la principauté de Monaco, de la plus grande partie de la Belgique et de quelques communes aux confins de la Lorraine et de la Sarre.

C'était une étape décisive de la politique extérieure de la Révolution, tous les historiens en ont souligné l'importance. Elle n'est pas moins capitale dans l'évolution de la pensée et dans la carrière de Carnot, mais elle n'a guère été retenue à cet égard. Pourquoi Carnot fut-il le rapporteur du Comité diplomatique ? Pourquoi et comment justifia-t-il les annexions ?

Le Comité diplomatique était constitué en majorité de Girondins. Ceux-ci, menés par Brissot, préconisaient depuis des mois une politique de propagande ; ils avaient une conception universaliste de la Révolution, qui devait être non seulement française, mais européenne et mondiale, et ils n'étaient pas éloignés de penser qu'elle n'aboutirait vraiment en France qu'en s'imposant au reste du monde. Il leur semblait, d'ailleurs, que les peuples n'attendaient qu'un signe pour se soulever. Déjà un citoyen du monde, le Prussien Cloots, voulait annexer l'univers à la France, selon une loi d' « attraction universelle vers le centre de la gravitation politique » ; la France ne serait plus la France, mais le foyer de cette future organisation mondiale : la République universelle.

En vertu de cette politique, la Convention avait décrété, le 19 novembre 1792, « qu'elle accorderait fraternité et secours à tous les peuples qui voudront recouvrer leur liberté ». On ne sait pourquoi certains historiens, Sorel notamment, ont refusé à ce décret plus de valeur « qu'un pompeux incident de séance » ; il fut au contraire le principe de décisions ultérieures.

Restait à préciser si cette fraternité et ce secours aboutiraient à la République universelle, par coagulation des territoires, libérés et annexés à la France, ou par création de républiques nouvelles et alliées. Politique d'annexions ou politique d'États satellites ?

Les Girondins n'étaient pas fixés sur ce point, ni d'accord entre eux, pas plus qu'ils ne l'étaient en politique intérieure.

Les Montagnards n'avaient pas beaucoup plus de cohésion ni de doctrine. Le tumultueux Chabot, capucin défroqué mais toujours prédicant, avait déclaré, dès le 28 septembre 1792, que « les limites de la France étaient déjà posées », que les annexions feraient entrer des contre-révolutionnaires dans la République, qu'il fallait laisser les pays libérés se gouverner à leur guise, quitte à passer avec eux des traités d'alliance, les acheminant ainsi vers une fédération universelle. Chabot n'était pas le seul Montagnard qui préférât les frontières naturelles, Bréard, Marat, Robespierre lui-même partageaient cette opinion. Les *Révolutions de Paris* voulaient aussi les limites naturelles, fleuves et montagnes, Rhin, Alpes et Pyrénées ; elles voulaient arrêter la marche conquérante et libératrice de nos troupes, et susciter l'imitation spontanée de la France par l'étranger envieux de connaître notre bonheur. « Qui fait les révolutions ? Ce n'est pas la force des armées, c'est l'opinion. » Quant à Marat, tantôt il voulait s'en tenir aux annexions fournissant un supplément de forces à la République, ainsi le 3 février, tantôt il prêchait la « croisade », ainsi le 5 mars.

Qu'on n'aille pas croire qu'il s'agissait là de querelles d'école ! Le sujet du débat était précis : la Savoie, à propos de laquelle s'affrontaient la politique d'annexions et celle des frontières naturelles, celle de la propagande et de l'idéologie, celle de la sécurité politique et militaire et de la sagesse. Les Girondins étaient plus révolutionnaires, les Montagnards plus réalistes, dans la mesure où l'on peut lier les diverses politiques extérieures à ces partis fluctuants [13].

Une troisième politique s'affirmait avec plus de discrétion : celle du financement de la guerre. Clavière l'avait envisagée, toujours à propos des opérations en Savoie et à Nice. « Il faut parler des finances, écrivait-il à Montesquiou en octobre 1792. Nous serions bien maladroits si nous négligions les avantages de notre position pour leur faire quelque bien. » Son projet était d'exiger des emprunts à l'étranger sous la pression des armes : « Nous avons près de Gênes une armée qui doit le convaincre que nous n'avons pas envie de perdre

notre solvabilité. » Ainsi, contrairement à ce que l'on a prétendu, les besoins du Trésor n'exigeaient pas la politique
d'annexions, il suffisait d'imposer des contributions de guerre,
Custine n'y manqua pas en novembre.

On a beaucoup insisté sur le décret du 15 décembre, pris
à la demande de Cambon et dont le projet avait été présenté
aux Comités de la Guerre et des Finances réunis, le 9 et le
13 décembre. « Nous nous battons pour la liberté commune,
avait affirmé Cambon, il faut donc partager les frais ». En
conséquence, il voulait introduire les assignats comme
numéraire dans les pays conquis, et frapper la noblesse, le
clergé et les prêtres. Les membres du Comité firent remarquer
qu'on risquait de perdre ainsi l'amitié des peuples libérés.
Cambon riposta qu'on épargnerait le peuple aux dépens des
privilégiés, et que la Belgique, où se trouvaient des partis
hostiles à la Révolution, méritait moins de douceur que
tout autre pays [14].

On se garda bien, à la tribune, de se montrer aussi explicite ; le décret donnait des directives aux généraux dont les
troupes occupaient des territoires étrangers, il ne prononçait
pas l'annexion mais bien la « municipalisation ». Ces pays
pourraient être appelés à se donner une constitution, celle-ci
devrait être républicaine, Danton s'était déjà expliqué sur
ce point le 29 septembre. Mais on se heurtait à Dumouriez
qui voulait faire de la Belgique un fief qui assurât son pouvoir personnel, si bien que l'annexion pouvait être le moyen
de tenir Dumouriez.

Ce fut à propos de la Savoie qu'il fallut arrêter une politique. Déjà les Savoisiens avaient formé une assemblée pour
réclamer leur rattachement à la France. Le Comité de constitution et le Comité diplomatique réunis furent chargés de
présenter un rapport. Celui-ci fournit les données nécessaires
pour comprendre les propositions de Carnot. Ce fut Grégoire,
le fameux abbé Grégoire, qui le présenta, le 27 novembre.

Avant tout il faut noter que Grégoire balayait, comme
une « chimère », le projet de la République universelle : les
peuples n'étaient pas mûrs pour la liberté ; la diversité des
langues, des mœurs, des idées, des climats, s'opposait à
l'unité, enfin il fallait tenir compte de l'histoire et de la
géographie. On pourrait puiser dans ce discours tous les
éléments d'une réponse à cette question célèbre : « Qu'est-ce
qu'une nation ? » Grégoire faisait intervenir les « barrières
naturelles » et se préoccupait aussi bien des exigences mili

taires — « raccourcir notre ligne de défense » — que des exigences financières — disposer de biens nationaux, de mines et de ressources nombreuses.

La politique de la République française devait être dominée par le principe de la souveraineté nationale : l'annexion ne saurait être envisagée que sur le désir des intéressés. C'était la politique du plébiscite.

Après quoi intervenait l'intérêt respectif des deux partis : celui de la France et celui du pays qui demandait l'annexion. Grégoire en fit l'application à la Savoie et prouva que les trois conditions étaient remplies : la Savoie voulait l'annexion, la France et la Savoie y trouveraient chacune leur avantage.

Le problème savoyard se reproduisait dans toutes les contrées où nos armes triomphaient, où nos agents favorisaient la révolution : en Belgique, à Nice, dans l'évêché de Bâle. Les villes belges demandaient leur annexion, Cambon se plaignit, le 31 janvier 1793, de la lenteur du Comité diplomatique. Lasource fit l'application stricte, à Nice, de la méthode créée par Grégoire, l'annexion fut décrétée le jour même. Danton fit un grand discours en faveur des frontières naturelles, en faveur de la révolution dans les pays conquis, en faveur de l'annexion de la Belgique. Mais, avant de décider cette dernière mesure, l'Assemblée voulut entendre le rapport du Comité diplomatique, fondé sur une consultation effective et légale des populations belges ; ce rapport fut confié à Carnot.

En attendant la Convention fut saisie du cas de l'ancien évêché de Bâle, où Carnot s'était rendu après le 10 août, et où s'était établie une république, dite de Rauracie. Un ami bourguignon de Carnot, Guyton-Morveau, présenta le rapport. Il proposait l'annexion en s'appuyant lui aussi sur le précédent posé par Grégoire.

C'était le 10 février 1793. Quatre jours plus tard Carnot présentait à son tour un rapport et un décret d'annexion, mais il dépassait et renouvelait les arguments de Grégoire. Après en avoir rappelé les trois points fondamentaux, il les complétait par d'autres, auxquels il donnait une importance à la fois toute nouvelle et durable. Pour le mieux comprendre, résumons les idées de Carnot en politique extérieure, telles qu'il les avait lui-même antérieurement présentées.

La question des annexions avait été abordée et résolue

négativement par Carnot depuis longtemps. D'abord en ce qui concerne le principe : dès l'Ancien Régime, Carnot avait préconisé une politique pacifique, le territoire français ne devait pas être accru, il correspondait aux intérêts comme aux droits de la France. Carnot ne pouvait pas être indifférent à l'autorité de Vauban : « La France a des bornes naturelles, avait écrit le maréchal, au-delà desquelles il semble que le bon sens ne permette pas de porter sa pensée. Tout ce qu'elle a entrepris au-delà des deux mers, du Rhin, des Alpes et des Pyrénées lui a toujours mal réussi. » Telle était l'opinion des ingénieurs militaires.

En ce qui touchait à l'application pratique, Carnot n'avait pas été moins net. Lors de sa mission à l'armée du Rhin, il avait affirmé aux Suisses la bonne volonté de la France, et il avait recommandé à l'Assemblée de ne rien faire qui pût compromettre la neutralité helvétique. Non qu'il répudiât la propagande, mais il la jugeait bonne à favoriser les mouvements spontanés d'un peuple mûr pour la liberté. Tel n'était pas le cas des Suisses, à son avis.

Le compte rendu de la mission aux Pyrénées fournit une étape de l'évolution. Les commissaires voulaient porter la propagande sur les rives de l'Èbre. Était-ce pour annexer toute une partie du territoire espagnol ?

Carnot et ses collègues se montraient résolus à « respecter le gouvernement et l'indépendance des autres nations ». Toutefois — et c'était tout le problème de la coexistence, en Europe, d'un État révolutionnaire parmi des États conservateurs — ils se demandaient si la Convention voudrait traiter avec un roi, et surtout avec un Bourbon. Enfin ils signalaient les inconvénients stratégiques du tracé de la frontière, et les inconvénients économiques du régime commercial. C'étaient là deux défauts qui exigeaient réparation, par la diplomatie ou par la guerre.

Ainsi la pensée politique de Carnot manifestait le souci des exigences militaires, ce qui ne saurait surprendre, et aussi celui des exigences économiques, ce qui est plus remarquable. Mais il n'est pas douteux que les Pyrénées, moyennant quelques retouches, fourniraient la démarcation entre la France et l'Espagne.

Était-ce fidélité aux anciennes frontières, aux frontières naturelles de la France ? Était-ce parce que les Espagnols n'étaient pas « mûrs » pour la République ? Le rapport de Carnot fournit la réponse et s'éclaire par tous les précédents, celui de Grégoire et celui de Carnot lui-même.

Si Carnot présenta le projet, c'est parce qu'il en avait été chargé par le Comité de la Défense générale. Il est curieux qu'on ne s'en soit pas avisé jusqu'alors, sans doute parce que Carnot a parlé au nom du Comité diplomatique. Mais c'est bien le Comité de Défense générale qui lui avait confié, le 25 janvier, la responsabilité de préparer un rapport général sur « les réunions et incorporations au territoire de la République ».

Ce Comité comptait trois autres membres appartenant au Comité diplomatique, il est douteux qu'ils eussent parlé le langage de Carnot.

Dans la suite, le rapport fut transféré au Comité diplomatique. En effet, il s'agissait des principes directeurs de la politique étrangère plutôt que des mesures pratiques concernant la défense générale. D'ailleurs les anciens Comités étaient jaloux de défendre leurs attributions. C'est donc au Comité diplomatique que le rapport de Carnot fut présenté le 13 février, avant d'être lu à la Convention [15].

Le 24 février, Carnot présenta son premier rapport, le seul où il abordât les principes. Il le fit avec une méthode stricte qui l'amena à examiner et résoudre tour à tour les problèmes.

La base était le droit des peuples à disposer d'eux-mêmes, droit déjà affirmé, mais que Carnot précisait dans une véritable déclaration des droits des nations, couronnant les droits de l'homme et du citoyen. C'est là un rapport aussi remarquable par sa nouveauté que par sa fermeté. Trois droits étaient définis : l'indépendance, la sûreté au-dehors, l'unité au-dedans. La sûreté au-dehors peut admettre des conséquences opposées au droit des peuples à disposer d'eux-mêmes et à l'indépendance qui en découle. Carnot, loin de vouloir le dissimuler, en faisait l'application à la France. Il établissait donc sur le plan des principes ce que Sieyès avait envisagé sur le plan des opportunités : l'intérêt de la France à se rattacher des territoires étrangers. Pour Sieyès l'absence de cet intérêt entraînait le refus de rattachement, pour Carnot la réciproque elle-même s'appliquait : l'intérêt de la France pouvait commander le rattachement, même si les intéressés n'y consentaient pas : « Il serait odieux qu'une nation eût l'intention de blesser les intérêts des autres *sans une nécessité indispensable pour elle-même.* » C'était le retour offensif de la raison d'État aux dépens des principes, Carnot le proclamait avec brutalité : « Toute mesure politique est légitime dès qu'elle est commandée par le salut de l'État. »

Pour la première fois, Carnot assumait les responsabilités des décisions suprêmes, il le faisait avec un réalisme inattendu, annonciateur de son action au Comité de Salut public.

Ainsi l'État, la nation, se posait comme une fin en soi, et qui menaçait la notion même de république universelle. Carnot n'en disconvenait nullement, il reléguait celle-ci au rang d'un idéal souhaitable, mais dont la « possibilité » ne lui était nullement démontrée. Pour y atteindre, le mieux était de réaliser, dans le cadre naturel de la France, des conditions de vie telles que les autres peuples voulussent les imiter. Il reprenait ainsi un thème montagnard.

Ce qui souligne cette orientation plus montagnarde, c'est la condamnation formelle de la sécession, de l'indépendance, en faveur d'une partie quelconque du territoire français. Carnot condamnait nommément la « fédération », sous la forme que lui donnaient alors les Girondins. C'est probablement pourquoi il ne voyait pas de solution intermédiaire entre l'annexion et l'indépendance.

Enfin il déclarait que chaque nation était seule juge des exigences nécessaires à sa vie, au salut de l'État.

Ce que ces déclarations, apport personnel de Carnot, auraient pu avoir d'inquiétant, de conquérant et d'impérialiste, il l'atténuait en se ralliant à la théorie des frontières naturelles : « Les limites anciennes et naturelles de la France sont le Rhin, les Alpes et les Pyrénées. »

Naturelles, elles étaient imprescriptibles, comme les droits de l'homme. Anciennes, elles pouvaient être niées par le droit des peuples à disposer d'eux-mêmes. A plusieurs reprises Carnot récusait le droit historique, argument des despotes, non des peuples libres.

C'était donc dans le cadre géographique du Rhin, des Alpes et des Pyrénées que le salut de l'État pouvait faire jouer l'annexion imposée de force. Il eût été intéressant de préciser si le Rhin devait former la frontière tout au long de son cours, ou dans quelle section, et si les Alpes et les Pyrénées devaient être annexées jusqu'à une hypothétique ligne de partage des eaux. Carnot n'en dit rien à cette époque. Mais il laissait deviner ses intentions quand il énonçait l'idéal d'un État « massif », pourvu de « barrières formidables », arrondi et facile à défendre. De plus Carnot ne pouvait ignorer que le ministre des Affaires étrangères avait confié au Comité de la Guerre, le 18 décembre 1792, que le Conseil exécutif se proposait de borner le territoire français au Rhin [16].

Déjà Grégoire avait esquissé ces conditions, mais elles figuraient antérieurement dans la tradition des ingénieurs militaires, dans Vauban et dans Maigret. Carnot, donc, était depuis longtemps familiarisé avec ces données que la guerre rendait plus actuelles. Pour lui, la frontière naturelle était la frontière stratégique.

Ces impératifs n'ont pourtant pas commandé les décisions. Ainsi le Comité diplomatique avait été saisi de vœux émanant des Flandres, du Hénaut et du pays de Liège, belle occasion pour annexer au nom du salut de l'État. Carnot s'y refusa. En effet, les fortifications dressées sur la frontière du Nord assuraient la sécurité de la France, Carnot l'avait souvent déclaré. En conséquence, le salut de l'État ne jouait pas nécessairement ici, il admettait également l'annexion ou l'indépendance de la zone conquise, entre l'ancienne frontière et le Rhin. La décision dépendait donc de la volonté des peuples.

Pour connaître cette volonté, Carnot avait dépouillé les dossiers renfermant les demandes de réunions, il les avait jugées presque toutes « dénuées de formes légales ». Seules les demandes de la principauté de Monaco et de divers territoires voisins du département de la Moselle constituaient un vœu « libre et formel », seules elles étaient retenues, les autres étaient ajournées.

C'est donc sur ces territoires que Carnot fit porter les premiers projets de décrets. Les attendus rappellent exactement le précédent par Grégoire et ne méritent pas d'être rappelés. L'annexion fut votée sans discussion. Carnot avait fait prévaloir ses vues, il avait mis l'accent sur la raison d'État et lui avait subordonné la volonté des peuples ; exactement à l'inverse du rapport de Grégoire.

Les demandes belges rejetées furent transmises de nouveau quelques jours plus tard, Carnot présenta les décrets d'annexion au début de mars. On pouvait attendre quelques précisions sur les avantages et les inconvénients d'une frontière située au-delà des lignes fortifiées et en deçà des limites naturelles. Carnot éluda délibérément le problème.

« Je n'examinerai point quels peuvent être les intérêts

respectifs des deux peuples.... Dans ce moment un seul doit nous fixer, la gloire nationale, l'engagement que nous avons pris d'aider et de conquérir tous les peuples qui veulent conquérir leur liberté. »

La contradiction était flagrante : le 14 février Carnot avait déclaré que l'engagement pris obligeait la France à secourir les peuples, non à les rattacher. Toutefois, à propos du Hainaut, Carnot parla de la « proximité et de la facilité des secours », de « l'étendue et de la population d'un vaste département » et de « ressources... immenses ». De plus, il s'agissait toujours de territoires situés à l'intérieur des frontières naturelles, et de territoires riches.

Ce dernier mot laisse apparaître un mobile que nous avons entrevu : les besoins financiers. Carnot n'en ignorait rien et le salut de l'État pouvait jouer ici. Aussi bien était-on toujours en deçà du Rhin et pouvait-on espérer que les armées françaises sauraient conquérir les frontières naturelles. C'était bien ce qu'avait laissé entendre Carnot le 14 février. Et si quelques localités se refusaient à devenir françaises, tant pis pour elles : « Que les réclamations partielles se taisent devant les grands intérêts de la République ! » C'est ce qui explique l'étrangeté de l'annexion fragmentaire de villes et de provinces dispersées. Marat ne cachait pas que c'était le bon moyen d'exercer une pression irrésistible sur les régions intermédiaires.

En fait, la guerre nous fit perdre aussitôt la Belgique et menaça le nord de la France. Il n'en restait pas moins que la voie était tracée avec beaucoup de fermeté : conquête des frontières naturelles, avec l'assentiment de la majorité de la population, refus d'annexions au-delà, mais secours et alliance aux peuples libres. La République universelle s'estompait devant la raison d'État, l'idéologue le cédait, chez Carnot, à l'homme de gouvernement. L'ami des Brissotins préférait Danton et apportait aux vues de celui-ci l'autorité du militaire.

Or les circonstances allaient appeler Carnot à la frontière.

CHAPITRE III

L'INVASION ET LA TRAHISON

« L A LIBERTÉ qui s'assoupit dans les succès se relève à la voix du danger, et son réveil est un triomphe. Les victoires de cette campagne répareront bientôt le léger échec que nous venons d'essuyer. Vainqueurs de l'Argonne, retournez devant les satellites de l'Autriche et de la Prusse, ils sont accoutumés à fuir devant vous ; et vous, jeunesse bouillante qui n'avait pas encore porté les armes, soyez sensibles aux chants de la gloire, courez à votre poste ; il est à Liège, il est partout où la République est attaquée. Citoyens, le peuple souffre de cette lutte prolongée entre la liberté et le despotisme, entre des armées et une nation. Le destin du despotisme est fixé : il doit périr. Eh bien, hâtez son heure dernière, ne faites la paix qu'avec les peuples libres et sans rois, et préparez la paix universelle [1]. »

Ainsi parlait Carnot, le 9 mars 1793. Le « léger échec » était la perte de la Belgique, l'invasion menaçante, ramenant avec elle la fermentation parisienne et l'atmosphère terrible de septembre ! Pour sauver la Révolution, et la Convention avec elle, Danton avait fait décider la levée de trois cent mille hommes et l'envoi de commissaires dans les départements. Carnot avait été chargé de rédiger un appel et de préparer un décret fixant les attributions des commissaires.

Nous avons entendu cet appel. Loin d'avouer le danger, il sacrifiait à l'emphase et à la forfanterie coutumières, il faisait briller la gloire et l'approche de la paix dans un monde libre et sans rois. L'amour de la gloire et la volonté de renverser tous les rois conduiraient-ils à la paix ? Peu importait alors, pourvu que les jeunes vinssent aux armées.

Quant aux attributions des commissaires, elles étaient si étendues que la levée d'hommes serait exigée, même si la jeunesse n'était pas « bouillante ».

Lorsqu'on élut les commissaires, Carnot fut choisi pour le

Pas-de-Calais et le Nord, en compagnie de Lesage-Senault, député du Nord, assez falot pour n'être qu'un second.

Par une progression fortuite mais efficace, Carnot avait été amené à connaître successivement les volontaires à Soissons, l'armée républicaine sur le Rhin, les problèmes de recrutement et d'organisation aux Pyrénées ; il retrouva le tout dans une région qui lui était familière, le Nord, et il y rencontra l'ennemi victorieux.

Il avait observé à Paris la violence des passions partisanes, il avait assisté aux débats concernant le tribunal révolutionnaire, qui fut créé, et le gouvernement révolutionnaire, qui fut ajourné. Une guerre à mort était engagée contre les réactionnaires, Carnot allait s'y consacrer.

Le 12 mars, Carnot roulait sur la route d'Arras en compagnie de son collègue. Le 14, ils étaient à Bapaume. Le district et la municipalité y travaillaient justement à lever des hommes. Une réunion se tenait, au milieu d'un mécontentement orageux. Les commissaires ne purent ramener le calme, et le bruit courut que leur vie avait été en danger.

La situation était inextricable, car la Convention demandait le contingent pour les trois cent mille hommes, et les commissaires envoyés en Belgique exigeaient le départ du dixième des citoyens en état de porter les armes, soit le triple, et « quelquefois jusqu'au sextuple », de la première demande. Les contre-révolutionnaires attisaient le mécontentement, les hommes ne partaient pas aux armées, les esprits s'échauffaient. La levée des trois cent mille hommes était pour la Révolution une épreuve dangereuse qui en changea le cours ; Carnot le comprit et il contribua à cette transformation.

Il tenta de maintenir les deux levées, en tenant compte des soldats déjà fournis, et en attribuant un caractère tout provisoire aux demandes des commissaires en Belgique. La confusion fut profonde, coupée de violences et de refus, elle aboutit assez généralement à la désignation, par le scrutin, de volontaires récalcitrants et inutilisables. Il fallut interdire le scrutin et renforcer l'action des commissaires départementaux.

Alors le conflit s'élargit, opposant les démocrates aux libéraux, les Montagnards aux Girondins, et le peuple aux notables. Comme à Paris la gauche menaçait de faire une nouvelle révolution. Il y avait là des démocrates, des Robespierristes, Darthé, Thérouanne, Lebas, prompts aux mesures extrêmes, prêts à dénoncer les commissaires de la Convention, et hostiles à la plus grande partie des administrations locales.

Le 12 mars, Thérouanne avait tenu une réunion à Hesdin. L'effervescence fut telle qu'il fit mander Darthé, l'un des administrateurs du département. Celui-ci stigmatisa les « motions insidieuses suscitées par des contre-révolution- naires et des agitateurs ». Aussitôt les cris fusèrent : « A bas ! A bas ! » On réclamait l'arrestation de Darthé, on injuriait des citoyens qui « s'étaient déclarés démocrates », on criait : « Pas de contingent », on menaçait un officier muni- cipal qui notait les noms des manifestants.

L'affaire fut transmise à Carnot et à Lesage-Senault. Ils firent emprisonner les délinquants. Aussitôt éclatèrent des contre-manifestations, des « fanatiques » voulurent assom- mer les administrateurs d'Hazebroucq, il fallut faire donner la troupe. Pour la première fois, Carnot se montra impla- cable. On le vit partout où des troubles étaient signalés, dis- tribuant des piques — ces fameuses piques[2] —, propageant le patriotisme et la crainte. Il fit envoyer au tribunal révo- lutionnaire tous les prévenus de conspiration, même l'ancien maire de Calais, que soutenait pourtant le Conventionnel Merlin de Douai, et qui fut exécuté. Ainsi Carnot pourvoyait l'échafaud. Était-ce parce que Darthé le surveillait[3] ? Non pas : il jugeait la terreur indispensable. Il l'a proclamé dans une lettre dont l'essentiel est demeuré jusqu'à présent inconnu.

« Quiconque a suivi la marche de la Révolution doit être bien convaincu qu'il n'y a point de paix sincère à attendre de nos ennemis, moins encore de ceux du dedans que de ceux du dehors, *qu'il faut les pulvériser ou être écrasé par eux*, que toute mollesse est fatale, que toute temporisation perd la chose publique, et que, si des considérations particulières, et même de justice distributive *(sic)*, font perdre un instant de vue la justice suprême, *le salut de l'État*, il n'y a plus d'espoir d'échapper à la fureur des conjurés. »

C'est l'alternative présentée à propos de la mort du roi : pulvériser ou être écrasé. L'explication de la terreur, le secret de l'action de Carnot tiennent à cette situation. Il fit donc traquer les suspects et poursuivre les ennemis.

En revanche il était humain lorsqu'il demandait que l'on secourût les familles des soldats et des volontaires, et que

l'on payât exactement les ouvriers qui travaillaient pour la
défense nationale : « Chaque instant est un siècle pour ceux
qui souffrent. » Mais c'était aussi une nécessité politique :
« Tout est perdu si les promesses des représentants de la
nation sont illusoires, si leur parole n'est pas sacrée, s'ils
ajournent la reconnaissance de la patrie lorsqu'ils exigent en
son nom des services actuels [4]. »

Survint la défaite, le 18 mars, à Neerwinden. Dumouriez
avait résolu de jouer sa carrière et le destin de la République
sur une bataille ; il avait perdu. Il décida de passer à l'ennemi
en entraînant son armée. Carnot, et les collègues de Belgique
qui l'avaient rejoint, se rendirent compte que la situation
devenait catastrophique : l'armée était en déroute et son
général menaçait de trahir, « le pillage, la désertion, la
cohue étaient à leur comble », des troubles éclataient partout, et les contre-révolutionnaires ne dissimulaient pas leur
joie.

Au bout de quelques jours il ne s'agissait plus que de
savoir s'il était préférable d'arrêter le général immédiatement, ou s'il valait mieux reprendre en main, d'abord, les
troupes et les administrations. Carnot préférait le second
procédé. Il décidait « dans le calme des mesures fortes »,
réclamant des généraux qui ne fussent ni traîtres, ni imbéciles — « j'ai peur que ce ne soit là le plus difficile » — et se
reposant sur les places pour sauver la situation militaire, « la
frontière est inexpugnable ».

Le danger — en dépit des apparences — n'était pas là,
mais bien dans la trahison, à l'intérieur. Pour le conjurer,
l'accord des patriotes était indispensable, pour « écraser les
égorgeurs et les intrigants », en prenant des « mesures terribles contre les ennemis du dedans [5] ».

Voilà donc comment Carnot en venait à la terreur, lui qui,
aux Pyrénées, réprouvait la dureté et redoutait la marche vers
la barbarie. « Il faut pulvériser ou être écrasé... », l'implacable dilemme s'imposait. Carnot et Lesage-Senault se rendirent à Arras pour y procéder aux épurations nécessaires.

Il se trouva que cette décision sauva Carnot.

En effet, le 30 mars, la Convention avait confié le soin à
quatre commissaires — dont Carnot — de se rendre au
quartier général de Dumouriez pour le suspendre, et avec lui
tous ceux qui paraîtraient suspects. Les commissaires — et
le ministre de la Guerre — rencontrèrent Dumouriez, qui les
fit arrêter et livrer à l'ennemi. Carnot, prévenu trop tard,

n'était pas avec eux, il organisa la riposte, encore que Dumouriez eût donné l'ordre à un officier de s'emparer de lui.

L'instant était angoissant : Dumouriez allait-il entraîner son armée dans la trahison ? Allait-il marcher sur Paris en compagnie des Autrichiens ? Rien n'était prêt pour les arrêter. Carnot le comprit et il agit en conséquence.

Dumouriez lança une proclamation pour entraîner ses hommes au nom de la France et au nom de l'obéissance, « tous les braves soldats se souviendront que l'armée est essentiellement obéissante ».

Carnot évoqua la fidélité à la Révolution, il circula à travers toute la région, montrant aux troupes la félonie du général en chef.

Le flottement fut très marqué chez les chefs et chez les hommes. Les premiers étaient pour la plupart des officiers d'Ancien Régime, des ci-devant. Ils avaient subi la Révolution sans l'appuyer, beaucoup étaient âgés et dépassés par les événements.

Quant aux hommes, on leur avait naguère donné Dumouriez comme un sauveur. Ils l'avaient cru, certains le croyaient encore, beaucoup ne croyaient plus à rien, surtout dans les troupes de ligne. On estimait que les deux tiers d'entre eux préféraient « la constitution et le roi de 1789 » à la République.

On vit un général, Tricotel, naguère appuyé par Carnot, placarder l'appel de Dumouriez, puis écrire au ministre de la Guerre ces lignes déconcertantes : « Les commissaires... ont trouvé fort mauvais que j'avais fait afficher ces dites proclamations, que je me mettais dans le cas d'être suspendu,... s'il y a du mal, général ministre, je l'ignore.... »

Un commandant de place informait les commissaires qu'il recevait des ordres de Dumouriez : « Je suis dans une position bien critique », s'écriait le pauvre homme.

A Lille des soldats murmuraient contre les commissaires ; au camp de Maulde, l'hésitation fut grande. D'autant que Cobourg avait accordé un armistice et que les Autrichiens se tenaient dans l'ombre.

Quant à la population, elle était en partie acquise à Dumouriez comme le prouvait l'attitude du journal conservateur *La Gazette du Département du Nord*.

Carnot put évoquer sa mission à l'armée du Rhin ; en dépit des changements, c'étaient toujours la même option et le même risque d'incompréhension. Il fit preuve d'adresse,

fournissant, malgré les moqueries, des vivres aux soldats
du camp de Maulde qui, appartenant à la vieille armée,
se tournaient vers Dumouriez. Il fit preuve d'énergie,
cassant de nombreux administrateurs, accordant à leurs
remplaçants des pouvoirs discrétionnaires — mais dont
l'exercice était contrôlé jour par jour —, réclamant le zèle
et la vigilance des sociétés populaires. Sans parler des
mesures militaires pour renforcer les places. Carnot fut tel,
en ces jours, qu'il força l'estime de Ronsin : il agissait en
révolutionnaire.

Quelques maladresses de son adversaire favorisèrent le
succès. Ainsi Dumouriez voulut-il transporter le trésor de
l'armée chez l'ennemi, alors « nous avons clairement aperçu
que nous étions vendus », écrivit un chef de corps. Cobourg
jugea bon de lancer une proclamation pour appuyer Dumouriez, il obtint un résultat tout opposé.

Ainsi Carnot incarnait déjà le patriotisme et, revêtu de sa
seule autorité, en présence d'un général entouré de son armée,
il l'avait emporté. C'est ce qu'exposait un autre Conventionnel, Duhem : « Nous trouvâmes à Lille Carnot et Lesage-
Senault qui avaient puissamment concouru, quoique sans
pouvoir *ad hoc*, à déjouer l'infâme Dumouriez[6]. »

Les commissaires à l'armée du Nord furent fréquemment
remplacés : ceux du 30 mars avaient été livrés à l'ennemi,
ceux du 4 avril furent en partie renouvelés le 8, puis le
12 avril. Enfin le 30 avril une réorganisation générale provoquait de nouvelles mutations. Au milieu de ces fluctuations,
Carnot restait. Bientôt il devint le collaborateur habituel de
Duquesnoy.

Ce personnage devait tenir un rôle assez important dans la
carrière de Carnot. Ce n'était pas un second, actif, déférent,
amical, à la façon de Prieur, de Garrau, de Lesage-Senault.
Il était rude et singulier. Il avait vécu dans le Pas-de-Calais,
tour à tour cultivateur et avocat, député à la Législative et
à la Convention, proche de Carnot par ses fonctions, éloigné
par son caractère et par ses opinions plus radicales. On le vit
en mission, vêtu en paysan, alors que ses collègues portaient
les insignes de leurs fonctions. On le trouva parfois ivre
mort. Le 25 mai il demandait son rappel parce que ses connaissances étaient inférieures à son zèle, mais il resta.
Quelques jours plus tard il fut en désaccord avec son collègue.

Les Girondins venaient d'être expulsés de la Convention,
le 31 mai, tous les hommes en place devaient se rallier à la

Montagne triomphante et ratifier cette journée décisive.
Carnot se serait montré réticent et aurait refusé de signer
l'adhésion enthousiaste rédigée par Duquesnoy. Du moins
c'est ce qu'a écrit son fils, s'appuyant sur une lettre — aujour-
d'hui disparue — de Carnot, et sur une note dont la sub-
stance se trouve dans la biographie de Körte. Or cette note
fut écrite après thermidor, dans un esprit de polémique, et ne
paraît pas avoir été l'œuvre de Carnot [7]. Le seul fait significatif — jusqu'alors négligé — c'est que la circulaire du
ministre de la Guerre, Bouchotte, faisant l'apologie du 31 mai,
et dénonçant comme fauteurs de guerre civile ceux qui critiquaient cette journée, ne fut pas publiée à l'armée du
Nord [8]. Deux mille exemplaires y avaient été envoyés,
Custine s'opposa à leur distribution. Les représentants en
mission, Duquesnoy lui-même, s'inclinèrent. L'eussent-ils
fait si Carnot avait été d'avis opposé ?

Ce dissentiment entre Duquesnoy et Carnot laissa des
traces. Il fut aggravé par le refus de Carnot de suspendre ou
de faire arrêter certains généraux, comme O'Moran, que
Duquesnoy fit incarcérer en l'absence de Carnot, le 6 août.

Les commissaires du pouvoir exécutif n'obtinrent pas
davantage les destitutions massives qu'ils réclamaient, leurs
relations avec les représentants en mission étaient tendues :
« Il est certaines opérations de MM. *(sic)* les députés qui
sont presque inconnues de tout le monde, surtout quand il
s'agit de personnes qu'ils soutiennent contre les autorités. »
A ces insinuations des commissaires, les députés ripostaient,
par la plume de Levasseur, que « la plupart de ces agents
étaient des hommes à tête exaltée, animés de passions
haineuses, ne voyant partout que complots, que conspirations [9] ». N'étaient-ce pas là « les égorgeurs et les intrigants » naguère flétris par Carnot ?

Toutefois celui-ci ne se mêla guère aux débats qui divi-
sèrent ces deux catégories de commissaires, mais il se plaignit des hommes de l'exécutif : « Ils n'ont été que nuisibles ;
sans eux, l'opération [les levées d'hommes] se serait faite par
les administrations elles-mêmes et serait achevée maintenant. »
Carnot dut pourtant reconnaître que les administrations
manquaient de zèle et de compétence.

Finalement les résultats des levées furent médiocres.
Carnot répétait les plaintes de Lacuée : les hommes ne
veulent « s'assujettir à aucune discipline, ils sont le fléau de
leurs hôtes et désolent les campagnes, dispersés dans les

cantonnements où ils ne font que boire et courir,... ils sont toujours nus,... il en est qui vendent jusqu'à leurs habits, leurs fusils, leur pain et leur bois... ».

Le manque de qualité tenait en partie à la pratique qui permettait aux recrues les plus aisées d'acheter un remplaçant. Carnot s'indignait de « ce trafic d'hommes... établi dans le pays qui a proclamé les droits de l'homme ». Au nom de la raison d'État il réclamait instamment l'obligation du service personnel.

Il s'élevait aussi contre la licence qui régnait dans le camp : « Un fléau terrible détruit nos armées : c'est le troupeau de femmes et de filles qui sont à leur suite ; il faut compter qu'il y en a autant que de soldats.... Elles énervent les troupes et détruisent, par les maladies qu'elles y apportent, dix fois plus de monde que les ennemis. » Un décret fut pris pour chasser les « catins », mais sans grand résultat.

Carnot intervint aussi dans l'habillement, l'équipement, la comptabilité et surtout les vivres. Ce dernier point était absolument capital. Carnot agit en conséquence et recourut à des procédés d'exception, véritables procédés de terreur. Des commissaires des guerres furent lancés dans les campagnes, accompagnés d'un préposé aux fourrages et appuyés par des troupes. « La force armée va se mettre en campagne, écrivait Carnot le 1er août, on va faire des visites domiciliaires partout. » L'effet fut immédiat : « Dix hussards ont produit en vingt-quatre heures plus que toutes les réquisitions depuis trois mois. »

L'esprit critique n'abdiquait pas devant les passions déchaînées. Carnot traquait les conspirations qui lui étaient dénoncées, mais démentait « les contes... ridicules » qui prophétisaient une subversion universelle, ainsi à Saint-Omer aux premiers jours d'août 1793 [10].

Mais pour vaincre la trahison et refouler l'invasion, il fallait aussi mener rigoureusement les opérations. Ce fut pendant cette mission à l'armée du Nord que Carnot fit ses débuts comme stratège, d'avril à août 1793.

CHAPITRE IV

DÉBUTS STRATÉGIQUES

L<small>E 31 MARS</small> les commissaires avaient fait observer à Dumouriez que la façon dont il paraissait ordonner sa retraite laisserait un vide découvrant dangereusement Lille, ils lui demandaient de protéger la ville en établissant un camp. Ce fut la première incursion de Carnot — et de ses collègues — dans la conduite des opérations. Ils n'avaient aucune qualité pour en user de la sorte, mais l'attitude plus qu'équivoque du général les justifiait pleinement : le lendemain la trahison était consommée. Alors Carnot prit sur lui d'intervenir dans le commandement, d'autant plus que le successeur de Dumouriez, le général Dampierre, était timoré et craignait que le premier échec ne lui coûtât la vie.

Les débuts stratégiques du futur organisateur de la victoire eurent lieu presque exactement dans la situation qu'il avait imaginée à plusieurs reprises : la France assaillie, les troupes entamées dans leurs qualités militaires. Le salut se trouvait alors dans les places fortes, c'est pourquoi, dès la nouvelle de la trahison de Dumouriez, Carnot avait prescrit aux généraux de rallier les troupes sous le canon des forteresses. Puis il avait entrepris de porter au maximum la puissance de résistance de ces places.

Il redevint ingénieur, inspecta Douai, Bouchain, Lille, Bergues, Dunkerque ; il renforça surtout la « véritable barrière », la « ligne cent fois inexpugnable formée par Gravelines, Calais, Saint-Omer, Aire, Saint-Venant et Béthune ».

Étrange inspection, sans cesse coupée par les problèmes politiques, parfois interrompue par une pointe ennemie, ou déviée par l'urgence de se porter sur un point menacé.

Chemin faisant Carnot galvanisait la défense, s'assurait que les garnisons étaient prêtes, que les officiers du Génie occupaient leurs postes ; parfois, il les déplaçait pour les mieux utiliser. Car ces officiers étaient en nombre très insuffisant, bien que le ministre ait organisé un recrutement hâtif du Génie.

Carnot ne pouvait pourtant ni entrer dans le détail, ni prolonger cette inspection. Il demanda au ministre d'envoyer un technicien, à titre de commissaire du pouvoir exécutif, Carnot-Feulint. La nomination fut prononcée, le 6 mai 1793 [1]. Feulint rencontra Lazare à Dunkerque, puis se mit à la tâche. Dans l'ensemble, il jugeait la défensive solidement assurée, en dépit du manque de fonds, de la rareté des officiers du Génie et de la médiocrité de quelques places, comme Arras et Cambrai. A cette occasion il établit un questionnaire-type et proposa au ministre de l'envoyer dans toutes les places de la République [2]. Ce qui fut fait [3]. Feulint fut félicité par le ministre pour ses « talents militaires » et son « patriotisme ».

Lazare partageait l'optimisme de son frère, il estimait que Valenciennes en particulier était « dans le meilleur état de défense possible »; ailleurs on effectua quelques travaux, « pas toujours ceux qu'avaient projetés les deux frères [4] ».

Par bonheur, les ennemis perdaient leur temps en contestations. A la conférence d'Anvers, les 7 et 8 avril, ils s'étaient disputé les gains probables d'une future victoire. Ils avaient décidé de porter tout leur effort sur les places fortes et de s'emparer de Condé, Valenciennes, Le Quesnoy, Lille, qui formeraient éventuellement une « barrière » opposée à la France. L'Angleterre refusait de se battre pour le roi de Prusse et pour l'empereur, elle exigeait Dunkerque. Les forces adverses s'étaient donc étalées en « cordon » et allaient diviser leurs efforts. Elles n'étaient pas encore complètement rassemblées et ne combinaient guère leurs mouvements. En somme, la politique l'emportait sur la stratégie, la lenteur de l'action militaire sauva l'armée du Nord et la Révolution [5].

Les coalisés étaient d'autant plus assurés de leur victoire, et par suite peu empressés à déclencher la lutte, que leurs services d'espionnage avaient souligné la faiblesse des Français. L'armée du Nord, d'après leurs renseignements, ne s'élevait pas à plus de trente-cinq mille hommes, desquels on pouvait défalquer, tant ils étaient médiocres, deux mille à trois mille hommes de nouvelle levée, environ douze mille hommes d'infanterie de ligne qui ne tenaient pas au régime, le dissentiment entre les volontaires et la ligne ayant été aggravé par les premiers efforts pour les amalgamer. De plus, leur disait-on, les bataillons de volontaires étaient incomplets, la plupart des généraux, et même des officiers, étaient hostiles à la Convention, Dampierre était un fol, sans talent, O'Moran manquait de convictions, La Morlière était cupide, et, si Favart et La Valette étaient révolutionnaires, le premier seul avait des connaissances, encore manquait-il de caractère. Enfin la cavalerie, peu nombreuse, manquait de chevaux, les places n'avaient guère de provisions, de munitions, de garnisons, leurs habitants préféraient capituler pour éviter la ruine [6].

Ces données étaient exactes dans l'ensemble, elles correspondaient à peu près aux rapports fournis au ministre Bouchotte, mais, le temps aidant, et aussi les efforts de Carnot, des renforts survinrent, l'armée fut reprise en main et les chances des alliés diminuèrent.

Les premiers mouvements de l'ennemi eurent lieu le 9 avril, le lendemain du jour où Carnot se félicitait de la rentrée de toute l'armée et de sa protection par les places de guerre. Dampierre parvint à contenir la pression adverse, il voulut même riposter en déclenchant une attaque, le 1er mai, pour dégager Condé, mais Carnot traversa ses desseins. Le 28 avril, il s'opposa au départ d'un escadron de cavalerie, le 29, il retint les trois mille hommes que réclamait Dampierre pour l'attaque qui devait avoir lieu le lendemain. Carnot déclara, le 30 avril, au Comité de Salut public, qu'il ne fallait pas livrer une bataille, qui pourrait devenir des plus funestes si on était vaincu. Dampierre fit pourtant sa sortie, qui échoua, sans que l'ennemi s'émût.

En effet, le 1er mai précisément, les armées coalisées avaient fixé leur plan d'opérations. Il s'agissait toujours de presser les sièges : dès la chute de Condé, ce serait le tour de Valenciennes. D'ici là, on recevrait renforts et matériel. Jusqu'alors Carnot avait paré au plus pressé, recourant aux solutions traditionnelles, les seules possibles dans une armée désorganisée par la trahison. Au début de mai, il proposa pour la première fois une opération offensive : « Il est honteux, écrivait-il, de rester sur la défensive lorsqu'on a dix mille hommes disponibles contre six mille. »

Ces chiffres indiquent assez le caractère très limité des projets, ce qui apparaît mieux encore dans les explications de Carnot : « faire diversion et forcer peut-être les ennemis d'abandonner le blocus de Condé ». L'offensive était destinée à renforcer la défense, la pensée restait celle d'un ingénieur [7].

L'opération pourtant reposait aussi sur une idée straté-gique : détruire Ostende, point de débarquement des forces britanniques. Pendant des années, Carnot s'attachera à ce plan comme au moyen d'affaiblir les liaisons entre coalisés et de renforcer la sécurité française. Pourtant il ne manquait pas d'autres ports, tel Anvers. L'entreprise fut d'abord réduite à son rôle de diversion ; elle pourrait s'arrêter à Furnes ou à Nieuport et serait réalisée par sept mille hommes, divisés en trois colonnes soutenues par une qua-trième qui tromperait l'ennemi en marchant sur Ypres. Plan compliqué qui morcelait les effectifs.

Les généraux objectèrent l'arrivée des renforts ennemis sur les points visés — ce qui était exact [8] — et parvinrent à ajourner l'expédition.

Sur ces entrefaites, l'ennemi attaqua le 23 mai, il fit reculer les Français et ouvrit le siège de Valenciennes. D'autre part, le Comité de Salut public prescrivait aux commissaires de ne pas intervenir dans les opérations. Enfin Custine était nommé général en chef de l'armée du Nord. La venue du « général Moustache » était un événe-ment, car ce chef avait du caractère et du prestige. « Il doublera notre espoir », écrivait-on. Mais s'entendrait-il avec Carnot ?

En dépit de ces changements, Carnot s'intéressa de plus en plus à la stratégie. Le 26 mai, il faisait la critique de la journée du 23 et adressait ses conclusions au Comité de Salut public, recommandant de suivre sur la carte : « L'enne-mi doit périr là, si nos affaires sont bien conduites.... » « Au lieu d'agir sur les flancs et les derrières de l'ennemi, nous lui résistons toujours de front ; c'est le moyen d'être perpé-tuellement battu. Qu'on laisse donc l'ennemi s'engouffrer, qu'on porte toutes les forces disponibles aux camps de Lille et de Maubeuge, et qu'une belle nuit on tombe avec furie sur Mons et Tournai, au même instant, et l'on verra bientôt l'ennemi, manquant de magasins et de communications, demander grâce à genoux. »

Ce plan n'était ni très neuf, ni très ample. Il ne liait pas les opérations des diverses armées. Toutefois, il avait le mérite de commencer le groupement des forces, de recourir à l'at-taque violente et d'être d'une réalisation relativement aisée. La pensée stratégique de Carnot évoluait [9].

Pour passer à la réalisation, Carnot saisit le moment où

le général Lamarche quittait le commandement et où Custine n'était pas encore en fonctions. Il décida le général O'Moran à marcher sur Furnes dans la nuit du 30 au 31 mai. Il ne s'agissait que d'un « coup de main pour essayer nos soldats », Carnot déclarait : « Nous ne comptons point rester à Furnes, mais faire quelques prisonniers et prendre quelques pièces de canon. » La suite des faits et de la correspondance ne permettent pas d'accepter cette déclaration comme le fond de la pensée de Carnot.

L'affaire eut lieu dans la nuit du 30 au 31 mai. Environ trois mille hommes, deux cents cavaliers et dix-huit pièces de canon allaient converger, en deux colonnes, sur Furnes. Ces effectifs devaient avoir facilement raison des mille trois cents hommes qui gardaient Furnes. Pour leur couper la retraite, les deux colonnes encercleraient la place. A vrai dire, le détail de l'opération restait flottant — comme Custine le remarqua dans la suite — et le général O'Moran était un médiocre qui marchait à contresens.

Le 31 mai, Carnot rendit compte de l'opération. Exercice malaisé lorsque l'auteur du compte rendu est aussi l'auteur du projet, et que ce projet a échoué. Carnot s'en tira médiocrement.

Il rédigea d'abord un bulletin de victoire : Furnes « avait été enlevée de vive force », on avait pris neuf hommes, onze chevaux et les magasins, sans doute y avait-il eu « quelque pillage », mais les hommes auraient voulu continuer sur Nieuport.

Il fallut pourtant préciser les faits, les deux colonnes n'avaient pas coordonné leur action, la garnison ennemie s'était retirée, les troupes françaises avaient tout abandonné pour piller et saccager. En vain les généraux et les représentants avaient voulu rétablir l'ordre, « le soldat ivre n'entendait plus rien et le nombre des coupables était trop grand pour songer à une punition violente, qui était d'ailleurs inexécutable dans pareille circonstance ». Du moins c'était l'opinion de Carnot, au contraire O'Moran se plaignit à Custine que les représentants eussent arrêté les sanctions.

En revanche, l'ennemi jugea que l'alerte avait été chaude, il attachait la plus grande importance à Ostende, c'était même, a-t-on dit, une manière de superstition pour le ministre de la Guerre britannique, Dundas, mais le duc d'York s'y intéressait beaucoup moins [10]. L'affaire avait prouvé que, comme on le supposait, les troupes hollandaises manquaient de qualité [11]. Les Hollandais, de leur côté, étaient humiliés et furieux, on les avait chargés d'occuper ces postes peu auparavant, et ils se plaignaient d'avoir été exposés sans nécessité et sans être soutenus [12].

Au total, le résultat était dérisoire, il n'y avait plus guère de chance de surprendre Ostende, et l'attitude des troupes françaises inquiétait Carnot. L'inconduite des volontaires fut l'une des rares occasions qui lui fit perdre tout sang-froid. Lui, partisan d'une discipline raisonnée, faisant confiance aux hommes, il alla jusqu'à écrire au Comité de Salut public : « Votre *nouveau code pénal militaire ne suffit pas* ; *si tout soldat qui vole une épingle n'est pas fusillé sur-le-champ, vous ne ferez jamais rien.* » Lui qui plaçait au plus haut les qualités de ténacité, d'opiniâtreté dans l'adversité, il était déprimé au point de ne pouvoir « soutenir le spectacle de semblables désordres », et de demander son rappel à la Convention « le plus tôt possible ».

C'était son premier contact avec les violences des pillards, il l'empêchait d'apprécier pleinement l'élan de leur attaque, leur valeur dans le choc, leurs qualités pour une guerre révolutionnaire.

Il n'eut pas de repos que les soldats eussent été morigénés et désavoués par leurs chefs et leurs camarades. Il parvint même, fait inouï, à renvoyer à Furnes un plein convoi d'objets volés.

Pour l'avenir, il voulut réorganiser les tribunaux militaires, déclarant que « la discipline [faisait] la force des armées ». L'événement avait donc profondément modifié sa conception de la discipline, son idéalisme n'avait pas résisté au choc de la réalité. D'ailleurs les circonstances avaient changé, le danger était pressant.

En conséquence, Carnot publia un arrêté qui permettait aux commissaires d'organiser un tribunal et il demanda aux administrateurs du Pas-de-Calais de lui fournir une liste de vingt-cinq citoyens « dont ils connaîtront le civisme pur et désintéressé, les lumières, la capacité, l'intégrité et l'activité ».

Mais Custine allait-il se dessaisir de la discipline, dans sa propre armée, au profit des commissaires ?

Quant à l'échec et à sa portée stratégique, après les premiers bulletins victorieux, il fut commenté par Carnot en termes tels qu'on y trouve la preuve de desseins très différents d'un simple coup de main. Carnot-Feulint affirma que

l'échec était dû à l'absence de moyens pour faire un pont [13].
Son frère, à plusieurs reprises, déclara que le pillage seul
avait empêché de prendre Nieuport, Ostende et d'y brûler
les vaisseaux anglais.

Il ne renonçait pas à ce projet : dès le 1er juin, il tenait un
conseil de guerre pour reprendre l'affaire ; trois jours plus
tard, il en entretenait le général O'Moran, mais celui-ci se
retranchait derrière l'autorité de Custine. Le 10 juin, Carnot
proposait au Comité de Salut public la prise d'Ypres et
d'Ostende, « chose très facile », mais que les généraux refusaient d'entreprendre ; il renouvelait cette proposition le 16,
en ajoutant qu'il « pressait, en vain, le général O'Moran »,
et qu'il espérait que Custine serait plus entreprenant. Le 27
et le 30 juin, il dénonçait au Comité de Salut public « notre
bêtise », qui laisse les ennemis fortifier Ostende. Le 17 juillet,
il déplorait que les ennemis eussent mis Ostende « sur un
pied assez respectable » et que l'attaque fût devenue dangereuse, à moins d'y consacrer des forces considérables. Le
6 août enfin, appelé au Comité de Salut public pour fournir
des renseignements sur une situation soudain aggravée par
la chute de Valenciennes, il faisait adopter un projet d'offensive sur Ostende. Faut-il ajouter qu'en juillet 1794 Carnot
insistait encore sur l'importance de cette place ?

La preuve est donc aveuglante, Carnot tenait à cette
opération, il lui attribuait une vertu militaire irrésistible,
puisqu'il écrivait à Lesage-Senault, dans l'accablement provoqué par la nouvelle de la chute de Valenciennes : « Si l'on
eût marché sur Ostende quand je le voulais, l'état des
choses serait bien différent. »

Carnot en était donc resté aux conceptions stratégiques
traditionnelles, et ce furent ces conceptions qui le firent
appeler au Comité de Salut public.

Pourtant une allusion, le 27 juin, à propos de Custine,
montre que Carnot songeait à combiner les opérations sur
le Rhin avec celles du Nord. Mais ce n'était qu'une allusion.

En attendant, sur les deux points qui lui tenaient au cœur,
la discipline et la marche sur Ostende, il s'était heurté à
Custine.

Dès le 13 juin, Custine s'était opposé à l'intervention des
commissaires dans le domaine disciplinaire : « Je respecte
les commissaires de la Convention nationale, mais je sais,
s'ils veulent être sages et s'ils prennent un intérêt réel aux
succès de la République, où ils doivent borner leurs fonctions. »

Le surlendemain, il avait interdit une attaque prescrite par O'Moran, et pour laquelle Carnot avait maintenu un général dans un commandement. Enfin il n'approuvait pas l'opération d'Ostende.

Le conflit entre Custine et les commissaires, tant nationaux qu'exécutifs, fut marqué par la violence du caractère même de Custine. Le général en chef était dénoncé pour son incivisme, accusé de trahison et personnellement pris à partie par les hommes de Bouchotte qui distribuaient dans l'armée des journaux bafouant et menaçant Custine. Les commissaires nationaux n'approuvaient pas cette campagne qui ruinait l'autorité du général, certains d'entre eux firent même arrêter quelque temps des commissaires exécutifs. Mais ils critiquaient la stratégie de Custine, ce qui provoquait des éclats. Un témoin a évoqué « une crise violente qui eut lieu entre les représentants du peuple et Custine, au sujet de ses opérations militaires [14] ».

Le discrédit civique et militaire de Custine renforça la position de Carnot ; il lui permit d'insister sur ses projets d'offensive auprès du Comité de Salut public. Les nouveaux membres de ce Comité firent savoir, dès le 12 juillet, qu'ils allaient consacrer la plus grande attention à ce « système d'attaque ou de défense », alors qu'ils négligeaient des projets d'une tout autre envergure, mais dont tous les auteurs semblaient suspects [15]. De plus, Carnot se faisait remarquer par son optimisme, son sang-froid et sa singulière énergie, au milieu du désarroi angoissant.

D'abord, il continuait de déclarer la frontière inexpugnable grâce aux places fortes : « Laissez les ennemis s'épuiser devant Valenciennes qu'ils ne prendront pas », écrivait-il au Comité de Salut public, le 30 juillet. Quelques jours plus tard, la place étant tombée, Carnot — comme tous les ingénieurs — répéta qu'elle aurait pu « tenir au moins un an » et que la capitulation était « infâme ». Mais la situation ne lui paraissait toujours pas dangereuse : « On assure que le projet des ennemis est tout simplement d'enlever la première ligne de nos places de guerre. » C'était exact, nous l'avons vu. Comment Carnot le savait-il ? Un espion anglais affirmait, à la même époque : « Il est certain que, dans l'armée du prince de Cobourg, il y a des officiers généraux, et même dans son conseil, qui rendent compte de ses mouvements. On croit que ce sont des officiers hollandais qui correspondent avec le député Carnot qui rôde dans la Flandre maritime [16]. »

Quel crédit accorder à cet agent qui attribue à Carnot le rôle d'intermédiaire entre la Convention et Londres, pour y faire passer des documents dans l'entourage de Fox ? Il est possible que Carnot, bien placé, à portée de Dunkerque et de Calais où il avait des amis, ait eu à jouer ce rôle, quelques indices permettant de croire que Carnot recevait des informations secrètes [17].

Que l'information soit parvenue directement à Carnot ou par quelques intermédiaires, le général Chérin par exemple, il était vrai que l'ennemi concentrait ses efforts sur les places de guerre de première ligne, laissant ainsi aux Français le temps de se reprendre et de préparer la riposte.

Carnot s'y employa, en organisateur lucide, énergique et adroit, s'occupant des hommes, du matériel et des armes.

Pour les hommes, Carnot acheva de lever le contingent, mais il refusa de l'accroître, même provisoirement, ce qui eût risqué d'aggraver l'esprit public sans aider à la défense, car cette cohue de paysans, avec leurs fourches et leurs faux, conduirait à une « déroute effroyable, comme celles de Crécy et d'Azincourt ». Carnot était hostile au mythe de la levée en masse.

Pour le matériel, Carnot s'appliquait à empêcher le gaspillage des soldats et les abus de certains négociants ; il multipliait les démarches et les ordres pour la fabrication d'affûts.

Quant aux armes, Carnot réclamait toujours la fabrication de piques, non plus à défaut de fusils, mais pour arrêter la cavalerie ennemie, si active, si nombreuse, et d'autant plus redoutable que la cavalerie française était insuffisante.

Carnot demandait aussi, et réquisitionnait dans les arsenaux, des canons. Il s'intéressait spécialement à l'artillerie à cheval : une compagnie d'artillerie à cheval « vaut, selon nous, deux régiments de cavalerie ». Il en voulait cinq [18]. Carnot songeait aussi, avec ses amis Guyton et Buissart, à l'emploi tactique des ballons auxquels il s'était intéressé depuis longtemps, « mais c'est aux généraux à faire usage de toutes les ressources de leur art, on ne peut rien leur prescrire à ce sujet et il est à craindre qu'ils ne suivent encore longtemps leur routine ».

Au point de vue tactique, Carnot s'opposait à tout procédé inhumain. Il ajournait la mise en place des nappes d'eau destinées à couvrir les forteresses, tant que celles-ci n'étaient pas menacées ; ç'eût été ruiner les paysans et peut-

être provoquer des soulèvements. « Dans les siècles de barbarie, la férocité tenait lieu d'héroïsme ; dans le siècle de la
raison, l'humanité, la justice, la probité doivent toujours
accompagner le courage », tel était alors le vœu de Carnot,
exprimé par les officiers qui avaient flétri les désordres
survenus à Furnes.

Cet ensemble de propositions, et d'actes, explique l'appel
de Carnot au Grand Comité de Salut public pour y diriger
les opérations. Ce Comité ne souhaitait pas la guerre sauvage
que prônaient des Hébertistes : « Allez ! braves défenseurs,...
précipitez-vous sur ces esclaves féroces,... foulez aux pieds
leurs crânes sanglants [19]. » Il se défiait des convictions politiques de tant de stratèges novateurs, qui émirent des projets intéressants au cours de l'été 1793 et qui furent suspendus et arrêtés peu après. Mais le choix tint aussi à des questions de personne, Barère et Prieur de la Côte-d'Or furent
les auteurs immédiats d'un choix qui eut une immense
répercussion sur les destins de la France et sur la vie de
Carnot : ils le firent entrer dans l'Histoire.

CHAPITRE V

DÉBUTS AU COMITÉ DE SALUT PUBLIC

L A NÉCESSITÉ primordiale du rétablissement de l'ordre, de l'autorité, proclamée par Carnot depuis quelques mois, s'imposait à tous les esprits. Le Comité de Salut public avait été créé, et bientôt réorganisé, pour apporter la solution.

Il était spécialement indispensable d'assujettir les généraux, la trahison de Dumouriez l'avait prouvé avec éclat.

La victoire était exigée par le salut public, elle supposait le talent et le pouvoir, elle réclamait la coordination de l'action des armées. Il n'était pas question de créer un état-major général et encore moins de nommer un généralissime, qui auraient une existence indépendante de la Convention et du gouvernement. Donc il fallait faire entrer au Comité un technicien patriote, un stratège citoyen et même conventionnel.

Parmi les représentants en mission aux armées, Carnot s'était fait remarquer : ses idées militaires paraissaient intéressantes, son action était énergique, sa puissance de travail étonnait, enfin son civisme n'avait guère donné prise à la critique. Pourtant il semble que Prieur de la Côte-d'Or ait d'abord retenu l'attention. Peut-être même est-ce lui qui fit admettre Carnot au Comité lorsque, le 4 août, il y fut lui-même appelé par Barère[1].

Le seul fait incontestable, c'est que Carnot, appelé par le Comité pour lui fournir des renseignements, s'imposa d'emblée et fut aussitôt retenu : il avait reçu le 6 août la lettre l'appelant à Paris, dès le 7 il signait comme membre du Comité, le 11 il se chargeait de porter ses plans au général Houchard commandant l'armée du Nord, le 14 il se fixait à Paris. Ce même jour, Barère faisait régulariser cette cooptation en obtenant de la Convention l'élection de Prieur et de Carnot. Ces procédés étranges prouvaient la gravité de l'heure et l'urgence de l'action.

Le Comité de Salut public, le second par sa composition, a conservé un prestige redoutable, une grandeur farouche ; admiré par les hommes de la Révolution et leur lignée politique comme le sauveur de la France nouvelle, haï par les antirévolutionnaires comme une sanglante dictature, il n'a laissé personne indifférent : il fut le « Grand Comité ». Ce fut, tout ensemble, un gouvernement de guerre, galvanisant les énergies patriotiques, terrorisant les ennemis et les traîtres, mobilisant toutes les ressources nationales, comme il est souvent advenu depuis ; ce fut aussi une dictature révolutionnaire, s'appuyant sur une manière de parti unique — les Jacobins —, imposant son idéal et terrorisant les adversaires — réels ou supposés — du régime par la guillotine et la prison. La durée de ce gouvernement tenait au vote mensuel de la Convention, qui pouvait ainsi contrôler ou transformer l'organe qu'elle avait créé et qui restait son émanation : « Comité de Salut public de la Convention nationale. » D'autre part, la population parisienne : artisans des faubourgs, meneurs des « sections », journalistes et orateurs des Jacobins et des Cordeliers pouvait peser sur le Comité en le soutenant ou en le menaçant. Ce puissant Comité était à la merci d'une « journée », d'une disette, d'une défaite. Pour durer, il fallait obtenir non seulement la prorogation mensuelle du Comité par la Convention, mais l'appui des Jacobins qui tenaient une bonne partie de la France révolutionnaire, et sinon la faveur, du moins la neutralité des sections, des chefs les plus remuants de l'opinion extrême, les Hébert, les Jacques Roux, les Vincent et autres « enragés ». Or chacun de ces groupes avait sa politique sociale, économique, religieuse et même militaire. Résoudre les grands problèmes de l'heure sans heurter de front ces courants, telle était la servitude de ces puissants.

Le travail venait ensuite. Il embrassait toute la vie nationale, comme dans un régime où l'État est amené à pratiquer le dirigisme, sinon la planification, dans certains secteurs. Un personnel improvisé, nécessairement, et qui comportait à la fois des ratés et des profiteurs, des timorés et des exagérés, alourdissait encore cette accablante tâche. Les solutions prises par arrêtés, sauf quand il fallait un décret à la Convention, se heurtaient aux intérêts particuliers, à l'incompréhension, à la routine, parfois aux croyances, aux idéaux, voire à l'opposition royaliste, mais toujours masquée, sauf dans les vastes zones insurgées : dans l'Ouest, en Vendée, chez les Chouans, dans le Sud et le Sud-Est, à Toulon, à Lyon. Les membres du Comité connaissaient la situation. Ils fournirent un labeur acharné pour parvenir à la dominer. A vrai dire ce fut la continuation et l'intensification d'un effort commencé depuis longtemps. Ni le 10 juillet, quand le Comité avait été épuré pour assurer une majorité monta-gnarde, avec Hérault de Séchelles, Jeanbon-Saint-André, Couthon, Saint-Just et Prieur de la Marne, ni le 26 juillet, date de l'entrée de Robespierre au Comité, ni le 14 août, jour de l'élection de Carnot et de Prieur de la Côte-d'Or, ni même le 6 septembre, quand on reçut Billaud-Varenne et Collot d'Herbois, Hébertistes résolus, on ne créa pas une institution nouvelle, rompant avec le passé, faisant face à des nécessités imprévues. Il s'agissait de poursuivre la tâche du Comité de Défense générale, créé en janvier, dénommé Comité de Salut public en avril, et revêtu de pouvoirs accrus à mesure que les circonstances intérieures et extérieures exigeaient de plus en plus impérieusement une autorité incontestable, que peu eussent recherchée et que nul n'eût admise auparavant.

D'abord organe de surveillance et de contrôle, stimulant et menaçant, comité parlementaire informant la Convention et lui soumettant les actes de l'exécutif, le Comité de Salut public devenait peu à peu, et par saccades, un pouvoir d'exception, ce gouvernement de guerre et cet instrument de révolution sociale, qui prit enfin le titre équivoque de « gouvernement révolutionnaire ».

Cette transformation continue, cette création incessante, voilà le trait essentiel d'une organisation bâtarde exigée par les circonstances, voulue par les hommes en place, sollicitée par des groupes passionnés et rivaux, dont l'influence rela-tive variait au gré des événements internes et externes, des ressources, des craintes et des espérances.

La haine commune de la tyrannie monarchique, de la réaction politique, sociale, religieuse, la nécessité d'être vainqueurs pour sauver la situation et la vie des régicides et des hommes nouveaux de la Révolution, l'amour de la patrie jaloux de protéger la frontière et l'honneur natio-naux, l'idéal de liberté et d'égalité, ces sentiments ani-maient les membres du Comité et les unissaient profondé-ment aux conventionnels, aux fonctionnaires, aux clubistes, aux cadres innombrables de la France nouvelle. Mais les rivalités personnelles, les divergences politiques et sociales,

les conflits d'intérêts, un esprit de corps dans la bureaucratie et dans l'armée nouvelles, un esprit de clocher persistant malgré tout entamaient l'union des révolutionnaires à tous les degrés d'une mouvante hiérarchie.

L'existence des ministres, formant le Conseil exécutif provisoire, composé au gré de la Convention, mais soumis au Comité et influencé par la population parisienne ; la présence aussi de nombreux comités parlementaires, comme le Comité de la Guerre, le Comité diplomatique, et surtout le Comité de Sûreté générale, complètent le signalement de ce régime étrange et compliqué, qui postulait et redoutait tout ensemble la concentration des pouvoirs entre les mains de quelques hommes résolus.

Carnot entrait au Comité, dans ces conditions redoutables et attirantes, pour redresser la situation militaire. Il jouait sa réputation, sa carrière et sa vie. Il y devint le Grand Carnot.

***

Inévitablement, Carnot fut pourvu d'une autorité énorme et mal définie. Il partageait avec les autres membres les pouvoirs immenses et incertains du Comité, avec eux aussi il partageait les responsabilités et les risques, soumis comme eux aux remous de la Convention et de la rue il devait obtenir sa prorogation à la fin du mois d'août, il dépendait enfin de la victoire et de la défaite. Pour obtenir l'une et conjurer l'autre, il devait utiliser à la hâte et impérieusement des institutions, des chefs, des troupes, des ressources en matériel, transports et vivres, qui fonctionnaient mal et que l'on était en train de transformer radicalement.

Plus que jamais l'action de Carnot était désormais collégiale. Sans doute ses missions, au Rhin, aux Pyrénées, à l'armée du Nord, étaient déjà des tâches collectives, mais partout Carnot avait dominé ses collègues, il avait imposé, avec une aisance relative, ses vues et son autorité, sauf peut-être à Duquesnoy, qu'il allait encore rencontrer. Cette fois il devait compter avec de puissantes personnalités. Jusqu'alors il était relativement aisé de discerner dans les missions, dans les comités, dans les assemblées, ce qui était l'œuvre personnelle de Carnot ; désormais toutes les décisions étaient prises au nom du Comité, dans un acte impersonnel et qui portait plusieurs signatures. Est-il possible de discerner le rôle propre de Carnot ? Beaucoup ont tenté de le faire, dont les conclusions discordantes montrent les difficultés de la tâche et le jeu des passions. On s'en aperçut dès la chute de Robespierre, quand on rechercha les responsabilités.

En effet les assertions des intéressés furent presque toujours postérieures au 9 Thermidor, et dictées par un souci de légitime défense : il s'agissait de sauver sa vie en se désolidarisant de la politique générale du Comité, en rejetant les mesures impopulaires sur Robespierre, Couthon et Saint-Just, qui venaient d'être renversés et exécutés. Dans la suite le risque s'affaiblit, mais le discrédit des terroristes subsista longuement. Il ne saurait donc être question de prendre au pied de la lettre les déclarations tardives des membres du Grand Comité.

Pour départager les responsabilités, les contemporains voulurent faire état des signatures. Une farouche polémique s'engagea sur ce point, d'autant plus âprement que la guillotine pouvait sanctionner les conclusions. On ne s'étonne pas, dans de telles conditions, que les signataires aient récusé leurs signatures. Il était humain de voir les membres du Comité, traqués et honnis par ceux-là mêmes qui les craignaient, les flattaient et les imitaient naguère, minimiser la portée de leurs écrits.

Le meilleur plaidoyer fut celui de Carnot, prononcé le 23 mars 1795, et répété par tous ses amis et biographes : Beffroy de Reigny, l'ami des jours plaisants, naguère, à Arras, Körte, l'historiographe, dans l'amertume de l'exil en 1820, Tissot, en 1824, Hippolyte enfin, dans ces fameux *Mémoires sur Carnot* qui inspirèrent les travaux ultérieurs [2]. Selon Carnot ces signatures n'impliquaient ni participation à la décision, ni approbation de la mesure prise, ni même connaissance de cette mesure ; c'étaient de simples « vu », pas même un certifié conforme, en somme une « opération purement mécanique », du moins en ce qui concerne les signatures « en second ».

Seul le premier signataire, et souvent rédacteur de l'arrêté, engageait sa responsabilité dans les mesures qui relevaient de sa spécialité. Affirmant ainsi une stricte spécialisation des membres du Comité, Carnot rejetait tout l'odieux de la police générale sur le triumvirat déchu — Robespierre, Couthon, Saint-Just — et n'assumait que les responsabilités liées à la guerre.

Encore récusait-il certaines décisions militaires bien qu'ils les eussent signées, et parfois rédigées ; c'étaient celles que le Comité lui avait imposées, et qu'il n'avait minutées que « parce qu'elles étaient dans les attributions qui lui étaient confiées», mais il avait, disait-il, déposé à l'avance sur le bureau une protestation contre ces mesures.

Il exposait aussi que la multitude des décisions quotidiennes, exigeant quatre cents à cinq cents signatures, qu'il fallait donner à la hâte, au cours de longues séances de nuit, amenait à signer sans lire. C'est ainsi qu'il avait signé les décrets faisant régner la terreur à Orange et à Arras, prescrivant l'arrestation de son restaurateur, et même de ses employés.

Cet argument fut l'un des moyens de défense les plus usuels des anciens membres du Grand Comité, soit dans leur justification collective, soit dans leurs plaidoyers personnels. N'était-ce pas rigoureusement indispensable quand on retrouvait des arrêtés terroristes qui portaient leur signature et les mettaient en danger de mort ?

Ils sauvèrent ainsi leur vie, mais au cours d'âpres débats qui laissent échapper de brèves et vives lumières sur la valeur des signatures, c'est-à-dire sur la spécialisation ou l'action collective des membres du Comité.

Ainsi doit-on éliminer les signatures apposées sur les copies, une fois la décision prise ; ce sont là les certifiés conformes, les « vu », les « opérations mécaniques » ; comme l'ont fait remarquer les accusés, on trouve « sur les différentes expéditions d'un même arrêté, tantôt la signature des uns et tantôt celle des autres».

Reste la signature du texte original, de la minute. Écoutons le plaidoyer de Billaud-Varenne : « Quoique Carnot paraisse être celui qui le premier a apposé sa signature sur l'arrêté [créant la commission terroriste d'Orange], je pense que tu n'iras pas jusqu'à dire qu'il est son ouvrage ; car on sait que, dans un comité où l'on a quelquefois jusqu'à deux cents signatures à donner par jour, on ne peut répondre que de son travail personnel. » Nous reconnaissons l'argument, audacieusement appliqué à la signature en premier. Mais Billaud ajoute que la signature est donnée « de confiance», et il répète que c'est un acte de confiance ! D'autres, aussi bien des amis, comme Beffroy de Reigny, que des adversaires, comme Dubois-Crancé, et aussi Saladin, le rapporteur de la commission d'enquête, employèrent cette expression dangereuse de « confiance». C'est bien ce que signifie la décision inspirée par Carnot à ses collègues hostiles au triumvirat de « ne pas signer les arrêtés de police générale ». Pache, avec la pénétration que donne parfois la haine, tira la conclusion menaçante : « Carnot a dit, m'a-t-on appris, qu'il signait de confiance,... mais d'après qui signait-il de confiance ? »

Comment contester cette solidarité ? Carnot a reconnu que la signature faisait passer sous le regard des divers collègues le travail de chacun d'entre eux et l'exposait à une censure, et aussi que cette censure était rare pour éviter qu'elle ne fût réciproque : chacun approuvait les yeux fermés ce que proposaient les autres, afin d'obtenir l'approbation de ce qu'il proposait lui-même.

C'est si vrai que, pour rompre la solidarité, il suffisait de ne plus signer. Ainsi le voulut Carnot pour les actes du bureau de Police générale. Ainsi fit Robespierre pour les actes du bureau de la Guerre ; Billaud-Varenne, Collot d'Herbois, Barère le lui ont reproché, mais moins catégoriquement que Carnot : « Robespierre, a-t-il écrit, ne voulait point signer les ordres du Comité relatifs aux opérations militaires : il se ménageait ainsi la faculté de dire, en cas de revers, qu'il s'était opposé aux mesures prises. »

Le refus de signature prouve la signification de la signature. Ainsi en jugeait Robert Lindet, qui ne signa pas l'arrestation de Danton.

A plus forte raison la rédaction d'un arrêté par un membre engage-t-elle fortement sa responsabilité. Et si Carnot déclare que, chargé de la section de la Guerre, il rédigea et signa des mesures contre lesquelles il protestait, cela revient à dire qu'il faisait passer d'abord la solidarité du Comité. Ainsi pour la tactique appliquée en Vendée : « Il m'était pénible de marcher suivant l'autre système [la violence], mais l'opinion de la majorité m'en faisait une loi. » Comme l'écrivit le haineux Fréron : « On n'a point insisté sur les aveux précieux de Carnot.... Il fallait demander à Carnot quelle était cette majorité. »

Finalement les signatures guident l'étude des actes de ces membres du Comité. Signatures apposées à la fin d'un texte écrit de la même main, témoignage le plus puissant, signature unique authentifiant une minute dictée à un secrétaire, preuve aussi concluante, signature enfin, mêlée à d'autres — sans que nul aujourd'hui puisse discerner qui a signé « en premier » —, indice d'une participation à l'activité générale.

L'observation du nombre, de la nature des actes, aux diverses époques, signés dans ces conditions, est presque le seul moyen de reconnaître l'action et la pensée d'un membre du Grand Comité.

Or, comme l'avait déjà remarqué Pache, « il n'y a aucun membre dont il y ait plus de signatures sur les minutes d'arrêtés que Carnot [3] ».

**

Cette remarque suggère l'ampleur du rôle qu'il tint. Loin d'apparaître comme un spécialiste des questions militaires, « enseveli » dans son bureau, comme on a dit pour Lindet, il se présente comme l'un des plus actifs. « Je l'ai vu, ce Carnot, séant à la table ronde, prenant part à toutes les délibérations, y donnant son avis sur les choses et sur les personnes non seulement concernant la partie militaire, mais concernant tous les autres objets de politique interne et externe. Nul n'a été plus que lui assidu au Comité. Barère, Robespierre, Collot, Saint-Just et les autres arrivaient quelquefois en retard, parce qu'ils allaient au spectacle ou aux Jacobins ; Carnot, matin et soir, y arrivait toujours le premier, en sortait toujours le dernier [4]. »

Si l'on voulait contester ce témoignage de Pache, les relevés de présence des membres du Comité, d'après les procès-verbaux, d'après les pièces signées, d'après les tableaux dressés à l'époque en prouveraient l'exactitude. Mais pourquoi chercher si loin ? Carnot lui-même n'a-t-il pas déclaré publiquement, au moment où il était courageux et dangereux de le faire : « J'ai assisté à toutes les délibérations du Comité ; il est faux, comme on l'a avancé, que j'aie été relégué dans mon bureau [5] » ?

Pour saisir et suivre l'action de Carnot, il faut abandonner les généralités et parcourir successivement les étapes de cette année cruciale, l'an II, depuis l'entrée de Carnot au Grand Comité jusqu'à la chute de Robespierre, du 7 août 1793 au 27 juillet 1794.

**

Il n'est pas douteux que Carnot, aussi bien que Prieur, fut appelé pour s'occuper de la direction de la Guerre et que ce fut d'abord sa tâche. Dans quelle mesure avait-il les mains libres ? Quelle était son autorité ?

Dès l'origine le Comité de Salut public avait comporté un « bureau chargé des questions militaires », certains membres s'en occupaient spécialement. Saint-Just depuis le 30 mai 1793 avait été amené à diriger le bureau, dans la suite, il avait pris la tête de la section chargée de la guerre vendéenne. Lorsque Prieur et Carnot entrèrent au Comité, Saint-Just et Robert Lindet étaient « attachés à la partie militaire » et assistaient à la séance du Comité de la Guerre tous les samedis à huit heures du soir. Dès lors Lindet s'occupa plus spécialement des subsistances, mais Saint-Just ne laissa pas carte blanche à ses deux nouveaux collègues. Le Comité lui-même examina les plans de Carnot. L'œuvre militaire, si elle fut inspirée par Carnot — comme le prouve l'adoption de ses thèmes familiers, notamment pour les opérations de l'armée du Nord —, n'en fut pas moins une œuvre collective : Carnot devait obtenir l'assentiment du Comité.

S'ils n'avaient pas de compétence, les membres du Comité n'en avaient pas moins des idées en matière militaire.

Billaud-Varenne voyait le salut dans la masse : « Au lieu d'armées inférieures et disséminées, vous allez avoir des armées formidables [6]. » Il était en correspondance avec des généraux — Moulin, Vachot — qui lui proposaient des plans d'opérations.

Collot d'Herbois affirma, le 20 septembre, à la Convention, qu'il serait bon de se désaccoutumer des fusils [7]. Couthon fit prévaloir le politique sur le militaire : « On veut toujours de la tactique, et la tactique est l'opium des révolutions populaires [8]. »

Hérault de Séchelles a laissé des notes sur la cavalerie, sur l'armée révolutionnaire et sur la nécessité de « saisir l'ensemble des plans de campagne de chaque armée », ainsi Schérer l'entretenait d'un plan pour la campagne de l'an II. Les agents du ministre des Affaires étrangères, surveillés par Hérault, contrôlaient les généraux et les états-majors.

Pour Robespierre, le cas est à la fois plus important et plus complexe. On croira peut-être qu'Hippolyte Carnot se donna le plaisir de caricaturer Robespierre lorsqu'il le présenta, la tête appuyée sur ses deux mains, accablé devant des cartes et des mémoires militaires, s'écriant : « Je n'y comprendrai jamais rien ! » Mais récusera-t-on le témoignage de Simon Duplay : « Je sais même que Robespierre n'entendait rien à l'art militaire [9]. » Pourtant Robespierre ne contestait pas l'importance des plans et des tacticiens, son carnet le prouve indubitablement, mais il ne se mêlait pas de préparer les projets. On peut cependant constater qu'il comptait sur le patriotisme, sur la haine, qui devait animer les Français contre leurs ennemis, et sur le rôle des places fortes, ce qui était proche des idées militaires de Carnot [10].

Saint-Just était le seul qui fût souvent intervenu dans le domaine militaire, sa correspondance avec Bouchotte prouve qu'il ne s'intéressait pas seulement à la lutte contre les Vendéens. Son rôle au Comité lui avait donné l'occasion de former un « bureau militaire » et de rédiger des « notes militaires », juste avant l'arrivée de Prieur et de Carnot.

Ces notes révèlent le souci d'une information précise, mais ne comportent aucune indication stratégique ou tactique. Dans la suite, notamment au cours de sa mission à l'armée du Rhin, Saint-Just ne craindra pas d'intervenir dans le système de guerre et dans les opérations. Le sens de son action correspond exactement à l'orientation générale qui prévalut en automne 1793, comme nous le verrons. Il était partisan d'une nouvelle méthode de guerre.

Dans ces conditions, on ne s'étonne pas que Saint-Just ait été uni à Carnot et à Prieur dans une organisation des sections du Comité. Sans aucun doute, Saint-Just s'occupait-il de toutes sortes de problèmes, mais il fut, parmi les membres du Comité, le plus attentif aux questions militaires [11].

Ainsi le rôle militaire de Carnot, bien loin de s'isoler dans un bureau, s'inscrit-il dans un cadre collégial. D'ailleurs, l'organisation des bureaux du Comité s'accomplit lentement, après maints tâtonnements au cours desquels on s'appliqua plus à l'obtention de résultats immédiats qu'à la méthode de travail.

Les membres du Comité étaient aux prises avec une tâche d'autant plus écrasante que leur nombre était toujours très réduit, six en moyenne, en raison des missions qui écartaient une partie d'entre eux. De plus, sur les six, deux ou trois se rendaient aux séances de la Convention et aux réunions des Jacobins, si bien que la journée ne suffisait pas au travail, il fallait poursuivre fort avant dans la nuit. On avait décidé, le 3 août, que le Comité se réunirait le matin à huit heures. Après avoir pris connaissance d'un extrait de la correspondance établi par le secrétaire général, il délibérerait « sur toutes les mesures de salut public», c'était là l'œuvre collective. La séance de la Convention séparait les membres, mais ils se réunissaient de nouveau, à sept heures du soir, et travaillaient jusqu'à épuisement des questions. Pendant les séances de l'Assemblée les membres qui n'y assistaient pas — c'était généralement le cas de Carnot — pouvaient poursuivre leurs travaux. En fait les séances du soir se prolongèrent souvent après minuit, surtout quand le Comité eut pris l'habitude de s'entretenir avec le Conseil exécutif à partir de dix heures du soir. De ce travail acharné, Collot d'Herbois a fait un tableau que corroborent tous les témoins : quinze heures de travail par jour, sans pouvoir même prendre ses repas chez soi, ni parfois son repos : « Je prenais à la hâte, chaque jour, un repas frugal dans le voisinage du Comité. Carnot était forcé de faire de même, ainsi que Prieur de la Côte-d'Or. Ils savent quelle fut mon assiduité ; la leur et celle de Lindet pouvaient seules la surpasser [12]. »

* *

Si le Comité de Salut public était le centre de son action, Carnot devait la coordonner avec celle des autres rouages, tels que le Comité de la Guerre et le ministère de la Guerre.

Depuis le début de juillet, Billaud-Varenne présidait le Comité de la Guerre, quatre séances avaient lieu chaque semaine, le soir à huit heures, sans compter les séances extraordinaires. Ce Comité étudiait les dossiers des militaires inculpés ou frappés de sanctions, l'avancement, l'organisation des unités, la solde et la comptabilité ; à l'occasion, il stimulait les bureaux et même le Comité de Salut public lui-même. Mais toujours il se comportait comme un organe consultatif. « Tu sais comme nous que le Comité n'est point autorisé à donner des décisions, et qu'il ne peut que proposer des lois à la Convention ou des arrêtés au Comité de Salut public [13]. » De sorte que le Comité de Salut public trouvait là une aide, à la condition que les membres, renouvelés chaque mois, ne lui fussent pas hostiles.

Le rôle du ministre de la Guerre était beaucoup plus important. Le Comité de Salut public, en effet, avait été créé pour contrôler l'action du Conseil exécutif, c'est-à-dire des ministres. Le 15 juin encore il s'attribuait pour tâche la surveillance des départements ministériels et la dénonciation des abus. Le 29 juin, préoccupé des échecs militaires, le Comité avait chargé deux de ses membres « de suivre spécialement les opérations du ministre de la Guerre et de surveiller l'exécution des décrets et de tous les arrêtés ». En principe l'action appartenait aux ministres, tandis que le Comité surveillait, contrôlait, dénonçait [14]. En fait des réunions communes avaient coordonné le rôle du Comité et des ministères, spécialement du ministre de la Guerre, permettant ainsi le passage du contrôle à l'action. Pourtant le ministère de la Guerre conservait le choix et l'avancement des officiers, même des généraux, la direction des armées, leur équipement, leur armement et leur ravitaillement, tâche immense et multiple qui l'exposait aux critiques, mais qui lui donnait un rôle de premier ordre, tel que le Comité de Salut public ne pouvait interrompre une collaboration de tous les instants avec le ministre et ses bureaux. Il fallut des mois pour que le Comité imposât son autorité et substituât la subordination à la coopération.

Le ministre Bouchotte, révolutionnaire convaincu, bureaucrate consciencieux, était prisonnier de son personnel ministériel. Il avait pour secrétaire général un Hébertiste volcanique, Vincent, qui avait introduit ses amis dans la place. Une sorte de pacte liait le ministre à ses adjoints : le premier fermait les yeux sur l'activité des seconds qui se consacraient à l'action politique, aux clubs, et négligeaient le travail administratif; en échange, ceux-ci soutenaient le ministre dans l'opinion parisienne, dans les sections, aux Cordeliers, aux Jacobins, dans la presse, et lui permettaient ainsi de se maintenir en place. On en avait eu la démonstration aux mois de juin et de juillet, Bouchotte avait été officiellement remplacé et, finalement, il était resté.

Robespierre estimait en Bouchotte le démocrate qui avait « la confiance des patriotes et la haine des aristocrates et des généraux perfides », mais il en connaissait la médiocrité. « Il est possible que Bouchotte soit plus propre à délibérer dans un conseil qu'à régler les opérations de nos armées. » Carnot ne lui fut guère favorable : « Bouchotte, écrivait-il, avait une prédilection particulière pour les ignorants [15]. »

Une rivalité d'armes contribuait à séparer les deux hommes, Bouchotte était un cavalier qui s'accordait mal avec les ingénieurs. Ce dissentiment s'était aggravé avec la Révolution, surtout depuis le 10 août qui avait montré que les « hommes à talents » n'étaient guère démocrates et que

beaucoup de démocrates étaient hostiles aux talents. Bouchotte nourrissait une défiance tenace à l'égard des officiers
du Génie et de l'Artillerie. En mai, il déplorait les exigences
des examinateurs chargés de recruter les officiers du Génie,
parce qu'ils demandaient trop de connaissances ; en août,
il dénonçait l'incivisme des élèves de l'École du Génie, qui
« provient de ce que ces jeunes gens ne sont pas autres que
les parents ou les enfants des officiers du Génie. Il me semble
qu'on pourrait proposer une maison d'éducation où l'on
mettrait les fils des sans-culottes ; on leur donnerait une
instruction propre au Génie, et ce serait un moyen de le
régénérer » ; en novembre, il ordonnait de suspendre « tout
ce qui est le moindrement suspect dans l'Artillerie et le
Génie [16] ».

Toutefois le ministre avait confiance en Carnot ; il le
prouva dès les premiers jours en déférant aux désirs de
Carnot, ainsi pour la nomination d'un commandant de place
dans le Nord et en maintenant à son poste le général Stetten-
hofen dont Carnot répondait [17].

Depuis longtemps Bouchotte travaillait en accord avec le
Comité de Salut public. Ils entretenaient une correspondance active, le ministre fournissait des comptes rendus
périodiques, suggérait des mesures concernant l'armement
ou les opérations, et le Comité transmettait au ministre
un relevé quotidien de la correspondance reçue et qui pouvait
intéresser le département de la Guerre. Cette correspondance se poursuivit, de plus en plus fréquente et détaillée [18].
Il y eut bien quelques incidents, par exemple une ferme
mise au point par Bouchotte d'une question que Carnot
avait cru pouvoir trancher contre lui, à propos d'un général
Falk qui se prétendait commandant d'armée, alors qu'il
dirigeait seulement un corps d'armée et n'avait point à
correspondre directement avec le ministre [19].

Ces petites difficultés ne troublèrent pas des rapports de
travail incessants. Bouchotte notait minutieusement toutes
les demandes, transmettait les informations, assumait
une besogne accablante mais peu efficace, en raison de
l'incurie de ses bureaux. Le Comité confiait au ministre
l'exécution des mesures qui lui semblaient utiles.

Pourtant le Comité s'appliqua bientôt à obtenir directement les renseignements militaires, en s'adressant aux représentants en mission et aux généraux en chef ; sans compter
qu'il acceptait une multitude de notes, suppliques, réclama-

tions et dénonciations envoyées par des officiers de tout grade et par des soldats.

La correspondance avec les représentants en mission était traditionnelle, alors que les généraux se tenaient à l'écart ; en vain firent-ils observer qu'ils informaient le ministre, il leur fut enjoint d'adresser directement au Comité le double de leurs lettres [20].

Ainsi le Comité, s'il ne prenait pas pour lui seul les leviers de commande, les doublait en quelque sorte. Cette dualité pouvait se maintenir grâce à l'accord entre le Comité et le ministre, mais elle provoqua des incidents entre les agents de la Convention, représentants en mission en liaison avec le Comité, et les agents du ministre.

Carnot avait observé la guerre sourde qui opposait l'un à l'autre ces deux personnels. Les représentants se jugeaient, conformément aux principes, investis de la souveraineté ; les agents du pouvoir exécutif se considéraient comme les seuls révolutionnaires authentiques. Hébertistes quand ils étaient choisis par Bouchotte, ou plutôt par Vincent, ils entretenaient avec ce secrétaire général une correspondance active et violente, proposant des épurations massives parmi les généraux et les états-majors, des rappels de représentants en mission, jugés trop faibles, des offensives gigantesques, montées comme des journées révolutionnaires.

Le cas de Celliez et de Varin à l'armée du Nord, hostiles à Custine, mais aussi aux commissaires de la Convention, tour à tour arrêtés et dénonciateurs, menacés et menaçants, capables de dresser en leur faveur les chefs locaux et les clubs parisiens, de s'appuyer sur les officiers jacobins et hébertistes, et, finalement, imposant les épurations, montre sur le vif que la lutte entre les partis ne se cantonnait ni dans la Convention, ni dans Paris, mais que l'organisation militaire, l'administration du personnel, et même la conduite de la guerre étaient en jeu.

Si Carnot n'avait guère été personnellement en conflit avec les agents du pouvoir exécutif, il n'approuvait ni leurs prétentions, ni la politique qu'ils préconisaient, mais toute décision les concernant était un problème de gouvernement. Pour assurer l'autonomie relative de son action, le Comité fut amené à manœuvrer, les uns par les autres, les représentants en mission — et la Convention dont ils faisaient partie — et les agents du pouvoir exécutif — et les clubs auxquels ils appartenaient.

Au début de l'action entreprise par Carnot, il n'était sûr ni des uns ni des autres ; le Comité était à la fois surveillé par la Convention et par les Hébertistes. Le mérite de Carnot et du Comité fut d'oser ; le succès militaire pouvait lui donner l'autorité [21].

CHAPITRE VI

SUR LE CHAMP DE BATAILLE DE WATTIGNIES

« CARNOT est venu nous voir. » Ces quelques mots étaient un message d'espoir ; Levasseur, représentant en mission à l'armée du Nord, les avait écrits le 16 août ; il concluait allégrement : « Si le Comité adopte les mesures que Carnot a proposées au général, et que Vernon et le général, de leur côté, avait arrêtées,... nous ne tarderons pas à voir la Belgique [1]. »

Le Comité adopta en effet le projet d'une offensive sur Ostende. Houchard, le nouveau général en chef de l'armée du Nord, fut chargé de le réaliser. Trop timoré pour risquer, il se laissa devancer par l'ennemi : les Anglais assiégèrent Dunkerque, et les Autrichiens Le Quesnoy. Entre ces points extrêmes, les forces coalisées s'égrenèrent en semis de garnisons et de camps, en « cordon », comme on disait alors.

Ce morcellement fut la grande chance des Français, il leur permit de rétablir les armées, de les renforcer en hommes, en matériel, en énergie, en décision. Avec une ardeur passionnée, les partis et les techniciens proposaient leurs remèdes : levée en masse, irruption torrentielle de tous les civils pour pulvériser les mercenaires sous les coups des hommes libres ; solution simpliste dans son héroïsme, telles les idées de sorties hors de Paris assiégé de 1871, telles les tentatives de percée du front ennemi lors de la première guerre mondiale.... Fusion intime des troupes de l'ancienne armée de métier avec les volontaires nationaux sous un même uniforme, dans des corps mixtes, pour créer un alliage nouveau, un « amalgame », doté des qualités militaires des uns et du patriotisme des autres ; telle la fusion de l'armée régulière et des forces du « maquis » de la deuxième guerre mondiale ! Grandes opérations coordonnées, combinant toutes les armées sur les frontières pour harceler l'ennemi en tous lieux, le frapper au point choisi, libérer le territoire et dicter une paix victorieuse ;

rêve traditionnel des états-majors, mais élargi à la taille de la Révolution et de la coalition, comme dans toute guerre opposant l'une à l'autre deux idéologies incompatibles.

Les Hébertistes, les sectionnaires, les Jacobins prônaient cette « insurrection générale » qui étoufferait tous les ennemis, ceux de l'intérieur étant poussés en première ligne, « enchaînés et sans armes », devant le front des patriotes. Le Comité de Salut public voulait écarter cette vision romantique qui eût conduit aux catastrophes, Robespierre y décelait une « conspiration de la réquisition », Carnot avait déjà combattu les essais localisés de levée générale. L'opinion était pourtant si ardente qu'il fallut tourner la difficulté pour ne pas se briser sur l'obstacle [2].

Le 23 août Carnot lançait un appel claironnant : « Tous les Français sont en réquisition.... Les jeunes gens iront au combat, les hommes mariés forgeront des armes et transporteront les subsistances, les femmes feront des tentes, des habits et serviront dans les hôpitaux, les enfants mettront les vieux linges en charpie, les vieillards se feront porter sur les places publiques pour exciter le courage des guerriers.... » Ce tableau qui unissait Greuze et David escamotait la levée insurrectionnelle. N'iraient au combat que les hommes non mariés, âgés de dix-huit à vingt-cinq ans. C'était la mobilisation de sept classes, l'application des idées de Carnot sur le service militaire universel. Cochon, le Conventionnel dont la carrière dut tant à Carnot, a justement défini le rôle de son protecteur dans la circonstance : « Vous avez sagement pensé qu'il fallait donner un régulateur à ce grand et sublime mouvement [3]. » Au surplus le tableau de la résistance totale des populations à l'ennemi était celui même qu'un officier du Génie rencontrait dans une place assiégée, comme à Landrecies, où les vieillards firent mieux que d'encourager les guerriers, ils fabriquèrent des gargousses et des cartouches.

L'amalgame avait d'abord séduit les Feuillants, qui espéraient absorber les volontaires; après le 10 août il fut repris par les républicains pour infuser, comme avait dit Feulint, le patriotisme aux troupes de ligne. Le champion de cette réforme était Dubois-Crancé ; il en avait fait arrêter le principe par le décret du 21 février 1793, sous la forme de l' « embrigadement », juxtaposant, dans une seule brigade, deux bataillons de volontaires et un bataillon de ligne. Depuis février on avait constaté la difficulté de regrouper des unités dispersées et de vérifier leur situation en hommes, en matériel et en comptabilité pendant la campagne. Robespierre reprochait à Dubois-Crancé d'avoir fait adopter « ce mode d'organisation lié à une profonde machination »; Carnot estimait que l'embrigadement n'était pas l'amalgame, son expérience de l'armée du Nord lui faisait dire que « nos ci-devant troupes de ligne et nos gardes nationaux [commençaient] à s'entendre parfaitement ensemble », ce qui était optimiste [4]. Pourtant la Convention pressa l'embrigadement par un nouveau décret, le 12 août ; Carnot ajourna la réalisation, la question ne se posa vraiment que dans l'hiver 1793-1794.

Quant aux plans stratégiques, Carnot put en trouver un nombre important dans les papiers du Comité. Jusqu'au 19 juillet, le fameux général Grimoard avait été le conseiller technique du Comité ; il laissa des idées et des projets, il recommandait de « suppléer... à l'art par le nombre », de faire une « guerre de masses », d'adopter l'offensive, « à coups de baïonnette, sans songer ni à tirailler, ni à faire des manœuvres ».

Dumouriez avait légué l'idée d'une invasion de la Belgique et de la Hollande, celle de faire campagne en groupant les forces au lieu de les éparpiller en garnisons inutiles, de tourner l'ennemi au lieu de l'attaquer de front, et de mener une grande offensive dans le Nord. Il est vrai que Grimoard, Dumouriez et Custine n'étaient guère des inspirateurs dont on pût alors se réclamer ; suspects ou traîtres, ils faisaient planer la suspicion sur tout ce qui les touchait. Des officiers d'état-major, ingénieurs militaires, Tardy, Gobert, Sauviac, préconisaient la guerre de mouvement, l'offensive par une armée formidable, des opérations combinées sur toutes les frontières suivant un plan général [5].

En somme une prolifération de plans d'opérations traduisait l'urgence d'en adopter un et la nécessité de renouveler la stratégie et la tactique. Or Carnot n'apportait rien de ce genre, ce qui le préoccupait c'était la frontière et l'armée du Nord. En vain lui fit-on savoir que les coalisés menaçaient l'Alsace, il ripostait le 23 septembre : « Ce n'est pas là qu'est le danger, c'est entre Cambrai et Péronne que le sort de nous tous est fixé. »

Il laissa donc Bouchotte s'occuper du Rhin, des Alpes où les Sardes s'avançaient, des Pyrénées même où Carnot avait pourtant réclamé tant de choses lorsqu'il était commissaire. A peine se souciait-il des troubles intérieurs, à peine répondit-il à l'énorme courrier qui affluait au Comité. Le plus urgent était de sauver Dunkerque, de sauver Le Quesnoy, de s'appuyer sur ces places fortes du Nord qui jouaient cette fois le rôle salutaire qu'il leur avait toujours attribué. Ensuite, à l'abri de cette cuirasse, un grand plan de campagne décisive pourrait être élaboré, à moins qu'une victoire écrasante n'arrêtât soudain l'ennemi.

L'action militaire du Comité de Salut public se modela sur ces vues. D'abord soutenir l'armée du Nord. Avant l'arrivée de Carnot, des renforts avaient été prévus, d'autres furent décidés. On s'aperçut alors que le manque de coordination tenait beaucoup aux généraux et aux représentants, qui prenaient sur eux de réduire les contingents demandés, et qui les acheminaient à loisir. Il fallait accroître l'autorité du Comité.

En même temps Carnot prescrivit d'envoyer des vivres, des fourrages et des munitions dans les places fortes. Feulint, qui avait naguère inspecté ces places, fut nommé directeur des fortifications à Saint-Omer, le 29 août. Les commandants des places furent sommés de tenir « à quelque prix que ce puisse être ». Le général chargé de défendre Dunkerque ayant émis quelques doutes sur la force de résistance de la place fut vertement rabroué : « Nous croyons qu'un général doit toujours trouver, soutenir et prouver que sa place est imprenable. » Carnot, en effet, attachait une importance décisive au sort de Dunkerque : « La France voit son salut dans Dunkerque. » Routine de fortificateur ? Non pas. Carnot et le Comité croyaient faire tomber Pitt s'ils l'empêchaient de prendre cette tête de pont sur le continent. C'est bien cette illusion politique, et non un système de guerre, qui commanda leurs décisions.

Houchard fut donc sommé de déclencher une bataille pour libérer le port assiégé. Le général prépara une manœuvre enveloppante qui permettrait de capturer l'armée anglaise assiégeante ; puis, reculant devant les risques, il se contenta d'une attaque de moindre portée, mais plus sûre.

Le premier plan était un « grand coup », propre à terminer la guerre, lui répondit Carnot, « mais si vous avez pensé que le succès fût douteux, nous ne pouvons qu'approuver la résolution que vous avez prise ».

La bataille fut livrée à Hondschoote, les 6, 7 et 8 septembre. Les Anglais levèrent le siège, Dunkerque était sauvé, Carnot exprima « la plus vive satisfaction du Comité », regrettant toutefois que l'ennemi n'eût pas été poursuivi [6]. La victoire améliorait pourtant la situation militaire et aurait dû avoir d'heureuses répercussions à l'intérieur. Il n'en fut rien.

Le Comité ne plaisait pas aux Hébertistes, non seulement à Vincent et à ses amis du ministère de la Guerre, mais aux extrémistes des clubs et des sections. Ils lui reprochaient d'être timoré, même dans la conduite de la guerre. A leurs yeux le décret du 23 août avait réalisé une caricature de la levée en masse.

En vain rappellera-t-on que ce décret préparait une œuvre de longue haleine et de portée formidable. Effectifs assurant la supériorité numérique sans dépasser les possibilités d'encadrement, d'armement, d'équipement et de ravitaillement, sans suspendre non plus la vie économique du pays. Droit de réquisition permettant d'employer des techniciens, des artisans, des ouvriers, des ateliers pour transformer les réquisitionnaires en armées équipées et puissantes. Les Hébertistes songeaient non pas à la campagne de 1794, mais à celle de 1793, non pas à l'armée disciplinée et régulière, mais à l'insurrection torrentielle, non pas au rôle et à l'autorité du Comité, mais à leur tâche propre que le Comité ajournait et compromettait. De plus, l'armement même n'était pas conçu selon les idées révolutionnaires. Carnot et Prieur lui consacraient une large place dans l'activité du Comité, ouverture ou utilisation de forges, d'ateliers, de manufactures, mais, partisans du libéralisme économique, convaincus que les ateliers nationaux entraînent « les voleries et le gaspillage », ils se refusaient à nationaliser les entreprises.

De même pour le ravitaillement des civils et des militaires. Ce dissentiment devint même inquiétant et pesa sur la politique du Comité. Exploitant la vie chère et l'insuffisance du ravitaillement, les « Enragés » — Roux, Leclerc, Claire Lacombe — et les Hébertistes avaient réclamé que l'on mît « la Terreur à l'ordre du jour », ils avaient menacé de renouveler les « journées » et les massacres, ils avaient même envahi la Convention le 5 septembre.

Alors des décrets avaient accru l'activité du Tribunal révolutionnaire, les menaces contre les « suspects », la législation contre les étrangers et les ci-devant, « une armée révolutionnaire » avait été créée contre les ennemis de l'intérieur, la taxation des grains et du fourrage avait été généralisée, Billaud-Varenne, enfin, et Collot d'Herbois étaient entrés au Comité.

Mais les concessions s'accompagnaient de résistances, les

chefs des Enragés avaient été rappelés, les réunions des assemblées de section avaient été ramenées à deux par semaine.

Une riposte fut montée au ministère de la Guerre. Bouchotte avait fait passer une circulaire aux « agents du conseil exécutif » pour définir leur rôle d' « œil du ministre », surveillant les chefs, recueillant les plaintes, maintenant le moral des troupes par la distribution des journaux patriotiques. Le 17 septembre les abonnements officiels au *Père Duchesne* furent portés à 12 000 exemplaires. Au même moment Vincent envoyait à des agents du Conseil exécutif une lettre explicite : « Presque tous les généraux méritent mille morts, partout ils ont arrêté la valeur des armées » ; il faut surveiller les états-majors, dénoncer leurs membres véreux, fédéralistes, muscadins porteurs d'épaulettes. Le 18 septembre, au nom des Cordeliers, le même Vincent réclamait que la Convention rétablît les commissaires du pouvoir exécutif et diminuât les attributions des représentants en mission [7].

Carnot était resté à l'écart de cette lutte. Pourtant les mesures contre les nobles et les étrangers rappelaient ses propositions à la Législative, mais il n'acceptait pas la mise en demeure de Claire Lacombe : « Ne dites pas que ce serait désorganiser nos armées en les privant de chefs inexpérimentés : plus ils ont de talents, plus ils sont dangereux. » Il était au contraire en relations avec le ci-devant Montalembert et avec Champmorin ; il recevait de Duvignau une lettre où celui-ci jugeait la suspension des officiers nobles « injuste, impolitique et désastreuse » ; il s'abstenait de signer des décrets d'arrestation frappant des officiers, il faisait le silence sur certains pour les sauver, recommandant au Conventionnel Lecointre — que nous retrouverons dans des circonstances dramatiques — de savoir se taire, car « la justice peut se trouver étouffée par la haine ». Il s'appliquait à imposer la discipline militaire à l'armée révolutionnaire [8].

Cette attitude explique l'opposition persistante des Enragés et des Hébertistes à l'égard du Comité de Salut public et de Carnot.

D'autre part, depuis Hondschoote, Houchard avait essuyé des échecs : Le Quesnoy avait capitulé, la garnison de Cambrai avait été détruite. Ces échecs avaient précipité les séries de destitutions déjà commencées sur les injonctions du personnel de Bouchotte.

Ce fut une hécatombe. Depuis le mois de mai les suspensions se multipliaient ; quand Hondschoote avait été saluée comme grande victoire, Vincent s'était écrié : « Eh bien, ça va-t-il depuis que Bouchotte a arraché cinquante scélérats de cette armée ? » Celliez et Varin avaient dressé les listes d'officiers à frapper, et de remplaçants ; généraux en chef, divisionnaires, brigadiers, adjudants généraux furent suspendus par dizaines et remplacés aussitôt. On suspendit ainsi les généraux en chef des armées du Nord, du Rhin et de la Moselle ; parmi les remplaçants se trouvait Jourdan ; on avait arrêté les tacticiens Berthelmy et Gay-Vernon [9].

L'opération avait été réglée par le ministère de la Guerre, préparée par Vincent et ses amis, élargie par plusieurs représentants en mission, concertée entre les ministres et le Comité de Salut public. Carnot y avait donc été mêlé, toutefois il n'avait pu que modifier sur certains points le projet ministériel. Il connaissait encore mal le personnel militaire, son autorité était mince ; il signait Laz. Carnot, il n'était pas Carnot — le seul — et encore moins le Grand Carnot.

Le 24 septembre la Convention, mécontente de tous ces bouleversements, fit une véritable interpellation ; Robespierre y répondit en posant la question de confiance, affirmant ainsi la solidarité des membres du Comité : « Je demande que le Comité soit renouvelé. » Il retourna la majorité et fit acclamer le Comité.

Houchard servit de bouc émissaire. Général victorieux, et naguère félicité, il fut accusé de ne pas avoir appliqué un plan « dont le succès était infaillible ». En fait ce plan était l'œuvre du chef d'état-major de Houchard — qu'on venait d'arrêter — et Carnot, au nom du Comité, avait accepté que ce plan fût abandonné. La raison d'État, comme la haine, faussait la justice, Houchard était sacrifié au profit du Comité de Salut public ; il fut guillotiné [10].

Toutes ces mesures ne pouvaient avoir leur effet que si elles étaient suivies par la victoire. C'est ce que voulait le Comité. Il crut que le plus sûr moyen d'y parvenir était d'envoyer Carnot vers Jourdan.

Carnot quitta Paris le 25 septembre au matin. Il rencontra Jourdan le 26 ; ils décidèrent « d'employer de grands moyens pour chasser les tyrans du territoire de la République ». Le 28, Carnot avait déjà regagné Paris.

Jourdan soumit son plan au ministre et au Comité dès le 29. Il proposait d'entreprendre une double offensive sur les deux ailes de l'ennemi pour le contraindre à se replier, peut-être même pourrait-on le cerner. Toutefois Jourdan, craignant que son projet parût trop aventureux, avait aussi proposé un plan défensif pour libérer Maubeuge, si l'ennemi l'assiégeait comme cela semblait probable. L'alternative rappelait, fâcheusement, les hésitations de Houchard. Comme lui Jourdan se prononça finalement le 1er octobre en faveur du plan le plus modeste et le plus classique, en raison des menaces qui pesaient sur les places fortes.

On peut penser que Carnot abonda en ce sens. Le Comité décida de l'associer à l'exécution comme il l'avait été à la préparation.

Ainsi Carnot devenait le lien vivant entre le Comité et l'armée la plus importante, il paraissait destiné à faire le va-et-vient pour arrêter les plans et surveiller les opérations, contrôlant ainsi de très près l'action des généraux qui avait provoqué tant de déboires et de catastrophes antérieurement.

Carnot quitta Paris le 6 octobre dans la nuit, Duquesnoy l'accompagnait. Le 7, ils rejoignaient Jourdan à Péronne.

Ce fut l'un des points culminants de la carrière de Carnot, l'un des trois épisodes de combat — avec la prise de Furnes et la défense d'Anvers —, la seule victoire enfin gagnée sur le champ de bataille par ce stratège sédentaire, mais cette victoire eût suffi à fonder sa réputation, selon le mot de Napoléon. Encore faut-il distinguer ce qui doit revenir à Carnot et ce qui doit rester à Jourdan[11].

A l'arrivée de Carnot, Jourdan avait arrêté ses dispositions et songeait à livrer bataille le 12 octobre. Tous les ordres de mouvement furent écrits par lui. Il est peu probable que dans les entretiens antérieurs Carnot eût envisagé les détails. Ce qui est assuré, c'est que Jourdan dut retarder l'opération faute de munitions, et c'est là que les représentants intervinrent, comme le montre la correspondance de Carnot.

Une sorte d'allégresse animait Carnot et colorait son style :
« Il nous faudrait au moins quinze mille baïonnettes ; nous ne pourrons pas charger les ennemis à la française, si nous n'en avons point.... Les bataillons de nouvelle levée sont supérieurement vêtus, tandis que ceux qui viennent de faire la guerre, et qui vont encore marcher à l'ennemi, sont tout délabrés. Cependant les premiers sont parfaitement inutiles, car ils n'ont pas même de bâton à la main, ils sont d'ailleurs de la plus grande beauté, mais ils ne font que consommer

des subsistances qu'on a bien de la peine à se procurer....
L'affaire sera chaude, mais nous vaincrons et la patrie sera
sauvée. »

Duquesnoy a fourni un exemple saisissant des procédés
des représentants. Un officier d'artillerie signala le manque
de munitions, aussitôt le général en chef convoqua le général commandant d'artillerie et lui demanda s'il ne manquait de rien ; celui-ci l'affirma, mais au nombre de cartouches qu'il mentionna on constata l'insuffisance. Aussitôt
les représentants destituèrent, firent arrêter et juger le
responsable. Il y eut beaucoup d'autres sanctions, frappant
des capitaines ou lieutenants, un quartier-maître, parfois
pour simple absence irrégulière.

En même temps des proclamations enflammées, exaltant
les succès obtenus sur les autres frontières, s'appliquaient à
relever le moral des troupes. Finalement, malgré l'insuffisance de leur cavalerie, les Français étaient en mesure
d'aborder l'ennemi sans appréhension ; ils étaient deux fois
plus nombreux — quarante-cinq mille contre vingt et un mille
—, leur artillerie était plus fournie, et le terrain, s'il se prêtait
peu au feu de l'artillerie, devait gêner plus encore la cavalerie adverse. Sans doute les Français connaissaient mal les
effectifs qui leur étaient opposés, toutefois Carnot, écrivant
la veille de la rencontre, déclarait : « Notre position est
plus avantageuse que la sienne [celle de l'ennemi] et, dans
deux ou trois jours au plus, nous espérons avoir de grandes
et heureuses nouvelles à vous annoncer.... Ça ira. »

La bataille fut livrée le 15 octobre. Jourdan voulait
« attaquer le centre des alliés... lorsqu'il apprendrait les
succès des colonnes de la droite et de la gauche, et réunir
ensuite son armée », c'est ce qu'il a écrit dans ses *Mémoires*,
et ce qui résulte des ordres qu'il avait donnés avant le
commencement du combat. Le plan fut vraisemblablement
adopté en accord avec Carnot, puisque Jourdan ne cessait de
solliciter son approbation. Avec un peu de chance l'armée
adverse aurait pu être non seulement refoulée, mais fortement éprouvée. Cette chance manqua.

L'aile gauche française, commandée par le général Fromentin, après quelques avantages, se risqua dans la plaine,
où la cavalerie autrichienne la mit en fuite. Jourdan a dénoncé
le manque de talents de Fromentin, et Carnot avait peu
d'estime pour les chefs qui servaient sous Jourdan. Mais les
ordres de Jourdan auraient dû être d'autant plus précis et

détaillés que ces lieutenants étaient médiocres, ce ne fut pas le cas.

L'aile droite, commandée par le général Duquesnoy, frère du représentant, marcha sur Wattignies, fortement appuyée par l'artillerie, mais elle dut finalement se replier.

Tous les témoins français, autrichiens, voire anglais, sont d'accord sur les opérations des ailes; le récit anglais insiste même sur l'énergie de la colonne conduite par Duquesnoy. Mais la lutte au centre, où se trouvaient Jourdan et Carnot, fut l'occasion d'un débat, d'abord entre eux, puis entre les historiens, qui rejetait de l'un à l'autre la responsabilité de l'échec.

Jourdan a écrit, dans ses *Mémoires*, que Carnot voulut déclencher l'attaque centrale prématurément; le général lui répliqua qu'il fallait « attendre que la gauche eût gagné plus de terrain ». A vrai dire la gauche, accablée par la cavalerie ennemie, ne pouvait gagner du terrain qu'à la condition de recevoir du renfort. C'est ce que dit Hippolyte Carnot :

« Allons au secours de l'aile gauche ! s'écria Jourdan.

— Général, voilà comme on perd une bataille », riposta Carnot.

Ce récit correspond à un passage des *Mémoires* de Vaublanc. C'était après le coup d'État de 1797, Vaublanc se trouvait en Suisse, en compagnie d'un émigré, Vintimille, qui avait combattu à Wattignies, et qui évoquait ses souvenirs, en présence de Carnot réfugié, rendu méconnaissable par une volumineuse perruque. « Il me semble que je vois encore cet homme grêle, pâle, de mauvaise mine, qui n'avait pas un habit uniforme, et qui, un drapeau à la main, conduisait la droite des Français... », disait Vintimille. Carnot intervint : « J'étais au centre de l'armée avec le général Jourdan, lorsque vous enfonciez notre aile gauche. Le général se prépara à la soutenir et même donna ordre de faire marcher les bataillons de la droite pour renforcer le centre. Je lui dis aussitôt : « Général, c'est ainsi que l'on perd des batailles. « Ne voyez-vous pas que l'ennemi affaiblit son aile gauche « pour renforcer sa droite ?... C'est là qu'il faut marcher. Dès « ce moment, je prends tout sur moi, comme représentant du « peuple. »

Si l'on se reporte à Jourdan, celui-ci confirme ces récits : « Carnot persista dans son opinion, parla d'énergie et d'audace et donna à entendre que cette prudence laissait échapper la victoire. » Alors Jourdan, craignant de passer pour timoré, fit donner la colonne du centre, mais elle ne put forcer l'adversaire, et il fallut se replier ; c'était l'échec, et c'est là ce qu'oublient de dire Hippolyte Carnot et Vaublanc.

Si Jourdan attribue cet échec à l'intervention de Carnot qui commit une « faute grossière », il reconnaît aussi « qu'il avait eu tort de multiplier ses attaques ». Quoi qu'il en soit, Jourdan donna pour le lendemain des ordres conformes aux désirs de Carnot, il décida de frapper l'aile gauche ennemie et de porter le principal effort sur Wattignies, considéré comme la clef de la position. A vrai dire, comme l'ennemi avait aussi renforcé son aile gauche, la difficulté restait la même, l'essentiel était plutôt la concentration de l'effort sur Wattignies.

Le 16 au matin, trois colonnes d'attaque s'élancèrent contre l'aile gauche ennemie. La partie fut rude, car les Autrichiens résistèrent sur leur position, qui était forte, et leur cavalerie riposta. Les généraux et les représentants durent payer de leurs personnes. Jourdan a signalé le rôle de Carnot et de Duquesnoy à la tête des troupes. Les représentants ne se contentèrent pas d'entraîner les hommes, ils destituèrent un général qui n'avait pas accompli sa mission. Dans la suite, ce général fut soutenu par les sans-culottes de sa section, et acquitté ; mais Carnot n'oublia pas. Un an après il écrivait : « Il est impossible de réintégrer ce général après la conduite qu'il a tenue à la bataille de Wattignies. »

Finalement la victoire était due au nombre et au mordant des troupes, malgré leur inexpérience et celle des généraux. On a, dès l'époque, souligné la maladresse des chefs placés sous les ordres de Jourdan. Il faut ajouter que Jourdan et Carnot, animés par un patriotisme ardent et une volonté implacable, n'avaient jamais dirigé une bataille ; le coup d'œil leur fit défaut, et leurs plans laissèrent finalement échapper un adversaire beaucoup moins nombreux.

L'artillerie joua un rôle que les Autrichiens ont souligné, mais l'essentiel ce fut l'élan des colonnes chargeant à la baïonnette. Carnot, qui avait déjà tendance à exalter l'arme blanche, tira d'importantes conclusions de cette expérience, la seule de sa carrière.

Jourdan écrivit au ministre de la Guerre le 19 octobre 1793 : « Les conseils de ces citoyens [Lazare et Feulint] m'ont été infiniment utiles et je vous avoue avec franchise que, me voyant réduit à moi-même, je me défie de mes connaissances. » En retour, Carnot attribuait tout le mérite à Jourdan. Seuls les agents du pouvoir exécutif, ceux qui avaient provoqué la chute de Custine, reprochaient à Jourdan d'avoir accordé trop d'importance aux représentants en mission, qui avaient été « pour ainsi dire les généraux de l'armée ». Ils prétendaient que Jourdan avait craint d'être dénoncé par les représentants et que le général et les représentants avaient fini par faire l'éloge les uns des autres. Ces insinuations annonçaient une campagne d'opinion hébertiste : Duquesnoy fut le plus visé, mais Carnot était déjà menacé comme nous le constaterons.

Alors que Wattignies avait été l'opération classique de la levée d'un siège par une armée de secours — comme Hondschoote pour Dunkerque —, certains avaient pensé que l'on avait mieux à faire : « Nous ne faisons qu'une guerre d'imitation, ou pour mieux dire de bamboche ; nous n'avons aucun plan, nous suivons les ennemis partout où ils se présentent.... écrivait Hoche. N'allons pas chercher les ennemis à Maubeuge, pour leur faire lâcher prise.... Réunissons deux masses, que l'une se porte sur Tournai, l'autre sur Ypres et Ostende. » Ces idées devaient faire leur chemin [12].

En attendant la situation était améliorée sur la frontière, puisque le siège de Maubeuge était levé, mais Carnot ne cachait pas au Comité que l'ennemi avait conservé son armée en bon ordre,... « plus que nous-mêmes ». Il s'agissait de tirer le meilleur parti de la victoire. Jourdan estimait la défensive indispensable pendant quelque temps, Carnot voulait l'offensive, mais reconnaissait la valeur des arguments de Jourdan. Il prescrivit à celui-ci d'attendre de nouveaux ordres que le Comité de Salut public allait donner.

De l'aveu de Jourdan, il fit valoir les raisons du général, mais le Comité passa outre, mené par « ceux qui croyaient que le peuple pouvait tout écraser de sa masse », en dépit des réticences de quelques membres « qui n'étaient pas entièrement étrangers à l'art de la guerre ». D'où l'ordre tranchant et optimiste expédié à Jourdan le 22 octobre ; mais Carnot lui-même jugeait ce projet hasardeux et les opérations fort délicates, dans une lettre qu'il adressait personnellement à Jourdan.

Le 26 octobre, Carnot remaniait les instructions en s'inspirant des écrits d'un tacticien anglais, Lloyd ; il proposait à Jourdan d'aller l'assister lors de la prochaine grande bataille. Jourdan temporisa et appela Carnot. Celui-ci ne

6

put quitter le Comité, mais réduisit ses ambitions et finit par admettre, le 3 novembre, que les opérations fussent suspendues. Il tint à répéter, le 6 novembre, à Jourdan, dans une lettre personnelle, qu'il lui gardait toute sa confiance et se rendait à ses raisons. Or, le même jour, le Comité s'indignait : « Reculer devant l'ennemi n'est ni du génie de la liberté, ni du caractère du soldat français.... Nous sommes affligés de voir un général républicain parler de démission,... le défenseur de son pays ne peut trouver rien d'impossible. »

La preuve est donc flagrante que Carnot, à cette époque, ne dirigeait pas à son gré les opérations militaires [13].

Il regagna Paris le 19 et reprit son poste au Comité.

Pourtant la victoire de Wattignies avait donné de l'autorité à Carnot. C'est en se référant à ce succès que Robespierre appuyait les nouveaux plans de Carnot et que Saint-Just sollicitait des instructions et des plans d'opérations. De plus les missions de Saint-Just, son rôle considérable dans la politique générale, d'autre part le travail de plus en plus lourd imposé à Prieur de la Côte-d'Or par l'armement accrurent le rôle de Carnot dans la conduite de la guerre.

Or, au même moment, le 10 octobre 1793, à la suite d'un grand rapport de Saint-Just, la Convention avait décrété « que le gouvernement serait révolutionnaire jusqu'à la paix ». De ce fait le Comité de Salut public, déjà consolidé par la victoire, reçut des pouvoirs puissants, son autorité fut en mesure de l'emporter, et l'action des membres du Comité, dans le domaine militaire, devint plus efficace et plus libre.

Depuis peu Carnot signait de son nom, sans prénom ni initiale. Il s'était imposé. Pourtant il avait échappé à une perfide attaque, liée à la politique générale et à l'action des Hébertistes, et qui avait contribué à faire contester ses conseils concernant le rôle de Jourdan et de l'armée du Nord.

CHAPITRE VII

GOUVERNEMENT RÉVOLUTIONNAIRE

LE GOUVERNEMENT révolutionnaire était une organisation ; il restait — après avoir posé le principe — à
imposer l'autorité de cette organisation, à en arrêter
les méthodes, à en fixer le but. Tâche accablante et redoutable, les contre-révolutionnaires n'étaient pas les seuls adversaires, il y avait encore ces extrémistes hostiles aux pouvoirs
du Comité, hostiles à la plupart de ses membres, disposés à
recourir à la terreur, par préférence, et peu préparés à
considérer la paix — terme officiellement proclamé du gouvernement révolutionnaire — comme une fin suffisante. Il
fallut donc lutter sur deux fronts.

Carnot fut intimement mêlé à cette lutte, parce que le
ministère de la Guerre était le quartier général des extrémistes, mais aussi parce que Carnot était opposé à la fois au
programme et aux hommes de ce groupe. Il se disait pourtant démocrate et ami de l'égalité, mais plus encore, il
était l'homme à talents, le partisan d'une direction — gouvernementale et administrative — confiée aux plus intelligents et aux plus instruits. L'égalité qu'il préconisait, portait
sur l'origine sociale, non pas sur la qualité intellectuelle et
sociale. La violence lui paraissait utilisable, faute de mieux,
quand elle s'exerçait dans le sens de la volonté générale et
qu'elle seule pouvait permettre d'aboutir dans un temps trop
limité pour recourir à d'autres moyens. Rien ne pouvait
justifier une violence inutile — la violence pour la violence,
« au gré des égorgeurs » — ni la violence intéressée — au
« profit des intrigants ».

Ajoutons que son mariage, celui de Feulint, les alliances
de la famille Dupont, l'orientation politique et sociale de
Feulint contribuaient à l'opposer aux extrémistes, et l'on
comprendra pourquoi Carnot fut au centre du combat. Pendant la première période du Comité, il se trouva du même côté

que Robespierre ; la solidarité gouvernementale en fut renforcée. Tout changea lorsque les extrémistes eurent été traqués et que les ministres eurent été supprimés — donc le ministère de la Guerre.

La lutte commença en même temps que l'établissement du gouvernement révolutionnaire.

Au moment où Carnot s'était rendu à l'armée du Nord pour prendre part à la bataille de Wattignies, un journal arrageois l'avait attaqué — lui et les siens — en termes violents et directs. « J'ai su que toute la famille était dans la plus vile aristocratie ; j'ai vérifié le fait, et j'ai trouvé que les aristocrates seuls avaient l'entrée chez elle. » L'attaque se précisait ensuite aux dépens de Lazare et de Feulint. Le premier était accusé d'avoir obstinément soutenu un officier du Génie aristocrate, puis de l'avoir remplacé par Feulint quand l'indignation des patriotes l'avait contraint de céder. Feulint avait reçu, de ce fait, un avancement scandaleux, et tous les bons citoyens de la région étaient consternés de voir s'installer à Saint-Omer cet officier « auquel personne n'avait confiance, et qui, malgré l'égalité, conservait encore le titre de Feulint ». A l'appui de ces dires, la seule preuve invoquée était le témoignage de patriotes comme Niou et Billaud-Varenne.

Cette attaque avait paru dans un journal que l'on distribuait alors aux armées, une espèce de *Père Duchesne*, le *Rougyff*, anagramme du nom de son directeur, Guffroy.

Personnage taré, démagogue versatile, Guffroy cherchait sans doute à consolider sa situation. Il avait naguère commis une sottise en essayant d'empêcher le mariage de Lebas et d'Élisabeth Duplay ; il s'était ainsi attiré l'hostilité du groupe robespierriste. Peut-être même Robespierre se rappelait-il que Guffroy avait combattu sa candidature à la Constituante, et que, au début de la Législative, ce même Guffroy lui avait écrit que, « parmi les députés, Carnot seul était patriote » ? Guffroy comptait s'appuyer sur Duquesnoy, le compagnon de Carnot, et aussi sur Lebon et Darthé, hostiles à Feulint.

Le 11 octobre, il accentua sa manœuvre et prit Carnot personnellement à partie. Il l'accusait d'avoir favorisé un aristocrate dont les parents avaient émigré, il l'informait qu'il avait remis à Robespierre les pièces à conviction appuyées par la lettre d'un représentant du peuple. Il ajoutait toutefois avec une feinte bonhomie : « Carnot, si tu es digne de siéger à la Montagne et de délibérer sur le salut de la France au Comité de Salut public, tu ne te fâcheras pas. Je t'ai cru républicain, c'est le moment de faire voir que le seul salut de la République t'anime. » Et, pour en fournir la preuve, Carnot devrait doter les armées de francisques. « La guerre ne finira qu'avec des francisques, ou l'équivalent. » Il faut dire que le *Rougyff* s'appelait aussi le *Frank* — racisme pitoyable.

Carnot était donc dénoncé à Robespierre par l'intermédiaire de Duquesnoy. Celui-ci n'avait pas pardonné à Carnot son refus de signer l'adhésion chaleureuse au 31 mai et son opposition à l'arrestation d'O'Moran.

La situation était d'autant plus embrouillée que, de son côté, Hébert attaquait violemment Duquesnoy, aux Jacobins, le 8 novembre, lui reprochant d'avoir fait donner un avancement abusif au général Duquesnoy, son frère. Celliez, l'agent du ministère de la Guerre à l'armée du Nord, appuya Hébert et reprocha à Carnot de protéger, lui aussi, son frère, Feulint. L'issue de cette escarmouche dépendait de Robespierre.

Le cas de Carnot fut d'abord tranché au Comité. L'on entendit Duquesnoy, on examina les documents, on écouta Carnot qui se justifia et qui fournit aussi la preuve que Duquesnoy avait couvert les dilapidations commises à l'armée du Nord. Mais, loin de demander une sanction contre son ancien collègue, Carnot détruisit les pièces qui l'incriminaient. Tel est le récit d'Hippolyte.

D'autre part, aux Jacobins, le 9 novembre, Robespierre prit la défense de Duquesnoy. Le lendemain le *Rougyff* publia un démenti, appuyé par Niou et par Billaud-Varenne. La gloire de Wattignies était évoquée. La modestie et le désintéressement de Carnot étaient exaltés : « Il s'est fait un devoir sacré de renoncer à tout avancement tant qu'il serait représentant du peuple. Loin de contribuer par ses sollicitations à celui de son frère, il a trouvé fort mauvais que tel avancement eût lieu à son insu, et il s'en est expliqué assez énergiquement vis-à-vis du ministre de la Guerre, en présence de tous les membres du Comité. »

Ainsi la preuve de la solidarité gouvernementale venait d'être administrée : Carnot, Billaud-Varenne, Robespierre et les autres membres se soutenaient mutuellement.

Feulint ne bénéficiait, en revanche, d'aucune louange, il crut prudent de se procurer un certificat de civisme. Un adjoint au ministre de la Guerre, Dupin, le rassura :

« Pareilles lettres, écrivit-il en faisant allusion aux papiers de Guffroy, servent à faire ressortir les vertus des bons patriotes [1]. »

Carnot, défendu par Billaud-Varenne et indirectement par Robespierre, s'était uni à eux pendant cette période pour organiser le gouvernement révolutionnaire. Le départ en mission de plusieurs membres lui avait interdit de répondre à l'appel de Jourdan, il lui fallut se fixer — provisoirement au moins — et intervenir même hors du domaine militaire, mais toujours — ou presque — dans les zones de combat.

Le 26 octobre il avait rédigé l'arrêté envoyant Hérault de Séchelles dans le Haut-Rhin, « pour y prendre toutes les mesures de sûreté générale qui lui paraîtront nécessaires ». Trois jours plus tard il avait signé l'arrêté envoyant Lebon dans le Pas-de-Calais pour y accomplir une tâche analogue ; il signa aussi les lettres des 13, 16 et 21 novembre, qui recommandaient à Lebon de suivre une « marche révolutionnaire » et l'autorisaient à déférer les prisonniers au tribunal criminel du département : « Toutes les mesures sont permises, ou plutôt commandées, par vos pouvoirs et par le salut de la patrie », déclaraient Billaud-Varenne et Carnot. A quoi Lebon répondit : « Malheur aux traîtres, aux dilapidateurs, aux prévaricateurs de toute espèce ! Leurs têtes vont tomber comme la grêle. » Ce qui ne tarda guère [2]. Haut-Rhin et Pas-de-Calais étaient dans la zone des armées, mais la terreur frappait aussi les insurgés de l'intérieur, dans l'Ouest, à Lyon et à Toulon.

Dans l'Ouest le premier rôle incombait à Prieur de la Côte-d'Or. Carnot prescrivit simplement l'établissement de camps pour interdire l'accès du Cotentin, suivant la leçon de Vauban et le souvenir du séjour de Carnot à Cherbourg [3]. Mais il voulait l' « extermination » des Vendéens et couvrit pleinement les agissements de Turreau : « Tu te plains, citoyen général, de n'avoir pas reçu du Comité une approbation formelle de tes mesures. Elles lui paraissaient bonnes et tes intentions pures.... Extermine les brigands jusqu'au dernier, voilà ton devoir [4].... »

Lyon, révolté, était alors investi ; le Comité prescrivit une répression « la torche à la main et la baïonnette au bout du fusil ». D'après Dubois-Crancé, Carnot serait l'un des promoteurs de cette consigne, mais l'arrêté du 24 septembre n'existe plus sous forme originale. En revanche l'arrêté du 1er octobre, qui réitérait le même ordre, a bien été signé de Carnot [5].

Pour Toulon, Carnot prescrivit le bombardement « à boulets rouges pour incendier la ville [6] ».

En somme, il était fidèle à la terrible consigne qu'il avait donnée dans le Nord, dès qu'il avait vu la nécessité d'une lutte à mort. Dans la suite — outre la nécessité militaire et révolutionnaire —, il a invoqué la volonté du peuple : « Votre manière de voir, fût-elle la meilleure, ne peut être substituée à celle du peuple. » Il ne s'agit pas de toute la nation, mais seulement « de la volonté apparente, la seule sur laquelle un gouvernement puisse prononcer... », et qu'il n'aurait pu méconnaître sans danger. Ainsi, disait-il aux représentants : « Lorsque vous avez voté la loi du maximum, par exemple, la question n'était pas de savoir si vous, négociants ou philosophes, trouviez cette loi mauvaise, mais si le peuple la voulait oui ou non. » Or, disait encore Carnot, « à cette époque la volonté du peuple était entièrement ultra-révolutionnaire [7] ».

Ainsi la méthode s'affirmait avec l'organisation. Le 25 novembre, le Comité obtint un décret de la Convention qui enjoignait aux représentants en mission de se conformer exactement aux arrêtés du Comité, et qui informait les agents du pouvoir exécutif — et les généraux — qu'ils ne pourraient s'autoriser d'aucun ordre particulier pour éluder les arrêtés du Comité. Comment Carnot ne se serait-il pas associé étroitement à une action qui empêcherait le dédain de ses prescriptions ? Son ami Garrau, lui-même, n'avait-il pas refusé de confier le commandement de l'armée des Pyrénées-Orientales au général Dumas (le père d'Alexandre Dumas) ?

L'un des instruments de terreur était l'armée révolutionnaire, décrétée sous la pression des Hébertistes, le 5 septembre 1793. C'était une force de police, une armée de l'intérieur, destinée à traquer les suspects et les contre-révolutionnaires. Hébert aurait voulu qu'elle fût suivie d'un tribunal et d'une guillotine, Billaud-Varenne avait contribué à cette création. Carnot avait présenté, le 9 septembre, le statut de l'armée nouvelle : la Commune pouvait contrôler le recrutement, mais le Comité se réservait de choisir les officiers supérieurs. Ceux-ci pourtant furent assez généralement favorables aux Hébertistes. Mais Carnot s'efforça d'imposer à cette force révolutionnaire la discipline militaire.

C'est dans ce sens qu'il rédigea les ordres concernant le détachement qui fut envoyé à Lyon. Ces ordres ne restèrent pas lettre morte : Carnot rappela, le 30 novembre, à l'armée révolutionnaire, « que la force publique est essentiellement obéissante, et qu'elle n'a aucune action directe et spontanée sur les autorités constituées et sur les citoyens ». Un peu plus tard, le 18 janvier, il spécifiait que les divers détachements de l'armée révolutionnaire étaient aux ordres des généraux, là où ils se trouvaient, et aussi des représentants. Carnot avait cédé, mais il refrénait peu à peu. « Ce fut Carnot qui, heureusement, écrit Barère, fut chargé de cette organisation au Comité »; il lui donna les formes militaires, l'assujettit aux lois militaires et refusa les tribunaux ambulants, les états-majors, les soldes et les effectifs excessifs.

En même temps le Comité réduisait à rien l'influence des agents ou commissaires de l'exécutif, comme ces Varin et Celliez envoyés à l'armée du Nord par Bouchotte. Le ministre lui-même était assujetti; on lui rappelait l'obligation de communiquer au Comité les lettres que lui adressaient les généraux; Carnot se montrait strict, même avec Dupin : « Nous t'observons que, lorsqu'on demande une décision au Comité, ce doit être avant que les ordres ne soient donnés [8]. » Si Carnot put diriger les armées, ce fut bien grâce à l'établissement d'un gouvernement qui assurait l'autorité des membres du Comité. La consécration de cette tendance fut obtenue par le décret du 4 décembre, qui soumettait encore plus étroitement les ministres, les généraux, les autorités et les représentants en mission à ce même Comité de Salut public. Carnot en tira les conséquences, le 8 décembre : « Le Comité, écrivait-il, se consacre aux affaires majeures, il n'a pas de bureau pour les détails, ceux-ci doivent être étudiés par le Conseil exécutif, qui prépare un rapport sur un projet d'arrêté, sur chaque question. »

Pourtant le bureau de la Guerre, au Comité de Salut public, prit une activité plus considérable et plus autonome. Les arrêtés le concernant étaient enregistrés séparément; sa correspondance fut de plus en plus importante. En conséquence le personnel s'accrut.

Le recrutement de ce personnel souligne le rôle de Carnot. C'est lui qui choisit les principaux employés. Il les prit parmi les hommes qu'il avait eu l'occasion d'apprécier soit à l'armée, soit dans les administrations. Par exemple, dans le Nord, il avait remarqué un commissaire ordonnateur, Chaalons, un commissaire des guerres, Bourotte, un garde-magasin militaire, Morel ; il les appela tous trois à la section de la Guerre du Comité, où ils demeurèrent longtemps. On trouve trace aussi d'une vingtaine de secrétaires, souvent originaires du Nord ou de Bourgogne.

Carnot organisa de même le personnel du Cabinet historique et topographique du Comité, lui donnant une équipe de secrétaires, de traducteurs et de cartographes.

D'ordinaire, Carnot rédigeait lui-même les minutes des arrêtés et des lettres, souvent même les expéditions originales. Les secrétaires dépouillaient la correspondance, tenaient les registres, copiaient les extraits, classaient les archives. Parfois l'un d'eux se rendait aux armées, soit seul, soit pour accompagner un représentant en mission.

Les signatures étaient, habituellement, celle de Carnot, accompagnée, suivant les cas, de celles de Saint-Just, de Prieur de la Côte-d'Or, de Barère [9].

La solidarité se combinait ainsi avec la spécialisation, l'œuvre collective avec l'initiative personnelle. Carnot était l'inspirateur, le plus souvent, mais les propositions étaient soumises au Comité de Salut public et communiquées aux Comités de la Guerre, des Fortifications, et aussi au ministre de la Guerre.

Cette solidarité se poursuivait dans la politique générale au service de laquelle travaillaient l'organisation et la méthode, le Comité et la Terreur.

A cette époque, Robespierre et l'ensemble du Comité se refusaient aux mesures extrêmes ; la Terreur n'était pas la Grande Terreur, il ne s'agissait nullement de subversion totale, de révolution sociale, de dictature, toutes choses que les Thermidoriens devaient indistinctement reprocher au Comité. L'assentiment de Carnot était donc d'autant plus facilement acquis. Carnot prescrivait de s'appuyer sur les sociétés populaires pour épurer les autorités constituées, défendre les patriotes, « maintenir le mouvement révolutionnaire » et placer « l'esprit public à la hauteur des principes ». Il signait, avec Robespierre et Billaud-Varenne, une circulaire aux sociétés populaires : « Vous serez nos plus puissants auxiliaires [10]. »

Avec Robespierre encore, Carnot s'opposait à la déchristianisation. Il prescrivait aux représentants en mission, dans la Somme ou dans la Corrèze, de ne pas donner « occasion de dire que l'on viole la liberté des cultes et qu'on fait guerre à la religion elle-même ». Il leur donnait pour consigne ce qu'il avait proclamé et réalisé aux Pyrénées : « la paix et l'union des citoyens » par la liberté : « Que chacun croie ce qu'il lui plaira pourvu que sa conduite ou ses erreurs ne trouble jamais l'ordre public. » Ce qui ne l'empêchait pas de déclarer, le jour où un couvent de chartreux devenait une manufacture d'armes, que ce lieu passait de l'ennui à l'activité utile et offrait « le tableau d'une population heureuse [11] ».

Avec Robespierre encore, et Billaud-Varenne, et Barère, il interdisait les visites domiciliaires à Paris pour rechercher les subsistances. Cette mesure extrême avait pu lui paraître indispensable dans le Nord, à Paris elle prenait une signification politique hébertiste enragée. S'il acceptait le maximum, c'était — il ne l'a pas caché — sans conviction. S'il pressait les fabrications de guerre, s'associant étroitement à l'œuvre de Prieur de la Côte-d'Or, c'était en évitant les entreprises d'État, les nationalisations, qui accroissent les frais et diminuent le rendement.

En tout, il restait libéral et ne se résignait — avec décision et autorité il est vrai — à toutes les mesures d'exception que pour hâter la fin de la guerre, et la fin même de ces mesures d'exception. A plusieurs reprises il a conjuré les généraux de faire l'impossible pour qu'une proche victoire mît fin à cet « état violent » qui épuisait la France.

CHAPITRE VIII

LES ARMÉES DE LA RÉPUBLIQUE

Après son long séjour à l'armée du Nord, Carnot savait les qualités et les défauts des troupes révolutionnaires ; il les avait vues combattre, vaincre et fuir ; il lui incombait d'en faire l'instrument de la victoire.

Pour y parvenir, il lui fallait élargir ses horizons jusqu'à l'ensemble des armées et des frontières, devenir leur centre, redistribuer leurs forces, les articuler, leur donner des chefs, des ressources et des plans.

Tâche déconcertante et formidable, tant l'armée était incohérente et instable, avec ses soldats d'Ancien Régime, ses volontaires enthousiastes de 1791, ses médiocres et ses rebuts de 1792, et le tout-venant de 1793. Masse énorme et inarticulée, où fleurissaient l'individualisme et l'esprit grégaire, le patriotisme et la désertion, l'héroïsme et l'anarchie. Encadrée d'officiers aussi divers, où les ci-devant coudoyaient les officiers improvisés, et dont l'administration était un chef-d'œuvre ahurissant de gaspillage et d'incompétence accompagné d'improvisation, cette armée était un monstre.

Rien ne pouvait irriter davantage l'esprit mathématique de Carnot organisateur. Mais il avait beaucoup appris depuis son entrée à la Législative et savait subir et utiliser ce qu'il ne pouvait intégralement et immédiatement transformer : il employait les instruments disponibles et tentait de les rendre plus efficaces sans les refondre. Il s'y résignait d'autant mieux qu'à ses yeux l'instrument était tout provisoire.

D'autre part, Carnot, ancien officier sans troupe, et savant, avait toujours vécu en dehors des milieux dont sortaient une grande partie des volontaires et de leurs chefs. L'ignorance profonde, où il demeurait volontiers, du peuple, surtout de celui des villes, des soldats, surtout de ceux de l'armée révolutionnaire, de leurs sentiments profonds, de leur condition de vie, de leurs aspirations, compliquait beaucoup sa tâche. Mais il voyait de haut ; sa connaissance de la psychologie collective des troupes — douloureusement acquise —, ses contacts avec les chefs lui suffisaient à diriger cette étrange armée.

Ce monstre était animé d'une puissante vitalité, mais risquait de périr pourtant, à la fois de présomption et de consomption.

Le Grand Comité s'appliqua à la tâche, menée par la résolution opiniâtre, la volonté impérieuse et l'esprit lucide de Carnot, réalisée avec l'aide de toutes les bonnes volontés que sollicitait largement Carnot. L'œuvre fut collective : outre le Comité de Salut public, celui de la Guerre et les bureaux ministériels y participèrent largement et efficacement. Il est assez plaisant de voir chaque biographie tirer la couverture en faveur de son héros, et, si nous cherchons à définir ici le rôle de Carnot, ce n'est pas pour céder à ce penchant.

La victoire appartenait au nombre. Carnot, dédaignant la tirade banale suivant laquelle un citoyen soldat valait dix esclaves des tyrans, voulut assurer à la République une puissante supériorité numérique sur ses ennemis : six contre un [1]. Encore fallait-il connaître les effectifs sous les armes.

Certes les bureaux du ministère possédaient des états de situation ; le seul ennui c'est que, là où les états indiquaient plus de cent quarante mille hommes, Jourdan déclarait ne disposer que de dix-huit mille hommes !

Carnot réclama, le 18 novembre, des états détaillés de tous les corps de la République, en distinguant les armes, en précisant l'époque de la formation, la force effective, la tenue, la discipline et l'esprit, et en indiquant l'armée et le lieu où ce corps était employé. Beau sujet d'enquête, mais dont le cadre semble ne jamais avoir été rempli.

Des renseignements incomplets arrivèrent peu à peu. Les relevés de détail ne correspondaient pas aux récapitulations. Les chefs avouaient parfois qu'ils ne pouvaient connaître l'effectif de leurs troupes et Dubois-Crancé constata, lorsqu'on voulut embrigader, qu'il n'y avait ni registres, ni états de revue en règle [2].

L'armée comprenait bien autre chose que des régiments d'Ancien Régime et des bataillons de volontaires. Des particuliers, et des décrets, avaient créé toutes sortes de corps

francs et légions, de composition très disparate et variable.
Les cadres n'étaient ni capables, ni désireux de faire des
relevés précis. Les chefs de corps déclaraient des effectifs
grossis pour percevoir davantage. Les officiers étaient tous
d'accord pour cacher l'appauvrissement de leurs unités, car
ils craignaient les fusions qui diminuaient les cadres ; les
sous-officiers et soldats les appuyaient pour ne pas être
séparés, ce qui serait arrivé en cas de fusion. En revanche,
les généraux proclamaient toujours qu'ils manquaient
d'homme tant pour obtenir des renforts, qui accroissaient
leur importance, que pour excuser par avance des échecs
éventuels. Enfin les chefs, pour faire leurs rapports, attribuaient des effectifs arbitraires aux unités sur lesquelles
ils n'étaient pas informés [3].

L'effectif général était donc mal connu, et il fut systématiquement exagéré pour donner confiance et tromper l'ennemi. De là naquit ce compte de un million deux cent mille
hommes que reproduisent les journaux et la correspondance
de Carnot.

Approximativement Saint-Just comptait quatre cent
soixante-dix mille hommes au 15 juillet. Grâce à la levée en
masse, on en indiquait plus de six cent mille au 15 octobre,
puis six cent soixante-dix mille, en janvier 1794. Faut-il
rappeler qu'en mars 1793 on avait décidé de lever trois
cent mille hommes, et que la levée en masse aurait dû en
fournir quatre cent mille [4] ?

Dans l'ensemble ces résultats assuraient à la France une
supériorité numérique sur ses ennemis, mais relativement
modeste et qui ne prit sa valeur qu'en fonction de la répartition des forces respectives. Cependant cet accroissement
posait une série de problèmes : comment utiliser une masse
de recrues ni exercées ni aguerries? Comment maintenir une
proportion satisfaisante entre les différentes armes, alors
que les recrues étaient des fantassins? Comment rendre
maniables des armées de plus en plus importantes ? L'issue
de la campagne dépendait de la solution.

L'amalgame avait été la première réponse : les hommes
de toute origine seraient unis, mêlés et fondus. Pourtant, en
dépit des décrets du 21 février et du 12 août 1793, Carnot
avait négligé la réalisation d'une opération qui ne lui donnait
pas satisfaction.

La loi uniformisait les unités en groupant par demi-brigades trois bataillons, l'un de ligne, les autres de volon-

taires ; ainsi les premiers bénéficieraient du patriotisme des
autres, et ceux-ci profiteraient de l'expérience des premiers.
Vieille question que Carnot étudiait depuis longtemps [5].
Vieille solution aussi, dépassée par les événements.

La loi prescrivait l'embrigadement et non pas l'amalgame,
les unités étaient juxtaposées et non pas fondues. Le texte
ne tenait pas compte de la guerre, quand il ordonnait de
réaliser l'opération de régiment en régiment, et de bataillon
en bataillon, dans l'ordre numérique, en groupant les
bataillons du même département. Malgré les retouches, Carnot le jugeait inapplicable et inefficace. A ses yeux l'opposition entre ligne et volontaires, blancs et bleus, était déjà
effacée. Ce qui comptait, c'était la présence de recrues inex-
périmentées, qui ne tenaient pas au feu si elles n'étaient pas
étroitement unies aux troupes aguerries.

Le Comité tout entier était défavorable à l'embrigadement. Robespierre pensait que ce «mode d'organisation
était lié à une profonde machination». D'autre part, le
ministre de la Guerre s'étonnait que l'on voulût rompre, en
campagne, les liens qui unissaient les hommes entre eux et
à leurs chefs [6].

Il suffisait d'incorporer les recrues dans les unités incom-
plètes. C'est ce que fit Saint-Just à l'armée du Rhin, ce que
conseilla Carnot partout, et ce que décréta la Convention,
le 22 novembre, à la demande des comités réunis de Salut
public et de la Guerre [7].

Carnot voulut même faire suspendre et modifier la loi
d'embrigadement. Il se rendit au Comité de la Guerre et fit
préparer un projet qui fut présenté à la Convention, le 8 janvier 1794, par Cochon, au nom des Comités de Salut public
et de la Guerre. Mais Dubois-Crancé s'y opposa, ce fut un
échec pour Carnot et pour le Comité. L'opération, ainsi
prescrite, traîna longtemps, bien que des commissaires
fussent chargés de la réaliser. Le Comité intervenait sans
conviction : «Le Comité n'ignore pas toutes les difficultés
qui s'opposent à l'exécution de l'embrigadement tel qu'il a
été décrété par la Convention, et il y a longtemps que tu
connais son opinion sur ce sujet.» De son côté Carnot avait
obtenu que les bataillons non embrigadés seraient dotés
d'un conseil d'administration. En revanche, toutes les unités
irrégulières, corps régionaux créés au gré des circonstances,
comportant même parfois des hommes non mobilisables,
furent refondues, afin d'assurer l'homogénéité de l'armée.

Dans cette affaire, Carnot avait travaillé avec l'aide du Comité de la Guerre qui comptait nombre de spécialistes. Il lui arriva souvent de s'adresser à eux, pour des questions d'organisation et d'administration. A plusieurs reprises il s'inclina devant leur opinion, par exemple quand il s'agit de numéroter les bataillons, alors que Carnot, pour fouetter l'émulation, aurait voulu leur donner un nom : République, Liberté, etc. De même pour les méthodes d'incorporation des bataillons de nouvelle levée. Le Comité de la Guerre appelait à l'occasion des représentants du ministre de la Guerre et aussi des diverses armes [8].

En effet les volontaires, presque tous fantassins, avaient dangereusement réduit le rôle des autres armes : Cavalerie et Artillerie.

Traditionnellement la Cavalerie correspondait au quart des effectifs de l'Infanterie, ce qui lui permettait d'assurer ses missions de reconnaissance, de couverture et de combat. Depuis la guerre cette proportion était tombée au-dessous du sixième du nombre des fantassins, alors que l'ennemi disposait de cavaliers nombreux et bien entraînés. Cette disproportion nous avait infligé des pertes sévères, sans parler de la démoralisation des fantassins. En vain leur donnait-on des piques pour arrêter les escadrons, ils lâchaient le terrain plutôt que d'affronter le choc.

Depuis longtemps déjà des levées de chevaux, de sellerie et de cavaliers avaient été entreprises ; les résultats restaient décevants. En janvier 1794, on pensait disposer de quatre-vingt-seize mille cavaliers, les tableaux n'en comptaient que soixante-quatorze mille, dont cinquante-quatre mille seulement étaient présents ; la proportion s'abaissait de plus en plus. La qualité n'était pas mieux assurée que le nombre. Carnot n'était pas compétent. Il s'en rapporta soit au Comité de la Guerre, soit à des spécialistes comme Pflieger. Il avait constaté, notamment à l'armée du Nord, notre faiblesse. Il fit de son mieux pour y remédier. Il ne confia jamais un rôle essentiel à cette arme dans ses plans stratégiques [9].

En revanche, tout portait Carnot à s'intéresser à l'Artillerie : arme savante, travaillant souvent en liaison avec le Génie, dotée d'un passé glorieux qui s'enrichissait de nouvelles pages et sur laquelle son intention avait été attirée aux Pyrénées. Carnot proclamait donc, le 22 janvier 1794, « qu'il était de la plus haute importance de procurer au service de l'Artillerie toute l'activité dont il était susceptible et de lui conserver la juste célébrité qu'elle s'était acquise ».

Les bataillons de volontaires comportaient chacun deux compagnies de canonniers ; ainsi la rupture d'équilibre avait été moins grave que pour la Cavalerie. Mais ces canonniers étaient improvisés, ils ne disposaient que de petites pièces, et surtout leurs officiers étaient souvent peu qualifiés. Carnot, là encore, confia les réformes à des spécialistes : Eblé, Verrières, Belair et le singulier marquis de Montalembert.

Les officiers de canonniers furent soumis à une instruction contrôlée. Un huitième régiment d'Artillerie fut créé ; on apprit même qu'un neuvième s'organisait sans en avoir reçu l'ordre. D'autre part, l'Artillerie montée fut l'objet de gros efforts : le nombre des compagnies passa de vingt à quarante.

Le Comité de la Guerre s'inquiéta de cet accroissement : « Serait-il politique de donner une aussi grande consistance politique au corps de l'artillerie, déjà trop puissant peut-être dans une république, et qui doit nécessairement avoir une grande influence par la nature des services dont il est chargé et par la réunion de ses moyens et de ses connaissances [10] ? »

Cette défiance à l'égard des talents — des techniciens mus par un esprit de corps — allait exactement à l'encontre des vœux de Carnot. Celui-ci, au contraire, fit soutenir les techniciens et obtint que les officiers ci-devant nobles de l'Artillerie et du Génie seraient maintenus dans leurs fonctions, alors qu'ils étaient suspendus partout ailleurs. Notons que Robespierre admit volontiers cette exception, lui qui s'était élevé, à plusieurs reprises, contre la destitution générale des officiers nobles. En revanche, Bouchotte recommanda de ne réintégrer que les officiers qui étaient « incontestablement reconnus pour bons citoyens [11] ».

D'autre part, en coopération intime avec Prieur de la Côte-d'Or, Carnot pressait les fabrications de matériel et de munitions. La puissance de l'Artillerie fut donc progressivement accrue.

Quant au Génie, Carnot put enfin réaliser l'un de ses vieux projets : lui attribuer des troupes de travailleurs, sapeurs et mineurs, qui étaient rattachés jusqu'alors à l'Artillerie. C'était encore une idée de Vauban, comme beaucoup d'autres réformes de Carnot. Les décrets furent obtenus par Letourneur et Delmas. Carnot se contenta d'approuver le règlement d'organisation pris par le Conseil exécutif. Nouvelle preuve du caractère collectif de l'œuvre de Carnot. En même temps le nombre des officiers adjoints s'élevait jusqu'à deux cents, auxquels s'ajoutaient des officiers tirés des Ponts-et-Chaussées, trente-six, ce qui doublait presque les deux cent cinquante officiers du corps. D'autre part le nombre des élèves, à l'École du Génie, était accru, mais à la demande de Bouchotte et de Hentz, qui déploraient l'aristocratie de l'École de Mézières, celle-ci était transférée à Metz. Elle était d'ailleurs en pleine désorganisation. Cette mesure confirme l'amertume des souvenirs que Carnot avait conservés de Mézières [12].

Les troupes de la République — Infanterie, Cavalerie, Artillerie et Génie — étaient distribuées en armées. L'une après l'autre, celles-ci étaient nées. Au début de la Convention, Servan en distinguait huit. Cinq grandes sur la frontière active : celles du Nord, des Ardennes, de la Moselle, du Rhin et des Vosges. Deux armées secondaires, sur les montagnes : armée des Alpes et armée des Pyrénées. Enfin une armée de l'Intérieur.

Avec les circonstances, cette répartition avait changé. Les soulèvements de l'Ouest avaient supprimé l'armée de l'Intérieur au profit de l'armée des Côtes. L'armée du Rhin avait absorbé celle des Vosges, au contraire les armées de montagnes s'étaient dédoublées : armée des Alpes et armée d'Italie ; armée des Pyrénées-Orientales et armée des Pyrénées-Occidentales. Enfin l'armée de l'Ouest se subdivisa à son tour en armées de l'Ouest des Côtes de Brest et des Côtes de Cherbourg.

Onze armées étaient donc placées sur la périphérie du territoire, leur composition était calculée en fonction du rôle qu'elles devraient remplir. En janvier 1794, on observait la répartition suivant le tableau, p. 98.

Il apparaît que le principal effort continuait de porter sur la frontière nord-est, de la mer à la Suisse. On trouvait là les deux tiers de l'effectif total, la presque totalité de la Cavalerie et de l'Artillerie. Mais la supériorité sur l'ennemi était réduite à trente-cinq mille hommes environ ; ce qui était loin des désirs de Carnot. Par bonheur, il put renforcer les armées de cette zone au cours des mois qui suivirent. De quatre cent mille hommes environ, elles s'élevèrent à quatre cent soixante-dix mille à la fin du mois d'avril et quatre cent quatre-vingt mille au mois d'août, sur un effectif

Armées.	Effectif total.	Infanterie.	Cavalerie.	Artillerie.	Dont en garnison.
Nord.............	197 000	168 000	18 000	11 000	51 600
Ardennes	38 000	30 000	6 000	2 000	19 000
Moselle	71 000	55 000	12 000	4 000	21 000
Rhin	88 000	71 000	13 000	4 000	30 700
Alpes	54 400	51 000	2 000	1 400	17 800
Italie	38 300	36 400	300	1 600	8 500
Pyrénées Orientales.	51 600	48 000	2 000	1 600	9 800
Pyrénées Occident.	42 000	39 000	1 000	2 000	9 800
Ouest.............	23 200	20 000	1 600	1 600	—
C. Brest..........	20 000	—	—	—	14 600
C. Cherbourg	11 900	11 000	400	500	12 000
Total...........	635 400	529 400	56 300	29 700	194 800

total qui finissait par dépasser huit cent cinquante mille hommes.

L'armée principale était l'armée du Nord, en raison des intentions stratégiques. Elle fournit un exemple saisissant de la mauvaise utilisation des hommes : sur plus de deux cent cinquante mille, environ le tiers était immobilisé dans les forteresses ; les malades et quelques détachés, permissionnaires ou prisonniers, enlevaient encore près de vingt-sept mille, si bien qu'on ne comptait, pour l'armée active, que cent trente-huit mille hommes. Carnot s'élevait énergiquement contre ce gaspillage. « C'est une chose inconcevable, écrivait-il à propos de l'armée du Rhin, que sur quatre-vingt mille hommes à peu près il s'en trouve la moitié d'inactifs.... »

Parmi les causes d'affaiblissement, la désertion continuait de tenir une place importante. A peu près toutes les catégories de militaires avaient leurs motifs pour quitter le service. Les volontaires estimaient que leur engagement valait pour une campagne, ils étaient donc dégagés de toute obligation, leur départ n'était pas, à leurs yeux, une désertion. Ceux qui n'étaient partis que sous la contrainte se donnaient le droit d'échapper à la première occasion. Enfin ceux qui ne cherchaient que l'argent désertaient pour reprendre du service en se faisant payer. Certes la Convention avait décrété de terribles sanctions, les 3 septembre et 22 novembre 1793, mais comment les appliquer alors qu'une partie de la population était de connivence avec les déserteurs ? Mieux valait tenter de réduire les occasions de désertion. C'est ainsi que les permissions agricoles, accordées le 25 janvier 1794, furent supprimées le 11 mars. De même les congés de convalescence. On ne les accorda désormais que « dans le cas où le malade [était] atteint de la nostalgie, ou maladie du pays ». Ce trait inattendu révèle l'attachement à la petite patrie. La plupart des volontaires, et surtout les recrues de la levée en masse, n'avaient jamais quitté leur village, sinon pour se rendre au marché voisin. Ils étaient aisément dépaysés. Cette maladie se manifestait par de violentes fièvres et par la prostration.

Carnot recommanda de sévir contre la désertion, mais sans éclat : « La publicité ne serait peut-être pas sans inconvénients. » Il entreprit aussi de lutter contre les maladies. D'abord en assurant le vivre et le vêtement. Puis en améliorant les hôpitaux et en les multipliant. Il accordait la plus grande attention aux variations du pourcentage des malades, et n'admettait pas qu'il s'élevât jusqu'au tiers ou à la moitié des effectifs, comme on le constatait dans certaines unités.

Finalement les résultats permirent de ne pas effectuer de nouvelles levées, de ne pas appeler d'autres classes de conscrits comme on l'avait envisagé. La République disposait d'une véritable masse armée [13].

Pour tirer parti de cette masse, il était indispensable de la soumettre à un minimum de discipline. Carnot n'avait plus aucune illusion sur la discipline spontanée qu'il avait vantée à la Législative. Il ne devait jamais oublier les scènes de désordre qui s'étaient déroulées sous ses yeux, à Furnes ; aussi était-il revenu à la doctrine traditionnelle : « La force armée est essentiellement obéissante. » La justice militaire fut réorganisée par le décret du 22 janvier 1794, et l'envoi de députations par les troupes fut interdit par celui du 14 janvier. Cependant on n'assista pas à une réaction ramenant aux pratiques d'Ancien Régime, la discipline que prescrivait Carnot ne devait pas être minutieuse. On fut de plus en plus sévère pour tout ce qui compromettait les opérations ou la politique générale, et l'on passa sur le reste. Il appartenait aux généraux — et aux représentants en mission — d'agir en conséquence. Carnot n'intervint pas dans le détail.

Mais il voulut susciter l'émulation, tellement préférable à la répression. Les prouesses étaient citées à la Convention, et ce procédé était assez efficace pour que des réclamations fussent adressées quand un rapport exaltant les hauts faits d'une unité n'avait pas été lu à l'Assemblée et cité au procès-verbal. L'esprit de corps était encouragé. Carnot aurait voulu que les armées françaises obtinssent une réputation d'invincibilité. Enfin le patriotisme, l'ardeur républicaine, la furie française constituaient les suprêmes rappels, auxquels il paraît bien que les chefs et les hommes étaient sensibles.

L'armée française connut alors la période la plus brillante de son histoire au cours de la Révolution. Les étrangers et les officiers d'Ancien Régime s'étonnaient du mordant extraordinaire des troupes, de l'autorité terrible des représentants en mission, de l'alliage inouï de liberté et de discipline, de désordre et d'audace, de patriotisme et de dédain à l'égard des ennemis. Cet équilibre précaire entre l'anarchie héroïque et le militarisme chauvin permit les victoires [14].

Ainsi la Révolution avait-elle enfin provoqué dans le domaine militaire ses conséquences révolutionnaires : l'armée nationale était née.

*
* *

Ce bouleversement devait entraîner de multiples répercussions profondes et souvent imprévisibles, sur la guerre, sur la politique internationale, sur la politique intérieure, les finances, l'économie, la société. Sans céder à l'emphase chère aux Conventionnels, on peut parler d'ère nouvelle dans la vie des peuples ; c'est ce qu'on n'a pas manqué de faire souvent depuis ce temps. Mais, alors que la postérité n'a pas manqué de regretter les maux accompagnant cette transformation, les contemporains — spécialement Carnot, confiant dans la supériorité démographique de la France — ont jugé qu'il s'agissait d'un effort tout à fait exceptionnel et qui resterait unique en son genre, comme le gouvernement révolutionnaire lui-même. La France victorieuse se contenterait ensuite de ses virtualités : elle aurait à sa disposition du matériel et des armes, elle ferait accomplir un bref entraînement aux hommes, et la seule possibilité d'une levée gigantesque contiendrait les autres puissances et garantirait la paix. Rêve de la dernière des guerres....

En attendant, la France était la première « nation armée » qui se fût organisée.

Ce ne fut pas l'œuvre personnelle et exclusive de Carnot, mais il y avait contribué dans toute la mesure de ses pouvoirs qui étaient immenses, et il devint, de plus en plus, le chef de toutes ces armées, grâce à l'autorité souveraine du Comité. Il avait contribué à organiser les forces de la France, il avait puissamment coordonné les initiatives et les réalisations, il lui appartenait de tirer le meilleur parti des troupes ainsi préparées. Ce fut l'organisation de la victoire.

CHAPITRE IX

ORGANISATION DE LA VICTOIRE

« CE CARNOT, sans même avoir cette magie de science qui se dissipera quand on voudra l'apprécier.... » Xavier Audouin allait même jusqu'à prétendre que jamais le Comité n'envoya ni plans, ni instructions aux généraux. C'était là l'une des premières manifestations d'une opposition de gauche qui n'a guère désarmé depuis. D'autre part, un émigré attribuait les plans à une équipe d'officiers d'Ancien Régime, cachés dans les bureaux du Comité : « On leur promit la vie pour prix de leurs talents et de leurs veilles. » Opposition de droite cette fois, s'appliquant à diminuer le régicide, et qui s'est longuement prolongée [1]. Mais, avec le temps, une coalition s'est nouée entre gauche et droite, unies contre un courant traditionnel et familial qui célébrait dans Carnot l'organisateur — le seul — de la victoire. Ce conflit a suffisamment brouillé toutes les données pour qu'il soit indispensable de définir le rôle de Carnot à partir des documents.

Lorsque Carnot arriva au Comité, la conduite de la guerre souffrait d'une crise profonde, d'ordre politique et technique. Politiquement le pouvoir glissait du Conseil exécutif au Comité de Salut public. Le premier hésitait à imposer ses vues, d'autant plus que le ministre de la Guerre était sur le point d'être remplacé. Le second manquait de compétence. Saint-Just, qui s'occupait de la section militaire, était accablé de travail, car il intervenait dans beaucoup d'autres domaines. L'un et l'autre ne savaient plus à quel général se vouer. C'était même là le point crucial : les chefs qualifiés pour conduire la guerre avaient tous trahi la Révolution : le roi d'abord, La Fayette ensuite, et Dumouriez ; enfin on croyait voir Custine trahir à son tour. Le régime suspectait, redoutait et détestait les généraux dont il ne pouvait se passer. Il avait tendance à grouper autour de lui quelques généraux retraités, ou suspendus, donc à sa discrétion parce qu'ils n'avaient pas d'armée. Mais les uns avaient prouvé leur incapacité, d'autres paraissaient encore dangereux, ainsi ce Grimoard, que le Comité venait de congédier. On avait donc introduit au Comité des militaires républicains, Prieur de la Côte-d'Or et Carnot [2].

Ceux-ci se heurtèrent à la crise technique. Les méthodes traditionnelles n'étaient plus applicables. Les sièges en règle, les cordons de troupes veillant aux frontières, les opérations lentes et méthodiques destinées à contraindre l'ennemi au repli, par la menace pesant sur ses communications et sur ses magasins, toute cette stratégie classique exigeait des troupes exercées, des techniciens, des délais. La Révolution n'avait plus de troupes de métier, fort peu de techniciens, et surtout elle ne disposait d'aucun délai. Chaque mois coûtait des hommes, du matériel, des dépenses telles qu'il paraissait essentiel de vaincre et de clore la campagne et la guerre. Il fallait inventer une stratégie exploitant la supériorité numérique — la masse — et l'élan révolutionnaire, à défaut du métier, pour abréger la durée de la guerre et, avec elle, toutes les contraintes. C'est là que le problème technique rejoignait le problème politique ; le gouvernement était révolutionnaire jusqu'à la paix, raison impérieuse pour obtenir une paix prochaine, sinon la France serait épuisée et l'élan révolutionnaire se briserait ou s'épuiserait.

Carnot était profondément convaincu de la nécessité primordiale d'une prompte et définitive victoire, mais il n'apportait ni plan général, ni système prémédité. Il avait cependant des vues précises sur des points limités : l'armée du Nord devait jouer le rôle principal, sa tâche initiale devait être la prise d'Ostende. Ces vues furent modifiées par l'initiative ennemie qui le contraignit à sauver Dunkerque et Maubeuge. Il y parvint, en recourant aux méthodes classiques, mais en présentant d'autres procédés : dans les deux cas il songea à quelque grande bataille qui eût mis l'adversaire hors d'état de poursuivre la lutte.

Sans aucun doute il ne voulut agir ni seul, ni impérieusement. Toutefois son rôle fut assez personnel pour être signalé, à la Convention, par ses collègues. Robespierre vantait à Saint-Just les plans de Carnot; Jourdan, comme Saint-Just, sollicitait ses conseils [3].

Au long de l'automne 1793, Carnot élabora lentement le

plan d'opérations de l'an II, mais il s'appliquait à modifier immédiatement les méthodes de combat. S'il ne présenta un résumé cohérent de la nouvelle méthode qu'à la fin de janvier 1794, il s'en faut de beaucoup que celle-ci ait été conçue et révélée à cette date. Elle prit corps, lentement, au cours de l'été et de l'automne 1793.

L'idée maîtresse était de faire une guerre de masses ; il faut « agir toujours en masse ». La formule était opportune, la masse était alors un mot d'ordre inlassablement répété, dont les résonances plaisaient aux révolutionnaires. La masse était associée à la démocratie, au suffrage universel, à l'émancipa-tion du citoyen. La levée « en masse » répondait au vœu des Hébertistes et des Enragés, nous l'avons vu. La guerre de masses découlait de la levée en masse. Idée-force, mythe révolutionnaire, notion confuse, la guerre de masses pouvait se clarifier et devenir une méthode, comme la levée en masse était devenue une conscription. Ce fut l'œuvre de Carnot, et de beaucoup d'autres.

La guerre de masses devenait l'art d'utiliser le nombre, mais aussi le soldat révolutionnaire. A une situation révo-lutionnaire correspondit une méthode révolutionnaire Elle rompait radicalement avec la méthode traditionnelle qui reposait sur l'emploi d'armées de métier peu nom-breuses, mais exercées. Dès janvier 1793, Grimoard avait écrit que « le moyen le plus simple de suppléer à l'art par le nombre [était] de faire une guerre de masses », et il avait précisé la signification de ce conseil : il s'agissait de « diriger toujours, sur les points d'attaque, le plus de troupes et d'artillerie qu'on pourra ». Il s'agissait non plus d'effectifs énormes, répartis peureusement dans toutes les places fortes, dans toutes les villes menacées, au long de toutes les fron-tières en camps plus ou moins improvisés, pour former des cordons, mais au contraire de condensations volontaires, préméditées, là où le coup serait asséné à l'ennemi.

L'idée fit fortune, les généraux, représentants, ministres, membres du Comité la reprirent et la développèrent. Ils prescrivaient de réduire les garnisons, d'attaquer avec des forces aussi élevées que possible, d'accabler l'ennemi sous le nombre. Carnot ne fit que la reprendre et que l'ériger en règle formellement prescrite à tous. Il était de ceux, innom-brables, pour qui la nouvelle méthode n'excluait pas le rôle protecteur des forteresses en cas d'échec. Hoche se montra beaucoup plus novateur — et sans succès — quand il proposa de « raser les places fortes que nous ne pouvons défendre sans nous disséminer ». Réveil d'une farouche controverse à la veille de la Révolution : les forts ou les hommes ? les sièges ou la bataille ? — la ligne Maginot ou l'armée motorisée ? pourrions-nous dire. Le prudent Carnot refusait l'alternative.

Cette contradiction entre la doctrine et les faits éclaire une opposition qu'on pourrait être tenté d'expliquer par le parti pris de certains historiens. Les uns, exaltant son rôle, voient en Carnot l'homme de la guerre de masses, ce sont ceux qui s'en tiennent aux écrits. D'autres, minimisant l'influence de Carnot, nient qu'il ait transformé l'art de la guerre : ils s'appuient sur les faits. Pourquoi ne pas tenir compte des écrits *et* des faits ? Pourquoi ne pas reconnaître que si Carnot n'eut pas seul la volonté de mener une guerre de masses, il ne fut pas non plus le seul responsable des maladresses et des erreurs ?

La possibilité de manœuvrer les masses, pour les grouper sur des points choisis, avait pourtant fait des progrès. Une armée de cent mille hommes, divisée en petites unités, demi-brigades d'Infanterie, escadrons de Cavalerie, compagnies d'Artillerie se prêtait au morcellement plus qu'à la masse. Le mouvement exigeait un épuisant effort de l'état-major qui devait s'adresser à une multitude de chefs subalternes, l'action combattante s'organisait malaisément. L'articulation fut accomplie, à partir du mois d'août 1793, par un officier d'état-major — officier de circonstance, car c'était un ingénieur des Ponts-et-Chaussées —, Berthelmy, nommé adjudant général par Custine, et qui dirigea l'état-major de Houchard [4].

En prenant possession de ses fonctions à l'armée, Berthelmy avait constaté le mal qui paralysait l'armée du Nord. « Il y a un nombre prodigieux d'hommes, et elle n'est pas forte, parce qu'elle est disséminée sans ordre. » Il avait trouvé et imposé la solution : organiser cette foule en « masses agissantes », de cinq mille hommes en moyenne, et qui rassemblaient, sous les ordres d'un général de division, deux brigades d'Infanterie, avec leurs généraux de brigade, de l'Infanterie légère, et, selon les besoins, de la Cavalerie. C'étaient les divisions. A leur tour les divisions se distribuaient en trois corps, des corps d'armée.

Bouchotte ne comprit pas la portée de cette innovation : « en révolution, fit-il observer à Berthelmy, le mieux est l'ennemi du bien ». En dépit de cette incompréhension, la réforme se généralisa : dans les diverses armées, on trouva des divisions — de dix mille hommes en moyenne — et qui dosaient les diverses armes conformément aux intentions tactiques.

Carnot ne paraît pas s'être particulièrement intéressé à cette organisation, ni aux divisions, ni aux corps qui restèrent — à la différence des divisions — assez exceptionnels. Pourtant l'endivisionnement favorisa l'exercice de son autorité [5].

Mener une guerre de masses, c'était aussi « se jeter brusquement à coups de baïonnette, sans songer ni à tirailler ni à faire des manœuvres, auxquelles les troupes françaises ne sont nullement exercées, ni même préparées », c'était adopter une « manière de combattre analogue à l'impétuosité et au caractère naturels de la nation ». A cette déclaration de Grimoard, Saint-Just avait fait écho, huit mois plus tard, lorsqu'il avait déclaré, à la Convention, que « le système français [devait] être impétueux », et qu'il avait préconisé « l'ordre de choc ».

Tout ce qu'on avait écrit sur l'attaque et sur l'arme blanche, entre les déclarations de Grimoard et celles de Saint-Just, s'inscrivait dans la même ligne, qu'il s'agît de Bouchotte, des Hébertistes ou des Enragés, de Danton ou de Hoche. Celui-ci avait peut-être frappé l'une des formules les plus outrées : « Point de manœuvres, point d'art, du fer, du feu et du patriotisme. » Nous retrouvons là le thème extrême de la masse révolutionnaire insurgée.

La position de Carnot était singulière : l'homme à talents répugnait à cette négation de l'art, mais il concevait un art nouveau pour employer des troupes sans talents. Depuis le fameux discours sur les piques, il était acquis au combat à l'arme blanche, à l'attaque exploitant l'élan patriotique, sinon le caractère national. Dès février 1793, il s'était rallié à l'offensive, lui qui avait longtemps professé que la défensive seule était justifiable, civilisée, et conforme au régime constitutionnel, lui pour qui la guerre était un art de conservation. Il avait déclaré : « La guerre est un état violent ; il faut la faire à outrance, ou rentrer dans ses foyers. »

Cette conversion correspondait aux circonstances — et ne devait pas durer plus qu'elles, ce n'était pas seulement au point de vue politique qu'on adoptait des solutions révolutionnaires « jusqu'à la paix ». Il fallait s'adapter aux soldats des armées républicaines. Il fallait surtout faire une guerre courte, pour arrêter l'effusion du sang, le gaspillage de l'argent et du matériel et empêcher l'épuisement de la France.

La guerre de masses était offensive, mais l'offensive devait être destructrice, trait plus neuf encore. Barère a prononcé un mot fameux : « Il n'y a que les morts qui ne reviennent pas. » Carnot a souscrit à ce mot. Sa correspondance est bourrée de rappels de cette farouche obligation : il faut anéantir, exterminer, détruire définitivement l'ennemi. Généraux et soldats, représentants en mission ne doivent jamais l'oublier. Houchard fut guillotiné pour ne pas l'avoir fait.

Là encore deux écoles d'historiens s'opposent. Les uns reprochent à Carnot cette forme terrifiante de la guerre. Les autres lui font grief de n'avoir pas détruit l'adversaire. Il s'agit encore, nous le verrons, du contraste entre les mots d'ordre et les réalisations. En thermidor, à la fin du Grand Comité, l'adversaire n'était pas détruit : aucune des batailles ne fut une bataille de destruction. Les opérations ne furent pas couronnées par l'anéantissement de l'adversaire. Mais Carnot ne fut pas le promoteur unique et spécialement représentatif de la guerre de destruction, il s'y convertit et il ordonna de la réaliser. Et si elle n'aboutit pas, il n'en fut pas le seul responsable : les exécutants eurent leur part de responsabilité dans cet échec, comme ils l'eurent dans les victoires. Enfin Carnot échoua par ses erreurs dans les ordres donnés, mais non par son intention.

Son rôle dans le recours à la haine fut plus nuancé. La haine entre les adversaires éclate toujours dès que se heurtent des conceptions irréductibles et intransigeantes : la guerre étrangère participe alors de la guerre civile. Mais le recours à la force terrible que donne la haine suppose une volonté consciente, une décision préméditée. Robespierre, dans un discours fameux, se faisait un devoir de propager parmi les Français la haine contre les Anglais, contre le peuple anglais. Carnot, lui aussi, a rappelé aux armées qu'elles devaient « faire profession de haïr et de mépriser » l'ennemi. Il a écrit qu'il ne voulait pas voir le soldat français mollir et s'apitoyer sur le sort des hypocrites et sanguinaires ennemis de notre liberté. Il voulait vaincre par la terreur : « Il faut exterminer [l'ennemi] jusqu'au dernier s'il est possible, pendant que la *terreur* est chez lui à l'ordre du jour. »

Ce recours à la terreur est encore plus évident dans les

décrets concernant les places assiégées : les ennemis occupant des places françaises seraient passés au fil de l'épée s'ils ne se rendaient pas dans les vingt-quatre heures. Carnot recommandait à Jourdan de publier ce décret et de l'appliquer, il prescrivait de faire un exemple avec la garnison de Nieuport, « autrement celles des villes envahies s'attendraient à une pareille condescendance et ne se rendraient point ».

Les Britanniques furent spécialement visés, un décret ordonnait de fusiller ceux qui tomberaient entre nos mains : pas de prisonniers !

La propagande attisait systématiquement la haine, en représentant les troupes adverses comme des bandes d'esclaves, dégradés et féroces....

> ... ces féroces soldats,
> qui viennent jusque dans vos bras
> égorger vos fils, vos compagnes !

Réciproquement, les coalisés montraient l'armée française sous l'aspect d'une horde sanguinaire, dévastatrice et barbare. On se prêtait mutuellement des atrocités qui soulevaient la colère, la peur et appelaient la vengeance.

Carnot ne fut pourtant pas le principal promoteur de cette méthode, il hésita parfois à en exiger l'application. Il doutait de l'efficacité de cette guerre totale. Il refusa de déclencher les forces sauvages que lui proposèrent quelques contemporains. Comme celui qui voulait propager une épidémie générale chez l'adversaire — guerre bactériologique avant la lettre — ou comme cet autre qui, pour mater le fanatisme espagnol, proposait de terroriser l'ennemi par des exécutions systématiques, notamment de moines, sans parler de celui qui voulait charger les canons des vaisseaux avec des briquets phosphoriques. Carnot et ses collègues reculaient devant la « guerre de Tartares » qu'avait prophétisée d'Arçon. Mais il contribua à semer et à faire éclore la haine entre les nations, à pousser l'Europe vers la guerre inexpiable, tant par les sentiments qu'il cultiva que par les dommages matériels qu'il ordonna.

On en venait à cette cruelle perspective de voir, selon un mot de Carnot, le 27 mai, la guerre « se nationaliser contre nous ».

Renoncer à la guerre de propagande républicaine, ce n'était pas forcément développer le respect pour la liberté de chaque peuple. Si l'on déclarait y renoncer parce que ces peuples n'étaient pas mûrs pour la liberté, qu'ils en étaient indignes, on incitait à les mépriser. Exalter la République et le caractère national tournait aisément au chauvinisme.

Nourrir la guerre par la guerre, c'était une nécessité plus qu'une méthode, mais cette nécessité provoquait la haine.

Ainsi la mobilisation des passions ne pouvait se limiter aux hommes sous les armes, elle devait galvaniser contre les peuples voisins la nation tout entière, puisque la guerre l'affectait profondément. La presse, officieuse ou non, ne s'en fit pas faute. Les historiens de la littérature de propagande en temps de guerre devraient chercher là les origines d'un genre spécial qui a connu depuis un essor inégalement apprécié. Depuis longtemps Carnot s'y intéressait, sans songer aux lointaines répercussions, simplement pour hâter la victoire.

Mais les civils étaient touchés plus directement encore par la guerre. Carnot n'admettait pas que les paysans français des zones occupées fussent autorisés à obéir aux réquisitions de l'adversaire, et moins encore qu'ils lui vendissent des denrées, grains ou bétail. Il en vint à prescrire l'évacuation des populations.

En revanche il tenait absolument — par nécessité — à lever chez l'ennemi toutes les réquisitions et contributions imaginables. Même si cet ennemi se montrait favorable à la France et aux idées républicaines : ce ne pouvait être qu'hypocrisie afin de nous trahir. Sans doute Carnot voulait-il respecter le mot d'ordre : « paix aux chaumières »; il souhaitait que « le pauvre se réjouisse» dans les régions qu'occuperaient nos armées, mais l'essentiel à ses yeux était la réquisition.

Carnot prescrivit de dépouiller systématiquement et intégralement les pays occupés. Il fut obéi. Un volontaire écrivait à son père : « Le pays que nous occupons est très beau, il était riche avant notre entrée, mais les commissaires de la Convention pour l'évacuation du Palatinat ont tout fait partir pour Strasbourg et Landau.... Ce pays est totalement ruiné, pour dix ans au moins. » Un autre écrivait, de Puycerda, à sa famille : « Nous pillâmes avec énergie. » Le souvenir de ces prouesses n'est pas encore effacé[6].

Tous ces résultats lointains n'ont été ni voulus, ni prévus par Carnot; seule la victoire prochaine et indispensable explique ses efforts. Les nouvelles méthodes de la guerre sont nées de la situation et non d'une volonté préméditée. Carnot a dû tirer des conclusions révolutionnaires d'une situation révolutionnaire. Mais il ne fut ni le premier, ni le seul. Sa fonction et son esprit méthodique l'amenèrent cependant à systématiser et à généraliser ce que lui-même et d'autres avaient imaginé. Il se sépara nettement des autorités supérieures du Corps du Génie qui en étaient encore à réclamer une armée spéciale pour chaque camp retranché !

Les profondes transformations de l'armée et de la guerre ne paraissent avoir été comprises par l'ennemi qu'assez tardivement, après les circulaires de Carnot qui les résumaient. A cette époque, en effet, les rapports des agents secrets révélèrent que l'armée française ne dépendait plus ni du ministre, ni du Comité militaire, ni de l'Assemblée, mais du seul Comité de Salut public, qui traitait le ministre en commis. Ils exposèrent que le Comité avait lancé le mot d'ordre d' « attaquer toujours, et toujours en grandes masses », pour exploiter le nombre et l'ardeur du soldat révolutionnaire. L'armée française disposait, savaient-ils, de 600 000 à 700 000 hommes, et la population de la France pourrait permettre de porter cet effectif jusqu'à 1 300 000. Le soldat était fanatisé par la propagande, il manifestait des qualités redoutables de « célérité et d'impétuosité ». Le gouvernement comptait les hommes pour rien, et l'Europe s'effrayait de cette innovation, de cette force terrible : un peuple-soldat [7].

La mise en œuvre de cette force nouvelle appartenait au Comité. Il la prépara en tenant compte des moyens et des intentions de l'ennemi. Le recours aux espions fut l'un des aspects typiques de cette guerre. Français et Anglais, notamment, se plaignaient que leurs villes fussent infestées d'agents équivoques et perfides; le Comité fut amené à dénoncer une « conspiration de l'étranger », mais il soldait aussi une nuée d'agents, et Carnot — dont nous avons déjà rencontré l'activité dans ce domaine — recommandait aux représentants et aux généraux d'agir de même, il fournissait des fonds à cet usage. « Aie de bons espions, écrivait-il à Pichegru, sache tout ce qui se passe chez les ennemis, jette la division parmi eux, tous les moyens sont bons pour écraser la tyrannie ; nous ferons à cet égard tous les sacrifices pécuniaires qu'il faudra. »

Cet espionnage est très mal connu. On sait pourtant que

les Anglais étaient parvenus à couvrir la France de chaînes
et de réseaux d'agents secrets qui couvraient le territoire, à la
façon des réseaux de la deuxième guerre mondiale. Les ports
étaient les aboutissements où se pressaient ces agents ; en
France, Calais paraît avoir joué un grand rôle, de même que
de petites rades, aux environs de Dunkerque par exemple.
A l'étranger, les conditions étaient encore plus favorables,
car la circulation était plus aisée. Hambourg fut un foyer
d'intrigues où se combattaient sourdement les envoyés
français et étrangers. Dans le voisinage de la Suisse rayon-
naient les émissaires que dirigea — et paya — longtemps
Wickham. De ces points, des relais permettaient de parcourir le territoire de la République, d'atteindre les points
névralgiques, les régions insurgées par exemple, ou mieux
les centres d'informations, les ministères, les comités,
l'Assemblée. A Paris même un Anglais, Sommers, dirigeait
l'espionnage ; à Londres, c'était Burges. Ils gagnaient des
fonctionnaires, tant en les payant qu'en s'appuyant sur leurs
convictions politiques, hostiles à la République et à la
Terreur. Les agents étaient spécialisés au point qu'un
espion chargé de s'informer sur la marine et les ports négli-
geait d'utiliser les renseignements qu'il aurait pu obtenir
sur la défense de l'intérieur et des frontières. Un agent avait,
le 19 juillet, dénoncé Carnot, comme chargé de diriger
l'action clandestine en Angleterre. Un autre signalait que,
parmi les décisions majeures du Comité dans la conduite
de la guerre, figurait le développement de l'espionnage,
spécialement en Angleterre.

Le Comité n'ignorait pas l'action des agents de l'étranger,
singulièrement les informations reçues sur les décisions et
les discussions du Comité lui-même. On connaît aujourd'hui
l'officine que tenait d'Antraigues à Venise. Ce fait explique
bien des mesures : le renforcement de l'espionnage, la Terreur, la suspicion quasi universelle.

Pourquoi les biographes ont-ils ignoré cet aspect important et encore obscur de l'activité de Carnot [8] ? Les plans
furent arrêtés en s'appuyant sur des renseignements ainsi
obtenus, mais ils furent aussitôt connus des adversaires par
leurs agents. La surprise n'a pas joué.

***

Le « système général des opérations militaires de la
campagne prochaine », communiqué le 30 janvier 1794 aux

commandants des armées, fournit le plan stratégique qui définit la conduite de la guerre en l'an II. On a souvent étudié ce document capital, manuscrit autographe de Carnot. Nous le reprenons ici avec l'intention de dégager le rôle personnel de son auteur, en replaçant ce document dans la série des pièces que rédigea son auteur et des plans dus à d'autres stratèges.

La pensée se présente sans détours, aussi nettement formulée que dans les œuvres scientifiques de Carnot. La précision des vues et la vigueur des motifs justifient cette expression de système, si volontiers usitée à l'époque.

L'idée maîtresse est de lier étroitement l'action de toutes les armées au service d'un plan commun et dont les moments et les tâches se distribueraient impérieusement. Vieille règle fondamentale, et jusqu'alors non appliquée. Carnot, grâce à l'autorité du Comité, grâce à ses relations personnelles avec les généraux et les représentants en mission, pouvait enfin lui donner vie.

Cette action concertée devait aboutir à décider la guerre dans le Nord. Carnot motivait fortement cette décision : c'est dans le Nord que le danger est menaçant, par les forces et les intentions d'un ennemi qui vise Paris, c'est aussi dans le Nord que l'ennemi est le plus vulnérable, car la Flandre est ouverte, sans places fortes, et parce que la population peut être soulevée contre lui.

Projet et arguments bien classiques, auxquels Carnot était d'autant plus sensible qu'il tenait à la région et à l'armée du Nord par une grande partie de son passé. Dumouriez, Custine, Houchard avaient conclu comme lui ; les chefs d'état-major novateurs, Gobert, Tardy et Sauviac, avaient fait la même proposition. Hoche voulait attaquer Tournai et Ostende, Sauveur Chénier envisageait la conquête de la Belgique. Le mémoire classique de l'ingénieur Lafitte-Clavé se prononçait dans le même sens [9].

On aurait tort, cependant, de croire que personne n'avait entrepris de porter ailleurs le principal effort. Naguère Custine songeait à forcer le Rhin. Au moment même où Carnot écrivait, Kellermann préconisait un système d'opérations autrement neuf et audacieux : une offensive en Allemagne pénétrant jusqu'au cœur de l'Empire, une autre en Italie, sur Turin et la plaine du Pô, en soutenant Gênes, pour « porter par là un coup mortel aux coalisés ». Ailleurs on se contenterait d'une défensive active. Ce plan, jusqu'alors inconnu, fut présenté à Carnot, puisqu'il est conservé dans ses archives.

Dans les mêmes circonstances, un plan était fourni par Grimoard ; lui aussi visait l'Allemagne, et spécialement la zone comprise entre les montagnes et la rive droite du Danube ; il comportait en outre l'occupation des passages qui conduisent en Italie par les Grisons. Ce plan était adressé à Robert Lindet. Nous n'insistons pas sur un projet démesuré où Sauviac conduisait simultanément l'offensive dans le Nord, sur le Rhin, en Italie et en Espagne. Ces indications prouvent que Carnot avait le choix, qu'il pouvait puiser à des sources très diverses, et qu'il refusa d'être aventureux et novateur.

Vouloir battre l'ennemi dans le Nord parce qu'il y avait rassemblé ses forces principales était un raisonnement contestable. L'alternative se répéta dans la suite : offensive au nord ou à l'est. La proposition de Carnot était la moins neuve et la plus prudente : l'offensive répondait surtout à la préoccupation politique de sauver Paris.

D'autre part l'action dans le Nord était l'aile droite d'une grande action politico-militaire qui devait porter son aile gauche en Angleterre au moyen d'un débarquement. Là serait l'offensive proprement dite. Elle permettrait de disloquer la coalition. D'autant mieux que les Prussiens, systématiquement ménagés, pourraient être amenés à se retirer. Carnot se rencontrait là avec d'Arçon, qui prêchait depuis janvier 1793 la descente en Angleterre, et avec Hoche, qui, en automne, insistait de plus en plus sur l'opportunité et l'efficacité d'une telle opération. Mais, là encore, Carnot sacrifiait à la prudence : l'action en Angleterre ne serait entreprise que le jour où le danger aurait cessé dans l'Ouest et serait atténué sur les frontières continentales. En somme, l'idée de la pointe sur Ostende restait la dominante [10].

Les modalités de réalisation ne sont pas exposées dans le « système » qui se présente comme « général » ; elles firent l'objet de lettres ultérieures, comme celle que Carnot écrivit à Pichegru, le 11 mars.

Dans le Nord, Carnot insistait sur la prise d'Ypres, qui couvrirait les places, raccourcirait la ligne de défense et inquiéterait l'ennemi. Comme on l'a observé, Carnot appliqua les idées de Lafitte-Clavé, tout comme l'aurait voulu Sauviac [11].

La prise d'Ypres devait être favorisée par deux offensives : celle de l'armée des Ardennes sur Charleroi, et celle d'un corps de l'armée de la Moselle sur Liège, idée souvent émise depuis Custine.

Le tout serait l'occasion d'une « grande bataille... qui [devrait] décider du sort de la campagne ». Cette bataille serait livrée entre la Lys et l'Escaut, pour couper toute retraite à l'ennemi, « dans l'entonnoir que forment ces deux rivières ». C'était la tactique de la masse. Ainsi se dessinait la méthode de destruction. Carnot disait encore : « Quand, par des opérations partielles, nous serions venus à bout de détruire la moitié de l'armée ennemie, il lui resterait encore les moyens de nous attaquer de nouveau l'année prochaine. » Il prescrivait donc un anéantissement total.

Les armées du Rhin, de la Moselle et des Alpes étaient associées à ce plan. Les premières devaient prendre le fort de Kehl, marcher sur Trèves et s'en emparer ; la troisième prendrait possession des passages alpestres, Petit-Saint-Bernard, Petit et Grand Mont-Cenis [12].

Ce plan a été critiqué abondamment et, en même temps, on a voulu en retirer la paternité à Carnot. Ce qui prouve que les adversaires de Carnot ne s'entendaient pas. On a dit que les dispositions arrêtées n'empêchaient pas les ennemis de se replier. Effectivement la bataille d'anéantissement n'eut pas lieu. Mais l'intention de Carnot n'est pas douteuse, il voulait couvrir Paris *et* détruire l'ennemi. Une fois de plus nous constatons la contradiction entre l'intention et l'événement : Carnot voulait mener la guerre dans une voie nouvelle, il avait grand-peine à y parvenir. Comment établissait-il ses plans ?

La première réponse est fournie par lui-même : il étudiait les ouvrages des spécialistes, stratèges français et étrangers, généraux qui avaient raconté leurs campagnes. Sa correspondance et sa bibliothèque en font foi. Ainsi se réclamait-il du stratège anglais Lloyd ; il rassemblait autour de lui les principaux ouvrages militaires, dans la bibliothèque du Comité, puis dans la sienne, d'où beaucoup sont passés dans les collections appartenant aujourd'hui encore à sa famille. Ce travail de cabinet était une méthode classique à laquelle il se tint. Les étrangers le savaient : un rapport du 25 janvier 1794 exposait que les auteurs des plans étaient « aidés de secours immenses en cartes, plans, reconnaissances, recueillis au dépôt de la Guerre », ainsi travaillaient-ils

« réellement d'après l'expérience et les lumières des plus grands généraux de l'ancienne monarchie ». Quelques années plus tard, un mémoire s'en expliquait plus catégoriquement encore : « Ses connaissances militaires [celles de Carnot] sont hors de doute, mais il manque de génie ; et là où finissent les renseignements que pouvait lui fournir le dépôt de la Guerre, s'est aussi terminée sa gloire. »

Cette méthode livresque n'était pas le fait du seul Carnot, elle était traditionnelle — elle le resta fort longtemps après lui. Grimoard ne cachait pas ses emprunts à Turenne et Créqui, par exemple, et il en concluait, non sans présomption, que ses projets, « présentant les résultats de nos plus grands généraux, devaient produire les mêmes effets que de leur temps ». La plupart des généraux instruits faisaient comme lui. Bonaparte recourut aussi à une large information. Carnot, pourvu de ses dossiers, étudiait les cartes et tentait d'appliquer les idées stratégiques à la situation respective des forces républicaines et étrangères [13].

Mais il n'agissait pas seul, a-t-on dit ; il recourait à une équipe ; c'est même là que s'accomplissait le véritable travail d'adaptation et de création. Carnot était le rapporteur de cette équipe au Comité.

Cette accusation se trouve d'abord dans les papiers anglais. Un rapport du 25 janvier 1794 montre « un conseil de guerre » formé d'officiers d'Artillerie et du Génie, préparant les opérations et rédigeant les plans. Le 23 mars, l'agent fameux qui informait d'Antraigues déclara « que le Comité de Salut public ne fait jamais autre chose que de revêtir de son nom, en forme de décret, les délibérations du Comité de la Guerre ». Celui-ci était formé de quinze personnes dont il désignait les principales : d'Arçon, Lafitte [Clavé], Bosting [Rostaing], Larivière et Latour. Cette information a été reproduite plus souvent qu'elle n'a été soumise à la critique. On se serait aperçu que la plupart des personnages énumérés étaient dans l'impossibilité absolue d'accomplir la tâche qu'on leur attribuait. Le caractère hypothétique de cette liste apparaît mieux encore lorsqu'on la compare avec celle que Mallet du Pan proposait de son côté, et où seuls d'Arçon et Lafitte-Clavé étaient communs avec la précédente, mais en compagnie cette fois de Meusnier, Favart, Saint-Fief. Mallet exaltait les qualités de son ancien ami d'Arçon et affirmait que Carnot assistait aux séances de ce petit Comité, en transmettait les résultats au Comité

— tâche que les *Dropmore Papers* confiaient à d'Arçon —, les défendait, les développait et transformait en arrêtés ou en lettres. Ces divergences doivent mettre en garde, comme la présence supposée de personnages morts ou éloignés. Selon toute apparence les espions ont confondu le Comité parlementaire de la Guerre et le Comité des Fortifications avec ce Comité fantôme, dont aucune trace n'a subsisté ailleurs que dans ces lettres.

Il n'en reste pas moins que Carnot ne travaillait pas seul : il consultait, comme on avait toujours fait avant lui. Ainsi il invita son ami Garrau à venir à Paris pour discuter les plans. Il recevait des propositions, sans même les avoir demandées, mais les apostilles prouvent qu'il les examinait : Expédie ton plan « sous le couvert du citoyen Carnot, l'un de nous, et tu peux être sûr qu'il sera examiné avec soin », répondait le Comité à un correspondant.

Il suffit de prendre le mémoire que Dumas aurait fait lire par Bouchotte, les 30 et 31 janvier 1794, et qui aurait inspiré le « système général ». L'analyse fournie par l'agent montre bien que Carnot n'a pas chaussé les bottes de Mathieu Dumas, il n'a pas décidé « d'avancer dans l'Empire », et encore moins de faire la guerre « la plus offensive » sur les Alpes et en Italie. Mais le dossier de Mathieu Dumas prouve qu'il s'appliquait à se justifier, à rendre des services et à fournir des suggestions [14].

On aboutit ainsi à considérer Carnot comme le lien entre les auteurs les plus divers, du passé et du présent, et le Comité de Salut public. Carnot s'informait et accueillait tous les projets ; il en renvoyait à Bouchotte, d'autres au Comité de la Guerre, au Comité parlementaire, pour les faire analyser et critiquer. Il reprenait le tout et l'étudiait sur la carte ; il rédigeait lui-même les projets. La section de la Guerre du Comité de Salut public ne comportait alors que des travailleurs subalternes qui se livraient à un travail de secrétariat. N'est-ce pas exactement l'œuvre d'un organisateur ? Sauviac a formulé à ce propos une remarque judicieuse. « Il y a autant de mérite à faire un bon choix qu'à créer, écrivait-il. Au reste, la réunion des ordres et des moyens d'exécution, entièrement due au représentant Carnot, est sans contredit au-dessus même de l'invention. » Carnot a pris partout son bien, empruntant ainsi à des courants divers parfois contradictoires ; il a synthétisé, adapté, recréé, discutant avec les généraux de passage à Paris, et aussi avec les membres du Comité de Salut public. Il a rédigé les ordres, il les a précisés et commentés dans sa correspondance avec les généraux, il a envisagé à diverses reprises d'en poursuivre l'application sur le champ de bataille. Il ne fut ni Guibert — seul créateur d'un système nouveau de guerre — ni Bonaparte, réalisateur dominant son état-major et donnant sa pleine mesure sur le terrain ; il fut l' « organisateur » de la victoire [15].

CHAPITRE X

LA GUERRE EN L'AN II

L'APPLICATION du « système général » supposait un accord entre le Comité, qui établissait les plans, et les généraux, qui devaient les réaliser. Sans doute l'autorité du Comité était-elle devenue assez redoutable pour imposer la docilité, sous peine de destitution, voire d'arrestation, sinon d'exécution. Mais la docilité serait-elle compréhensive ? Les généraux devaient entrer dans la pensée du Comité et imaginer les manœuvres qui en assureraient le succès. L'esprit d'indépendance, ou l'inintelligence, eussent entraîné des incohérences et des mutations fréquentes, dont les inconvénients s'étaient depuis longtemps affirmés. La composition des états-majors généraux, le choix des commandants d'armée, c'étaient là deux problèmes conjoints, dont la solution avaient préoccupé tous les gouvernements depuis le début de la guerre, sans que jamais d'heureux résultats eussent été obtenus.

Le commandement en chef des armées avait été affecté par la grande crise de septembre. La lutte des diverses tendances révolutionnaires avait atteint le personnel des généraux, les Hébertistes et les Enragés avaient obtenu de nombreuses destitutions, le ministre de la Guerre s'y était prêté, la Convention s'était émue et le Comité tout entier avait dû couvrir cette épuration ; Barère avait précisé à la Convention que Carnot avait fourni des informations sur chacun des destitués.

Dans la suite le même mécanisme joua — partis, ministre, assemblée, comité —, le choix des généraux en chef relevait de la politique générale. Mais le rôle de chacune de ces autorités se modifia. Le régime du gouvernement révolutionnaire avait formellement attribué à la Convention la nomination des généraux en chef, sur présentation du Comité. Ce furent donc les membres du Comité qui effectuèrent les choix ;

Carnot avait à faire valoir les exigences techniques ; ce n'étaient pas les seules ; les autres membres intervinrent, et les résultats ne lui sont que partiellement imputables. Qui s'étonnera qu'après coup chacun ait réclamé le mérite des meilleurs choix et récusé la responsabilité des mauvais ? Et que les historiens et biographes aient parfois agi de même en faveur de leur héros ? Les documents, insuffisants et souvent obscurs, ont permis ces interprétations ; ils permettent aussi des conclusions plus nuancées.

Un remaniement profond avait été provoqué en septembre par le renvoi des ci-devant et par l'épuration hébertiste. Sur dix commandants en chef, trois étaient classés comme nobles — Landremont à l'armée du Rhin, Schauenbourg à l'armée de la Moselle, Canclaux à l'armée des Côtes de Brest ; Houchard avait été inculpé et quittait l'armée du Nord, Dagobert avait renoncé au commandement de l'armée des Pyrénées-Orientales. Delbhecq, qui dirigeait l'armée des Pyrénées-Occidentales, venait de mourir. Carnot avait joué un rôle bien réduit dans ces changements ; Collot d'Herbois avait tenu souvent la plume.

Parmi ceux qui étaient en fonction se trouvait le fameux Kellermann, mais c'était en raison de l'indocilité de Dubois-Crancé qui l'avait maintenu, malgré un décret de la Convention. Pour faire exécuter la mesure, ce ne fut pas Carnot qui intervint — il était à l'armée du Nord —, mais Robespierre.

Ces vides furent l'occasion de mutations. Jourdan fut porté de l'armée des Ardennes à celle du Nord, sur l'initiative, semble-t-il, de Bouchotte. Nous avons vu que Wattignies l'avait mis en relations étroites avec Carnot. Les commissaires de Bouchotte déclaraient que c'était un « pur ». Robespierre avait voulu réconcilier les généraux, mais il notait sur son carnet : « Jourdan et Ernouf suspects par leur inaction et leur correspondance ». La destitution et l'arrestation de Jourdan, le 6 janvier 1794, furent décidées. Carnot rédigea l'arrêté, Jourdan lui en attribua l'initiative, mais Robespierre était d'accord avec Carnot [1].

Le cas de Hoche n'est pas moins remarquable, bien qu'il ait été obscurci par une abondante littérature. Hoche plaisait à Carnot parce qu'il lui proposait les opérations que celui-ci souhaitait : la prise d'Ostende, l'offensive en Belgique, l'action en masse ; il avait pris part aux expéditions de Furnes, Nieuport et Ostende, sous Vandamme ; pourtant il avait jugé qu'on aurait pu faire mieux que la bataille de

Wattignies, mais ce n'est pas à Carnot qu'il l'avait écrit. Il était en excellents termes avec Bouchotte et Audouin, Robespierre et Couthon, avec qui il entretenait une correspondance suivie, après avoir été protégé par Marat. Soutenu chaleureusement par les représentants en mission de l'armée du Nord, il avait plus d'appuis qu'il n'en fallait pour être porté au commandement de l'armée de la Moselle, le 23 octobre 1793. La mesure, proposée par Bouchotte, fit l'objet d'un arrêté rédigé par Carnot et signé par lui ainsi que par Collot d'Herbois, Prieur de la Côte-d'Or, Robespierre. Deux mois plus tard les représentants en mission, Baudot et Lacoste, en conflit avec Saint-Just et Lebas, lui attribuaient le commandement des deux armées, de la Moselle et du Rhin.

Cette mesure devait le mettre dans une situation difficile à l'égard de Saint-Just. Carnot intervint alors pour remettre les hommes et les choses en place, mais il demeura une gêne, sinon une rivalité, entre les généraux, et aussi une présomption favorable de Saint-Just pour Pichegru. Celui-ci a connu un avancement non moins rapide : nommé général de brigade le 22 août 1793, il avait été porté au commandement de l'armée du Rhin le 20 octobre. Bouchotte l'avait patronné; depuis, il ne cessait d'étaler son civisme et il était l'homme de Saint-Just, de Lebas et de Collot d'Herbois. En somme ni Hoche ni Pichegru — non plus que Jourdan — ne peuvent passer pour créatures de Carnot.

Pour rompre cette irritante et dommageable rivalité, le 6 janvier, le Comité fit passer Pichegru à l'armée du Nord, au moment même où Jourdan était décrété d'arrestation. La pièce était de la main de Carnot, mais la nomination de Pichegru était une satisfaction donnée à Saint-Just, Lebas et Robespierre. La solidarité ne cessait pas de s'affirmer entre les membres du Comité; d'autre part, le rôle de Bouchotte demeurait considérable : c'est lui qui était chargé de présenter une liste de généraux pour compléter les états-majors des armées du Nord, des Ardennes, de la Moselle et du Rhin.

Quant à Hoche il fut peu docile et, quand Carnot lui prescrivit de marcher sur Trèves, il éluda l'ordre et laissa passer le temps. Bouchotte et Carnot, Saint-Just et Collot d'Herbois s'impatientèrent. Hoche riposta : « Dois-je rendre compte tous les jours de mes opérations au Comité?... Suis-je le maître de faire camper, ou dois-je attendre les ordres du Comité ? » La rupture fut singulière : Hoche fut envoyé à l'armée d'Italie, le 10 mars 1794, où il reçut un ordre d'arrestation, daté du 20 mars. L'arrêté avait été écrit par Carnot, mais le même jour Robespierre avait écrit de sa main : « Nous avons la preuve que le général Hoche est un traître.... Il est nécessaire de le faire arrêter sur-le-champ. » Carnot avait ajouté la date de l'en-tête, comme pour souligner que la mesure avait été prise en plein accord [2].

Et c'est Jourdan qui remplaçait Hoche ! Levasseur avait insisté pour obtenir cette nomination. Jourdan croyait que Carnot s'y opposerait. Levasseur le trouva au contraire très favorable. Ce fut donc avec Pichegru à l'armée du Nord et Jourdan à l'armée de la Moselle que Carnot entreprit la campagne de printemps ; l'autorité du Comité s'était exercée assez lourdement pour qu'on pût croire que les généraux seraient disposés à le seconder.

Le commandement des autres armées donna lieu à des mutations nombreuses : en moyenne quatre généraux s'étaient succédé à la tête de chaque armée, entre l'arrivée de Carnot au Comité et le début des opérations du printemps 1794. Toutefois une certaine stabilisation eut lieu alors, de sorte que, si Carnot n'a pas nommé ces chefs, il les a du moins maintenus, sauf exception.

Le rôle des généraux en chef se rattachait à la politique générale, et le sort de ceux qui étaient accusés de trahison était soumis au Comité de Sûreté générale [3]. Mais pour les autres officiers c'est le Comité de Salut public qui décidait, après consultation du ministre de la Guerre. Si celui-ci, ou des représentants en mission, avaient déjà pris des mesures, ils devaient les justifier [4].

Carnot apprit à connaître l'état-major ou, du moins, les plus importants de ses membres. Des répertoires avaient été adressés au ministre de la Guerre, accompagnés de dossiers. Le Comité fit établir ses fiches [5].

Nombre de mesures importantes furent prises par Carnot. Par exemple l'arrestation, le 22 décembre, de trois officiers, deux généraux sortant du Génie, Bernède et Delattre, qui furent décapités par la suite [6]. Il contresigna des arrêtés d'arrestation, il provoqua l'arrestation de Rouget de Lisle, qu'il poursuivait opiniâtrement. Il prononça des mutations, des nominations, des mises à la retraite [7]. Il partageait la direction du personnel de l'armée avec Bouchotte [8]. Pourtant d'autres membres du Comité intervenaient parfois : le 15 décembre, Couthon rédigea l'arrêté de destitution et d'arrestation du général Carteaux ; celui-ci, il est vrai, avait commandé en chef [9].

**

Le pouvoir du Comité facilita la préparation et la réalisation de l'offensive de printemps, que Carnot avait préparée en exposant son « système général ». Mais l'application de ce système exigeait des instructions détaillées. Grâce aux archives familiales, il est possible de suivre la préparation de ces instructions, ce qui éclaire de façon assez neuve l'évolution de la pensée stratégique de Carnot.

Trois rédactions des instructions à l'armée du Nord furent tour à tour établies : la première à la suite du « système général », la seconde le 17 février, et la troisième le 11 mars. Carnot, peu à peu, créait ce rôle nouveau pour lui — et peu commun dans l'histoire militaire antérieure — de chef d'état-major général. Il apprenait à souligner ses desseins, et à laisser le choix des moyens aux généraux en chef. Dans le premier libellé, c'était lui qui précisait les buts et les voies, les mouvements des troupes, les effectifs, la répartition des diverses armes. Il fixait les enchaînements sans admettre que l'ennemi pût les rompre vraiment. Il transformait le général en chef en subalterne. La deuxième rédaction traçait simplement les grandes directives, elle prescrivait le premier but à atteindre, ajournant la suite pour le temps où la première étape aurait été parcourue. La forme était concise et impérieuse, l'instruction était devenue un arrêté du Comité. Elle fut envoyée à l'armée du Nord. La troisième rédaction reprenait toute la question et précisait le lieu de la rencontre entre les adversaires ; les vues étaient plus précises et le ton plus pressant. Carnot avait adopté un rôle moins tatillon que dans le premier texte, et plus large et circonstancié que dans le second.

Les opérations prescrites avaient été, elles aussi, sensiblement modifiées. La prise d'Ypres était toujours le pivot, attestant la continuité des idées de Carnot. Ce parti pris a été abondamment critiqué ; il est en effet très contestable ; les préoccupations politiques seules peuvent le soutenir.

Dans le premier de ses ordres, Carnot allongeait les troupes en « cordons » et les installait dans les camps, de telle sorte que, voulant tout protéger, il retombait dans l'erreur que condamnait son « système général » : il dispersait les forces. De plus, l'objectif était limité au gain de terrain et préparait le siège des places, ainsi que la prise des magasins. Pourtant, Carnot recommandait de disséminer le moins possible les forces ! Il y avait un désaccord entre sa pensée théorique et les ordres d'exécution.

Le deuxième texte était si bref qu'il ne permet aucune conclusion : rien n'y révélait une méthode nouvelle de guerre, celle du système.

En revanche, le troisième, s'il avait encore le souci d'assurer la protection en gagnant du terrain, prescrivait « une grande bataille » pour « décider du sort de la campagne », en acculant l'ennemi pour lui enlever tout « moyen d'échapper ». Il recommandait d'exploiter ensuite la victoire. Toutefois, il consacrait encore plus de cinquante mille hommes, dispersés en camps et garnisons, à défendre la zone voisine de Maubeuge. Il est vrai qu'il mettait l'armée des Ardennes à la disposition de Pichegru. Enfin Carnot proposait qu'un ou deux membres du Comité se rendissent sur place quand la bataille serait proche.

Le plan a été critiqué, notamment par Napoléon. On lui a reproché non seulement le choix d'Ypres, mais des dispositions qui ne concentraient pas assez les forces et n'anéantissaient pas l'ennemi. Comparé aux précédents, il montre pourtant une étape vers la guerre de masses. Quelques jours plus tard, le 18 mars, Carnot accentuait ce trait, en prescrivant à Richard et Choudieu, les représentants à l'armée du Nord, de presser Pichegru de livrer de grandes batailles, de cerner l'ennemi [10].

La réalisation fut profondément décevante. Pichegru agit tardivement ; il n'appliquait pas le plan de Carnot, il se faisait battre. Au bout d'un mois, la place de Landrecies était assiégée par les ennemis ; non seulement l'offensive française n'avait pas eu lieu, mais les chefs s'étaient laissé surprendre.

L'armée des Ardennes, qui devait appuyer Pichegru, tardait à entrer en action. L'armée de la Moselle aurait dû tout d'abord, nous l'avons vu, marcher sur Trèves, mais n'avait pas obéi. Un peu plus tard, le 9 mars, Carnot prescrivit de livrer une bataille et d'établir les troupes vers Arlon pour couper les communications entre le Luxembourg et le pays de Liège. Là il fut plus heureux, Arlon tomba entre nos mains le 18 avril. Alors Carnot exposa la suite du rôle de l'armée de la Moselle ; on lui recommandait

notamment de se concerter avec celle du Rhin pour continuer ses offensives.

Le général Michaud, qui commandait celle-ci, avait
demandé, le 30 mars, des instructions précises. Il lui fut
prescrit d'observer une « défensive active ».

Tous ces contretemps avaient irrité Carnot, dont les
ordres devenaient de plus en plus pathétiques : « Nous
sommes perdus si vous n'entrez pas bien vite en pays
ennemi, avait-il écrit à Pichegru le 31 mars, la défensive
nous déshonore et nous tue. » Il reprenait les thèmes du
« système général » : offensive, *furia francese*, attaque générale. Et aussi cette invitation qui devançait la proclamation
célèbre de Bonaparte à l'armée d'Italie famélique : « Indi-
quez-leur les richesses de la Belgique, de la Flandre et de
l'Allemagne, et que la victoire se charge de les conduire. »
Saint-Just et Lebas étaient envoyés en mission dans le
Nord « pour y suivre les vues du Comité de Salut public » ;
on leur faisait remarquer les effets de la désobéissance de
Pichegru.

La seule nouvelle favorable avait été celle de l'inertie des
Prussiens, ce qui avait atténué le choc porté à nos armées
par les coalisés.

Du côté des Alpes, Carnot avait dû intervenir avec brutalité et opiniâtreté pour forcer les généraux à l'action
— « tu réponds sur ta tête... » — et les cols alpestres avaient
été occupés. Cependant, l'armée d'Italie avait pris Oneille
et Loano.

Enfin, aux Pyrénées, Carnot avait prescrit des opérations
de diversion. Il n'avait pu fournir le matériel et les hommes
qu'on lui avait demandés pour cette zone, l'action ne s'y
engagea vraiment qu'au début de mai.

Les opérations de débarquement en Angleterre avaient
été réduites d'abord à une descente à Jersey et Guernesey,
puis elles avaient été ajournées, faute de moyens.

Des effectifs considérables étaient en effet fixés dans
l'Ouest de la France. Garrau avait cru pouvoir annoncer la
fin de la Vendée, le 18 mars, c'était se réjouir trop
tôt [11].

En somme la première phase du « système général »
s'était limitée à l'action résolue d'un ennemi nombreux,
bien organisé et qui avait déclenché une offensive victorieuse, tandis que les chefs français hésitaient et se montraient fréquemment indociles.

Mais c'est à cette époque que Carnot parvint à accroître considérablement ses pouvoirs.

Au nom du Comité, le 1ᵉʳ avril 1794, Carnot proposa à la Convention de supprimer le Conseil exécutif provisoire, donc tous les ministres. C'était la conclusion d'une crise ouverte dix-huit mois plus tôt, lors de la lutte contre Pache, et dans laquelle Carnot avait tenu un rôle actif. Depuis ce temps, à plusieurs reprises, le démembrement du ministère de la Guerre avait été proposé, et même, en novembre, Bourdon de l'Oise avait demandé la suppression de tous les ministères.

En fait leur rôle avait été amoindri, tant par leur stricte subordination au Comité que par la création de nombreuses commissions « dont les attributions, observait Carnot, [formaient] autant de démembrements des fonctions ministérielles ». Malgré tout, les ministres représentaient encore un pouvoir, celui des bureaux. C'était le cas au ministère de la Guerre, avec son personnel hébertiste, mêlé à la politique parisienne, et exerçant — malgré le Comité — une influence sur les cadres militaires.

On peut s'en faire une idée par la lecture des condoléances adressées à Vincent, en février. Le dossier contient des lettres d'agents du Conseil exécutif, de commissaires des guerres, de gardes-magasin, d'officiers d'état-major, de généraux, de commis du ministère : un Celliez, un Gateau, un Parein. Une lettre est écrite au nom de « tous nos bons républicains ».

Carnot était leur adversaire, son hostilité à l'égard des Extrémistes ne fait aucun doute. Il ne leur pardonnait pas leur dédain des talents, la suspicion dans laquelle ils tenaient à la fois les gens instruits et les intelligences supérieures — singulièrement parmi les hommes d'État et les militaires. Carnot avait un hautain mépris pour l'ignorance et pour la médiocrité intellectuelle ; il était certes orgueilleux, mais il appartenait surtout à ces générations du xviiiᵉ siècle élevées dans le culte de la raison et du progrès — les « lumières » — opposées à la superstition. Quand il vit poindre une nouvelle superstition, celle de la force, de la dureté, de la violence, superstition aveugle, nourrie d'illusions, de préventions et d'appétits — comme il l'avait vue aux Pyrénées —, il l'interpréta comme le signe d'une erreur pernicieuse et du danger le plus terrible qui pût menacer l'œuvre de la Révolution.

Par là il demeurait l'ingénieur, le savant qui s'était rebellé contre l'Ancien Régime, subordonnant les talents à la naissance. Il restait le collègue et l'ami de ces officiers instruits, surtout ceux du Génie et de l'Artillerie qui pouvaient être peu favorables à sa politique — comme Dubois-Crancé — mais réservaient leur estime au talent. Ce n'était pas une question de classe, mais d'esprit, puisqu'il accueillait volontiers des ci-devant, comme Montalembert, ou des roturiers de la plus modeste origine, comme Hoche. Il rêvait d'une république prodiguant l'instruction à tous et confiait les plus hauts postes aux savants. C'était, par avance, Saint-Simon et Guizot. Dans l'immédiat, il proscrivait les chefs politiques — et plus encore militaires — sans intelligence, instruction, ou sans ce génie qui remplace l'école. Hébert et Vincent incarnaient à ses yeux le plus grand danger pour la République et la civilisation.

Ceux-ci ne l'ignoraient pas. Ils considéraient Carnot et les siens comme des aristocrates qu'il fallait surveiller. Ils avaient pour cela au ministère de la Guerre assez de partisans, notamment parmi les chefs de service; ils avaient fourni aussi quelques-uns de ces commissaires du pouvoir exécutif qui avaient été en conflit avec Carnot. Les premières lances avaient été rompues au temps de la dénonciation faite par Guffroy, depuis chacun était resté sur ses positions, guettant l'occasion de perdre l'adversaire.

Celle-ci survint fin février, au moment du conflit hébertiste. L'offensive touchait Carnot, d'abord en ce qui concernait l'armée révolutionnaire dont on réclamait l'accroissement et, de ce fait même, un rôle politique plus actif que celui auquel Carnot l'avait reléguée. D'autre part, il était question du ministère, où il s'agissait de maintenir Bouchotte, et, par suite, de lui assurer une action plus considérable.

Dans les mesures et les discours qui marquèrent l'essai de conquête du pouvoir, Carnot fut attaqué indirectement. Hébert déclara, le 4 mars, aux Cordeliers, qu'un complot avait eu pour but de renverser Bouchotte et de le remplacer par Carnot-Feulint, intrigant et modéré. L'auditoire ne distingua pas nettement s'il s'agissait de l'un ou l'autre des frères Carnot, si bien que les témoins dirent tantôt que Lazare, tantôt que Feulint avait été dénoncé.

Lorsque les Hébertistes furent arrêtés, dans la nuit du 13 au 14 mars, il y avait parmi eux non seulement Vincent et Ronsin, mais Mazuel, aide de camp de Bouchotte et chef d'escadron de la Cavalerie révolutionnaire, Dubuisson, qui avait été commissaire du pouvoir exécutif à diverses reprises, Bourgeois, employé au ministère de la Guerre. Contre eux, on suscita le témoignage de personnages qui tenaient de près à la défense nationale : un agent national pour les poudres, un agent d'atelier d'armes, un administrateur de l'habillement des troupes, le secrétaire général du Comité de Salut public pour les poudres et salpêtres, et un employé du bureau de la Guerre [12].

Ainsi, en marge du conflit général, un règlement de comptes plus particulier s'accomplissait dans le personnel qui dépendait de Carnot. La lutte avait eu pour enjeu l'armée et son administration, facteur si important de la Révolution et de la maîtrise du pouvoir. Carnot avait été menacé, il sortait plus fort. D'autant que, nous l'avons vu, il en profita pour épurer l'armée. Il faut pourtant noter qu'il restait encore dans les bureaux de la Guerre nombre de Robespierristes.

Carnot ne cacha pourtant pas sa satisfaction : « Les conjurés ont reçu le prix de leurs forfaits, écrivait-il à Garrau le 24 mars, jamais plus grande joie ne s'est manifestée dans le peuple. »

Du coup il put se débarrasser de l'armée révolutionnaire, arrêter le général Rossignol, brider les agents du Conseil exécutif et supprimer ce Conseil. Son pouvoir militaire en fut puissamment accru.

Pour supprimer les ministères, Carnot exhuma le vieux grief : ces ministères étaient une institution monarchique, nobiliaire et fanatique.

La Convention accepta de remplacer les six ministères par douze commissions « rattachées au Comité de Salut public sous l'autorité de la Convention ». Singulières commissions, d'un ou de deux membres, plus un adjoint, tous proposés par le Comité qui contrôlait l'organisation, le personnel et le fonctionnement des bureaux. C'étaient désormais autant de services à la disposition du Comité ; le rôle de surveillance de celui-ci avait fait place à l'action gouvernementale.

Le nombre des commissions amenuisait l'importance de chacune ; les attributions du ministère de la Guerre étaient démembrées au profit de six d'entre elles.

Celle de « l'Organisation et du Mouvement des armées de terre » devait assurer aussi les opérations. Les fortifications, la défense des côtes et des frontières, relevaient de la commission des Travaux publics. L'armement formait toujours une commission spéciale. Le ravitaillement, l'équipement, le casernement et le campement des armées étaient confiés à une commission « du Commerce et des Approvisionnements ». Les hôpitaux militaires étaient rattachés aux hôpitaux civils, c'est-à-dire à la commission « des Secours publics ». Enfin les convois, charrois, relais militaires et la remonte dépendaient de la commission « des Transports, Postes et Messageries ».

Au total, six commissions sur douze intervenaient donc dans les questions militaires, et, réciproquement, Carnot était amené à intervenir dans trois commissions, à la fois civiles et militaires. La réforme était donc spécialement importante pour la guerre et pour Carnot ; on comprend qu'il l'ait rapportée. D'ailleurs, il l'avait réclamée dans son rapport sur la mission aux Pyrénées, ainsi que le lui rappelait, tout joyeux, son ami Garrau : « Quelle belle besogne !... Tu sais que, dans notre mission aux Pyrénées..., il fut convenu... que nous proposerions... de renverser ce colosse [13]. »

Carnot plaça le Bourguignon Pille à la tête de l'Organisation de l'armée de terre. Pille était auparavant au ministère. Il eut pour adjoint Sijas, ancien adjoint au ministère de la Guerre, appuyé par Saint-Just. Les deux hommes ne purent s'accorder ; Sijas démissionna le 21 mai ; sa démission fut refusée, alors il se déclara malade et, à son retour, refusa de revoir Pille. Peu après, il le dénonçait comme suspect, par ses relations avec des aristocrates et par le secret dont il entourait son travail. L'homme de Saint-Just attaquait l'homme de Carnot [14].

A la commission des Travaux publics, Carnot mit Dupin, officier du Génie qui venait du ministère de la Guerre et avec qui Carnot entretenait de bonnes relations. Le dépôt de la Guerre fut rattaché à la commission des Travaux publics.

Carnot s'occupa spécialement de réglementer le travail de la commission de l'Organisation et du Mouvement. Il interdit à toutes les commissions d'effectuer des nominations aux emplois militaires.

D'autre part le Comité augmentait ses services et ses locaux. La section de la Guerre fut agrandie et recruta de nouveaux employés. Carnot dut recourir à un secrétaire particulier, Mayeux, pour lui confier la rédaction des lettres dont il lui indiquait le thème.

Désormais Carnot avait bien en main le personnel militaire dont il réglait le sort : avancement, mutations, réintégrations, etc. Il accrut sa correspondance avec les représentants et les généraux ; en mai, elle devint presque quotidienne, du moins avec les principales armées. La liaison était directe et constante. On vit les représentants adresser leurs lettres officielles personnellement à Carnot, les militaires multiplier les sollicitations, se faire appuyer par les gens en place. Carnot était en situation de se faire une clientèle : il accordait des exemptions, il lançait des réquisitions pour mettre à l'abri ou « blanchir » qui en avait besoin. Toutefois il ne fut jamais accusé de favoritisme ni de vénalité. Il n'en reste pas moins que, si ces conditions nouvelles renforcèrent son rôle dans la conduite de la guerre, elles le compromirent aux yeux de Saint-Just et de Robespierre [15].

* * *

A la fin du mois d'avril, le « système général » semblait totalement anéanti par l'offensive coalisée. Pourtant, les méthodes de combat qu'il préconisait, adaptées aux forces — et aux faiblesses — du soldat républicain, faisaient leurs preuves. Les troupes combattaient avec âpreté, leur mordant restait redoutable, la cohésion s'affirmait, et l'on remarquait le rôle croissant des troupes légères d'Infanterie, Cavalerie et Artillerie. Là résidait notre espérance : il suffirait de diriger efficacement cette puissance, d'autant plus redoutable qu'elle s'accroissait, tant par le résultat des levées que par les renforts acheminés vers le Nord.

Au lendemain de la chute de Landrecies, 30 avril, les représentants Saint-Just et Lebas vinrent conférer au Comité auquel ils avaient demandé un plan. Par bonheur le repli prussien permettait d'exploiter la force de l'armée de la Moselle et de renforcer celle-ci en prélevant des renforts à l'armée du Rhin.

Carnot ne s'émut pas. A la nouvelle de la perte de la ville il avait immédiatement écrit pour prescrire de continuer l'offensive, recommandant de cerner l'ennemi et annonçant la marche de Jourdan. Celui-ci et Michaud, à l'armée du Rhin, étaient tenus d'agir d'urgence. Pourtant, un certain flottement se manifestait chez Carnot : fidèle à la stratégie du « système », il prescrivait l'offensive en Flandre maritime, où il voulait toujours prendre Ypres et Nieuport, mais les mouvements de l'ennemi l'amenaient à lui opposer partout des troupes et à disperser ses forces. C'est alors que Pichegru proposa, d'accord avec les représentants, Richard, Saint-Just et Lebas, le 6 mai, un plan d'attaque sur les ailes et de défense au centre, qui fut agréé par Carnot. Tout le monde était d'accord pour faire soutenir l'aile droite par l'armée des Ardennes et par celle de la Moselle. La lutte allait s'intensifier sur la Sambre. Elle fut acharnée pendant tout le mois de mai. Les généraux se montraient désormais dociles, ils sollicitaient les ordres du Comité. Celui-ci savait se tenir dans son rôle, il donnait des directives générales et laissait une large initiative aux généraux. Quand « la grande opération du passage de la Sambre » fut amorcée, Carnot écrivit : « La balle est lancée : vous n'avez plus à prendre conseil que des circonstances. »

Le flottement persista cependant, du fait des résistances rencontrées, des initiatives de l'adversaire et des hésitations de Pichegru. Ainsi, le 18 mai, c'était le centre qui subissait le choc, l'ennemi était battu, mais Pichegru n'exploitait pas sa victoire. La décision, vainement cherchée sur les ailes, aurait pu être obtenue là.

Pourtant, la consigne donnée par Carnot était catégorique, à propos de l'action sur la gauche il avait écrit, le 14 mai, ces lignes dont on ne saurait exagérer la signification : « Comment les ennemis fugitifs ne sont-ils pas taillés en pièces ?... La fuite des Autrichiens ne suffit pas à la France, *il n'y a que les morts qui ne reviennent pas.* »

Quelques jours plus tard, le 23 mai, il écrivait à Jourdan pour lui recommander les batailles de destruction : « Avant tout, il faut battre l'ennemi en rase campagne, le poursuivre, l'exterminer. Les villes alors tomberont d'elles-mêmes. » Carnot n'était plus l'ingénieur obsédé par les sièges, il exigeait la guerre d'anéantissement, du nom même que Cobourg avait donné à sa propre action, celle qui venait d'échouer. Mais si Carnot fournissait le mot d'ordre, il ne donnait pas les moyens de l'appliquer.

Pourtant, il en venait peu à peu au regroupement des forces et des commandements. Le 27 mai, il prescrivit à l'armée de la Moselle d'agir de concert avec l'armée des Ardennes et celle du Nord, et, « comme toutes les opérations

doivent être assujetties à un même système, la direction
générale en [était] remise à Pichegru ». Le 8 juin, un arrêté
du Comité ratifiait cette décision, la guerre de masses
s'unifiait.

Il n'en restait pas moins que Carnot continuait d'exiger
la conquête de la Flandre maritime, s'intéressant plus à
l'aile gauche qu'à l'aile droite et voulant renforcer la première en prélevant des effectifs sur la seconde. Il attachait
plus d'importance à la prise d'Ypres qu'aux combats sur
la Sambre. Il réclamait de Jourdan la prise de Namur, mais
aussi une grande bataille en rase campagne, et Jourdan se
plaignait de ces incertitudes.

Or Saint-Just, à l'armée de Sambre-et-Meuse qui venait
de se former par la jonction de l'armée des Ardennes et d'une
partie de l'armée de la Moselle, avait des vues toutes différentes. Saint-Just fut investi, le 6 juin, de pouvoirs extraordinaires sur l'ensemble des forces réparties du Rhin à la mer.
Il s'opposa aux mesures qui pouvaient affaiblir les troupes
de la Sambre. L'antagonisme s'aggrava par les sanctions
que prit Saint-Just contre les officiers qui dirigeaient le
siège de Charleroi, notamment contre Marescot, l'un des
meilleurs ingénieurs et des plus attachés à Carnot.

Ainsi s'opposaient deux membres du Comité, l'un accoutumé à diriger les opérations et peu enclin à céder, l'autre
détaché aux armées avec un immense pouvoir, assuré, au
cours de ses voyages à Paris, qu'il serait fortement appuyé,
convaincu que son système était le meilleur, et suspectant le
le civisme du premier. Mais les pouvoirs de Saint-Just
avaient pour objet de tenir la main à l'exécution des décrets
de la Convention et des arrêtés du Comité de Salut public.

Les questions de personne ont joué un rôle excessif dans
le différend, aussi bien à l'époque même que dans la suite
entre historiens passionnés pour Carnot ou pour Saint-
Just. A voir les choses sans parti pris, il apparaît que ni l'un
ni l'autre des deux stratèges du Comité ne parvenaient à appliquer les directives de la guerre de masses : Carnot s'en
prenait à Ypres et aux places de la Flandre maritime, Saint-
Just voulait tour à tour assiéger Charleroi, Namur et Mons.
Et, là, au contraire, Carnot eût préféré la guerre en rase campagne, quelques troupes bloquant simplement Charleroi.
La grande bataille décisive avait été souhaitée par Carnot,
elle fut livrée par Saint-Just, fortuitement, parce que
Cobourg venait au secours de Charleroi — comme Jourdan

était allé au secours de Maubeuge, et Houchard au secours
de Dunkerque —, mais, ici, la place avait capitulé ; les Français disposaient de la supériorité numérique, ils furent
victorieux à Fleurus le 26 juin. Pourtant, une fois de plus,
l'ennemi put se retirer : la technique de la bataille d'anéantissement n'était pas établie.

Carnot, toujours préoccupé de l'aile gauche, convaincu
que par là seulement la coalition pouvait être disloquée,
prépara — à défaut de la descente en Angleterre qu'il n'avait
cessé de préconiser, mais qu'il n'avait pu réaliser — une
expédition contre la Hollande. C'était le développement du
« système général ».

*
* *

Sur les autres fronts, Carnot dirigea aussi en assignant les
tâches, en exigeant l'application de la tactique nouvelle,
en fournissant les effectifs et le matériel.

Au début de mai, Carnot avait réuni les armées des Alpes
et d'Italie pour assurer l'unité d'action. Celle-ci s'accomplit
au profit de l'armée d'Italie, et l'initiative elle-même passa
aux généraux et aux représentants, qui proposèrent un plan
d'opérations, le 21 mai. Il s'agissait de faire une campagne
en Piémont. Derrière Dumerbion, qui commandait en chef,
se trouvait Bonaparte ; à ses côtés, il y avait Robespierre
jeune. Carnot ne se laissa pas forcer la main, il prit argument des renforts qu'on lui demandait pour rappeler, le
31 mai, qu'il s'agissait, pour le moment, de favoriser l'action
de l'armée du Nord et de tenir en échec l'ennemi sur les
autres fronts. Il rappela ces consignes le 13 et le 23 juin, prélevant en outre des renforts. Enfin, le 25 juillet, il reprocha
au général en chef d'avoir cédé à « l'esprit d'invasion », au
détriment de la sécurité de cette position. Augustin Robespierre vint à Paris, au début de juillet, « arracher, par la
tyrannie de son frère, le projet d'entrer dans le Piémont,
en abandonnant nos frontières, en laissant enlever la Corse,
en exposant Port-la-Montagne [Toulon] à une nouvelle
invasion, en livrant nos derrières à nos ennemis..., en faisant
dépendre notre sûreté des bonnes dispositions du gouvernement génois... » ; mesures « désastreuses », écrivait Carnot,
le 13 août, et qui eussent paralysé les armées des Pyrénées
et de l'Ouest.

Cette diatribe vibre de l'hostilité entre Carnot et Robespierre, mais elle révèle aussi que Carnot n'acceptait pas les risques et les calculs de Bonaparte. Celui-ci allait pourtant faire la vraie guerre révolutionnaire, la guerre d'anéantissement. On observe aussi la prudence de Carnot dans une zone frontière — la seule — qu'il ne connaissait pas, et enfin son désir, longtemps entretenu, d'éviter la prolongation de la guerre, que Bonaparte envisageait plus volontiers. Tel fut le premier différend stratégique — par personnes interposées — entre Carnot et Bonaparte.

Le « système général » avait prévu, aux Pyrénées, une action aussi limitée que celle qui devait avoir lieu dans les Alpes : l'armée des Pyrénées-Orientales assurerait à la France la Cerdagne et le Val d'Aran, tandis que celle des Pyrénées-Occidentales s'emparerait de Saint-Sébastien et de Fontarabie. Ce programme fut à peu près rempli par Dugommier à l'est et, plus tardivement, par Müller à l'ouest. Carnot intervint peu, sinon pour stimuler Müller. Carnot aurait voulu obtenir la paix avec l'Espagne, pour ôter la Méditerranée aux Anglais en reprenant la Corse, une alliance avec Gênes eût facilité la réalisation de ce dessein [16].

C'est encore les Anglais que devaient combattre les armées de l'Ouest — après avoir écrasé les révoltés — en effectuant la descente dont on parlait tant.

Jusqu'à l'établissement du « système général », Carnot s'était peu occupé de la guerre de l'ouest, il intervint davantage à partir de cette époque. Ce fut d'abord, le 13 février, pour proscrire la dissémination des forces et recommander la guerre de masses, comme partout ailleurs. Il envoya sur place son ami Garrau et aussi Hentz, qui avait sa confiance.

Garrau lui vanta l'efficacité de la méthode forte : incendie des repaires et des postes occupés par les Vendéens, incendie des fours et des moulins, « vivent les mesures rigoureuses et les hommes qui ont des c...! » et flétrit avec vigueur les indulgents : « Je n'appréhendais plus que la faction, trop écoutée, des modérés. Vivent les patriotes purs ! » C'était au temps de l'arrestation de Danton et de Philippeaux, et aussi des « colonnes infernales » de Turreau, qui ajoutaient les atrocités à la terreur.

Carnot resta muet. Tout au plus signa-t-il la lettre de Barère, qui, le 6 avril, signalait aux représentants l'avalanche des protestations contre les « mesures de sévérité », mais s'en rapportait finalement à leur patriotisme.

Les violences continuèrent, le Comité était tenu au courant par les récriminations des uns et les professions de foi des autres ; mais il faut reconnaître qu'il était malaisé de discerner la vérité. Le cas fameux du général Huché en est la preuve.

Personnage sinistre, sur qui les circonstances projetèrent une sanglante lumière qu'il n'eût pas connue s'il était demeuré ce soldat ivrogne, borné et brutal, qu'il était sous l'Ancien Régime. Il présida avec entrain aux incendies, aux massacres, aux viols, aux tortures et, par l'horreur, se fit une réputation. Les choses en vinrent au point que le Comité de surveillance de Luçon le fit arrêter le 3 mars. Mais, pour y parvenir, il avait recouru à un faux témoignage. Pille, qui était alors commissaire d'une commission exécutive, comprit que l'affaire était mal engagée, il envoya Huché à Paris « avec tous les égards dus à un citoyen accusé, mais non convaincu ». Les représentants s'indignèrent de cette arrestation d'un « général qui faisait son devoir ». Le Comité de Sûreté générale donna raison aux représentants et libéra Huché le 27 mai. Carnot rédigea l'arrêté qui renvoyait Huché à l'armée de l'Ouest ; Robespierre et Barère signèrent avec Carnot. Auraient-ils pu faire autrement ? Il a fallu lire les pièces un peu vite pour faire grief à Carnot et de la nomination, et des reproches qu'il fit ensuite à Huché. Il est vrai que la version qu'il donnait de l'événement n'était pas plus exacte.

De plus, Huché continua d'appliquer sa méthode dans son nouveau poste, alors que la consigne était de pacifier. Le 16 juillet, il dirigeait encore une colonne et allait surprendre les paysans chez eux ou dans les champs. Il se présentait comme un chef vendéen, puis massacrait tous ceux, hommes, femmes et enfants, qui n'avaient pas osé se prononcer contre les Vendéens. Aucune sanction ne l'atteignit avant le 9 Thermidor.

Ce triste individu, frappé sous tous les régimes, eut l'inconscience de demander sa réintégration à Carnot, ministre de la Guerre en 1800, après avoir protesté, auprès de Bonaparte, contre le « caractère haineux » de Carnot [17] !

Pendant que Huché était arrêté, le Comité modifia le personnel et les méthodes en Vendée. Les généraux Rossignol et Turreau furent remplacés ; il fut prescrit de frapper impitoyablement les chefs et les insurgés, mais de ménager la population ; de renoncer « à l'épouvante », mais d'inspirer la confiance. On comprit aussi qu'il ne s'agissait plus d'une guerre, sinon d'une « chasse au sanglier », comme écrivait Garnier de Saintes, mais d'une pacification.

Carnot, qui avait rédigé les principaux décrets, avait spécifié qu'il fallait poursuivre les prêtres réfractaires « non comme prêtres... mais comme rebelles ou factieux ».

La rigueur demeurait implacable. Les tribunaux d'exception étaient maintenus ; Carnot prenait des dispositions draconiennes pour opérer la récolte en recourant aux troupes, mais c'était une action cohérente, aux effets limités. Carnot maintint strictement cette ligne de conduite, rappelant tantôt qu'il fallait — le 2 juin — « prendre les mesures les plus fortes... pour anéantir des monstres », autorisant — le 4 juin — la destruction de Saint-Florent ; tantôt — le 2 juillet — il rendait les généraux « responsables de l'indiscipline des troupes, ainsi que des actes d'inhumanité qui ne pourraient qu'aigrir le mal ». Le 23 juillet, il formula clairement sa politique : « Nous n'avons qu'un seul but, celui de terminer enfin l'horrible guerre de la Vendée, objet dont on s'écarte également soit par une lâche indulgence, soit par des exécutions qui, en frappant sur la faiblesse, ne pourraient que révolter la justice et l'humanité. »

Ces longs efforts et la persistance imprévus de cette guerre ajournèrent les projets de descente en Angleterre. Carnot, pourtant, esquissa divers projets : dans les îles anglo-normandes, au début de 1794, dans l'île de Wight, à la fin de février, contre l'Angleterre même. Cependant, en raison de l'état des armées et de la flotte, rien ne put être tenté, le général Moulin déclarait le 5 juillet 1794 que la chouannerie interdisait l'expédition [18].

* *

Finalement, au début de juillet 1796, d'importants objectifs avaient été atteints : les frontières étaient dégagées, la Belgique était conquise, les insurrections de l'Ouest avaient échoué. Les résultats sauvaient-ils la Révolution ?

On peut dire, après Billaud-Varenne et sans doute avec Robespierre, que les victoires avaient leurs inconvénients : elles écartaient le danger qui avait galvanisé les énergies, provoqué le gouvernement révolutionnaire et consolidé la Révolution. « La guerre, qui paraissait devoir consommer notre ruine, est pourtant ce qui nous a sauvés. » Carnot n'en jugeait pas ainsi. Consterné par « l'état violent » qui éprou-

vait les forces vives du pays, il pensait que le ressort allait
se briser si la lutte n'était pas rapidement terminée par la
victoire et par la paix. Sa stratégie était politique, il se sou-
ciait sans cesse des gains définitifs et condamnait les aven-
tures inutiles et dangereuses. En vain a-t-on voulu comprendre sa grande idée — la marche sur Ypres et Ostende —
en fonction des seules opérations militaires, elle s'intégrait
dans un ensemble qui était d'ordre politique : rompre la
coalition, détacher les continentaux des Anglais. Avait-il
trouvé le meilleur moyen ? On n'oserait l'affirmer, mais tel
était son but. De même voulait-il ménager les Prussiens,
intimider les Espagnols et traiter avec les uns et les autres.

Le 16 juillet, il avait crayonné les articles de la paix,
renonçant à la frontière du Rhin, proposant une limite
stratégique incurvée, au long de l'Escaut et de la Haine,
entre Anvers et Namur. Ainsi serait tendue en permanence
la nasse qui se refermait derrière un agresseur éventuel.
C'était la leçon de Lafitte-Clavé. Les Anglais verraient leur
commerce s'effondrer, tant au nord que dans les Indes. Les
coalisés perdraient les ressources énormes de la banque
d'Amsterdam.

Mais Carnot était amené à reconnaître que la paix devait
être conquise par de nombreux efforts : les succès acquis
n'avaient ni écrasé les armées adverses, ni acculé les gouvernements aux négociations. Du moins l'armée française,
plus forte que jamais, pouvait-elle vivre sur l'ennemi. Et
les méthodes de guerre, progressivement perfectionnées,
devaient permettre d'aboutir à coup sûr, sinon par une
seule campagne.

Le drame se ramenait à une contradiction fortement
nouée : la fin de la guerre ne pouvait être atteinte que par
un suprême effort qui exigeait la prolongation du gouvernement révolutionnaire. Or celui-ci était déchiré et sapé,
divisé par la guerre et ses méthodes, comme par la politique
et ses procédés.

CHAPITRE XI

DÉCHIREMENT DU COMITÉ

L'ÉTABLISSEMENT et le développement du pouvoir du Comité étaient liés à un ensemble de conditions mouvant et complexe. Le Grand Comité, né sur les ruines de la Gironde, avait reposé sur la Montagne qui lui assurait la majorité à la Convention, et sur un accord avec les Extrémistes — Enragés et Hébertistes — qui avaient assuré le soutien parisien — Commune, Cordeliers et hommes de mains — moyennant des concessions, sinon à leur programme, du moins à leurs tendances.

Tant qu'il y avait eu à craindre pour l'existence même de la République, l'équilibre s'était maintenu ; quand l'avenir avait paru moins sombre, les Enragés et les Hébertistes avaient été sacrifiés, mais l'accord s'était maintenu entre les membres du Comité[1].

Il se brisa presque aussitôt, à propos du procès et de l'exécution de Danton. On croit volontiers Carnot quand il affirme qu'il avait de l'aversion pour Danton ; ces deux hommes avaient des tempéraments trop contraires, seul l'amour de la patrie avait pu les réunir. Et pourtant, ajoute Carnot, j'ai été, « au Comité de Salut public, contre l'arrestation de Danton ». Cette déclaration, faite après le 18 fructidor, pourrait paraître peu convaincante en face des minutes d'arrêtés frappant les Dantonistes et signées de Carnot, mais la correspondance avec Garrau vient la confirmer. Celui-ci disait sa grande satisfaction de voir écraser les modérés ; Carnot, qui l'avait approuvé quand il s'était agi des Hébertistes, regretta l'exécution des Dantonistes, par équité : « Vous n'avez pas une preuve contre lui... », par prudence : « Si vous frayez une fois le chemin de l'échafaud aux représentants du peuple, nous passerons tous par ce chemin. » Il s'agissait ici d'un « fondateur » de la République — « songez-y bien, une tête comme celle de Danton en entraîne beaucoup d'autres », et ces proscriptions tueraient la Révolution [2].

La mort de Danton laissait en tête-à-tête quelques hommes, Robespierre, Saint-Just, Carnot ; elle faisait disparaître le seul chef capable d'exercer une influence comparable à celle de Robespierre ; on pouvait redouter que Robespierre, d'accord avec Couthon et Saint-Just, voulût imposer sa politique et son autorité. Carnot s'y opposa.

Dès le 1er avril, il s'écria : « Malheur à une république où le mérite d'un homme, où sa vertu même serait devenu nécessaire. » Cet avertissement fut repris, trois semaines plus tard, par Billaud-Varenne. Mais, déjà, dans l'intervalle, l'opposition s'était affirmée [3].

Les anecdotes ne manquent pas, mais elles se situent à des dates imprécises ; on ne sait parfois si elles se rapportent ou non au même fait. Peu importe. L'essentiel se dégage clairement, à savoir que, d'avril à juin, la scission s'approfondit sans cesse davantage et aboutit à la mort de Robespierre et de ses amis, aussi bien qu'à la fin du Grand Comité, donc du grand rôle de Carnot.

Si Robespierre avait des partisans fanatiques, Carnot était en train de se constituer une clientèle. Il pouvait compter sur un certain nombre de représentants en mission, il avait contribué à les nommer, il leur faisait confiance et, parfois, il nouait avec eux des relations d'amitié. Le meilleur exemple est celui de Garrau, mais il y eut aussi Richard et surtout Choudieu, Lacombe, Saint-Michel, Hentz. D'autre part, les militaires étaient amenés à solliciter celui qui disposait des nominations, mutations, récompenses, voire des congés de moisson et de convalescence. Il procédait enfin aux réquisitions, plaçant les intéressés dans les administrations, les manufactures, les services de tout genre, ou même renvoyant les hommes à leurs entreprises. Les sollicitations venaient de toutes parts, de Couthon même ; et de nombreux Conventionnels comme Enlart, Laloy, Dubois.

Naturellement Carnot s'intéressait spécialement aux officiers du Génie et d'Artillerie. Il écrivait à Lebon pour les faire relâcher ; il en faisait libérer par le Comité.

Il protégeait et même secourait des ci-devant et des modérés, l'ex-marquis de Montalembert, l'ex-marquis de Marescot, d'Obenheim, Lacuée, Tholozé, d'Audreville. Il sauva aussi Pigault-Montbaillarcq, qu'il avait connu à Calais et qui appartenait à une famille de banquiers [4].

Il est frappant que, dans les premières altercations, Carnot ait traité Robespierre et Saint-Just de dictateurs et que ceux-ci lui aient reproché ses relations avec les aristocrates. Depuis longtemps déjà, Robespierre avait été l'objet, par les uns ou par les autres, de telles inculpations, mais elle venait cette fois d'un membre influent du Comité et au moment où la popularité et le rôle de Robespierre grandissaient. Quant à Carnot, on lui avait reproché sa famille — son frère Feulint —, leurs relations et les siennes avec des militaires « à talents », mais réactionnaires, aussi bien que les amis de la famille Dupont, qui était celle de sa femme et de sa belle-sœur. Mais la critique venait désormais de Robespierre et de Saint-Just, au moment où Carnot, par la suppression du ministre de la Guerre, disposait d'un pouvoir qu'il n'avait jamais eu — et ce pouvoir s'exerçait sur l'armée.

Il faut évoquer toutes les diatribes antérieures — et toutes les mesures prises — contre le pouvoir militaire, dangereux pour la République, surtout en cas de victoire, pour mesurer la puissance de l'accusation et des craintes qu'elle exprimait. Carnot prendrait-il la suite de Custine, de Dumouriez, sinon de La Fayette ?

Il est peu probable que Robespierre ait vraiment brigué la dictature ; il est sûr que Carnot ne voulait jouer ni les Dumouriez, ni les La Fayette, ni les Custine. Mais il suffisait que chacun fût persuadé de la réalité des desseins de l'autre, que chacun pût constater la réalité du pouvoir de l'autre, que chacun enfin fût exaspéré par le caractère et le tempérament de l'autre.

De Robespierre et de Saint-Just contre Carnot, nous n'avons guère que les quelques tirades violentes qui éclatèrent lors des scènes dont nous allons parler. Mais, de Carnot, il est resté toutes les déclarations antirobespierristes postérieures au 9 Thermidor. Les premières s'expliquent par la nécessité de justifier l'événement, les suivantes par celle de sauver son pouvoir et sa vie ; mais, dans la suite, Carnot n'a jamais désarmé, ni au Directoire, ni à Magdebourg.

En vain a-t-on voulu définir les divergences politiques : rien d'essentiel ne séparait les deux hommes dans ce domaine. Ni l'un ni l'autre n'avaient approuvé la déchristianisation, le dirigisme économique, la lutte à mort contre les commerçants, le partage des terres ; ni l'un ni l'autre n'avaient refusé d'y recourir quand il le fallait. Tous deux voulaient la république des lumières et se réclamaient de Rousseau ; ils aimaient la nature, la vertu, ils étaient déistes. Carnot n'était pas moins incorruptible que Robespierre. En politique extérieure, la raison d'État les guidait ; ils ne croyaient ni à la propagande, ni aux conquêtes, ils ne tenaient pas à l'intégralité des frontières naturelles, ils souhaitaient la paix, mais ils haïssaient l'Angleterre. Tous deux étaient amenés à recourir à la violence quand le salut public l'exigeait.

Sans doute Carnot ne trouva-t-il pas d'accents comparables à ceux de Robespierre quand, présidant la Convention, il eut à célébrer l'Être suprême. Sans doute limita-t-il le programme économique et social plus étroitement. Sans doute fut-il plus réticent quand il s'agit d'établir la Grande Terreur. Mais ce n'était que des nuances et toujours l'accord avait pu s'établir.

Il faut chercher ailleurs. L'un et l'autre étaient autoritaires, jaloux de leur pouvoir, impérieux et même violents. Cette ressemblance les opposait. L'un était un parlementaire, le doctrinaire, l'orateur et le tacticien des assemblées et des clubs ; l'autre était un scientifique, mais qui se voulut politique ; il réussit mal dans les assemblées et dans les clubs. Le premier mesurait l'importance énorme de la compétence militaire dans les circonstances que traversait la République, mais il fut incompétent. Il tenta de s'appuyer sur les connaissances et les aptitudes de Saint-Just ; alors il eût pu évincer Carnot. Ce dernier trait achevait la rupture.

Certes, en d'autres circonstances, dans un cadre différent, et surtout si Robespierre et le Comité n'avaient pas eu d'ennemis acharnés, le dissentiment n'aurait pas eu de vastes répercussions dans l'histoire nationale. Mais le Comité tenait à des circonstances qui s'étaient modifiées, le danger extérieur diminuait, la Vendée s'affaiblissait, l'opinion se divisait de plus en plus, et l'ardeur révolutionnaire s'éteignait chez le plus grand nombre. Des Conventionnels avaient de bonnes raisons de craindre pour eux. Enfin, si Robespierre s'appuyait sur Couthon et Saint-Just, Carnot avait pour lui Prieur et Lindet. La vie du Comité était menacée dans sa source.

A mesure que les deux groupes fortifiaient leur position, les altercations se répétèrent ; dans l'intervalle, ils s'accordaient pourtant contre leurs ennemis communs, du dehors et du dedans. Le Conventionnel Niou — celui-là même que

Guffroy prit à témoin de l'aristocratie de Carnot et qui avait appuyé Carnot — assista à une première scène le 7 avril. Niou était employé comme ingénieur aux armements et c'est à propos du personnel de l'administration des armées que Saint-Just déclencha l'attaque. Il s'indigna qu'un employé, très patriote, eût été incarcéré. Prieur, qui dirigeait le service, démentit le fait. Alors Saint-Just s'en prit à Carnot, comme si celui-ci avait manié Prieur à sa guise. L'employé en question était le beau-frère de Sijas, dont nous avons vu le rôle au ministère de la Guerre et dans la commission de l'Organisation et du Mouvement. Ainsi les deux groupes recrutaient une clientèle, noyautaient leur personnel et rivalisaient jusque dans leurs bureaux.

« Vous voulez renverser successivement tous les patriotes qui vous font obstacle, afin de rester seuls et de vous emparer du pouvoir suprême, s'écria Carnot. Mais les amis de la liberté sauront déjouer vos ruses.

— C'est toi qui es lié avec les ennemis des patriotes ; sache qu'il me suffirait de quelques lignes pour dresser ton acte d'accusation et te faire guillotiner dans deux jours.

— Je t'y invite, répondit froidement Carnot. Je provoque contre moi toutes tes rigueurs. Je ne te crains pas, ni toi, ni tes amis ; vous êtes des dictateurs ridicules. »

Saint-Just menaça de faire expulser Carnot du Comité.

« Tu en sortiras avant moi, Saint-Just. »

Saint-Just s'éloigna en proférant des menaces [5].

Cet éclat n'empêcha pas les membres du Comité de s'accorder contre les Hébertistes. Le 9 mai, chez Monge, un vif incident survint entre Carnot et Mme Audouin, fille de Pache, qui défendait Hébert. Le lendemain, Pache, sa fille et son gendre étaient arrêtés par le Comité de Salut public et le Comité de Sûreté générale réunis [6].

L'arrestation de Pache mettait le point final au conflit qui l'avait opposé aux Carnot depuis dix mois. A ce propos, Carnot s'était réconcilié avec Bourdon de l'Oise. Celui-ci avait été mal reçu au Comité le jour où il était venu dénoncer Hanriot, Pache et Bouchotte. Carnot, l'ayant appris, s'en excusa, et ils se mirent d'accord. Bourdon de l'Oise était si violemment hostile à Robespierre qu'il avait résolu de l'assassiner [7].

La collaboration avec le Comité de Sûreté générale marquait aussi la bonne entente entre une partie de ce Comité et Carnot. Quelques jours auparavant, deux secrétaires de

Carnot avaient été arrêtés en tant que ci-devant nobles. Carnot avait demandé au Comité de Sûreté générale de les libérer, s'il n'y avait pas d'autres griefs contre eux. Il eut satisfaction dans la journée[8]. La majorité du Comité de Sûreté générale ne pardonnait pas à Robespierre d'avoir créé, le 16 avril, sa police : le bureau de Surveillance administrative et de Police générale. Les autres membres du Comité de Salut public — hormis Couthon et Saint-Just — s'inquiétaient aussi de cette création redoutable.

Ils furent pourtant tous d'accord pour créer, le même jour, à Orange, ce fameux tribunal révolutionnaire qui annonçait l'effroyable loi de prairial[9]. Ce fut aussi le moment où la terreur s'aggrava dans le Nord ; Carnot y redoutait la trahison, notamment à Cambrai. Lebon — après avoir conféré avec le Comité — vit confirmer ses pouvoirs, malgré Buissart, qui se tournait vainement vers Carnot, comme vers Robespierre, pour se débarrasser de Lebon[10].

Le conflit entre les personnels des deux groupes se poursuivait. Un secrétaire de Saint-Just et Lebas fut arrêté, et aussi Lebas jeune, qui était aide garde-magasin à l'armée du Nord[11].

Le 25 mai, Carnot écrivait à ses « deux collègues » Saint-Just et Lebas, pour disculper le chef d'état-major du général Ferrand. Il leur faisait, en passant, une remarque significative : « L'expérience nous prouvant que de pareilles dénonciations [comme celle que Saint-Just et Lebas avaient transmise] sont souvent dictées soit par des haines particulières, soit par le désir d'obtenir les places de ceux qu'on veut faire destituer, soit enfin par l'envie de priver la République de ceux qui la servent avec goût et intelligence[12]. »

Deux jours plus tard Carnot écrivait à Hanriot en faveur de Viénot, receveur des domaines de Vincennes, capitaine de la garde nationale, et qu'Hanriot avait destitué. Viénot s'était adressé à Carnot, le 5 mai, « comme Français et comme républicain », puis, n'ayant pas obtenu satisfaction, il avait alors fait passer sa pétition par Lecointre[13]. C'était là un ennemi farouche de Robespierre, l'un de ceux qui se vantèrent le plus d'avoir préparé le 9 Thermidor. Cette rencontre — Bourdon de l'Oise, Lecointre, l'un et l'autre se tournant vers Carnot — montre que les ennemis de Robespierre comptaient sur lui. Robespierre lui-même s'en doutait ; il a consigné dans ses notes que Bourdon de l'Oise avait présenté un commis au Comité, que Carnot l'avait pris dans ses bureaux et qu'il avait fallu plusieurs interventions de Robespierre pour l'en faire chasser ; ce Conventionnel, observait-il, « joignait la perfidie à la fureur [14] ».

Précisément des tentatives d'assassinat furent alors répétées. Robespierre et ses amis ripostèrent par la terrible loi du 22 prairial (10 juin), qui ôtait toute garantie aux suspects. Cette nouvelle mesure provoqua une des plus violentes scènes qui aient eu lieu au Comité.

Le fameux accusateur public Fouquier-Tinville a raconté qu'il s'était rendu au Comité alors qu'on y préparait le projet de loi. Il avait constaté que Carnot et ses amis en laissaient toute la responsabilité à Robespierre. Le conflit éclata, semble-t-il, au lendemain du vote de la loi, quand on redouta qu'elle fût appliquée aux Conventionnels. L'affaire fut si vive qu'on décida de tenir désormais les séances au premier étage, « afin que le peuple ne fût pas témoin des orages qui nous agitaient ». Carnot serait resté muet, « étonné » en présence de la violence de ses adversaires, et Robespierre aurait « pleuré de rage [15] ».

Quoi qu'il en soit, la scission était désormais profonde. Robespierre ne vint plus au Comité ; Couthon dirigeait le bureau de Police, ainsi que Saint-Just quand il était à Paris. Collot d'Herbois et Billaud-Varenne faisaient cause commune avec Carnot, Prieur et Lindet. Les choses en étaient venues au point que les cours étrangères connaissaient l'antagonisme qui divisait les membres et qui opposait le Comité de Salut public au Comité de Sûreté générale [16]. Carnot pourtant prenait alors des mesures rigoureuses qui s'inscrivaient dans les cadres de la « Grande Terreur ».

Il fit, le 17 juin, cette implacable déposition sur la conduite de Victor de Broglie, qui contribua à le faire guillotiner. Il reçut au même moment un envoyé du conseil général d'Arras et lui demanda si Arras « était toujours à la hauteur » ; l'autre répondit affirmativement, parce que Lebon « y avait porté les choses au plus haut degré révolutionnaire et que tous ceux qui étaient contraires à la République disparaissaient tous les jours [17] ». Carnot laissa Lebon libre d'agir tant que les succès militaires n'eurent pas fait disparaître tout danger. Il signait aussi des ordres d'arrestation, même émanant du bureau de Police générale, des arrêtés pour surveiller les prisons et poursuivre ceux qui voulaient y organiser des conspirations, et il signa également des arrêtés envoyant dans les départements des agents chargés de l'action policière. En somme, il participait à la politique générale et ne se cantonnait pas dans la conduite de la guerre. Mais les crises reprirent précisément à propos de la guerre : Carnot fut accusé d'impéritie et d'incivisme.

Ce fut au retour de Fleurus, le 26 ou 29 juin, que Saint-Just déclencha une nouvelle attaque. Il lui reprochait cette fois d'avoir compromis la victoire de Fleurus par les renforts qu'il voulait prélever. La rancœur de Saint-Just appuya sur ce fait, et il le reprenait dans ce discours qu'il n'a pu prononcer le 9 thermidor, mais dont il a laissé le texte. Visiblement, l'opposition devenait beaucoup plus âpre depuis que Carnot était seul maître des armées et depuis que Saint-Just avait reçu sa grande mission militaire. Il y avait une compétition directe concernant la conduite de la guerre, le rôle de l'armée du Nord et celui de l'armée de Sambre-et-Meuse, l'activité des représentants, notamment de Choudieu.

Robespierre appuyait Saint-Just et trouvait dangereux que Carnot contrôlât les généraux, les principales commissions, un certain nombre de représentants et les troupes. Dans le fatras que d'Antraigues transmettait aux coalisés, on signalait ces craintes. Toute occasion était bonne pour attaquer la direction de la guerre : le déplacement des troupes, les projets sur la Hollande, l'envoi des canonniers parisiens aux armées, la non-exécution de la garnison de Nieuport, le refus de l'offensive en Italie.

Baudot, peu favorable à Carnot, raconte que Robespierre s'en prit aux plans de campagne, qu'il « osa dire que Carnot était d'accord avec les ennemis de la République » et qu'il prodigua les « calomnies », menaçant de dénoncer Carnot. Celui-ci, versant des larmes de rage, n'aurait rien répondu, mais les autres membres auraient pris sa défense. Levasseur et Barère ont parlé de l'affaire de Fleurus ; les discours de Robespierre et de Saint-Just ont repris ces divers griefs, bases d'un véritable réquisitoire [18].

Ses ennemis voulurent enlever à Carnot le prestige qu'il tirait des victoires. Dans une auberge, un agent du Comité déclarait que Carnot était « un foutu gueux », qu'il avait failli faire perdre la bataille de Fleurus et qu'il ne venait si ponctuellement au Comité que pour espionner. Florent Guiot confirma dans la suite que des envoyés du Comité traitaient Carnot de contre-révolutionnaire et qu'ils annonçaient que « le peuple ne tarderait pas à en faire justice [19] ».

Les querelles de clientèle continuèrent. C'étaient Bauche et

Rambourg, deux commis de Carnot, que Robespierre avait fait arrêter, au reçu d'une dénonciation venue des Ardennes. Carnot réclama vainement leur libération et de violentes récriminations eurent lieu le 29 juin [20]. Au même moment, Carnot s'appliquait à faire libérer le sous-chef du bureau de comptabilité de la commission de l'Organisation et des Mouvements de l'armée, qui avait eu maille à partir avec les commissaires du Comité de surveillance de la section de l'Indivisibilité. Cette fois, Robespierre fit arrêter les membres de ce comité, qui s'en étaient pris à l'Être suprême et à Robespierre lui-même, et Carnot les fit libérer, le 9 juillet [21]. Les intrigues se croisaient dans une étonnante confusion.

Les membres du Comité s'épiaient et se défiaient. Saint-Just a dit l'humeur sombre de Billaud-Varenne, il a dépeint ses traits altérés, son teint blafard et son regard fixe. Les autres, recrus de fatigue et rongés de fureur, n'étaient pas davantage en état de se contenir. Lindet a raconté que Collot d'Herbois s'était jeté sur Robespierre et qu'il avait dû les séparer, aidé de Carnot et de Prieur de la Côte-d'Or. Le conseiller Carnot affirme qu'un jour son frère lança une écritoire à la tête de Robespierre [22].

Le 9 juillet précisément, la défiance redoubla. Il avait été décidé que Couthon irait prendre les eaux, que Saint-Just se rendrait aux armées et que Carnot partirait pour la Hollande. Or un agent du Comité, Demaillot, dînant ce soir-là avec Carnot, apprit que tous ces départs étaient ajournés : les deux camps s'observaient.

Il avait aussi été question d'envoyer Billaud-Varenne à l'armée du Nord, où se trouvaient les représentants Richard et Choudieu, que Robespierre trouvait trop mous. Carnot s'y était opposé, répliquant que Richard et Choudieu observaient les ordres du Comité [23].

Le 21 juillet, les comparses s'affrontaient de nouveau; Sijas dénonçait aux Jacobins le chef de la commission de l'Organisation et du Mouvement des armées, Pille, le collaborateur de Carnot. Il lui adressait les reproches que l'on faisait à Carnot lui-même [24].

Ce conflit risquait d'avoir d'immenses conséquences, car il affaiblissait le Comité de Salut public au moment où celui-ci s'opposait au Comité de Sûreté générale et au moment où une partie des Conventionnels, mécontents et inquiets, cherchaient à perdre Robespierre et ses amis.

L'ampleur des répercussions amena une tentative de

rapprochement. Le 23 juillet, une réunion des deux Comités fut tenue « pour s'expliquer mutuellement sur la division qui, selon ce que Robespierre avait prétendu à plusieurs reprises aux Jacobins, subsiste entre les Comités de gouvernement ». Ainsi en parlait Ruhl, membre du Comité de Sûreté générale, et qui avait refusé de signer l'ordre d'arrestation de Danton.

Ce fut Saint-Just qui prit la parole. Il fit l'éloge de Robespierre et parla de la nécessité d'organiser une constitution. Robespierre intervint ensuite et se plaignit de ses ennemis, notamment de Carnot, « en leur reprochant l'acharnement avec lequel ils le déchiraient ». Carnot riposta et « lui dit en face qu'il ne l'aimait pas »; d'autres, Billaud-Varenne, Vadier, intervinrent à leur tour; les reproches habituels furent repris une fois de plus.

Finalement l'apaisement se fit et l'on décida que Saint-Just ferait un rapport au nom des deux Comités, « pour apprendre à la Convention qu'ils n'étaient pas divisés ». Dans cette euphorie, tous se mirent d'accord sur des points litigieux : Carnot accepta la création de quatre commissions populaires qui exécuteraient les décrets de ventôse sur le partage des biens des suspects, Saint-Just consentit au départ de quatre compagnies de canonniers parisiens [25].

Accord éphémère. Dès le lendemain, Couthon dénonçait le départ de ces canonniers comme une manœuvre contre-révolutionnaire tramée par Carnot. Depuis ce temps, les historiens se sont vivement opposés sur ce point, déterminant au dire des uns, insignifiant d'après les autres. De quoi s'agissait-il ?

Les canonniers formaient l'élément le plus important de la force armée parisienne. Il y avait quarante-huit compagnies, une par section, comptant chacune cinquante hommes et deux canons légers. Ils étaient capables d'emporter la décision dans un combat de rues; on avait mesuré leur rôle au 31 mai 1793, quand ils avaient fait reculer la Convention; on allait constater la puissance de l'artillerie encore plus nettement le 13 vendémiaire, quand Bonaparte écrasa l'insurrection, mais il ne s'agissait plus alors de canonniers parisiens. Un an plus tard, Babeuf s'appliquait à renouer avec tous les canonniers démocrates pour accomplir son coup d'État. Force politique, ils l'étaient plus encore au temps où ils avaient été rattachés à l'armée révolutionnaire, en septembre 1793. Ils devaient prendre du service par moitié, successivement tous les trois mois, pour aider l'armée révolutionnaire à « comprimer les

contre-révolutionnaires et accapareurs de l'intérieur ».
Le reste du temps, ils demeuraient à Paris dans leur section ;
en vertu de l'article 3 du décret du 9 septembre, ils pouvaient être appelés à défendre les autorités si des troubles
éclataient.

Certes il y avait des différences notables entre les sections,
c'est-à-dire entre les quartiers. Les plus révolutionnaires
étaient celles qui avaient marché le 31 mai dans les quartiers
de l'est de l'Hôtel de Ville au faubourg Saint-Antoine, de la
Villette et de Belleville au Panthéon. C'est vers elles que se
tournera Babeuf.

Quelques semaines après l'arrêté du 3 novembre, qui
avait organisé leur service, vingt-quatre compagnies avaient
été portées sur les points névralgiques : douze à Lyon, sept
dans l'Ouest, cinq dans la région parisienne.

Carnot eut le souci de les contrôler, comme l'ensemble de
l'armée révolutionnaire, pour les astreindre à une stricte discipline et veiller aux écarts politiques. Effectivement, malgré
leurs protestations, les compagnies de canonniers furent
soumises aux généraux commandant les troupes.

Trois mois plus tard, il s'agit de la relève. Carnot fit savoir,
le 24 janvier, qu'elle était incompatible avec les nécessités
du service aux armées, et, malgré des protestations, notamment à Lyon, les canonniers obéirent. Ces nécessités ces-
sèrent quand la crise hébertiste fut résolue ; or la situation
militaire ne s'était pas améliorée, à beaucoup près.

Pendant la crise hébertiste, le gouvernement avait éloigné
de Paris tous les détachements de l'armée révolutionnaire, et
au lendemain, il avait licencié cette armée. Mais les canonniers qui n'étaient pas de service et se trouvaient en conséquence à Paris avaient manifesté leur loyalisme. Ils furent
conservés et placés sous l'autorité exclusive du Comité de
Salut public. A cette date, il y avait, conformément aux
prescriptions, vingt-quatre compagnies en service, à Lyon,
dans l'Ouest et à Laon, Soissons et Chantilly.

La relève commença donc, mais, dès le 8 avril, on spécifiait
que la compagnie qui se rendrait à Laon serait mise à la
disposition du général commandant l'armée du Nord. Les
remplacements s'accomplirent si lentement qu'au milieu
de juin ils n'avaient assuré le retour que de neuf compagnies.
Hanriot, général de la force armée de Paris, réclama le retour
de quatre compagnies qui étaient à Brest depuis huit mois,
inutilement, et qui seraient nécessaires à Paris. Il désirait

donc installer des compagnies dans la capitale, en sus des vingt-quatre prévues. Carnot transmit la demande au général Moulin, mais une seule compagnie revint de Brest et elle y fut remplacée. Il y avait à l'armée de l'Ouest cinq autres compagnies, trois d'entre elles furent relevées. De même treize compagnies étaient revenues de Lyon au début de juillet. Le calcul d'Hanriot allait-il réussir ? Carnot intervint. Il argua des besoins de l'armée du Nord, soulignés par le bureau de l'Artillerie, et prescrivit, coup sur coup, les 8, 12 et 23 juillet, le départ de six compagnies vers le nord-est. Ce qui donna lieu à de véhémentes protestations, bien que les départs du 23 eussent été contresignés par Saint-Just. Effectivement, Carnot avait combattu la tentative d'Hanriot d'augmenter le nombre des canonniers à Paris ; mais les services de la Guerre prétendirent qu'il en restait trois de plus qu'il n'était prescrit, et l'on trouve même la preuve qu'il y avait vingt-huit compagnies au 9 Thermidor. Hanriot, dit un rapport, avait voulu se faire un parti des canonniers, car ils méprisaient la garde nationale. Il convoqua leurs capitaines, le 9 thermidor, et s'appuya sur Fontaine, adjudant-général d'artillerie et chef de leur état-major. Effectivement, des capitaines suivirent Fontaine de préférence au commandant de leur section. Le flottement fut considérable. D'après Coffinhal, Hanriot aurait disposé un moment de dix-sept compagnies de canonniers. Carnot n'avait donc pu conjurer ce risque.

D'autre part, il s'était soucié d'agir sur le moral des armées. Depuis longtemps, il connaissait l'influence des journaux, il en fit créer un, la *Soirée du Camp*, peu de temps avant la journée décisive.

Le 13 juillet, le Comité décida de le tirer à 10 000 exemplaires, le 16, une imprimerie fut réquisitionnée, le 19, deux employés du Comité furent chargés de préparer une douzaine de numéros, le 21, ils commencèrent de paraître. Dans ce journal, Hébert était attaqué comme « contre-révolutionnaire », la Convention était exaltée. Certains passages étaient significatifs. On parlait notamment des scélérats qui s'efforcent de « donner à la vertu l'apparence du crime, et à la bassesse du crime, la gloire qui n'est due qu'à la vertu ». On invitait les troupes à ne pas oublier « ceux qui ont guidé nos généraux dans le chemin de la victoire ». On s'appliquait aussi à prendre en main les élèves de l'École de Mars. Le numéro du 9 thermidor faisait allusion aux « calomnies contre les plus

fermes soutiens de la République »; il ajoutait ces mots menaçants : « Nos armées sauront leur répondre. »

Pourtant Carnot ne se liait pas aux antirobespierristes.
Legendre, le rencontrant le 25 juillet, lui disait :

« Je sais que tu as brisé une lance avec Robespierre,
crois-tu que nous devons le démasquer ?

— Ne précipite rien, répondit Carnot, le moment viendra.
Ne fais pas d'imprudences, car tu monterais à l'échafaud [26]. »

Les sollicitations des uns étaient renforcées par les menaces
des autres. Robespierre se plaignait, le 26 juillet, qu'on eût
semé la division parmi les généraux, persécuté ceux qui
étaient fidèles et protégé les aristocrates. Il dénonçait l'administration militaire et s'inquiétait des dangers de la
victoire [27]. C'était plus qu'il n'en fallait pour perdre Carnot
si Robespierre l'avait emporté, mais celui-ci, acclamé aux
Jacobins, n'eut pas de succès à la Convention.

L'atmosphère du Comité devint alors tragique :

« Tu rédiges notre acte d'accusation, disait Collot à
Saint-Just, le soir du 26.

— Eh bien, oui », répondit celui-ci, et, se tournant vers
Carnot : « Tu n'y es pas oublié non plus. »

Effectivement, ce projet de discours reprenait la question
des canonniers : « Je ne nie pas qu'on ait eu le droit d'en tirer,
mais je n'en connais pas le besoin. » A propos de Fleurus :
« Il n'y a que ceux qui sont dans les batailles qui les gagnent. »
Enfin ce trait direct : Je ne connais pas de « dominateur qui
ne se soit emparé d'un grand crédit militaire ». Saint-Just
quitta le Comité dans la nuit du 26, après avoir promis de
communiquer ses griefs à ses collègues.

Carnot était resté dans la salle avec les autres adversaires
de Robespierre. Il prit alors une part active à la lutte, rédigeant et signant des arrêtés. Il s'agissait surtout de s'assurer
des forces militaires placées sous le commandement d'Hanriot. Ce commandement fut supprimé au profit des chefs
de légion qui se succéderaient au pouvoir. Ce système était
le même que Feulint avait exposé le 10 août, aussi peut-on
penser que l'initiative en revint à Carnot.

Dans la matinée du 27 juillet (9 thermidor), Couthon survint. Il protesta contre les dispositions prises et invectiva
Carnot :

« Je savais bien que tu étais le plus méchant des hommes.

— Et toi le plus traître », riposta Carnot [29].

On apprit alors que Saint-Just, négligeant de tenir sa promesse, déclenchait son attaque à la Convention. Mais l'obstruction le paralysa ainsi que Robespierre, et la Convention vota l'arrestation d'Hanriot et la convocation des chefs de légion, la mise en accusation de Robespierre, Couthon, Saint-Just et Lebas.

La lutte éclata. Hanriot et la Commune firent appel aux forces armées, notamment aux canonniers. La Commune disposa bientôt de dix-sept compagnies de canonniers. Hanriot voulut délivrer Robespierre et ses collègues arrêtés, il se fit prendre, mais, grâce à l'incohérence générale, tous furent libérés dès la fin de l'après-midi.

C'est alors que les Comités ripostèrent, appuyés par la Convention, et reprirent leur autorité sur les sections. Carnot intervint pour ce qui touchait la force armée : il lui ordonna de demeurer dans les sections, de faire des patrouilles, de fournir des comptes rendus de demi-heure en demi-heure ; il fit donner des armes à la section des Tuileries et fit appel aux « jeunes patriotes » du camp des Sablons dont il changea le général.

Ce rôle de Carnot fut reconnu tant par les partisans de la Commune que par ceux des Comités. Parmi les premiers, à la section des Invalides, on affirmait que Sijas l'avait dénoncé dans la nuit, « avec les preuves les plus authentiques ». Parmi les seconds, à la section des Arcis, le 9 thermidor, dans la nuit, le commandant de la force armée envoya successivement trois lettres à Carnot. Il lui demandait s'il fallait envoyer des hommes en armes contre la Commune, pour libérer les prisonniers. Carnot fit savoir qu'on devait rester « tranquille, en force sur le terrain », et que les représentants allaient marcher « en force », en prenant des renforts sur leur passage [30].

Pourtant, Carnot n'intervint pas sur les lieux : c'est Barras qui reçut de la Convention le commandement. La tactique, dont l'initiative paraît revenir à Carnot, réussit pleinement : les forces retenues chacune dans sa section firent déserter l'Hôtel de Ville et amenèrent l'abandon de la Commune, d'Hanriot, de Robespierre et de ses amis. Quand les troupes de la Convention survinrent enfin devant l'Hôtel de Ville, il n'y avait plus de résistance, déjà Robespierre avait tenté de se suicider. Pour limité qu'il puisse paraître, le rôle de Carnot fut donc efficace ; d'ailleurs, on sent la joie du triomphe dans la proclamation qu'il rédigea.

Carnot informait les armées de l'événement en termes violents, selon une tradition déjà bien établie :

« Faites savoir aux incomparables armées de la République, écrivait-il, qu'un nouveau genre de scélératesse avait trouvé, dans leurs succès mêmes, des motifs pour les calomnier ; d'infâmes tyrans, qui avaient usurpé le nom de patriotes, voulaient désorganiser la victoire qui, sur toutes nos frontières, est à l'ordre du jour depuis le commencement de la campagne. Les traîtres ont reçu le prix de leurs forfaits, la représentation nationale a délivré la France, l'oppression a disparu, tous les cœurs s'ouvrent aux plus doux épanchements, et l'allégresse a pris la place de la consternation dans Paris [31].... »

Un an à peine s'était écoulé depuis l'entrée de Carnot au gouvernement. Ce peu de temps avait suffi pour lui permettre d'infléchir l'histoire nationale et le classer parmi les grands hommes de la Révolution. Par lui, la victoire avait sauvé la France et la Révolution même. Il avait été organisateur au plein sens du terme : précis, actif, tenace et méthodique. Stratège et tacticien, il n'avait pas eu la même lucidité, la même efficacité. Pourtant, par lui, l'art de la guerre et la nature des sentiments qui unissaient les membres d'une nation et les dressaient farouchement contre ceux des autres avaient promptement évolué. Il ne saurait être question de lui en attribuer tout le mérite, ou toute la responsabilité, les causes de cette évolution le dépassaient de tous côtés. Il n'en reste pas moins qu'il en fut l'instrument efficace et qu'il orienta et précisa le détail de cette évolution. Sans lui, le Comité aurait pu essuyer des défaites qui l'eussent balayé. En revanche, s'il avait eu le génie militaire d'un Bonaparte, peut-être aurait-il pu conclure plus tôt une paix durable qui eût éviter les campagnes mêmes de Bonaparte. Hypothèses aventureuses, mais qui aident à cerner le contour de l'action d'un homme.

A quoi s'ajoute l'œuvre intérieure. Elle demeure liée à celle des Robespierristes, comme celle d'un collaborateur puis d'un adversaire. C'est elle qui montre comment on cesse d'être révolutionnaire, après avoir fixé le terme des réalisations et des violences d'une révolution. Longtemps, on lui en fit gloire, au temps des historiens favorables à la conser-

vation sociale. Puis elle fut invoquée, pour l'accabler, par
ceux qui déplorèrent l'échec de la démocratie. Prisonniers
parfois de systèmes idéologiques commandant une philosophie de l'Histoire, ils eurent tendance, les uns et les autres,
à situer Carnot dans la lutte des classes. Mais le critère qui
distinguait riches et pauvres, bourgeois et prolétaires, n'était
pas propre à classer un Carnot. Pour lui, le talent était ce qui
distinguait et classait les hommes, le talent et l'instruction.
Celle-ci, démocratiquement propagée, décèlerait celui-là
partout où il se trouverait, chez des ci-devant, des bourgeois ou des pauvres.

Les plus doués, les plus travailleurs, les plus intègres,
devaient guider les autres pour le plus grand bien de tous.
L'État serait leur instrument ; il y avait en Carnot un saint-
simonien avant la lettre : le pouvoir devait revenir aux
savants.

Si importante qu'eût été pour Carnot cette année cruciale,
il devait connaître encore des jours d'action non négligeables.
Désireux désormais d'arrêter la réaction, il fut tour à tour
mêlé à l'activité des dernières assemblées républicaines et
des premières assemblées impériales. Il eut une part plus
ou moins grande du pouvoir républicain et du pouvoir napoléonien. Au gouvernement ou dans l'opposition, il ne fut ni
sans idéal, ni sans influence, ni même souvent sans grandeur.
Le suivre dans ses voies nouvelles est d'autant plus intéressant que les interprétations tendancieuses de sa pensée
et de son œuvre à cette époque foisonnent.

DE THERMIDOR A L'EXIL

CHAPITRE PREMIER

LE STRATÈGE SAUVE LE TERRORISTE

LES promoteurs du 9 Thermidor ne savaient pas que la chute de Robespierre déterminerait la fin de la Terreur et les menacerait à leur tour. Ils virent bientôt la Convention se dresser contre les Comités, les modérés devenir violents pour se venger d'avoir eu peur, les terroristes désavouer la Terreur et se dénoncer mutuellement, tous enfin attaquer les collègues de Robespierre et de Saint-Just.

La réaction atteignait tour à tour le Marais, les Girondins revenus, les hommes de 93 et ceux de 92 ; allait-elle anéantir la Révolution et ceux qui s'étaient glorifiés d'en être les auteurs ? Ceux-ci étaient assez nombreux et assez puissants encore pour sauver leur œuvre et leur personne; ils mirent un terme à la réaction thermidorienne et bâtirent le régime directorial.

Certains pourtant perdirent leurs fonctions, parfois leur liberté et même leur vie.

Les passions et les ambitions déchaînées se polarisèrent suivant de nouvelles lignes de force, parmi le fracas des invectives et les manœuvres perfides. L'organisation de la France était mise en question aussi bien que le sort des hommes de la Révolution.

Carnot ne fut épargné que de justesse, comme organisateur de la victoire. Il eut le courage d'essayer de sauver ses anciens collègues, mais il dut reconnaître qu'il n'en avait pas le pouvoir.

Son rôle déclina de semaine en semaine, comme celui du

Comité de Salut public, auquel il appartint encore pendant la première partie de cette période.

Ce Comité ne dirigeait plus que la politique extérieure et la guerre ; les six membres restants — Carnot, Lindet, Billaud, Collot, Prieur et Barère — étaient neutralisés par six thermidoriens, dont Tallien, le mari de Notre-Dame de Thermidor. Dès le 28 août, Billaud, Collot et Barère étaient accusés de terrorisme. Carnot n'était pas visé, mais son nom était prononcé par des accusés, comme Fouquier-Tinville, qui voulaient sauver leur tête ; par des accusateurs, comme Lecointre, qui exploitaient les papiers de Robespierre, de Saint-Just et du bureau de Police, où se trouvaient tant de signatures compromettantes. Naguère menacé par Robespierre pour son modérantisme, Carnot était soudain en passe d'être frappé comme terroriste. Il évita le pire à force d'adresse et de courage ; ce fut, à cet égard, la période la plus étonnante de sa carrière.

Les victoires étaient sa chance, on admettait d'ordinaire qu'il avait bien conduit la guerre et qu'il devait la diriger encore [1]. Carnot exploita cette chance. Le jour même où Lecointre dressait son réquisitoire contre les trois premiers accusés, Carnot vint à l'Assemblée, au milieu du tumulte, annoncer la prise de Condé ; dans le silence soudain rétabli crépitèrent les applaudissements. A chaque nouvelle victoire, Carnot renouvela cette démarche.

Une autre chance était offerte par ses attributions sur le personnel de la guerre. Il fit libérer et réintégrer des prisonniers politiques, des officiers, des généraux ; il reçut nombre de sollicitations, auxquelles il se montra complaisant. On en vint même à lui reprocher parfois des mises en liberté imprudentes [2]. En revanche, il prescrivit aux représentants en mission aux armées d'effectuer une épuration générale. Ce fut l'occasion qui lui permit de sauver ou de frapper des personnages qu'il n'avait pu atteindre jusqu'alors, mais qu'il n'avait pas oubliés.

Coup sur coup, vingt-six employés à la Commission furent renvoyés. Parmi eux se trouvaient le beau-frère de Sijas, plusieurs chefs de division et commis à qui l'on reprochait de pleurer Sijas et Robespierre, d'autres en qui on n'avait « point de confiance ».

Dans l'armée, la démission du général Santerre était acceptée, Montaigu, Lebas, Calendini étaient destitués, le général Huchet — destitué lui aussi — devait comparaître devant le Comité, le général Desbrulys était mis en arrestation, Declaye était destitué et incarcéré. Au total, une vingtaine d'officiers supérieurs ou généraux étaient frappés, tandis que trois représentants étaient spécialement chargés d'épurer les états-majors et les commandants des places fortes [3].

Enfin il donna des gages, insistant pour qu'on maintînt la fermeture du club des Jacobins, effectuée dès la chute de Robespierre.

Le tout était de savoir si cela suffirait à le désolidariser, non seulement de Robespierre, mais de ses collègues accusés. Déjà Lecointre incriminait sa conduite passée, faible et insouciante. Ces premiers griefs se fussent aisément aggravés si Lecointre avait mieux préparé son réquisitoire. Faute de preuves, provisoirement, ils ne furent pas retenus.

Carnot renforça sa position en prononçant, le 22 septembre, un grand discours sur la campagne de l'an II. Il ramassa en quelques traits vigoureux les caractéristiques essentielles, l'éclat des opérations, l'originalité et le mérite de la conception. L'Assemblée l'applaudit, l'acclama. Ce succès même fut l'origine d'un autre danger : les terroristes les plus menacés appuyèrent désormais sur la défense nationale leurs divers plaidoyers ; ils voulurent s'attacher à Carnot comme on saisit une bouée. Ainsi, à propos des colonnes infernales de Vendée, le 29 septembre, Carrier et Billaud-Varenne en appelèrent à Carnot. Il ne refusa pas ce rôle généreux et dangereux mais voulut rejeter les responsabilités sur la majorité de l'ancien Comité. « Ça a toujours été avec douleur que j'ai soutenu *(sic)* une opinion contraire à la mienne, mais c'était celle de la majorité du Comité. » Argument imprudent : non seulement Carnot avouait la solidarité, mais il posait la question de la majorité : les trois morts — Robespierre, Couthon et Saint-Just — n'avaient pu la former seuls, contre les trois accusés et Carnot.

Lorsque Billaud se réclama de lui, en affirmant que le Comité tout entier avait été hostile aux mesures de rigueur, et que seul Robespierre les avait imposées, Carnot se leva, dans une assemblée mal disposée, et, après avoir chargé Robespierre et Saint-Just, en résumant tendancieusement l'affaire du général Huchet, il put affirmer, sans soulever de protestations, « que Billaud avait été constamment opposé au système de Robespierre »; il parvint même à déclencher des applaudissements.

Dès lors Barère, Collot et Billaud se réclamèrent systématiquement de Carnot, celui-ci assuma cette triple charge. « Il y aurait de la lâcheté, déclarait-il, à se récuser », et il affirma sa pleine solidarité.

« Tout ce qu'ont dit mes collègues est de la plus exacte vérité ; j'ai assisté à toutes les délibérations du Comité ; il est faux, comme on l'a avancé, que j'aie été relégué dans mon bureau. » Tant de courage força les applaudissements, mais prépara de sourdes hostilités qui éclatèrent plus tard avec indignation. « N'avez-vous pas frémi comme moi, lorsque vous avez vu l'un d'eux plaider pour les chefs de nos bourreaux et s'identifier à leur cause ? »

Un risque contraire et non moins dangereux sortit de cette solidarité déclarée. Des hommes de gauche, des journaux, des sociétés populaires célébrèrent Carnot et voulurent lui faire patronner leur politique. Carnot remercia. « Je m'honorerai toujours du suffrage d'une réunion de républicains caractérisés par leur énergie et par leur franchise », répondit-il à la société populaire de Dijon, mais il refusa de s'engager. Son souci était, en excusant des collègues qui avaient péché par erreur, de maintenir la dignité et l'intégralité de la représentation nationale [4]. Ainsi put-il gagner du temps.

Éloigné du Comité par le sort, le 6 octobre, il continua de prendre part à ses travaux pour la conduite de la guerre. A peine le mois d'interruption obligatoire fut-il passé qu'on le réélut, le 5 novembre, à ce même Comité. Cette fois les Thermidoriens s'indignèrent. Fréron, le chef de la fameuse « jeunesse dorée » des muscadins et des merveilleuses, publia un article véhément, traitant Carnot de décemvir, d'acolyte de Barère, de terroriste enfin, qui avait établi le tribunal d'Orange, qui avait nommé Carrier et Fouquier-Tinville, qui avait assassiné Camille Desmoulins. Le *Moniteur* répliqua en exaltant le talent militaire de Carnot que les Anglais mêmes reconnaissaient [5]. Carnot s'en fut trouver Fréron et le menaça de son épée comme il avait fait pour Duesme, au temps de son mariage manqué. Ainsi le réduisit-il au silence.

D'autre part, il proposa à la Convention l'amnistie pour les rebelles de l'Ouest qui poseraient leurs armes. Malgré tout sa position parlementaire était fragile, il s'en aperçut à sa première imprudence. Le 2 janvier 1795, il annonçait à l'Assemblée les victoires spectaculaires des troupes franchissant sur la glace les rivières hollandaises.

« D'après ces événements, vous pardonnerez aux Anglais de regarder nos volontaires comme de grands terroristes.... » A ce mot, les murmures et les interruptions se déclenchèrent, Tallien se déchaîna. A son intention, sans doute, Carnot poursuivit : « On ne reprochera pas à nos terroristes d'avoir porté la terreur ailleurs que dans les camps des ennemis. » L'incident fut pourtant exploité, Carnot dut se déjuger. En vain un journal ami voulut-il en tirer une leçon d'apaisement : « Carnot, qui sait mieux combiner des plans de campagne que disputer pour se faire imprimer, a lui-même tranché la question de manière qu'on ne s'est point souvenu de ce qu'avait dit Carnot.... » Le temps n'était pas à l'oubli, Carnot confiait à son ami Garrau qu'il était « obligé de lutter pour [sa] défense personnelle contre des factions sans cesse renaissantes », et il unissait sa cause à « celles de la patrie, de la République [6] ».

Le 2 mars, les trois anciens collègues de Carnot étaient décrétés d'accusation et arrêtés, Carnot lui-même quittait le Comité, le 5 mars, pour n'y plus revenir. Se jugeant menacé, il prononça, le 23 mars, un nouveau discours. Sous couleur de soutenir les accusés, il se défendait lui-même. Évoquant son opposition à Robespierre et à Saint-Just, il rappelait l'autorité irrésistible dont ceux-ci disposaient alors à la Convention et dans tout le pays. Il affirmait que Paris et la France entière avaient approuvé le Grand Comité ; finalement, il laissait poindre la crainte que la réaction n'attaquât les anciens représentants en mission, qui étaient innombrables, et ne fît le jeu des royalistes. Ce morceau habile et bien construit parut d'abord atteindre son but, l'Assemblée en décréta l'impression. Ce succès fut éphémère, Carnot, traqué, fut invité à se désolidariser des accusés. Clauzel voulut lui faciliter cette opération délicate :

« Carnot vous a dit ici qu'il y avait dans le Comité une majorité, *dont il ne faisait pas partie*, qui ne voulait que des mesures atroces.

— Je ne l'ai pas dit.

— Tu l'as dit ! J'en atteste tous mes collègues. »

Plusieurs : « C'est vrai. »

Le débat prenait une grandeur tragique : pour Carnot, acquiescer, c'était condamner les trois accusés, s'obstiner c'était se perdre avec eux. Clauzel le comprit et coupa court :

« Vous voulez absolument conduire Carnot et Lindet à l'échafaud, et nous ne le voulons pas, parce que nous aimons la justice. »

Il eut le dernier mot.

Sur ces entrefaites, le 1er avril, les sectionnaires parisiens, tenaillés par la misère et la faim, soulevés contre la réaction envahirent l'Assemblée. La journée échoua, mais provoqua la déportation à la Guyane, sans jugement, des trois accusés. La poussée fut telle que plusieurs Thermidoriens furent arrêtés, même Lecointre, qui avait déployé tant de zèle. Nul ne parla de Carnot ; son courage l'avait sauvé, provisoirement du moins.

Le 20 mai eut lieu une nouvelle irruption populaire dans l'Assemblée, un député fut assassiné. Quelques Montagnards avaient soutenu ce soulèvement, Carnot — au dire de son fils — avait été sollicité, mais il avait refusé. Lors de la répression, il fut pris à partie.

« Comment as-tu pu, pendant quinze mois entiers, ne pas t'apercevoir qu'on assassinait journellement la patrie en fournissant ses meilleurs et ses plus utiles citoyens ? » s'écriait Larivière. « Je ne demande pas ta tête, mais je veux que tu ne sièges plus avec nous. »

Carnot se défendait plus aisément maintenant qu'il n'avait plus à sauver ses collègues : « Ce ne sont plus mes paroles ni mes opinions qu'il faut juger, ce sont mes actions. Je me suis constamment renfermé dans la partie dont j'étais chargé. » Ainsi, contre toute vraisemblance, renversait-il ses affirmations antérieures. Il alla jusqu'à déclarer qu'il avait défendu Barère, Billaud et Collot, uniquement parce que son nom était « accolé » aux leurs dans les journaux, mais, ajoutait-il, la façon dont se donnaient les signatures devait prouver qu'il était responsable des seules mesures militaires [7].

C'est alors qu'une voix s'écria :

« Carnot a organisé la victoire ! »

Mot historique, frappé pour la postérité comme une devise autour d'une effigie, titre et surnom même de Lazare Carnot, l'auréolant de gloire à l'instant même où le péril était le plus imminent. Carnot ne sut jamais avec certitude qui l'avait lancé.

Dès lors les remous s'apaisèrent peu à peu, malgré quelques réveils, ainsi, le 2 juin, sous la plume de Merlin de Thionville [8].

**

Les succès remportés tant que Carnot était resté à la tête des opérations, jusqu'en avril 1795, justifiaient le titre qui lui avait été décerné. Ce fut l'apogée de sa réputation.

Le 9 Thermidor n'avait eu aucune répercussion dans la conduite de la guerre, sinon l'abandon de l'offensive en Italie, préconisée par Robespierre et inspirée par Bonaparte.

L'effort principal portait toujours sur le front septentrional, comme au temps de la marche sur Ypres et Ostende. C'était alors Pichegru qui commandait l'armée du Nord. Maître d'Anvers, il avait l'ordre d'attaquer par mer la Zélande. Les moyens maritimes firent défaut et l'on se rabattit sur la Flandre hollandaise.

Carnot n'avait jamais cessé de penser que cette « grande opération » devait « briser la coalition et assurer le succès de la campagne ». Pour mieux y parvenir, il invitait Jourdan à concerter l'action de l'armée de Sambre-et-Meuse avec celle de l'armée du Nord, mais il laissait chacun libre et autonome. Il recommandait de rester en grande « masse », mais sans arrêter les mesures qui eussent déterminé ce résultat.

De même « l'attaque vigoureuse » était toujours le mot d'ordre; toutefois Carnot adoptait la prudence de Pichegru et ne voulait pas s'avancer avant d'avoir assuré les derrières des armées.

Il voulait notamment reprendre les places fortes, Valenciennes, Le Quesnoy, Condé, en faisant planer sur l'ennemi la terreur du décret qui ordonnait la mise à mort de tous les défenseurs opiniâtres. Mais Carnot, non plus que le Comité, ne tenaient à appliquer ce décret terroriste ; il conseilla un compromis pour que la « fierté républicaine ne fléchisse en rien, mais aussi sans nous mériter le nom de barbares ».

Pourtant Carnot pensait encore que, après l'extermination de l'adversaire, les places tomberaient d'elles-mêmes. En fait, elles tombèrent avant. Cependant, les deux armées françaises avaient laissé passer un temps précieux. Schérer, qui était en partie responsable de la lenteur des sièges, fut vertement tancé le 21 août, mais l'offensive ne put reprendre avant les premiers jours de septembre. Carnot songeait encore à attaquer la Zélande, cette fois par l'Escaut, mais il jugeait surtout nécessaire que l'armée de Sambre-et-Meuse rempor-

tât des victoires en rase campagne. La République en profi-
terait pour la guerre comme pour la paix.

Car, dès la mi-octobre, Carnot envisageait la paix.

Depuis longtemps il la jugeait indispensable au rétablissement des finances et de l'économie, à la consolidation de la
Révolution, à l'abandon des mesures d'exception. Avec le
9 Thermidor, avec les victoires et la lassitude des ennemis,
l'heure en était venue. Il était même possible de la conclure
en protégeant solidement la nouvelle frontière. Carnot envisageait la création d'une république hollandaise ; cette résolution
s'affermit avec l'espoir d'un soulèvement qui seconderait
les opérations. Carnot était informé des choses de Hollande
par son beau-frère Collignon, depuis longtemps chargé de
s'occuper des patriotes hollandais réfugiés en France. Carnot
avait même réuni ces patriotes sous la présidence de François de Vinck. Toutefois, il restait sur ses gardes et conseillait une « prudence révolutionnaire » — formule vraiment
thermidorienne. A peine eut-il appris que des réseaux d'inon-
dation avaient été tendus, qu'il parla, le 25 novembre, des
quartiers d'hiver. « Le salut de l'armée, c'est la loi suprême »
— autre formule thermidorienne. Pourtant, en accord avec les
représentants aux armées du Nord et de Sambre-et-Meuse, il
envisageait, depuis la fin de septembre, l'occupation de la
rive gauche du Rhin.

Ainsi conduisait-il la guerre de façon opportuniste. Si
l'on s'en fût rapporté à lui, l'action se serait arrêtée dans le
Nord à la fin de novembre, et les effectifs des armées mises au
repos eussent été réduits.

Cette fois, ce fut Pichegru qui décida d'exploiter la situation favorable offerte par le gel des inondations et des
fleuves et par le fléchissement de l'ennemi. Carnot, tenté
par la nouvelle que la flotte hollandaise, enserrée dans les
glaces, était vulnérable, le laissa libre d'agir. Au surplus les
pourparlers commençaient avec des envoyés hollandais :
Carnot touchait au succès final. Celui-ci aurait pu être
accru par l'anéantissement des troupes anglaises, si les hésitations et la prudence françaises ne leur eussent permis de
se retirer. La coordination entre les deux armées était
demeurée imparfaite ; Carnot avait attendu au dernier
moment pour assurer l'unité de commandement.

Il en était de même à l'aile droite. Les deux armées, de la
Moselle, sous Moreaux, et du Rhin, sous Michaud, devaient
coordonner leur action sans s'unir. Leur mission, définie

le 18 juillet, était secondaire : harceler l'ennemi, ramasser des approvisionnements, sans tenter de grandes conquêtes, sinon celle des pays situés entre Sarre et Moselle. Coblentz paraissait un objectif un peu éloigné. Une fois Trèves occupé, Carnot se proposait de dépouiller le pays et de frapper l'ennemi sans s'engager trop loin, car il faudrait s'attendre à une attaque.

Là encore, les missions étaient assez dispersées : blocus de Luxembourg, occupation de Kaiserslautern, prise ultérieure du Palatinat et de Mannheim. En fait, l'armée de la Moselle orienta bientôt son effort vers Trèves et Luxembourg, celle du Rhin fut inactive jusqu'au jour où Carnot s'impatienta : « Dans toutes les autres armées, on a établi le système d'agression, à l'armée du Rhin, on a juré, à ce qu'il paraît, de rester éternellement sur la défensive la plus passive. » Carnot préconisait, en octobre, le passage du Rhin et la mise à contribution des pays de la rive droite. Enhardi par la victoire, il déclarait même le 14 novembre : « Il ne sera pas dit que vous souffrirez que les ennemis conservent un pied sur notre territoire, car nous regardons comme tel maintenant tout ce qui est en deçà du Rhin. » Nouvelle et significative variation sur le thème du Rhin frontière. Il envoyait Kléber à l'armée du Rhin pour stimuler Michaud et il fournissait des indications détaillées sur la façon de prendre Mayence et Mannheim. La lenteur des résultats l'incita à proposer ici encore, le 20 décembre, des quartiers d'hiver, combinés avec l'ouverture des négociations avec la Prusse.

Le 19 février 1795, Carnot reprit le projet de passage du Rhin ; les négociations avec la Prusse étaient certes en bonne voie, on les rendrait ainsi plus promptes et plus favorables. De plus, il restait encore à battre l'Autriche.

La frontière du Rhin était acquise ; la mésintelligence entre Autrichiens et Prussiens, la volonté de paix de la Prusse avaient favorisé la progression de nos armées, mais l'adversaire n'avait pas été écrasé ; il conservait ses forces.

Pourtant, au moment où Carnot quitta le Comité et la conduite de la guerre, son objectif essentiel était atteint, la coalition était disloquée.

Les autres armées avaient eu un rôle beaucoup plus modeste. Celles des Alpes et d'Italie surveillaient la frontière. Carnot, refusant de s'engager dans les Alpes, avait envisagé de combattre les Anglais en reprenant la Corse ou en attaquant Livourne.

Aux Pyrénées, il avait au contraire poussé l'offensive. Il espérait créer une république satellite en Catalogne et fixer la frontière sur la ligne des crêtes. Pourtant, il ne fournit guère d'instructions ni de plans et n'intervint qu'exceptionnellement. Les succès furent suffisants pour presser les négociations, mais non pour établir la République catalane.

Restaient les troupes de l'Ouest — contre la Vendée et la chouannerie. Là encore, il s'agissait de pacifier plutôt que d'exterminer. Tout y contribuait : le procès des atrocités stigmatisées par les Thermidoriens, les inclinations personnelles de Carnot, les dispositions mêmes d'une partie des Vendéens et des Chouans. Dans la plus large mesure, Carnot se fia aux chefs qui étaient sur place, surtout à Hoche.

Les relations entre Hoche et Carnot ont donné lieu, nous l'avons vu, à de vives controverses. En présence d'affirmations aussi catégoriques et contradictoires que difficiles à vérifier, il faut préciser les faits : Carnot a signé la libération de Hoche dès le 4 août, puis il l'a appelé à Paris et lui a confié des commandements de plus en plus importants, contre les Chouans d'abord, sur toute l'armée de Cherbourg ensuite, et enfin sur les armées réunies de Cherbourg et de Brest, successivement les 16 et 21 août, et 13 novembre 1794. Il déclarait à Hoche, le 7 février 1795, qu'il lui confiait « exclusivement la direction générale des forces, afin que rien n'altère l'ensemble des opérations ». Il avait écrit dans le même sens aux représentants en mission, exprimant à l'un d'eux, le 18 janvier, toute la satisfaction que lui donnait Hoche, général actif, éclairé et qui voulait la fin de cette « guerre déplorable ». Ainsi fut conclue la paix de La Jaunaie, en attendant celle de Saint-Florentin.

L'œuvre militaire de Carnot paraissait donc achevée avec celle de la Révolution même. Sans doute restait-il encore des ennemis, mais le plus malaisé était fait, du moins le croyait-on. Déjà Carnot songeait à écrire l'histoire, il commençait d'en élaborer les matériaux au cabinet topographique, il faisait publier une chronologie sommaire — *Tableaux des Campagnes des Français* —, il dépêchait aux armées des « historiographes », il dictait une manière de testament, la veille de sa sortie du Comité[9].

« Toutes les vieilles routines, tous les préjugés militaires ont été frondés au cours de cette guerre. Il fera bon voir, dans les fastes de la République, comment des troupes mal armées, sans habitude des exercices militaires, sans autre discipline que la confiance, souvent dénuées d'habillement et de subsistances, ont arrêté ce débordement de légions réunies contre elles, comment de bons cultivateurs, forcés de combattre pour la défense de leurs foyers, menés par des chefs choisis par eux, chantant tous ensemble des hymnes à la liberté, ont vaincu ces cohortes. »

N'était-il pas prématuré de célébrer la fin de la guerre et la fin des transformations de la stratégie et de la tactique ? Cette image des armées révolutionnaires ne sacrifiait-elle pas à la légende ?

Les traités de paix de Bâle et de La Haye, négociés pendant que Carnot était éloigné du Comité, semblèrent justifier son optimisme et son action. C'est pourquoi, le 1er octobre, quand il s'agit de prononcer l'annexion de la Belgique, Boissy d'Anglas, modéré notoire, demanda que Carnot « dont la science militaire est connue », soit entendu. C'est ainsi que l'organisateur de la victoire sortit de la suspicion et de l'obscurité où il s'était réfugié.

Son argumentation porta sur la valeur stratégique de la nouvelle frontière. Il en vantait les mérites, dus au fossé de la Meuse et à la forteresse de Luxembourg et aussi aux forteresses de la frontière ancienne qui formaient une seconde ligne. Revenu à ses anciennes doctrines, il ne disait rien du Rhin qu'il avait préféré quelques mois auparavant. Un mot sur la guerre commerciale contre l'Angleterre précéda sa conclusion sur la nécessité de préparer une paix durable. Les applaudissements prouvèrent à Carnot qu'il avait retrouvé quelque crédit [10].

*

Qu'allait-il devenir ? Promu à l'ancienneté le 11 mai 1795, il était seulement chef de bataillon et nommé sous-directeur à Arras, pour le jour où il cesserait d'être représentant. Car il s'était refusé à tout avancement pendant l'exercice de ses hautes fonctions et il avait même préféré ne pas nommer général son frère Feulint quand un poste s'était trouvé libre. Ce rare désintéressement lui fermait à peu près la carrière militaire, son avenir était donc lié aux élections.

Carnot avait approuvé le décret fameux qui imposait aux électeurs le choix des deux tiers des nouvelles assemblées, celles du Directoire — Anciens et Cinq-Cents — parmi les Conventionnels. A ses yeux cette mesure était indispensable au maintien de la République.

Il s'intéressa donc aux élections. Le département du Pas-de-Calais, qu'il avait représenté tant à la Législative qu'à la Convention, était en proie à la réaction thermidorienne, surtout Saint-Omer qui était le lieu d'attache de Carnot. Le représentant en mission Florent Guyot épurait les terroristes, et, par une rencontre curieuse, il se trouvait que Feulint, si longtemps modéré, était en mauvaise posture.

Il était compromis, lui aussi, par de fâcheuses signatures, notamment celle d'une adresse à la Convention exaltant les journées du 31 mai et du 2 juin. On prétendit que le cosignataire avait pris seul l'initiative de cette démarche, ce qui sauva Feulint. Florent Guyot le maintint dans la société populaire de Saint-Omer ; il fut même membre de la commission d'épuration des autorités constituées. Il crut plus sage de se faire oublier. « Carnot ne se montre jamais dans les circonstances difficiles », disait-on en septembre 1794.

Dans ses rares interventions, il fut pris à partie violemment, car il tentait d'appuyer ceux dont les Thermidoriens dénonçaient le terrorisme. Sa situation était exactement à l'image de celle de son frère. Le 24 septembre 1794, on en avait eu la preuve. Feulint avait été vivement admonesté par le président du tribunal de Saint-Omer dans une réunion générale : « Un bon républicain peut être trompé et égaré, mais il ne persiste point dans son erreur. » Le même jour, à la Convention, une députation des Thermidoriens de Saint-Omer était entendue, puis violemment attaquée par Duhem et par Duquesnoy, qui l'accusaient de réaction, notamment son porte-parole, un certain Jadot. Les protestataires, surtout Duquesnoy, affirmèrent que Carnot avait fait arrêter ce Jadot, et, au milieu du tumulte, Duquesnoy s'écria : « J'adjure Carnot de dire la vérité. » Carnot resta muet et l'incident fut clos.

Dans de telles conditions, la situation électorale de Carnot était mauvaise. Les modérés et les Thermidoriens du Pas-de-Calais le honnissaient comme ancien membre du Grand Comité ; oublieux de la défense nationale, ils chargeaient Carnot des actes de Lebon [11].

Carnot se tourna vers Buissart, ce vieil ami arrageois qui avait été fidèle à Robespierre jusqu'au 9 Thermidor, et qui était resté lié avec Carnot. Buissart lui fit savoir quels électeurs avaient été choisis ; Carnot lui rappela la composition de la députation du Pas-de-Calais, « notre département ». A l'assemblée électorale, Carnot rallia les voix des patriotes, mais ce ne fut pas assez pour qu'il fût élu, même au titre de la liste supplémentaire, où l'on devait prendre le complément des deux tiers de Conventionnels [12].

Il fut plus heureux dans douze départements qui le proposèrent pour la liste supplémentaire, mais il ne fut élu directement que dans un seul, celui de la Sarthe [13].

Assuré de poursuivre sa carrière politique, Carnot prépara sa rentrée par un discours à l'Assemblée, le 22 octobre, à la veille de l'organisation du nouveau régime. C'était faire acte de candidature à la Direction des opérations, soit comme ministre, soit comme membre du Directoire.

L'occasion était fournie par les dires de la réaction qui amplifiait les échecs subis en Allemagne, qui parlait d'une débâcle et semblait vouloir une paix rétablissant le tracé des frontières de la France de l'Ancien Régime.

Depuis le départ de Carnot, la conduite de la guerre avait été incohérente. D'abord, le Comité de Salut public avait eu l'étrange idée de confier la direction de chacune des quatre principales armées à chacun de ses membres, bon moyen pour réduire la charge, mais aussi pour faire disparaître l'unité de direction. Un peu plus tard, en août, cette unité avait été rétablie au profit de Doulcet [14]. Celui-ci avait senti le besoin d'une compétence mieux assurée, il avait fait appel à Bonaparte. Ce fut le temps d'élaboration des célèbres plans qui préparaient la campagne d'Italie. Bonaparte travaillait pour l'avenir, il ne s'occupait pas des vicissitudes présentes [15]. D'ailleurs il reçut bientôt une autre affectation. Finalement, le 7 octobre, ce fut un collègue de Carnot, un officier du Génie que la Révolution avait fait entrer dans la vie politique, Letourneur, qui fut chargé de diriger la guerre. On a dit que Letourneur lui demanda conseil, il n'en reste pas trace [16]. Du moins apparaît-il qu'ils combinèrent leur action dans la journée parlementaire du 22 octobre.

Letourneur prit d'abord la parole pour défendre Jourdan, en attribuant les échecs aux violations de la ligne de neutralité allemande par les Autrichiens, et surtout au retard apporté au franchissement du Rhin. Carnot appuya ses dires: «Lorsque je quittai le Comité de Salut public, il y a six mois, on était prêt à le faire. Je ne sais pourquoi il a été tant différé.»

L'incident ainsi provoqué s'amplifia aussitôt, avec les interventions de Merlin de Douai, Bentabole, Hardy, Lesage-Senault, secondés par la gauche de l'Assemblée.

Aubry, qui avait épuré l'armée en prairial, fut pris à partie ; on l'accusa d'avoir remis les commandements à des royalistes ; on ne parlait pas de Pichegru, mais les éloges ne portaient que sur Jourdan. Finalement Aubry fut décrété d'arrestation, entraînant avec lui divers généraux et hommes politiques.

Ainsi Carnot avait posé sa candidature, il avait même esquissé un programme : offensive au-delà du Rhin, revision des nominations prononcées par Aubry [17]. Malgré la réaction thermidorienne et ses menaces, il ne s'était pas déjugé et n'avait pas été écarté. Cette réussite pouvait-elle se prolonger?

CHAPITRE II

DIRECTEUR DE LA RÉPUBLIQUE

« FAIRE régner la concorde, ramener la paix, rétablir l'abondance et le crédit public, remettre l'ordre social à la place du chaos, procurer enfin à la République française le bonheur et la gloire qu'elle attend... », telle fut la première proclamation du nouveau gouvernement, le Directoire, qui rétablissait l'ordre constitutionnel suspendu depuis le 10 août 1792 et qui devait clore la Révolution.

Que de précautions pour la stabilité et la légalité ! Deux assemblées élues — sauf par les pauvres —, l'une, le conseil des Cinq-Cents, apportant l'imagination, l'autre, le conseil des Anciens, apportant la sagesse. Un gouvernement collectif, cinq chefs d'État et de gouvernement, les Directeurs, élus par les Anciens sur propositions des Cinq-Cents, mais assurés de rester au pouvoir pendant cinq années et chargés de choisir et de renvoyer à leur gré les ministres qui n'étaient pas parlementaires. Au service de ces pouvoirs publics une administration de conseils élus, au canton et au département, mais surveillés par des commissaires que nommaient les Directeurs.

Carnot, d'après son fils, aurait voulu donner plus de place aux talents, ils eussent formé la deuxième chambre, celle des « lumières », éclairant de ses avis l'Assemblée qui incarnerait la souveraineté nationale. Ainsi persistait en lui le culte de la raison, des savants et des techniciens. C'était déjà l'appel aux « capacités », dont on parlera tant sous la monarchie bourgeoise et qui fut quelque peu réalisé sous Napoléon [1].

Le pluralisme directorial ne donnait guère confiance à Carnot, qui avait connu les âpres rivalités des membres du Comité : « Les destinées de l'État dépendront des humeurs de cinq personnes, plus ces humeurs seront en désaccord, plus l'État éprouvera de fluctuations. » Pourtant, Carnot accepta d'entrer au Directoire.

A vrai dire, on voulut d'abord se passer de lui. Les anciens Conventionnels, qui disposaient de la majorité dans les Conseils, choisirent bien cinq d'entre eux comme Directeurs : La Revellière-Lépeaux, Letourneur, Reubell, Barras et Sieyès. Parmi ces médiocres et ces tarés, deux militaires pouvaient être chargés de conduire la guerre : Letourneur et Barras. Sieyès seul faisait figure d'homme d'État, seul il refusa. Les quatre se réunirent, le 2 novembre 1795, convoquant d'éventuels ministres, parmi lesquels Carnot pour la Guerre. Celui-ci refusa, il eût perdu sa qualité de membre du Corps législatif, et l'inviolabilité qu'elle lui assurait. Peut-être aussi n'avait-il plus l'habitude ni le goût des fonctions subalternes [2].

Le lendemain, il était élu Directeur, rassemblant la majorité juste suffisante. Il accepta en termes qui ne l'engageaient pas [3].

Les difficultés initiales ont été ramenées à une image frappante : les Directeurs se rendant à leur palais — le Luxembourg — accompagnés d'une garde en guenilles et ne trouvant sur place ni table, ni chaise. Cette situation s'améliora bientôt ; il y avait des ressources, il suffisait d'organiser, or Carnot était organisateur.

Il contribua efficacement à monter les services. Il sut choisir un secrétaire général pour remplacer celui que La Revellière avait fait nommer, ce fut Lagarde, qui avait fait ses preuves en Belgique et qui remplit si bien ses fonctions qu'il les conserva même sous le Consulat. Carnot fit transporter au Luxembourg les dossiers et le matériel de bureau du Comité de Salut public, sous la direction de Pierre, secrétaire général de ce Comité et qui devenait chef de service de la secrétairerie directoriale. Pierre était un Bourguignon, ancien secrétaire personnel de Guyton de Morveau, cet ami de Carnot. Auprès de lui se trouvait Aubusson, qui avait travaillé deux années au Comité de Salut public.

Il y eut autant de bureaux à la secrétairerie qu'il y avait de ministères, pour faciliter la liaison, plus un bureau central pour coordonner, avec bibliothécaire, archiviste, imprimeur, service de renseignements sur le personnel administratif, la presse et les armées, comportant même un service statistique auquel Carnot songeait depuis longtemps [4].

A l'usage, la machine apparut lente et formaliste ; elle fut simplifiée, mais il subsista un bureau de l'intérieur, un bureau politique et un bureau militaire qui intéressait directement Carnot.

Là encore, il plaça des secrétaires qu'il avait utilisés au Comité de Salut public, des Bourguignons, des Dijonnais. On y retrouvait Bauche, qui avait donné lieu à un vif incident entre Carnot et Robespierre. Au total, une dizaine d'employés — beaucoup plus que dans les autres bureaux — répartis en bureau central de la Guerre, bureau de Renseignements, bureau de l'Artillerie et du Génie. Dans ce dernier, Carnot appela son beau-frère Toussaint Collignon. Ce personnel assez homogène et expérimenté semblait prolonger les services du Comité, Carnot s'y trompait parfois, employant un mot pour l'autre [5].

En outre, Carnot disposait toujours d'un Cabinet historique et topographique. C'était le même organisme et, dans une certaine mesure, le même personnel qu'il avait utilisés en 1793 et 1794. On y trouvait une vingtaine de personnes, notamment Duvignau, les deux Lacuée, Antoine et Gérard, les généraux Dupont et Clarke, l'un et l'autre tout dévoués à Carnot, les secrétaires Chaalons, Bourotte et Mayeux. Celui-ci continuait d'être le secrétaire habituel de Carnot. Les bureaux de ce service, aménagés par Chalgrin, étaient installés dans l'hôtel de La Trémoille, face au Luxembourg.

La correspondance de ce cabinet montre qu'il constituait une manière de grand état-major, où l'on préparait les opérations, et qui entretenait des relations suivies avec les commandants en chef des armées, leur transmettant les ordres du Directoire pour les opérations, observant la réalisation des mouvements prescrits et adaptant les dispositions aux conditions changeantes de la lutte. A l'occasion, ce service s'occupa de diplomatie, surtout quand les généraux furent amenés à négocier. Enfin tous les documents, écrits ou dessinés, y étaient rassemblés, classés et analysés, pour la rédaction de l'histoire des guerres.

Ni Dupont ni Clarke n'étaient de grands stratèges, ce sont eux cependant qui ont étroitement collaboré avec Carnot dans la direction des opérations.

Les attributions du Cabinet historique finissaient par se croiser avec celles du Dépôt de la guerre, ce qui amena Carnot, le 11 mai 1797, à fondre les deux organes. Du coup, il se débarrassait du chef du Dépôt, le général Calon, avec lequel il ne s'accordait pas.

Ainsi Carnot avait imprimé une continuité entre le Comité de Salut public et le Directoire, alors que tout semblait les opposer. A quelques éléments près, comme la présence d'un

Séguier, entré dans les bureaux pendant la réaction thermidorienne, on eût cru voir survivre les services du Grand
Comité [6].

De plus, ces services, à la disposition de l'Exécutif, donnaient au régime un caractère non prévu par la constitution
et que l'on pourrait appeler « présidentiel ». Carnot contribua
à imprimer ce caractère.

Le choix des ministres avait été arrêté avant l'entrée
en fonction de Carnot, sauf pour le ministre des Finances.
Celui-ci fut peut-être proposé par lui, c'était Faipoult,
officier du Génie. Le département de la Guerre avait été
confié au général Aubert-Dubayet, qui avait été frappé au
temps du Grand Comité, et que Carnot jugeait impropre
à cette fonction. En revanche Carnot estimait le ministre de
l'Intérieur, Bénézech, ancien commissaire pour l'Artillerie
et le Génie dans la Commission de l'Organisation et du
Mouvement des armées de terre.

L'essentiel était l'entente des cinq Directeurs qui devaient
travailler et vivre ensemble dans le palais du Luxembourg.
Ils n'avaient pas le droit de prendre de décisions séparément, l'autorité appartenait au Directoire et non aux Directeurs ; elle naissait de leur réunion et s'évanouissait avec
leur séparation. Quand ils étaient réunis, il fallait au moins
l'accord de trois d'entre eux. Or le Girondin La Revellière et
le Thermidorien Barras ne pardonnaient pas à Carnot son
rôle au Grand Comité. Reubell lui-même n'avait pas oublié
que ce Comité avait critiqué sa conduite à Mayence. Seul
Letourneur, officier du Génie, s'accordait vraiment avec
Carnot. Plus encore que le passé, l'humeur de chacun
— comme l'avait prévu Carnot — pesait sur leurs relations.
Sauf Letourneur, chacun était infatué de sa propre valeur ;
de plus, Reubell était violent, Barras était faux, La Revellière se montrait maladivement susceptible, Carnot avait
la passion de l'autorité et parfois éclatait.

Rien de plus cruel que le portrait des divers Directeurs
par chacun d'entre eux. Pour Carnot, Barras était le protecteur « des nobles tarés et des pourfendeurs », Reubell
celui « des gens accusés de vol », et La Revellière, celui des
« prêtres scandaleux », comme il convenait à cet être « hypo-
crite et immoral ». Celui-ci dénonçait à son tour la fausseté,
l'ambition et le caractère vindicatif de Carnot. Barras laissait
entendre que Carnot voulait le perdre en l'impliquant dans
une conspiration. Les mémoires de Reubell ont disparu,

ils eussent achevé de nouer ce nœud de vipères. Certes ces
haineuses caricatures furent tracées après le drame de fructidor, mais la défiance était antérieure même à la réunion des
Cinq, et ces sentiments grandirent progressivement [7].

Ce fut une raison supplémentaire pour distinguer les
attributions : Carnot géra la Guerre ; Letourneur, la Marine ;
Barras, la Police ; La Revellière, l'Instruction publique, les
Arts et Manufactures ; Reubell enfin, la Justice, les Finances
et les Affaires étrangères.

**

La « communauté » du Directoire exécutif ! Savoureuse
expression glissée sous la plume de l'intendant du palais ;
savoureuse, mais exacte.

En commun les Directeurs délibéraient pendant des heures
chaque jour, recevaient les ministres, donnaient audience,
figuraient aux cérémonies officielles. Dans ce palais du
Luxembourg, ils menaient en commun leur travail et s'acquit-
taient de leur rôle de représentation. Leur vie privée ne se
dégageait qu'imparfaitement de cette communauté.

Apparemment tout était réglé par le protocole pour se
dérouler dans la dignité qui convient aux magistrats
suprêmes. Ceux-ci portaient un uniforme somptueux :
manteau de satin pourpre, couvert de broderies d'or, habit
bleu brodé, large écharpe, glaive en sautoir, culotte de satin
blanc, chapeau empanaché. Carnot a été représenté dans
cette tenue. Des contemporains, français comme les observateurs des *Tableaux de Paris*, étrangers comme Wolfe
Tone, ont vu Carnot dans ses fonctions, et l'ont trouvé
imposant et affable, exactement semblable, dit Wolfe Tone,
aux personnages de Van Dyck.

Le retour à l'ordre s'accomplit malaisément, au milieu
d'une crise morale, économique et financière. L'organisation matérielle du Directoire en donnait la preuve. L'éclat
ne manquait pas, grâce au mobilier des rois et des émigrés.
On tendit des tapisseries des Gobelins, on distribua des
tapis d'Aubusson et de la Savonnerie. Des lustres de cristal
rivalisèrent avec les flambeaux et les appliques de bronze
pour éclairer les salles de réception garnies de meubles précieux. Mais il fallut se contenter du Petit Luxembourg,
naguère propriété des Condé, puis du comte de Provence, le
palais proprement dit étant inutilisable. Les officiels, en

tenue somptueuse, étaient peu accoutumés au cérémonial tout neuf, et le personnel, huissiers, gardes, domestiques et serveurs, était improvisé, ce qui donnait aux réceptions, aux dîners d'apparat et aux bals un caractère un peu singulier.

En toute hâte, on commanda au tailleur costumier du théâtre des Arts les uniformes officiels. Ceux des Directeurs coûtèrent plus de soixante-dix mille francs chacun, aux frais du Trésor. Le 10 frimaire — 1er décembre 1795 — Carnot signa un reçu : « Il m'a été fourni un manteau rouge de satin, la veste, le pantalon, une écharpe, trois collerettes. »

Il était plus difficile d'installer chaque Directeur et sa famille, et d'assurer leur vie quotidienne. Carnot, dernier nommé, fut d'abord relégué sous les combles, en attendant que son appartement fût prêt. Ensuite il occupa, avec La Revellière, l'hôtel du futur président du Sénat : Carnot disposait du rez-de-chaussée et du second étage, La Revellière se contentait du premier, chacun avait en outre un petit jardin attenant. Cette promiscuité ne laissait pas d'être bien gênante, entre collègues qui se heurtaient et finirent par se haïr.

L'hôtel, luxueusement décoré, fut pourvu d'un mobilier confortable. Carnot reçut notamment un salon de damas bleu et blanc, un tapis du Raincy, un piano forte, un lit de repos, un métier à broder. La réception était plus facile à organiser que les chambres et la cuisine. Pendant des mois, les achats utilitaires se succédèrent : batteries de cuisine, matériel pour l'office, les cabinets de toilette et les buffets. Un jour, on se procurait pour quatre cent mille francs de chaudronnerie, une autre fois c'était une emplette de vaisselle, de verrerie et de faïence dépassant cinq cent mille francs. Il n'y avait pas moins de sept douzaines de pots de chambre, les uns tout ordinaires, les autres décorés et venus de Rouen. Pendant longtemps encore, on compléta ces installations; chaque Directeur présentait ses desiderata — Carnot était l'un des moins exigeants, il donnait à étamer ses marmites abîmées et faisait souder sa « baignoire en sabot ».

Peu à peu la communauté directoriale fut pourvue d'une lingerie, d'une buanderie, d'un magasin de faïence et verrerie, de réserves de charbon, bougies et chandelles, lampes et huile. Grâce à cette organisation, les chefs de l'État purent traverser la période de terrible pénurie et de vie chère qui marqua l'hiver 1795-1796. Certes ils avaient un traitement honorable, et à l'abri de l'inflation, car il était stipulé en valeur de froment et montait avec le cours du blé, cinquante mille myriagrammes par an, ce qui représentait cent vingt-cinq mille francs-or en mai 1797. Mais il y avait des frais de représentation, et aussi l'esprit d'économie et d'épargne de la bourgeoisie française. Carnot songeait à assurer son avenir, après les cinq années de magistrature suprême.

Aussi, quand la pénurie fut atténuée et que les prix se fixèrent, au cours de l'été 1797, si l'on songea un moment à rompre la communauté, devenue pénible à mesure que les relations entre Directeurs s'étaient gâtées, l'intendant sut trouver les arguments qui dissipèrent ce propos — et lui conservèrent sa place. La communauté, faisait-il observer, est « avantageuse à tous et à chacun »; sans elle, « les premiers magistrats du peuple resteraient sans linge au bout de trois mois » et devraient payer la plupart des dépenses de leurs propres deniers. Si le Corps législatif était informé, « il serait possible qu'il prétendît que toutes ces dépenses doivent peser sur les appointements de chacun des membres ».

Non seulement la communauté continua, mais, après le départ de Carnot, elle en vint à employer les fonds secrets pour le service courant, tandis qu'on rognait le salaire du personnel.

Le ravitaillement fut assuré selon les mêmes principes, mais aux frais des intéressés. Le boucher du Bureau central du canton de Paris et l'École nationale de boulangerie assuraient le service.

Ainsi peut-on connaître la table de chacun. Les Carnot, trois ménages, celui de Lazare, celui de Feulint et celui de Collignon, consommèrent en ventôse 782 livres de viande, 12 queues de mouton, 13 ris de veau, 10 cervelles, 8 pieds et 4 têtes de veau, le tout pour 87 960 francs. Barras avait dépensé plus de 109 000 francs et Reubell moins de 33 000. Carnot avait aussi acheté 268 livres de pain blanc, 240 livres de pain bis et 6 boisseaux de farine pour 24 000 francs. C'était le temps où le ravitaillement était mal assuré, et de plus en plus onéreux.

La cave de Carnot était son œuvre personnelle. C'était une cave de Bourguignon, riche en centaines de bouteilles de Mâcon, rouge et blanc, ordinaire et fin, agrémenté de bons crus de Bourgogne, de Bordeaux, de Champagne, de Frontignan, de Calabre, de Malaga, de Madère et de Malvoisie.

Sans négliger une trentaine de bouteilles de cognac, et autant de liqueurs diverses. A peine ose-t-on mentionner cent soixante bouteilles de bière.

Les provisions comportaient 70 pots de confiture, 14 paquets de chocolat, 48 livres de café, du sucre, du thé, de la farine. Il est vrai qu'il fallait donner des dîners officiels. Mme Carnot était une maîtresse de maison prévoyante.

Elle avait aussi songé au linge. L'inventaire dressé au lendemain du coup d'État mentionne, pour Carnot, 30 chemises de coton, 27 de toile, 10 caleçons, 7 gilets de flanelle — sans parler de 18 chemises qui étaient à blanchir. On trouva, outre 6 bonnets de coton, 2 culottes de peau, 2 tricornes, 3 houppelandes, 3 habits, 2 redingotes, 1 uniforme militaire et 1 costume directorial.

Ainsi la maison était bourgeoise, cossue, sans autre luxe que la cave. Comme objets précieux, on ne signala que les médailles d'or de l'académie de Dijon, et trois montres en or [8].

La vie de famille tenait à coup sûr une place importante — la première. Dans ces trois ménages, en trois mois naquirent trois enfants, une fille chez les Collignon, le 10 mars 1796, un fils chez Feulint, le 20 avril, et un fils aussi chez Carnot, le 1er juin. On peut croire que les parents veillèrent d'autant plus jalousement sur ce fils qu'ils avaient déjà perdu un enfant, un garçon nommé Sadi — en souvenir des Rosati — qui était né le 19 juillet 1794, et qui était mort le 10 août 1795. Le nouveau garçon fut aussi appelé Sadi — c'était le futur fondateur de la thermo-dynamique. Carnot put utiliser sa connaissance des problèmes d'éducation, nous avons vu qu'il les avait étudiés depuis longtemps.

Toutefois des réceptions officielles étaient nécessaires, Carnot et sa femme surent faire les honneurs. Ainsi le 12 juillet 1796, quand ils reçurent Wolfe Tone, avec l'amiral Truguet, le général Chérin et quelque quatre-vingts convives. La table était abondante, mais sans ostentation, le menu comportait deux services et un dessert. Carnot était alors président du Directoire. En temps ordinaire, il semble avoir reçu peu de monde.

L'un de ses fidèles, Lomet, a déclaré que la femme du Directeur «se plaisait trop à encourager les visites. Elle mit la maison de son mari sur le ton du beau monde : c'étaient des salons de thé, de la musique, des bals brillants... ». On avait pris pour aide de camp un « joli cavalier » qui faisait les honneurs. Aussi les intrigants et les jolies femmes, « une partie de la clientèle féminine de Barras, débordèrent » chez Carnot. Quelle créance accorder à ces dires [9] ?

Carnot, de son côté, recevait des savants, Monge, Berthollet, Prony, Fourcroy, des littérateurs et des artistes, le poète Lebrun, et ce singulier Beffroy de Reigny, toujours fantaisiste et famélique, effaré et craintif, imprudent et réactionnaire, qui compromit son protecteur avec la plus inconsciente légèreté. Il était autorisé à faire venir, chaque lundi, deux convives à son choix. Ainsi amena-t-il Dalayrac, La Houssaie, et quelques autres, « et même des marchands, dit-il, mais respectables par leurs mœurs et leur probité ».

Carnot menait une vie bourgeoise qui correspondait bien au régime et à ses goûts personnels. Les autres Directeurs en usaient de même, à l'exception de Barras, plus largement installé dans une aile du Grand Luxembourg. Il était le seul qui vécût largement, dépensât beaucoup au jeu et au plaisir, qui donnât des dîners en ville et des fêtes dans sa maison de campagne à Suresnes. C'est lui pourtant que l'Histoire a trop souvent considéré comme donnant le ton !

Carnot resta laborieux, assidu au bureau, et chargé de lourdes tâches. Il compléta peu à peu sa bibliothèque, témoin de ses préférences intellectuelles et littéraires. Elle unissait les Modernes aux Anciens, les étrangers aux Français : Montesquieu à Tacite, Voltaire à Erasme, Rousseau, Mably, Condillac, Pope, Locke à Machiavel, Helvétius et Confucius, Charron, Ovide à Horace, voire à l'Imitation, et au Supplément à la magie blanche. En revanche elle ne renfermait aucun des grands classiques du XVIIe siècle, et si peu d'ouvrages sur la Révolution ! Carnot était bien de son siècle, sa pensée s'était fixée avant les événements qui l'illustrèrent [10].

CHAPITRE III

FAUX DÉPART JACOBIN

« JE NE sais sur quels fondements on avait imaginé que je favoriserais le parti de ces anarchistes », a écrit Carnot, après le 18 fructidor. Le fait est que l'opinion était unanime : aux applaudissements du *Journal des Hommes libres* correspondait l'indignation des amis de Beffroy de Reigny : « ton Carnot est un coquin » ; les observateurs de la police confirmaient ces dires et les agents de l'étranger s'exprimaient de la même façon : « Il a des principes exagérés, un caractère haineux et vindicatif, notait un agent de l'Angleterre, le besoin qu'on avait de lui l'a seul soustrait au sort de tous les autres membres du Comité de Robespierre [1]. »

L'occasion de vérifier la justesse de ces vues fut fournie par les nominations de fonctionnaires — dix mille postes à pourvoir — que les Directeurs devaient effectuer, chacun pour sa région. Pour sa part, Carnot avait reçu tout le nord de la France, sa patrie d'adoption et, naguère, son district politique. Non seulement la nature du choix mais le ton des solliciteurs indiquent clairement l'idée qu'on se faisait de Carnot et l'orientation de sa politique.

Le rôle de Carnot ne se limita pas strictement à la région qui lui était affectée : on s'adressa à lui de bien des points de la France ; par exemple Faure écrivit à son « ancien collègue et codéfenseur de la République » pour maintenir un républicain résolu au poste de commissaire de la Haute-Loire ; il obtint satisfaction.

Beaucoup d'autres anciens Conventionnels se tournèrent vers Carnot, soit pour appuyer des candidats, soit pour solliciter un poste. Ils se présentaient en vieux camarades des grandes luttes et usaient encore du tutoiement jacobin. On retrouve, parmi eux, Lamarque, l'ancien compagnon des missions aux armées, Lindet et Prieur, spécialistes mili-

taires du Grand Comité, Taillefer, Mallarmé, Garnier de
Saintes, Grégoire, Desgrouas, tous patriotes prononcés, et
dont certains furent mêlés à la conspiration de Babeuf,
ainsi Crachet, abonné du *Tribun du Peuple*, ainsi encore
Félix Lepelletier. On rencontre aussi des officiers connus de
Carnot : Clarke, Duquesnoy, Turreau, qui patronnaient des
candidats. Enfin quelques sociétés patriotiques, quelques
Thermidoriens et quelques rares membres du nouveau
tiers[2]. Ces demandes, surtout celles des Conventionnels,
furent bien accueillies.

Les choix de Carnot les plus significatifs eurent lieu dans
le département du Pas-de-Calais. Certes la députation tout
entière avait été consultée par le Directoire, comme dans le
reste de la France, mais sur les candidats, évidemment
modérés, qu'elle proposa, une huitaine seulement furent
nommés, encore étaient-ils parfois soutenus par d'autres
patronages. Or il y avait à pourvoir quatre-vingt-trois postes
de commissaires cantonaux, et huit postes de commissaires
auprès des tribunaux.

La plupart des désignations furent prononcées à la
demande des sociétés de patriotes ou des personnalités
locales. Le club d'Aire rappela que Carnot l'avait présidé,
Legay évoqua le souvenir des Rosati, Buissart ainsi que
son beau-frère et un autre de ses parents reçurent des fonctions. En revanche, Guffroy et Darthé furent évincés. Cependant Carnot nomma les protégés de Nicole et de Berlier. Le
commissaire auprès du tribunal correctionnel de Saint-
Omer fut Crachet, l'abonné du *Tribun du Peuple*.

La décision la plus importante était le choix du commissaire départemental, prototype du préfet. Carnot nomma
un protégé de Berlier, Coffin, terroriste amnistié, Jacobin
qui avait rattaché la société populaire d'Hesdin aux Jacobins de Paris, qui avait poursuivi, en les traitant de « sang-
sues du peuple », les commerçants qui vendaient au-dessus
de la taxe. Non seulement le commissaire départemental
exerçait une grande influence, mais il pouvait proposer des
candidats aux postes cantonaux. Coffin fit nommer commissaires une douzaine d'anciens Jacobins qui figuraient sur les
listes noires dressées par Guffroy. Il engagea bientôt la
lutte contre la municipalité d'Arras ; contre elle il soutint
les ouvriers et les pauvres, et il finit même par faire destituer
cette municipalité.

La droite s'indigna ; des pétitions collectives, des réclamations virulentes, appuyées par le nouveau tiers, des lettres anonymes furent envoyées au Directoire, accusant violemment Carnot. En vain.

D'autre part, Carnot accueillit volontiers les protégés de Daunou. Celui-ci présidait le conseil des Cinq-Cents ; il était originaire du Pas-de-Calais, auteur pour une large part de la Constitution de l'an III et d'opinion modérée. Il opéra, par l'intermédiaire de Carnot, une vingtaine de nominations ; plusieurs furent aussi l'objet de réclamations de la part des députés du nouveau tiers.

En somme Carnot prenait résolument le contrepied des élections locales et recrutait un personnel de gauche, bien fait pour obéir au Directoire et s'accorder avec un Corps législatif formé surtout d'anciens Conventionnels, mais destiné à combattre les élus locaux dans les diverses administrations [3].

Rancœur d'un candidat malheureux contre ceux qui ont préféré ses concurrents ? Revanche des persécutions subies pendant la période thermidorienne ? Conviction que le salut de la République était à ce prix ? Il faut noter que Carnot fut loin d'être le seul à effectuer de pareils choix ; le Directoire tout entier y contribua.

Les débuts justifiaient les alarmes et les invectives. Benjamin Constant y voyait même une manœuvre de grande envergure : « Les terroristes sont cette artillerie du gouvernement, toujours cachée mais toujours redoutable, et qui, toutes les fois qu'il sera forcé de l'employer, réduira en poudre ses adversaires. » Mais il signalait la contrepartie de cette tactique, la crainte des « hommes honnêtes » — républicains modérés et bourgeois — affolés de « ce qu'ils appellent des nominations jacobines [4] ».

Carnot fut l'un des principaux responsables de cette orientation ; il le reconnut dans la suite, non sans quelque embarras. A vrai dire, cette politique pouvait réussir, surtout au lendemain de la réaction thermidorienne, à une époque où il fallait poursuivre la guerre et appliquer la législation de combat de la Convention finissante. Mais à la condition de se poursuivre sans défaillance, et d'être appuyée par le Corps législatif. Le dernier point pouvait être acquis jusqu'aux prochaines élections, mais après devrait-on envisager de gouverner contre les deux tiers renouvelés ?

En somme, il s'agissait de savoir comment fixer la Révolution. Serait-ce par l'application immédiate et totale de la

Constitution ? Dans ce cas, le pouvoir appartiendrait aux représentants d'une opinion qui boudait le régime, refusait les places, éludait les lois et se plaignait d'un désordre qu'elle contribuait à créer. Encore étaient-ce là les dispositions les moins redoutables. Dans l'Ouest, dans le Centre, dans le Sud-Est, l'hostilité était ouverte. Le gouvernement devait recourir à la force armée, il décrétait l'état de siège, il entamait des opérations militaires, il employait encore — contre toutes les règles — des agents extraordinaires, survivance curieuse des envoyés en mission de la Convention, maintenus ou renforcés par le pouvoir exécutif : Fréron dans le Midi, Reverchon dans la région lyonnaise, d'autres dans le Centre, dans le Sud-Est. Comment renoncer à toute contrainte sans livrer la République à ses ennemis ? Comment continuer la guerre sans obliger les déserteurs à rejoindre leurs bataillons et les conscrits réfractaires à partir aux armées ? Or les administrateurs élus étaient complices des déserteurs et des réfractaires. Comment continuer la guerre et administrer le pays sans ressources financières ? Or les administrations tardaient à agir et manifestaient les plus mauvaises dispositions. Comment juger les infractions aux lois et règlements, les délits politiques et les actes de rébellion avec des juges élus, de connivence avec leurs électeurs et avec les délinquants ?

Il fallait assurer l'ordre et la sécurité, rétablir le ravitaillement et trouver l'équilibre entre les prix et le pouvoir d'achat, arrêter l'inflation et approvisionner les marchés.

Pouvait-on assumer de pareilles tâches par le seul jeu des rouages constitutionnels ? Le Corps législatif avait si bien compris la nécessité de mesures exceptionnelles qu'il avait accru les pouvoirs du Directoire, autorisé les nominations là où manquaient les élus, et là où ils étaient contre-révolutionnaires. Enfin le Directoire utilisait ses agents extraordinaires dans la zone la plus hostile et pour accomplir les tâches les plus impopulaires.

Mais les procédés d'autorité, s'ils étaient adoptés par d'anciens terroristes, s'ils faisaient bon marché des législateurs et des élus, risquaient de rappeler le Grand Comité honni et d'écarter ceux que Constant appelait les « hommes honnêtes ». Ils risquaient aussi de réveiller les Jacobins poursuivis pendant la Convention thermidorienne, et finalement amnistiés, et de les inciter à chercher une revanche dans le rétablissement de la terreur.

Entre ces risques opposés, le Directoire cherchait le « juste milieu ». Harcelé par des factions partisanes, qui tantôt menaient l'attaque à la tribune des assemblées, tantôt dans les colonnes des journaux, tantôt — plus sourdement — dans les clubs nouveaux, comme celui du Panthéon, et même dans les conspirations royalistes, que soutenait une partie du clergé, tandis que les émigrés et l'étranger, surtout l'Anglais, appuyaient le prétendant.

Comment trouver le juste milieu et combattre les extrêmes sans tomber dans cette politique de « bascule » qui risquait de conduire de Charybde en Scylla ? Carnot avait voulu prendre son appui à gauche, parmi des républicains éprouvés qu'il pensait assagis par les événements, et qui le seraient plus encore par leurs responsabilités. D'ici les prochaines élections — dans dix-huit mois —, ils devraient assurer la marche des nouveaux rouages, résoudre les problèmes les plus urgents, pacifier, stimuler et intimider suffisamment pour rallier la masse des électeurs et réduire à d'inoffensives minorités les extrêmes. C'est là ce qu'il attendait d'un Coffin, et ce qu'il en obtint dans une large mesure. Peu à peu il pourrait desserrer les contraintes, lever l'état de siège, retirer les troupes de l'intérieur, faire confiance enfin à la nation.

Autour de lui, parmi ses amis, se trouvaient des républicains ardents, comme Garrau, des modérés comme Feulint, Collignon, et des tièdes comme Lacuée, Clarke, ou Beffroy de Reigny.

Mais il fallait par-dessus tout éviter les à-coups, ne pas se déjuger, ne pas céder aux pressions, ni même paraître céder. Or ce fut l'erreur fatale du Directoire — et dans une mesure indéniable celle de Carnot — que de marquer des hésitations, de laisser paraître des flottements et des contradictions, au lieu de regrouper les Français, de réunir les Girondins et les Montagnards, de faire collaborer les fonctionnaires élus et les fonctionnaires nommés, les civils et les militaires, à la même œuvre de fusion pourtant annoncée au premier jour.

Quelle pouvait être l'autorité d'un gouvernement — et de ses agents — qui parlait en ces termes des nominations à peine terminées :

« Si, dans la multiplicité des choix que le Directoire exécutif s'est vu forcé de faire en même temps, l'intrigue lui en a surpris quelques-uns de mauvais, il s'empressera de réformer ces erreurs quand il aura été éclairé par les faits.»

Cette proclamation date du 26 décembre, c'est le temps où La Revellière place le ralliement de Carnot à la politique du « juste milieu ». Ainsi Carnot s'opposa aux manifestations jacobines à l'occasion de la fête du 21 janvier 1796, bien que les membres du club du Panthéon — le nouveau club jacobin — fussent autorisés à escorter les voitures des Directeurs [5].

La politique du juste milieu pouvait être poursuivie par une majorité directoriale constituée par La Revellière et Carnot, celui-ci étant généralement soutenu par Letourneur. Encore fallait-il qu'elle prévalût dans les problèmes majeurs : celui de la politique religieuse et celui de la politique sociale.

Au point de vue religieux, on avait adopté une politique de combat ; il eût fallu une politique d'apaisement, analogue à celle que Carnot et Hoche firent prévaloir dans l'Ouest et qui favorisa la pacification. Carnot était convaincu que la persécution renforçait la position adverse, que le temps seul pourrait saper le christianisme et que, dans le présent, la tolérance universelle était le seul dogme dont il fallût faire profession [6]. La Revellière était d'un avis tout contraire. Carnot le blessa en raillant la théophilanthropie. On fit donc la chasse aux prêtres réfractaires, exilés rentrés, septuagénaires ou infirmes. Ce fut l'une des causes de l'impopularité et de l'impuissance du régime [7].

Puis on rompit cette ligne. Cochon, nommé ministre de la Police le 14 germinal an IV — 3 avril 1796 —, sous l'influence de Carnot, se montra favorable au clergé, indulgent aux réfractaires, faible enfin au moment où ils manipulaient les élections.

Au point de vue social, Carnot resta d'abord fidèle aux démocrates qu'il avait fait nommer. Il ne signa pas ce singulier arrêté du 17 mars, qui chargeait les administrateurs départementaux de dresser des fiches sur les commissaires du Directoire, c'est-à-dire sur leurs propres surveillants, nommés par le pouvoir exécutif. Il ne signa pas non plus la proclamation du 14 avril. Il ne révoqua pas ceux qu'il avait nommés et qui — comme Coffin — avaient fini par se faire accepter, et avec lui l'autorité directoriale : « Il est l'homme que vous deviez choisir », répondaient les administrateurs du Pas-de-Calais, et le Directoire faisait écho à cette déclaration [8].

Toutefois ce personnel n'était pas favorable à la politique de tolérance religieuse. De plus, certains des chefs démocrates considéraient le régime directorial comme une étape, au sortir de la réaction thermidorienne, et qui devait ramener à la constitution de 1793, c'est-à-dire à l'égalité politique, au suffrage universel, au referendum, au triomphe de la souveraineté populaire.

Certains d'entre eux songeaient même à une démocratie sociale, combattant les riches, remaniant la propriété, complétant en somme la Révolution. Ce furent eux qui provoquèrent l'évolution de Carnot vers les conservateurs.

En effet, certains démocrates voulurent manœuvrer Carnot : « Nous avons compté sur toi et tes collègues pour être les premiers et principaux agents de ce plan régénérateur » (c'est-à-dire de la restauration de la constitution de 1793), avait déclaré Félix Lepelletier à Carnot. Et il avait refusé le poste que Carnot lui offrait ; Lindet avait fait de même [9].

Carnot infléchit sa politique. Cochon fut doté de larges crédits pour « surveiller et entretenir l'esprit public dans la commune de Paris », notamment dans les faubourgs Saint-Antoine et Marceau [10]. Il se persuada qu'il fallait combattre les démocrates pour faire prévaloir l'alliance du juste milieu.

Dans la correspondance de Carnot, on trouva, après le 18 fructidor, vingt-huit lettres du député Audouin — perdues depuis. Elles montrent qu'à partir du 16 germinal — 5 avril — il changeait de système, selon les termes mêmes du résumé de ces lettres. Il s'agissait « de ramener à la République ses ennemis par un système de modération qui obtienne leur confiance et celle des puissances étrangères [11]. » Ce que confirme une lettre du même Audouin, publiée dans le très officiel *Rédacteur*, le 17 juin suivant : « Tous les hommes de bon sens, quelles qu'aient été les nuances de leurs opinions pendant les crises révolutionnaires, ne forment plus qu'un faisceau infrangible dès le jour où la patrie a obtenu un gouvernement constitutionnel. » Le mot de ralliement était la constitution de 1795, comme le déclara Carnot dans un discours du 10 mai. Toute la question était de savoir si les ennemis à combattre se trouvaient seulement à gauche, si c'étaient seulement les démocrates, et non les royalistes. Le général Pille, ancien collaborateur de Carnot et commandant la division territoriale de Nevers, lui signalait les principaux ennemis à droite [12].

Or Carnot décida au contraire de combattre la gauche. Ce choix inattendu compromit le régime encore fragile et vulnérable. A coup sûr, Carnot a sous-estimé la force et l'organisation des royalistes. Il a cru pouvoir frapper l'extrême gauche sans favoriser la droite, supposant que les modérés sauraient se rallier et l'appuyer. Il misait sur un parti constitutionnel.

Ainsi décida-t-il d'abattre les partisans de la constitution de 1793, qui complotaient jusque dans l'armée et dans la Légion de police.

Cette Légion de police devait être un corps d'élite, de sûreté, composé d'éléments choisis d'infanterie et de cavalerie, et sur lequel on devait pouvoir s'appuyer en toutes circonstances. Bonaparte venait de lui donner des cadres. Si elle était suspecte, la situation paraissait extrêmement grave.

Ce fut Carnot qui décida ses collègues à une énergique répression, déclenchant ainsi une rupture avec la gauche, qui ne cessa de s'aggraver. La Légion fut d'abord frappée.

Le 23 avril, le Directoire la dénonça au Corps législatif, lui demandant une loi pour envoyer les légionnaires aux armées, après les avoir épurés. La loi fut adoptée sur-le-champ, un arrêté en prescrivit l'application. Quelques incidents eurent lieu : des femmes firent de la propagande auprès des officiers et des soldats en faveur de Babeuf et distribuèrent des numéros du *Tribun du Peuple*. On manifesta contre le Directoire, la presse jeta feu et flammes. L'un des chefs de la Légion était en même temps représentant du peuple et dirigeait un journal de gauche, *L'Ami du Peuple*. L'indice d'un complot parut se faire jour ; on dit que des soldats de la Légion pillèrent des commerçants. Si bien que, le 11 mai, le Directoire publia une proclamation sensationnelle : « Un affreux complot doit éclater la nuit prochaine.... [On doit] égorger le Corps législatif, tous les membres du gouvernement,... [pour rétablir la constitution de 1793],... le pillage [doit éclater] dans Paris. »

Cette proclamation était signée du président du Directoire, Carnot. Mais celui-ci n'agissait pas seulement en raison de sa fonction ; il apportait une énergie, une passion qui ont frappé tous les contemporains et tous ceux qui depuis étudièrent cette affaire encore ténébreuse, et dont il s'est fait gloire lui-même, après le 18 Fructidor.

La moindre suspicion suffisait pour lui faire disgracier des hommes qu'il avait jusqu'alors soutenus. Témoin ce Toulotte, de Saint-Omer, qui réclama vainement contre les conséquences d'une note de police.

« L'affreux complot » avait été suivi, soutenu, couvé par la police, à la suite des déclarations d'un mouchard, nommé Grisel, qui avait appris, vers le 15 avril, les projets de Babeuf et les avait fait connaître à Cochon et à Carnot.

C'était l'occasion d'un magnifique coup de filet ; sous prétexte de combattre les chimères puériles et incendiaires de Babeuf, on allait pouvoir frapper le reste des Montagnards et des Jacobins, les démocrates baptisés des noms redoutables et péjoratifs d' « exclusifs » et d' « anarchistes ».

L'opposition de Carnot à Babeuf va de soi. Le communisme de Babeuf contredisait les convictions maîtresses de Carnot, son tour d'esprit, son passé et ses projets, sa conception même de la civilisation et du rôle de la Révolution.

Carnot était rationaliste. Ennemi de tout fanatisme, de gauche ou de droite, de religion ou d'antichristianisme, il pensait qu'il fallait à tout prix en éviter les déchaînements, qui eussent nécessairement abouti au triomphe de la brutalité, aveugle et destructrice. Il s'en était clairement expliqué lors de sa mission aux Pyrénées. A ses yeux aussi bien le recours à la violence, le culte de la force, que les mesures de subversion totale, la loi agraire, la communauté des productions du sol, niaient les bases de toute civilisation, les droits et la dignité de l'homme, qui résidaient dans la raison, qui supposaient une libre adhésion après une équitable information. Une telle déviation marquait la faillite de la Révolution, la chute dans la barbarie, la condamnation de tous ses efforts, de tous ses espoirs, de toutes ses épreuves. C'est ce qu'il avait proscrit chez les Exagérés, chez les Enragés, et dans nombre de Conventionnels, de représentants en mission et de sociétés populaires. Le mouvement babouviste, amalgame confus d'idées simplistes, de sentiments de révolte et d'idéalisme utopique, ne valait pas mieux pour cet « homme à talents » que déconcertait Caliban.

D'autant que le babouvisme menait l'une des attaques les plus directes contre les gens instruits, les notables, la culture. On écrivait que la classe ouvrière est « la plus précieuse de la société ». « La supériorité de talents et d'intelligence n'est qu'une chimère, déclarait le *Tribun du Peuple*, ce n'est qu'une chose d'opinion que la valeur de l'intelligence..., il est peut-être encore à examiner si la valeur de la force toute naturelle et physique ne la vaut point. » Blasphème impardonnable ! Péché contre l'esprit.

Précédemment la démocratie s'était parfois dressée contre les hommes à talents, mais dans ce débat entre l'*intelligentsia* et les prolétaires, entre Minerve et Caliban, jamais encore on ne s'était avancé si loin, ni si agressivement. Cette fois les injustices sociales, l'exploitation de l'homme par l'homme, l'assujettissement des misérables étaient imputés aux « intelligents », c'étaient eux qui avaient attribué un « si haut prix aux conceptions de leurs cerveaux », et qui en avaient fait un « brevet d'accaparement ».

Ajoutons que Babeuf et ses amis se tournaient spécialement du côté des militaires, qu'ils prêchaient le refus d'obéissance au gouvernement, la prise d'armes en faveur du *Tribun du Peuple*, baptisé tribun militaire pour la circonstance. Les généraux étaient pris à partie, notamment Bonaparte. Déjà cette propagande portait ses fruits, des adresses d'encouragement étaient envoyées à Babeuf par l'armée des Alpes, par celle de l'Ouest et par l'armée de Rhin-et-Moselle [13]. Babeuf voulait ressusciter cette force armée parisienne, ces compagnies de canonniers contre lesquelles Carnot avait lutté. Il dressait, arrondissement par arrondissement, la liste des anciens canonniers, des anciens officiers de l'armée révolutionnaire, amis de Robespierre et Hébert, tel Hudin, bijoutier rue Pastourelle, naguère aide de camp d'Hanriot.

Tout le passé de Carnot, tout ce qui lui tenait au cœur le dressait contre un tel mouvement.

A bien des égards, le babouvisme était la revanche d'Hébert et des Enragés. Les conspirateurs recherchaient les anciens sectionnaires, les anciens démorates ; ils vantaient la valeur et les convictions d'un ancien aide de camp d'Hanriot, ils dessinaient la carte politique des démocrates parisiens et noyautaient les anciens amis de la Commune.

D'ailleurs les projets de Babeuf, « le complot des égaux », ne furent pas pris au sérieux par les contemporains ; « le dévergondage de leur projet portait en lui-même un contrepoison, a écrit Rousselin de Saint-Albin, Babeuf n'était qu'un instrument ; l'impulsion était celle de Conventionnels exclus [14] », les Amar et les Vadier, soutenus par la popularité quasi légendaire de Drouet, l'homme qui avait arrêté le roi à Varennes et qui venait de rentrer des prisons autrichiennes. Ceux-là n'étaient pas subjugués par l'idéal de

Babeuf, ils n'étaient pas hostiles aux talents ; pourquoi
Carnot les combattait-il si fort ? Par peur d'être impliqué
dans leur complot, a encore écrit Rousselin. Accusation
vraisemblable dans une certaine mesure, en raison de la
persécution essuyée par Carnot pendant la Convention thermidorienne. D'autres, Baudot par exemple, ont dit que
Carnot voulait faire oublier son passé [15]. L'argument prend
de la valeur si l'on tient compte de la lettre adressée à Carnot par Drouet, le 9 mai. Celui-ci condamnait l'orientation
réactionnaire du gouvernement, il condamnait aussi la violence. Il ajoutait qu'il s'adressait à Carnot non pas seulement parce qu'il présidait le Directoire, mais parce que,
précisait-il, « j'ai eu plusieurs conférences secrètes avec
Carnot à ce sujet, et je lui ai écrit plusieurs fois [16] ».

Tout donne à croire que Carnot voulut ostensiblement
se désolidariser des Jacobins, des démocrates, des anciens
terroristes qu'il qualifia, après le 18 fructidor, « d'êtres
immoraux et incorrigibles, qui portaient le désordre, le
mécontentement, la terreur dans toutes les parties de la
République [17] ». Il crut ainsi assurer son avenir, consolider la
politique du juste milieu et supprimer des risques dont il
affirmait la réalité à son ami Garrau, démocrate convaincu :
« Les troubles dont nous étions menacés ici sont prévenus
par les mesures rigoureuses du gouvernement, le licenci e
ment de la police a porté le dernier coup aux anarchistes [18]. »
Ce dernier terme souligne le point de vue de Carnot.

Cette volte-face déconcerta. Carnot a lui-même raconté
la stupeur d'un cordonnier à la nouvelle du rôle de Carnot
dans la répression des Babouvistes [19]. D'autre part, Poultier
s'adressait à Carnot pour lui demander de conserver et d'utiliser la Légion de police réorganisée : « Je m'adresse à vous,
citoyen Directeur, parce qu'autrefois vous m'avez témoigné
de l'amitié et que je crois encore la mériter. » Malo écrivait
dans le même sens [20]. Carnot gardait même des contacts
avec certains des personnages les plus compromis. Ainsi
prévint-il Félix Lepelletier qu'il y aurait des arrestations
au camp de Grenoble, Lepelletier se garda bien d'y aller et
avertit quelques amis [21].

Les journaux de gauche, comme *L'Ami des Lois*, se montrèrent favorables à Carnot, à plusieurs reprises, même après
ces événements. Ainsi, le 30 septembre, Carnot était mis en
scène comme un pur patriote : « Je ne m'appelle pas monsieur — lui faisait-on dire —, je suis citoyen et je m'en

honore. » Ces dispositions se maintinrent jusqu'en novembre.

En revanche, nombre d'amis ou de correspondants de Carnot — ou du Directoire — s'inquiétaient des chances qu'une telle politique pouvait donner aux royalistes. Sans parler de Hoche, qui attirait sur ce point l'attention des Directeurs, Buissart, le vieil ami arrageois, signalait la destruction des arbres de la Liberté, les menées royalistes des villes, et l'inexécution des lois ; il vantait l'énergie de Coffin, ce que Carnot appréciait volontiers, car Coffin combattait les Babouvistes et restait dans la ligne constitutionnelle [22]. Carnot fit l'honneur à Coffin de publier dans *Le Rédacteur* les félicitations qu'il lui adressait, document intéressant car il prouve que Carnot connaissait le risque et voulait le combattre : « Le Directoire est instruit, citoyen, que le royalisme essaie de se relever dans le département du Pas-de-Calais. Il sait que quelques hommes, autrefois la tête du mouvement réactionnaire, vont, compulsant les registres des sociétés populaires qu'il dominait alors, et sollicitent des signatures pour attaquer, dans des pétitions insidieuses, les républicains prononcés [23]. »

Garrau fut le plus franc critique de la politique nouvelle, et l'un des plus sévères, dans sa grandiloquence affectueuse. « Mon ami, j'ai l'âme triste jusqu'à la mort, confiait-il à Carnot le 31 août.... Que [le gouvernement] soit sévère, inflexible pour les anarchistes, c'est le vœu de tous ses amis, il le doit. Mais qu'il ouvre enfin les yeux sur un ennemi bien plus dangereux, bien plus cruel encore, c'est l'affreux royalisme. » Et Garrau faisait un sombre tableau de la réaction sous toutes ses formes, de ses collusions avec les ennemis, des troubles qu'elle entretenait et de ceux qu'elle allait susciter : « Il se prépare un nouveau 13 vendémiaire. » Il dénonçait la responsabilité de Carnot : « Ainsi sans le vouloir, mais par l'effet de la réaction royale qui s'opère, vous vous privez chaque jour de l'appui de ceux qui ont leur existence attachée à la vôtre. » Il montrait le danger que constituaient les nouveaux alliés du gouvernement, « ces hommes qui veulent vous livrer nus et sans défense à vos ennemis les plus mortels ». Pour conclure, il conjurait Carnot de renverser le courant : « Arrêtez-vous donc, il en est temps encore ; mon ami, arrêtez les progrès d'un incendie qui s'étend,... que les places, les emplois à votre nomination ne soient confiés qu'à des hommes dignes. Occupez-vous ostensiblement des besoins du peuple et des moyens de diminuer ses maux.... Et alors il ne sera plus à appréhender que votre juste sévérité contre l'anarchie ne devienne dans les mains du royalisme l'instrument de mort des républicains.... Alors vous aurez encore une fois sauvé la République, et peut-être prévenu l'établissement du régime militaire. » On ne saurait mieux définir les répercussions de l'option politique de Carnot, le rôle d'un homme dans l'Histoire.

Garrau était Jacobin, mais il écrivait en connaissance de cause. Ses fonctions de commissaire à l'armée d'Italie lui permettaient d'être largement informé de la politique française et de ses répercussions à l'étranger. Elles lui valaient aussi des persécutions de la part des militaires — et de Bonaparte — désireux de secouer la tutelle des civils. Garrau n'exagérait rien quand il redoutait le triomphe du royalisme ou du césarisme. Carnot était trop engagé, trop circonvenu, pour écouter Garrau ; il nota en marge de la lettre si perspicace : « C'est faux. Vous n'y êtes pas ! On se rallie au gouvernement qui veut la République [24]. »

CHAPITRE IV

FAUX DÉPART DIPLOMATIQUE ET MILITAIRE

PROFONDÉMENT engagé dans les luttes intérieures, Carnot n'en demeurait pas moins l'organisateur de la victoire.

C'était même sa principale activité, l'élément essentiel de son prestige, du moins dans la mesure où la victoire reviendrait sous nos drapeaux.

Apparemment la tâche était moins lourde qu'au temps du Grand Comité : la Prusse, l'Espagne et la Hollande avaient signé la paix. Carnot n'avait plus à s'inquiéter de cette frontière du Nord, qui avait si longtemps accaparé ses soins. Le jour était enfin venu où l'annexion de la Belgique et l'occupation de la Hollande avaient disloqué la coalition et affaibli considérablement les moyens militaires, économiques et financiers dont disposaient les derniers ennemis de la France. C'était ce que Carnot, depuis 1792, avait toujours prévu et voulu ; il pouvait en être fier.

Libéré de ses ennemis sur la Meuse et sur les Pyrénées, Carnot pouvait concentrer ses forces pour agir sur le Rhin et les Alpes. Mais il avait trouvé là une situation compromise. L'offensive tardivement déclenchée en Italie contre les Autrichiens et les Piémontais s'était interrompue presque aussitôt, à cause de l'incapacité du général Schérer. Rien ne put être fait avant le printemps de 1796, époque où Bonaparte commença sa légendaire campagne.

D'autre part les armées autrichiennes avaient refoulé Jourdan et Pichegru en deçà du Rhin à la fin de la campagne de 1795. Carnot en avait fait peser la responsabilité sur ses successeurs au Comité de Salut public, mais, depuis son retour au pouvoir, il n'avait pu enrayer le recul. Les Autrichiens tenaient une large tête de pont sur la rive gauche du Rhin, et le Directoire avait accueilli avec empressement l'armistice proposé par l'ennemi, en janvier 1796.

La situation n'était pas encore alarmante, mais exigeait

une solide préparation pour la campagne prochaine, préparation tout ensemble militaire et diplomatique. Les coups devraient être portés là où ils arracheraient la décision, c'est-à-dire la victoire et la paix. Les négociations importaient autant que les combats, encore fallait-il savoir quel but assigner aux unes et aux autres.

La question des frontières était la plus brûlante. Les ennemis — Angleterre, Autriche et Russie — avaient convenu, le 28 septembre 1795, d'unir leurs efforts pour ramener la France à ses anciennes limites. Le Directoire était lié par la constitution elle-même qui déclarait intangibles les nouvelles limites englobant Avignon, Nice, la Savoie et la Belgique. Ainsi la contradiction semblait-elle insoluble. D'autre part, le Rhin continuait de provoquer les contestations les plus passionnées ; la Prusse avait accepté qu'il devînt la frontière de la France si des compensations lui étaient accordées, et si l'Empire et l'empereur étaient consentants. Restait à obtenir, de bon gré ou de force, cet assentiment.

Reubell dirigeait la politique extérieure, mais toute question de frontière étant aussi question militaire Carnot ne pouvait s'en désintéresser. Il avait prôné, le 1er octobre 1795, la frontière de la Meuse, allait-il, malgré cela, lancer une offensive sur le Rhin ? Avec quels objectifs ? La conduite de la guerre amenait encore Carnot à s'occuper de politique étrangère pour trouver des alliés. Pour toutes ces raisons, il devait s'entendre avec Reubell, il y parvint aisément pendant les premiers mois. Pourtant Carnot avait ses informations personnelles, notamment par les généraux, et le Cabinet historique était quelque peu un cabinet diplomatique.

Reubell et Carnot travaillèrent les ambassadeurs des États qu'ils voulaient lier à leur politique. Ils reçurent et pressèrent Sandoz-Rollin, représentant de la Prusse, Boccardi, représentant de Gênes. Carnot se montrait courtois, mesuré, insinuant ; Reubell était rude, impétueux, menaçant. Leur action concertée pesait assez pour amener les diplomates à dépeindre à leurs gouvernements respectifs les risques d'une résistance et les avantages des concessions. Pourtant, les deux compères ne purent rien obtenir, et la France dut renoncer à des alliances souhaitables.

Carnot joua un rôle moindre dans les autres négociations, qui n'aboutirent pas mieux, et, quand le printemps devint proche, c'est à lui que revint le rôle d'emporter la décision au moyen des victoires. En somme, les débuts diplomatiques avaient été un faux départ, en grande partie à cause des exigences excessives du Directoire [1].

* * *

La reprise des grandes opérations avait préoccupé Carnot dès son arrivée au Directoire, tant elle apparaissait malaisée : l'armée se décomposait ! A la chute de Robespierre, elle comptait environ 800 000 hommes ; au début du Directoire, à peine en restait-il 450 000. Et dans quel état de désorganisation ! Des demi-brigades — ou régiments — amoindries de plus des trois quarts, réduites à 600 hommes, des escadrons de 20 et 25 cavaliers, et qui n'étaient pas tous montés et, encore moins, bien montés [2].

Cette pénurie ne tenait pas aux pertes sur les champs de bataille, mais à la maladie et à la désertion, l'une et l'autre imputables en partie au manque de ressources, en partie au fléchissement du patriotisme.

De toutes parts, on signalait les départs, par groupes de 20, 40, 60 hommes, aussi bien dans les armées de l'intérieur que dans la zone de combat. Des bandes de soldats, presque nus, sans souliers ni culottes, enveloppés dans de vieux sacs à distribution, revenaient chez eux, par petites étapes, mendiant ou maraudant tout au long de la route [3].

Ils justifiaient leur conduite par leur misère ; ils ne recevaient ni nourriture, ni solde, ni vêtements. Les officiers, ajoutaient-ils, les laissaient partir sans les signaler, pour continuer de les compter à leurs effectifs. La gendarmerie fermait les yeux, tant qu'il n'y avait pas de désordres et que les déserteurs n'abusaient pas de leurs armes ; mais, dans ce cas, les gendarmes étaient bien incapables d'intervenir efficacement [4].

Il y avait aussi les cortèges d'éclopés, de malades et de blessés.

Ils avaient traîné d'hôpitaux en hôpitaux, ils rentraient chez eux à la faveur d'une convalescence. A l'occasion, des médecins complaisants ou véreux leur délivraient de faux certificats.

La catastrophe financière qui s'était produite pendant la période thermidorienne avait provoqué la misère des armées ; elle avait été accompagnée d'une réaction, voire d'une propagande royaliste, qui avait entamé le moral des troupes et contribuait à la désertion [5].

Une connivence tacite et quasi universelle protégeait ces déserteurs. Ils revenaient dans leur famille et ne se cachaient pas ; les cultivateurs et les manufacturiers les employaient ouvertement ; les autorités élues — municipalités et tribunaux —, les gardes nationales, formées de leurs parents et de leurs amis, les ignoraient ou les protégeaient. La patrie n'était plus en danger, les troupes avaient pris les quartiers d'hiver, les volontaires étaient partis pour une seule campagne, les exempts et les réfractaires étaient nombreux ; tout cela — et la paix escomptée — conduisait les populations à considérer ces retours comme légitimes [6].

La tâche la plus urgente était donc le rétablissement des effectifs, le rappel des déserteurs, la levée des réquisitionnaires qui s'étaient dérobés, et peut-être l'appel de nouvelles classes. Il fallut promptement renoncer à cette dernière éventualité, tant l'opinion s'y montra hostile ; le ministre de la Police jugea même indispensable de publier, le 18 février 1796, un démenti officiel [7]. Les autres mesures n'allaient pas non plus sans quelque risque. Chaque fois qu'on avait tenté de saisir les déserteurs, ils avaient quitté leurs foyers et leurs travaux pour prendre le maquis, vivre de rapines et semer l'effroi. Parfois même ils passaient dans les rangs des bandes royalistes. Nul n'avait oublié que le refus du service militaire avait été la cause directe des insurrections de l'Ouest.

Carnot fut donc amené à organiser les rappels et les poursuites, intervenant ainsi dans les départements de l'Intérieur et de la Police, autant que dans celui de la Guerre. Tout se tenait. Comme il arrive souvent, les problèmes particuliers se rattachaient au problème général de l'autorité du régime.

Les rapports officiels manifestèrent l'optimisme le plus traditionnel : déserteurs et réfractaires auraient afflué à l'appel des chefs du gouvernement, les effectifs se seraient accrus de plus de 50 000 hommes en six mois [8]. La vérité est moins satisfaisante.

Carnot fit préparer par Lacuée un ensemble de mesures préventives et coercitives : suppression des congés de convalescence et des affectations spéciales, recensement des réfractaires et des déserteurs, battues de troupes et de gendarmerie pour les saisir, sanctions contre les recéleurs et les employeurs de déserteurs. Le Corps législatif adopta ces dispositions, des agents militaires furent chargés d'aider les autorités locales à les appliquer. Celles-ci y apportèrent la plus efficace mauvaise volonté.

Les commissaires, les gendarmes et les troupes raflèrent pourtant un nombre appréciable de déserteurs et de réquisitionnaires, un millier par exemple dans la région d'Agen. D'autres vinrent d'eux-mêmes demander des feuilles de route. Mais certains étaient désespérés au point de se mutiler ou de se suicider pour ne pas partir, tandis que les hardis se rebellaient, invectivaient les autorités et formaient des bandes. Plus simplement, un grand nombre faisaient semblant de partir, se laissaient escorter, puis revenaient tranquillement chez eux. Garrau écrivit à Carnot pour lui signaler l'inapplication des lois, l'abus et le trafic des congés de réforme.

Le gouvernement recourut à tous les moyens : promesses et menaces, amnisties et sanctions, appels à la gloire. Les résultats furent des plus médiocres, les sanctions ne paraissent pas avoir été réellement prises et, tout au long de l'année 1796, on dénonça la présence d'un grand nombre de réquisitionnaires et de déserteurs impénitents. Le temps de l'enthousiasme était passé, aussi bien que celui de la terreur ; la lutte contre les Jacobins arrêtait les seuls Français qui fussent encore disposés à combattre ; Carnot lui-même ne trouvait plus les mots que lui avait inspirés la patrie en danger ; il en venait aux menaces platoniques, ou il faisait appel à l'esprit de corps, ce qui n'était pas sans danger si l'on craignait le césarisme.

Pourtant il se montra strict et attaché à l'égalité. Les affectations spéciales ne permirent jamais de quitter les armées, les hommes qui avaient acheté un remplaçant durent servir personnellement, et, courage suprême, les personnages politiques réclamant des faveurs pour leurs protégés furent mal accueillis [9].

Les effectifs prévus ne furent pas rassemblés : on disposa respectivement de 95 000 et de 85 000 hommes aux armées de Sambre-et-Meuse et de Rhin-et-Moselle, au lieu de 103 000 qu'on avait prévu pour chacune. Au lieu de 531 253 hommes au total, à peine en avait-on 460 000.

Encore fallait-il les faire vivre. Un rapport du ministre de la Guerre, en janvier 1796, dressait un bilan décourageant : pas de ressources, des promesses non tenues, des

marchés sans fournitures, un arriéré insolvable très lourd,
pas de transports et pas de trésorerie. La transformation
des régies en entreprises accrut encore l'incohérence ; les
entreprises ne fonctionnaient pas encore quand la régie
s'interrompit. Le gaspillage était effroyable. Ce fut une
situation bien étrange et bien dangereuse que celle d'armées
si démunies qu'elles devaient se décomposer en minuscules
cantonnements pour vivre aux dépens des populations. Si
l'on s'avisait de les rassembler, elles ne pouvaient plus se
nourrir. Le manque de transports interdisait même la
répartition des ressources qui pouvaient se rencontrer. Non
seulement les opérations, mais les déplacements eux-mêmes
étaient devenus impossibles. C'était la ruine des plans de
campagne, c'était aussi celle de la discipline et de l'esprit
militaire. La maraude sévissait, préparant le pillage et les
violences. Les officiers, aussi démunis, fermaient les yeux
ou secondaient les maraudeurs, pour avoir une part de leurs
rapines. Dès qu'il y avait quelques envois — armes, équipements, vêtements —, ils donnaient lieu au trafic et au
troc. Il fallut subir la rapacité des manutentionnaires, et
exploiter au maximum tous les territoires à la disposition
de la République, pour parvenir à fournir le strict minimum
indispensable au déclenchement des opérations. Carnot
choisit et stimula un ministre de la Guerre honnête et laborieux, Pétiet, mais leurs efforts conjugués n'aboutirent
qu'à de médiocres effets. Cette situation résultait de l'organisation constitutionnelle qui assurait une indépendance
excessive à la Trésorerie. Celle-ci était régie par cinq commissaires, élus par les Conseils comme les Directeurs, et
formant une manière de quatrième pouvoir. Aussi, quand
il fut question d'organiser une république cispadane, en
avril 1797, Carnot prescrivit-il d'y faire nommer les commissaires de la Trésorerie par les Directeurs : « Nous nous
apercevons chaque jour qu'[un] autre ordre de choses amène
un tiraillement effroyable. »

De fait, tout gravita autour de l'impécuniosité incurable :
la guerre et la paix, la dépendance des généraux, l'autorité
du gouvernement [10].

Le problème posé par l'encadrement des troupes n'était
pas celui de la pénurie, mais de la pléthore : les officiers
surabondaient, on en comptait en moyenne un pour dix
hommes. Le Comité de Salut public avait adopté une solution
que Carnot appliqua sans en avoir suffisamment étudié les

conséquences. C'était la refonte des unités dont on réduisit le nombre pour accroître les effectifs des hommes et réduire celui des cadres.

La mesure était draconienne. Au lieu de 144 demi-brigades d'Infanterie, il n'y en aurait plus que 100 ; au lieu de 34 d'Infanterie légère, seulement 30 ; la Cavalerie était aussi réduite : 20 régiments de Cavalerie lourde, au lieu de 27 ; 12 de dragons et de chasseurs à cheval au lieu de 20 et de 23 ; 8 de hussards au lieu de 14.

L'Artillerie et le Génie conservaient seuls leurs effectifs : 16 régiments d'Artillerie — dont 8 à cheval — soit environ 30 000 hommes, y compris les ouvriers et 20 000 hommes dans le Génie, avec 400 officiers, 600 mineurs et 12 bataillons de sapeurs.

On supprimait 14 495 emplois d'officiers d'Infanterie de bataille sur 24 285 ; 1 139 officiers d'Infanterie légère sur 31 809 ; 1 170 officiers de troupes à cheval sur 3 880. Finalement on gardait 15 242 officiers et on en remerciait 15 634. Par bonheur il y avait nombre de postes vacants, et la suppression ne frappait qu'un tiers environ des emplois d'officiers. Le problème était ainsi résolu... sur le papier.

Comment choisir ceux qui resteraient ? Sous l'effet des habitudes administratives, on garda les plus anciens. Étaient-ils les meilleurs et les plus aptes à faire campagne ? Si l'on en croit le général Krieg, c'étaient les moins utilisables, de « vieilles mâchoires ».

Les autres ne pouvaient être laissés sans ressources. On leur attribua le tiers ou la moitié de leur traitement selon leur ancienneté, juste assez pour les empêcher de sombrer dans la misère. Ils étaient indignés et ne se gênaient pas pour clamer leur dégoût. C'était déjà le problème des demi-soldes. On les trouvait en groupes, chez les traiteurs et marchands de vin, menant grand train. Certains se faisaient entretenir par des filles. Ils étaient des recrues toutes désignées pour *Le Tribun du Peuple*. On leur enjoignit de quitter Paris. Ce n'était pas une solution. Leur rancœur se propagea, gagnant jusqu'à leurs camarades demeurés en fonctions et qui savaient désormais ce qui les attendait.

Un ancien collègue de Carnot, dans sa mission à l'armée du Nord, l'un de ceux qui lui avaient été les plus dévoués, Richard, lui écrivit à ce sujet, en mars 1796. Il lui signalait, en termes déférents, ces inconvénients et lui proposait d'y remédier en acceptant les démissions des officiers plus jeunes, maintenus aux armées, et qui pouvaient souhaiter de partir. « Ils ont assurément bien acquis ce droit après quatre années de campagne, et ceux qui seront jaloux d'une pareille exception seront à même de se la procurer au même prix. » Si cela ne suffisait pas, on pourrait attribuer aux demi-soldes les places réservées à l'ancienneté, et enfin mettre les derniers « à la suite » des unités, c'est-à-dire en excédent.

« Dans un moment comme celui-ci, les ménagements sont nécessaires en tout ce qui touche l'armée en grande masse. Le mécontentement est très grand dans toutes les armées. »

En fait, cette réforme précipitée ne fut jamais complètement appliquée : à peine publiée, il fallut la remanier. On avait d'abord décidé de conserver tous les officiers des troupes à cheval, quitte à verser provisoirement l'excédent dans l'Infanterie. Puis on avait résolu de conserver les sous-officiers en excédent comme surnuméraires. Enfin le 20 mars, au lendemain de la lettre de Richard, les généraux en chef avaient été autorisés à donner des congés de réforme aux officiers qui le désiraient et à conserver les officiers en surnombre comme officiers à la suite, avec leur traitement d'activité.

N'était-ce pas revenir sur la réforme et la condamner ? Celle-ci, d'ailleurs, était prématurée, comme le montra l'arrêté du 17 frimaire an V (7 décembre 1797), qui rappela tous les sous-lieutenants, lieutenants et capitaines démobilisés [11].

Le problème des cadres était aussi celui de leur entretien. La solde en papier-monnaie demeurait à peu près inutilisable. Il fallut accorder des secours en nature, théoriques le plus souvent. La misère fameuse de l'armée d'Italie à l'arrivée de Bonaparte lui était commune avec toutes les autres, et le dénuement des officiers mis en scène par Stendhal se retrouvait partout.

Aubry, successeur de Carnot à la direction du personnel, avait nommé tant de médiocres et de réactionnaires à des postes importants qu'il avait porté un coup au moral de l'armée. On avait réclamé une épuration, mais elle succédait à tant d'autres que les effets en étaient considérés comme provisoires ; d'autre part, rien ne prouve qu'elle fut judicieusement effectuée [12]. Les officiers exploitèrent les divisions politiques, s'appliquant à deviner quel parti l'emporterait, afin de le flatter, de l'aider à triompher, pour partager ensuite avec ses chefs les profits du pouvoir. L'armée

ouvrait une carrière aux ambitions. Pour les satisfaire, le
Directoire voulut, malgré l'article 368 de la constitution,
rétablir les distinctions honorifiques. D'où ce curieux arrêté
du 10 mars 1796 ridiculisant les croix, cordons et hochets du
despotisme, mais prévoyant des déclarations en faveur de
ceux qui ont bien mérité de la patrie, et la remise d'armes
d'honneur [13].

Pour maintenir le civisme, le Directoire envoyait les journaux aux armées ; Carnot fit créer, fin avril 1796, un quotidien officiel à leur usage, le *Journal des Défenseurs de la
Patrie*, comme il avait fait déjà, dans l'été 1794. C'était aussi
un moyen d'émulation, par la publication des hauts faits
individuels ou collectifs. Peu à peu ce journal supplanta les
autres, ceux qui précisément attaquaient Carnot, par exemple
L'Ami du Peuple [14].

Déjà les généraux étaient intervenus dans les luttes
civiles — Menou, Pichegru, Bonaparte. Leur ambition
rivalisa avec celle des hommes au pouvoir, certains faillirent
entrer au Directoire. Les militaires méprisaient de plus en
plus les civils, les « pékins ».

Des jalousies divisaient les armées, selon leurs succès, leurs
chefs, leurs misères respectives. On enviait l'armée du Nord,
qui recevait une solde en numéraire payée par la Hollande ;
mais les Hollandais refusaient de continuer à payer ces
troupes si elles quittaient leur pays pour participer aux
combats. Chaque armée souhaitait des conquêtes pour faire
cesser la pénurie et se dédommager.

Le grand remède à l'esprit prétorien des troupes et à
l'ambition des généraux avait été l'emploi de représentants
en mission aux armées. Il en restait encore quinze en fonction
au début du Directoire, quinze anciens Conventionnels,
répartis par trois entre les armées. Sept furent élus au Corps
législatif. Deux d'entre eux prirent immédiatement leurs
fonctions à l'Assemblée, Chiappe et Merlin de Thionville,
les autres restèrent à la disposition du Directoire, ainsi que
ceux qui n'avaient pas été réélus. Leurs fonctions furent
définies peu à peu par les soins de Carnot.

Il ne pouvait être question, sous ce régime constitutionnel,
de faire de ces agents du pouvoir exécutif des personnages
proconsulaires. Carnot les assimila aux divers commissaires
du Directoire qui surveillaient les administrations. Observateurs et non acteurs, ils encourageaient ou dénonçaient.
Ce statut s'expliquait pour des commissaires placés auprès

d'administrations élues ; il était moins logique pour des commissaires aux armées. Pourquoi, même « dans le cas d'urgence », Carnot voulait-il qu'ils n'intervinssent que « sur la demande écrite du général en chef ou du commissaire ordonnateur en chef » ? Avait-il une confiance si totale dans les généraux et dans les ordonnateurs ? Pourquoi n'avoir pas confié plus fermement aux commissaires les pouvoirs administratifs, la négociation des armistices et des traités ? Le problème capital des rapports entre les autorités civiles et militaires aurait été posé en termes plus favorables au régime.

Ainsi bridés, quelques commissaires jouèrent pourtant un rôle considérable. Ils n'étaient pas tous dévoués à Carnot, certains comme Rivaud et Haussmann étaient les hommes de Reubell. Même dans la direction du personnel de la Guerre Carnot devait donc compter avec ses collègues [15].

Les deux principales armées étaient alors celles de Sambre-et-Meuse commandée par Jourdan, et celle de Rhin-et-Moselle, commandée par Pichegru. L'un et l'autre disposaient d'une haute réputation, le premier passait pour plus patriote et jacobin, le second pour plus modéré — certains suspectaient même, à juste titre, sa conduite au cours des dernières opérations. Carnot les estimait l'un et l'autre et leur faisait confiance ; mais Jourdan avait gardé quelque ressentiment de la rudesse de Carnot ; quant à Pichegru, il poursuivait les fins politiques qui l'amenèrent à trahir le régime. Jourdan et Pichegru avaient signé — inconstitutionnellement — un armistice avec les Autrichiens, Carnot le fit observer à Jourdan, en rendant justice aux bonnes intentions du général, et l'armistice fut remplacé par celui que conclurent les commissaires du Directoire. Ainsi le principe était sauf, mais les armées restaient inactives. Cette inaction se prolongea au-delà de toute prévision.

Dans le domaine militaire comme dans le domaine diplomatique, c'était un faux départ ; mais les mécomptes militaires tenaient au régime plus qu'aux hommes.

La seule compensation — en attendant les succès de Bonaparte — était apportée par Hoche et ses victoires contre les insurgés de l'Ouest. Hoche était déjà en fonction, à l'arrivée de Carnot au pouvoir ; il avait donné la mesure de sa valeur. Carnot lui avait confié la haute direction, plaçant

les trois armées de l'Ouest sous son unique commandement,
renonçant à lui imposer un commissaire du Directoire, lui
demandant de rédiger lui-même les instructions sur la
conduite de la guerre et sur la pacification de l'Ouest. Le
général et le Directeur voulaient, l'un et l'autre, terminer au
plus vite cette lutte épuisante et sans gloire, ménager les
populations pour ne frapper que les chefs. Hoche eut donc les
mains libres.

Toutefois Carnot lui avait permis, le 13 janvier 1796, de
soumettre Charette et Stofflet, « et non de traiter avec eux
de puissance à puissance ». Or Hoche, en février, autorisa
Charette à fuir à l'étranger. Carnot censura Hoche et lui
prescrivit de saisir Charette et de le mettre à mort. Ainsi
Hoche risquait-il de se déshonorer en manquant à sa parole ;
il le fit remarquer à Carnot, sans refuser d'obéir, mais en
demandant qu'on employât des formes qui le missent à
l'abri d'une accusation de duplicité. La question fut résolue
par Charette lui-même, qui renonça à s'enfuir et préféra
continuer la lutte. L'incident avait prouvé la docilité de
Hoche, mais ne laissa-t-il pas quelque ressentiment, s'ajoutant à d'autres ? Il est remarquable que la correspondance
entre Hoche et Carnot fut constamment très officielle, bien
différente de celle qu'entretenait Carnot avec les autres
commandants d'armée, par exemple Bonaparte. Souvent
même elle n'était pas directe [16].

En février et mars, Stofflet et Charette furent pris et
mis à mort, puis les autres chefs posèrent les armes les uns
après les autres.

La pacification s'accomplissait. Hoche et son armée
devenaient disponibles pour lutter contre l'étranger au
moment où la victoire revenait sous nos drapeaux, du moins
en Italie.

CHAPITRE V

BONAPARTE, BRAVE MAIS BIEN JEUNE

Un lundi, aux premiers jours du Directoire, Beffroy de Reigny était chez Carnot au moment où se présenta un jeune général qui ne payait pas de mine.

« Qui est-ce ? demanda Beffroy.

— C'est le général de la force armée de Paris.

— Comment s'appelle-t-il ?

— Bonaparte.

— Est-ce un homme d'esprit ?

— Je n'en sais rien.

— A-t-il des talents militaires ?

— On le dit.

— Qu'a-t-il fait de remarquable ?

— C'est lui qui commandait les troupes de la Convention, le 13 vendémiaire. »

Bonaparte, héros de guerre civile, venait prendre les ordres, ses fonctions le plaçant à la disposition immédiate du Directoire, mais il brûlait d'obtenir un commandement pour donner sa mesure et faire carrière. Il lui fallait donc se faire apprécier des Directeurs, et spécialement de Carnot, qui dirigeait la Guerre. Bonaparte tenait alors en haute estime l'organisateur de la victoire et, nommé au Cabinet historique et topographique, il avait fait remarquer à son frère Joseph qu'il occupait la place de Carnot. Pour attirer l'attention du Directeur, Bonaparte lui présenta, remanié et complété, le célèbre plan d'opérations en Italie qu'il avait préparé au mois d'avril.

Le 19 janvier 1796, les projets de Bonaparte furent adoptés. Clarke venait d'écrire au général Schérer, qui commandait l'armée d'Italie ; il déplorait l'inertie de ces troupes, mais il s'y résignait. Carnot lui transmit le jour même le plan de Bonaparte, du coup la lettre déjà prête ne fut pas envoyée ; une autre la remplaça, où Carnot prescrivait, au nom du

Directoire, l'offensive immédiate sur des objectifs précis. Une nouvelle lettre, le 3 février, recommandait l'audace et non la lenteur « méthodique et quelque peu routinière », elle prescrivait la victoire sur les Sardes et l'armistice avec eux, selon les instructions et par l'intermédiaire du nouveau commissaire, Saliceti, qui venait d'être envoyé à l'armée d'Italie[1].

Les idées de Bonaparte s'imposaient donc, mais leur succès eût illustré Schérer, bien que l'origine du plan fût alors assez connue, comme le prouvent les allusions de Schérer et de Ritter. Schérer n'était pas l'homme que réclamait la situation, il s'écria que l'auteur d'un tel plan devait se charger de le réaliser et il démissionna. Le commissaire du Directoire attaché à l'armée d'Italie, Ritter, s'indignait plus violemment encore : « Souffriras-tu, écrivait-il à Letourneur, que l'armée d'Italie aille s'anéantir parce qu'il a plu à quelques forcenés *(sic)* de vous démontrer sur la carte... que l'on pouvait prendre la lune avec les dents[2] ? » Ritter fut rappelé.

L'heure était enfin venue, Bonaparte fut nommé, le 2 mars; date et décision historiques s'il en fut ! On a beaucoup chicané, dans la suite, pour savoir à qui appartenait l'honneur ou la responsabilité d'un tel choix. Barras s'en faisait gloire; peut-être intervint-il, bien que le mari de Joséphine dût passer à ses yeux pour un niais, comme on l'a justement remarqué[3]. Peut-être aussi Letourneur, mais il n'était pas en mesure d'imposer une décision. A coup sûr, Reubell regrettait Schérer et Ritter; quant à La Revellière, il faisait confiance à Carnot dans le domaine militaire. D'après Feulint, la nomination fut obtenue par Carnot, malgré Barras et Reubell, et contre le vœu de Feulint lui-même, qui redoutait l'ambition du jeune général[4].

Carnot, d'après Vaublanc, craignait plutôt l'inexpérience de Bonaparte. Le génie stratégique pouvait n'être pas accompagné des qualités du chef, surtout quand il s'agissait d'aller commander des Augereau et des Masséna. Il passa outre, et c'est lui qui doit demeurer le responsable : « Si Bonaparte eût échoué, déclara-t-il plus tard, c'est moi qui était le coupable; les autres ne se mêlaient point de la guerre, c'est sur moi que devait tomber la responsabilité[5]. »

Le nouveau général en chef devait demeurer subordonné au Directoire, lui soumettre les détails d'exécution, « autant que le temps et les circonstances permettront de le faire », et solliciter son assentiment « pour déterminer des mouvements militaires d'une importance majeure et qui n'auraient point été prévus». Ses fonctions seraient strictement militaires, le Directoire se réservant exclusivement la faculté de faire la paix et laissant à ses commissaires à l'armée d'Italie le soin de conclure les suspensions d'armes. Le commissaire Saliceti fut renforcé par Garrau, en qui Carnot pouvait avoir la confiance la plus absolue. Garrau serait-il de taille à contenir Bonaparte ? Sa carrière l'avait-elle préparé à conduire des négociations ? Son jugement était-il assez sûr et son caractère assez pondéré ? La nomination de Berthier comme chef d'état-major répondait au même souci, mais n'était pas une meilleure garantie, bien au contraire. Du moins Carnot serait-il informé ; il lui appartiendrait d'agir en conséquence [6].

* *

Les mesures concernant l'armée d'Italie s'inscrivaient dans un plan d'ensemble préparant la reprise des opérations. Coup sur coup, Moreau remplaçait Pichegru, Beurnonville était envoyé à l'armée du Nord, chacun d'eux recevait un chef d'état-major choisi par le Directoire et un nouveau commissaire. Carnot avait rédigé tous les arrêtés [7].

La reprise de la campagne était annoncée dans les lettres qu'il envoyait à Moreau et à Jourdan. Celui-ci devait se préparer à l'attaque pour libérer la rive gauche du Rhin, tandis que Moreau, franchissant le fleuve, envahirait la Souabe, et que Marceau assurerait la liaison. Déjà Carnot envisageait d'atteindre le Danube en combinant les efforts de l'armée d'Italie, comme diversion, à ceux des armées du Rhin.

Carnot faisait siennes les idées de Bonaparte, comme celles de Kellermann et de Sauviac [8].

Tout fut compromis par le dénuement des armées qui ne permit pas aux généraux d'entamer les opérations. Seul Bonaparte osa prendre la misère pour appui en faisant miroiter l'abondance. Quand l'armistice fut rompu sur le Rhin par les Autrichiens, le 21 mai, Bonaparte avait obtenu des résultats qui le mettaient hors de pair : il était victorieux, célèbre, puissant, presque indépendant.

Carnot, cependant, s'appliquait à le diriger, à le suivre, à le conseiller ; il voulait collaborer à son œuvre et la faire servir les vues militaires et diplomatiques du Directoire. Dialogue passionnant, dont on peut suivre toutes les reparties, enrichies des observations faites dans la suite par les deux interlocuteurs.

Au départ, Bonaparte devait suivre un plan, paraphrase de celui qu'il avait lui-même fourni, à quelques variantes près qu'il jugeait sévèrement à Sainte-Hélène : « Cette instruction est une mauvaise amplification, pleine de contradictions et de bêtises, d'un mémoire bref et lumineux que Napoléon avait présenté au Directoire, en janvier 1796. » Carnot avait recommandé « un système de guerre offensive », excluant les nombreux sièges qu'une campagne méthodique aurait exigés dans le Piémont. Il prescrivait pourtant la prise de plusieurs places — Tortone, Gavi, Ceva. Napoléon releva avec une humeur hautaine cette contradiction. Il exagérait certes, mais la divergence n'est pas contestable entre les vues de Carnot et celles de Bonaparte. Il restait toujours quelque chose du fortificateur en Carnot, par exemple quand il signalait le risque représenté par la garnison de Coni, tandis que Bonaparte voyait les problèmes à une autre échelle : « Ce n'est pas la garnison de Coni qui nuira, c'est toute l'armée piémontaise, la nation en marche[9]. » Ces indications tardives soulignent l'aspect militaire d'un débat qui était à peine perceptible en 1796. A cette époque le Directeur et le général rivalisaient d'amabilité : « Toute la France, toute l'Europe, ont les yeux fixés sur vous », écrivait Carnot après les premières victoires. « Ce projet est digne de vous, de l'armée et des destinées de la France, s'écriait Bonaparte. Je chercherai constamment à vous donner des preuves du zèle et de la bonne volonté où je suis de mériter votre estime et celle de la patrie[10]. »

Éperdument amoureux et pleinement confiant dans le Directeur, Bonaparte lui confiait même ses soucis intimes. « Je vous dois des remerciements particuliers pour les attentions que vous voulez bien avoir pour ma femme ; je vous la recommande, elle est patriote sincère et je l'aime à la folie. » Il lui écrivit même en termes plus vifs : « Je suis au désespoir, ma femme ne vient pas. Elle a quelque amant qui la retient à Paris. Je maudis toutes les femmes, mais j'embrasse de bon cœur mes bons amis[11]. »

Toutefois le général s'émancipait. On lui avait interdit de négocier, « quelle ignorance de la guerre, quelle jalousie des généraux », écrivait-il à Sainte-Hélène. Qu'importe ! Il avait pris sur lui d'accorder une suspension d'armes aux Piémontais. Il s'agissait de faire accepter cette infraction. Coup

sur coup, dans trois lettres, il s'enquit en termes pressants :
« Je suis fort inquiet de savoir si ma réponse est conforme
à vos intentions. » « Si je n'avais pas rempli votre but, écrivait-il le lendemain, ce serait le plus grand malheur que je
puisse imaginer. » Enfin, deux jours plus tard, il concluait :
« Je ne puis mettre en doute que vous n'approuviez ma
conduite. » Bonaparte avait tenu à mettre à l'écart les diplomates et les commissaires. « Cela me regarde seul », avait-il
déclaré à Faipoult. Il se fit appuyer de tous côtés. Saliceti
écrivit à Carnot une lettre exceptionnellement amicale :
« Adieu, mon cher Carnot, continue-moi ton affection et ta
confiance, mon désir est de les mériter. » Joseph Bonaparte
se rendit à Paris, muni d'une lettre personnelle de Napoléon
à Barras. Ce luxe de précautions réussit ; le 5 mai arrivait une
lettre du Directoire, datée du 25 avril, qui apportait des
instructions diplomatiques et se reposait sur la prudence du
général « dans ces transactions ». Le Directoire approuvait en
rappelant pourtant que le commissaire devait seul traiter
pour la paix, un traité était préparé, auquel Carnot avait
mis la main [12].

Triomphe ou désastre ?... La lettre d'approbation prescrivait aussi la division de l'armée en deux ; une partie, sous
Bonaparte, marcherait sur Livourne et intimiderait Gênes,
Rome et Naples, l'autre, commandée par Kellermann, occu-
perait le Milanais en attendant de pénétrer dans le Tyrol.

L'indignation de Napoléon n'était pas apaisée à Sainte-
Hélène : « On se demande ce qui avait pu faire adopter
au Directoire un plan aussi bête.... Les uns ont prétendu que
cela provenait de la jalousie naissante..., d'autres ont cru
que ce plan était l'effet de l'ignorance.... Toutefois, Napoléon,
en demandant sa démission plutôt que de souscrire à une
mesure si désastreuse, a de nouveau sauvé l'Italie et son
armée. »

Quand il ajoute que la lettre arriva peu avant l'entrée à
Milan, au moment même où il était saisi par la grande
ambition du pouvoir suprême, on comprend mieux sa déconvenue. Il se garda bien de rien brusquer. Il écrivit une lettre
personnelle à Carnot, annonçant sa marche prochaine sur
Livourne, comme il lui était prescrit, et lui confiant une
lettre officiellement adressée au Directoire, pour refuser le
partage de l'armée d'Italie. Astucieusement, il observait :
« Comme il serait possible que cette lettre... ne fût pas bien
interprétée, et que vous m'avez témoigné de l'amitié, je

prends le parti de vous l'adresser en vous priant d'en faire l'usage que vous suggéreront votre prudence et votre attachement pour moi. » Suivaient de vives protestations de respect et de dévouement. Ce qui lui permettait d'écrire dans la lettre officielle : « Je ne puis rendre à la patrie des services essentiels qu'investi entièrement et absolument de votre confiance. »

Si Carnot s'était inquiété de l'ambition du général, ces lettres auraient dû confirmer ses craintes. Il n'en fut rien. Sans doute avait-il simplement jugé que les opérations dans la péninsule exigeaient qu'un autre général vînt dans le Milanais. Or Kellermann avait été associé à la préparation de la campagne ; Bonaparte même avait prétendu, le 28 avril : « Je puis en même temps marcher du côté de Naples et de Mantoue. »

Carnot accepta les protestations de Bonaparte et lui répondit personnellement en termes flatteurs : « Nous avons à cœur que personne ne partage avec vous le titre que vous avez mérité seul, celui de vainqueur de l'Italie. » Il était loin d'imaginer ce que vaudrait ce titre, qu'il donnait volontiers à Bonaparte dans les articles du *Rédacteur* et les discours officiels, sans parler des communiqués de Berthier et de Bonaparte qu'il faisait publier, forgeant ainsi les premiers anneaux de la légende napoléonienne. Délicatement il ajoutait, comme au temps des poésies de l'*Almanach des Muses* : « C'est à grand regret que nous cédons au vœu de la citoyenne Bonaparte qui va vous joindre. Nous avions peur que les soins que vous allez lui donner ne vous détournassent de ceux auxquels la gloire et le salut de la patrie vous appellent, et nous avions résisté longtemps à son vœu [13]. »

C'en était fait, Bonaparte avait forcé le destin grâce à la faiblesse ou à l'erreur de Carnot. Désormais l'amitié régna entre les deux hommes : Bonaparte était pour l'un « mon cher général », et Carnot, pour l'autre, était « mon cher Directeur ». Le général adoptait un style flatteur digne de Talleyrand : « La récompense la plus douce des fatigues, des dangers, des chances de ce métier-ci se trouve dans l'estime du petit nombre que l'on apprécie. Je mériterai votre estime, je vous prie de me continuer la vôtre et de me croire pour la vie... », écrivait-il le 8 juin. Il prenait pourtant assez d'autorité pour conseiller Carnot en politique intérieure : « Faites en sorte de renverser à Paris toutes les factions. Nous sommes souvent très inquiets sur les bruits qu'on fait courir à chaque

instant dans l'étranger. Le pauvre Directoire *(sic)* périt
souvent, mais je crois qu'avec du courage et un seul point
de ralliement on ne périt jamais que les armes à la main. »

Notons bien que Bonaparte, à ce moment, avait déjà
proposé d'intervenir, par l'intermédiaire de Junot, le 9 mai,
avec l'armée d'Italie, « prête à comprimer les ennemis de
l'intérieur qui tenteraient d'anéantir le gouvernement républicain et la constitution de 1795 [14] ». Carnot aurait-il pu
provoquer l'avènement de Bonaparte dès cette époque, en
s'associant à lui ? Il écarta ces offres, jugées superflues :
« L'horizon politique s'éclaircit sensiblement à Paris, et
j'éprouve, mon cher et digne général, une grande satisfaction à vous dire que vos triomphes ont fait en cela plus que
tout le reste. » Il ajoutait d'aimables paroles sur Joséphine ;
« Elle emporte bien particulièrement les regrets de toute ma
famille, je vous prie de lui en donner l'assurance, quand vous
l'allez voir, comme elle vous donnera celle de mon inviolable attachement pour tout ce qui vous appartient [15]. »

Bonaparte ne demeurait pas en reste ; il félicita Carnot le
2 juillet, pour la naissance de son fils, sur un ton amical qui
était celui d'un égal. A la requête du général, Carnot prit
soin de Lucien Bonaparte, « mauvaise tête » et qui avait la
« fureur de se mêler de politique », et qui avait fait le Jacobin
en 1793, malgré les recommandations de Napoléon — osait
écrire sérieusement celui-ci.

Ainsi appuyé sur Carnot, Bonaparte en prenait de plus en
plus à son aise. Coup sur coup — le 9 mai et le 6 juin — il
avait signé, sans ordres du Directoire et sans avoir consulté
Saliceti, deux armistices, l'un avec le duc de Parme, et
l'autre avec le roi de Naples. Il déclarait tranquillement à
Miot de Mélito : « Les commissaires du Directoire n'ont rien
à voir dans ma politique [16]. » Ainsi se permit-il, le 20 mai, de
faire payer la solde moitié en numéraire, ce qui fit de ses
officiers et de ses soldats des priviligiés, attachés à leur armée,
jalousés par les autres. Le Directoire maugréait, mais s'inclinait. N'était-il pas tributaire, lui aussi, des gains et du
butin de Bonaparte [17] ?

La politique italienne de l'armée fut en contradiction avec
la volonté du gouvernement. Bonaparte et Saliceti patronnaient les patriotes italiens au moment même où Carnot
recommandait de « ne pas compromettre notre liberté en
voulant fonder celle des autres ». Qu'il s'agît du Milanais, de
Gênes ou du pape, Bonaparte poursuivait « sa politique [18] ».

Garrau venait d'arriver auprès de Bonaparte, au début de juin. Il comprit promptement les risques d'une telle situation et les indiqua, le 30 juin, à Carnot : « Il est permis à un jeune homme de vingt-cinq à trente ans, qui à la tête de cinquante mille républicains a, en deux mois, conquis ou soumis presque toute l'Italie, d'avoir l'amour de la célébrité. Mais je désirerais que cette passion, louable en elle-même, ne devînt pas funeste à la chose publique [19] ».

Garrau, trop perspicace, fut promptement calomnié, vilipendé, discrédité à l'armée d'Italie. Intègre, il fut persécuté par la multitude des trafiquants de tout poil qui pullulaient à l'armée, parmi les chefs, parmi les services, parmi les fournisseurs.

Mais Carnot ne fit rien pour soutenir son commissaire et ami. Garrau n'avait-il pas écrit pour dénoncer les risques de la politique intérieure de Carnot ? N'appuyait-il pas la politique de propagande de Bonaparte et de Saliceti auprès des patriotes italiens ? Garrau fut blâmé et comprit qu'il devait s'effacer : « Adieu, écrivit-il à Carnot le 18 septembre, je ne te demande que la continuation de ton estime et de ton amitié [20] ».

Carnot refusa cette démission ; son ami resta en fonctions tant que les commissaires furent maintenus aux armées, mais le coup n'en était pas moins fort, Bonaparte l'avait emporté.

* *

A la même époque Carnot éprouvait des déboires en Allemagne, au lieu des grandes victoires qui eussent assuré la paix : Bonaparte n'avait-il pas proposé, le 11 mai, de pénétrer en Bavière, après la prise de Mantoue, et de combiner son action avec celle des armées du Rhin ?

Celles-ci, dans le plan de Carnot, devaient marcher sur Vienne en convergeant à partir de Coblentz et de Strasbourg. Les attaques et les manœuvres, alliant la prudence à l'audace, devaient bousculer l'ennemi, le chasser, le tourner et le détruire. Pour y parvenir, Jourdan et Moreau devaient suivre les indications de Carnot, combiner leur action et prendre les initiatives nécessaires.

Au début de la campagne, la plus grande confiance unissait le Directeur et les deux généraux en chef. « Je tiens pour sûr que Jourdan va se couvrir d'une gloire immortelle », avait écrit Carnot à Garrau. En janvier, Jourdan était venu à Paris travailler avec Carnot. Moreau n'était venu à Paris qu'en avril, mais le ton de sa correspondance avec Carnot atteste l'estime et la confiance réciproques.

Les entretiens personnels furent complétés par deux lettres — des 29 mars et 10 avril. Jourdan, installé sur la rive droite, attaquerait l'ennemi et se porterait sur la Lahn, laissant un cordon protecteur et détachant vingt-cinq mille hommes sous Marceau pour couvrir la Sarre. L'adversaire ainsi fixé, Moreau ferait franchir le Rhin par Marceau et s'emploierait à nettoyer la rive droite. L'Autrichien, surpris au moment où il s'apprêterait à accabler Jourdan, devrait revenir vers le sud et sa volte-face offrirait à Jourdan l'occasion de l'écraser.

Les généraux objectèrent que leurs armées n'étaient pas prêtes et que tout risquait d'être déjoué par une offensive autrichienne. Ils contestaient aussi le mouvement du corps de Marceau, et le choix de ce général qui ne connaissait pas le pays. Carnot admit ces objections et autorisa l'assouplissement de ses instructions.

D'autre part, il tenta d'épauler l'action stratégique par les intrigues d'un agent secret, Poterat, qui se flattait de soulever l'Allemagne du Sud. Moreau lui déclara qu'un tel aventurier ne pouvait inspirer confiance.

Les Autrichiens étaient commandés par l'archiduc Charles, chef de vingt-deux ans, plus redoutable que les vieilles culottes de peau qu'il remplaçait. Ils étaient un peu plus nombreux que les Français et disposaient d'une meilleure cavalerie.

L'archiduc rompit l'armistice le 21 mai.

Moreau n'était pas prêt, Jourdan fut battu. Carnot dut harceler Moreau, lui faire passer des fonds que fournissait Bonaparte, le stimuler sans cesse : « Les moments sont chers, il faut les rendre décisifs. » Carnot prescrivait une guerre « audacieuse et terrible », des marches « rapides et imprévues », il citait Bonaparte en exemple. C'était enfin cette guerre de destruction dont on parlait depuis si longtemps. Mais Carnot ne pouvait fournir que ces conseils, si généraux, et Moreau était circonspect. L'archiduc Charles a dit tout le profit qu'il tira de cette lenteur.

En revanche, Jourdan obtint des succès, mais sans écraser l'adversaire. Il s'excusa : « Si je n'agis pas toujours comme vous le désirez... la faute n'en peut être imputée qu'à mon peu de valeur..., il y a quatre ans, je ne me doutais pas que j'occuperais le poste dont je suis honoré. »

Malgré tout, Jourdan s'avançait au long du Mein et Moreau gagnait le Danube, déjà Carnot les voyait convergeant sur Ratisbonne et Vienne. Il songeait à soulever la Bohême et la Hongrie....

De son côté Moreau déclarait, le 7 juillet : « On peut comparer notre marche à celle de l'armée d'Italie ; depuis le passage du Rhin, nous avons livré cinq combats et deux batailles que nous avons tous gagnés [21]. »

Il appartenait à Carnot de conjuguer les efforts des armées du Rhin et de l'armée d'Italie.

Précisément cette armée procédait à des sièges ; n'était-ce pas la spécialité de Carnot ? Le 18 juin la tranchée avait été ouverte devant la citadelle de Milan, le 29, celle-ci capitulait. Carnot recommanda de détruire cette bastille symbolique, instrument de la tyrannie autrichienne ; il restait fidèle aux idées qu'il avait présentées à la Législative [22].

Il s'agissait ensuite de prendre Mantoue, clef de la région, gage des échecs et des succès, de la perte ou de la prise de l'Italie. Bonaparte annonça qu'il allait procéder au siège. Carnot intervint : « Si le Directoire avait sous les yeux un aperçu des vivres qui peuvent être dans cette place, il eût pu déterminer *(sic)* s'il était préférable d'ouvrir la tranchée ou de se contenter d'un simple blocus. » Reproche effacé aussitôt, en considération de l'extrême insalubrité des marécages avoisinants. De plus, Carnot faisait confiance à l'officier du Génie qui dirigeait les opérations. Celui-ci, Chasseloup, était un excellent technicien et un caractère rudement trempé ; il ne s'était pas toujours bien accordé avec Carnot, ni avec Bonaparte.

La tranchée fut ouverte le 18 juillet. Bonaparte tenta de pénétrer dans les lieux par surprise, ce que Carnot approuva, un peu doctoralement : « Les stratagèmes et les coups de main audacieux sont en effet une partie essentielle de l'art d'attaquer les places [23]. »

L'entreprise tourna court. On apprit soudain que le général autrichien Wurmser s'avançait à la tête d'une armée pour sauver Mantoue. Une fois de plus, comme à Wattignies, mais en sens inverse, une armée de secours faisait lever un siège. Bonaparte n'avait ni le temps ni le désir de consulter qui que ce fût : il abandonna la place. La centaine de pièces d'artillerie de siège, si difficilement rassemblées, fut jetée dans les marais, et l'armée d'Italie fit face à l'assaillant le 31 juillet.

Bonaparte se trouvait en difficulté, il parvint cependant à redresser la situation au cours de la manœuvre de Castiglione. Carnot ne tenta ni de le morigéner, ni de l'endoctriner, mais il reconnut, en dépit des termes voilés de la correspondance d'Italie, toute la gravité de la situation : « Nos succès sont grands, disait-il ensuite à Sandoz-Rollin, ministre de la Prusse à Paris ; ils ont tenu néanmoins à peu de chose. » Et il ajoutait ces mots, qui montrent Carnot, fort de son âge et de son passé, juge et critique de Bonaparte : « Le général Bonaparte a eu besoin de tout son sang-froid et de toute sa capacité pour n'être pas déjoué par la fortune. Il a failli être la victime de deux fautes : d'avoir trop dispersé son armée, et d'avoir trop méprisé son ennemi. »

Carnot ne fit pas observer à Bonaparte que le Génie — c'est-à-dire Chasseloup — affirmait que Mantoue aurait pu être enlevé la nuit même où le siège avait été abandonné. Il le félicita pour la victoire de Castiglione.

Il faut dire que Bonaparte donna lieu de penser que cette victoire avait été totale, au point que Carnot, le 23 août, le mit en posture de se joindre à Moreau, alors qu'il était urgent de refaire l'armée d'Italie, sur qui allait fondre une nouvelle menace [24].

Exactement à la même date, Jourdan battait en retraite devant l'archiduc Charles, qui avait massé la plus grande partie des Autrichiens contre lui. C'était l'effet d'un manque de coordination entre Moreau et Jourdan, imputable à Moreau, mais aussi à Carnot. Celui-ci avait pressé Jourdan d'avancer, même sans être assuré de l'avance de Moreau. Il l'avait aussi maintenu loin de Moreau, vers le nord. C'est qu'il voulait, d'une part, précipiter les opérations, et de l'autre exploiter les ressources de la région du Mein.

La retraite de Jourdan fut désordonnée, l'armée se décomposait. Le général, désespéré, démissionna, il écrivit à Carnot pour le prier de faire accepter cette démission, il lui répétait, à cette occasion, sa confiance et son attachement en raison de tant de témoignages de bonté qu'il avait reçus de lui. Jourdan fut porté au commandement de l'armée du Nord, pour s'y reposer provisoirement.

Mais la campagne était manquée. L'armée de Jourdan étant revenue en deçà du Rhin, Moreau ramena la sienne sur ce fleuve, par une retraite méthodique et peut-être trop célébrée.

Carnot était indigné, désolé, il dénonçait la « misérable

reculade » de Jourdan. Sans doute admirait-il la retraite de
Moreau, « son cher Fabius », mais tous ses plans n'en étaient
pas moins anéantis, et ceux qui l'approchaient notaient
que, malgré ses efforts, « son dépit et son chagrin se déce-
laient à chaque instant [25] ».

Bonaparte, au contraire, menait brillamment les opérations qui enfermèrent Wurmser dans Mantoue. Il annonçait
victoires et profits : « L'armée d'Italie a produit dans la campagne d'été 20 millions à la République... elle peut en produire le double pendant la campagne d'hiver [26]. » Son prestige
croissait, le Directoire attendait la chute prochaine de la
place ; déjà il envisageait la fin de la guerre.

Or ce fut une troisième armée de secours qui survint,
menée par Allvinczi. L'armée d'Italie fut à son tour en péril,
mais Bonaparte, après tant de victoires, ne pouvait être
traité comme Jourdan, il le savait. Aussi cette fois, loin de
dissimuler les risques, il jugea opportun de les exagérer pour
obtenir de puissants renforts : « Je désespère, écrivit-il le
13 novembre, d'empêcher le déblocus de Mantoue. L'armée
d'Italie, réduite à une poignée de monde, est épuisée.... Nous
serons bientôt derrière l'Adda, et plus loin, s'il n'arrive pas
de troupes. »

Carnot fournit des renforts. Bonaparte accomplit la
manœuvre d'Arcole. Carnot admira et félicita Bonaparte.
Ce fut lui qui rédigea le message annonçant la nouvelle au
Corps législatif. Mais il confiait à Sandoz-Rollin : « Bonaparte
est brave, mais il est bien jeune, il ne prévoit pas assez le
danger et il n'agit que par impétuosité. » De fait, l'épisode
fameux du pont d'Arcole montrait tout ensemble la bravoure du général, mais aussi une sous-estimation des
risques, puisque — contrairement à la légende — la colonne
commandée par Bonaparte ne put franchir le pont. Il n'en
reste pas moins que la manœuvre d'ensemble fut admirable.
Carnot vantait les « ressources » du génie de Bonaparte [27].

Cependant les difficultés restaient assez grandes, et l'indépendance de la politique de Bonaparte assez redoutable,
pour que le Directoire voulût éviter de nouveaux retours
de fortune ; il décida de tenter de négocier avec l'Autriche.

Dans l'intervalle, la paix avait été signée avec Naples,
le 10 octobre 1796. Carnot avait été mêlé aux négociations,
c'est même lui qui les avait fait aboutir [28].

CHAPITRE VI

LA GUERRE ET LA PAIX EN L'AN V

LA VICTOIRE de Bonaparte, les armistices qu'il avait imposés acheminaient la guerre vers sa conclusion logique :
la paix générale. La nation, les Conseils, le Directoire
voulaient cette paix. Carnot avait souvent secondé Reubell
dans la conduite de la politique extérieure, l'ambassadeur
de Prusse les désignait l'un et l'autre comme « les plus
influents ». Mais, dans les derniers mois de 1796, Carnot
prit une part à la fois plus directe et plus indépendante. Il
mena de front la guerre et les négociations, il les fit converger vers un but commun, la paix, sur des ennemis enfin
lassés et convaincus de la possibilité d'une coexistence
pacifique du régime français, issu de la Révolution, et des
États européens de l'Ancien Régime.

La politique nouvelle de Carnot, hostile aux Jacobins, aux
Exclusifs, le détachait aussi de leurs tendances à développer
la propagande et les conquêtes, pour l'incliner vers les
Modérés, désireux de conclure une paix prompte, donc
généreuse, et, par là même, pensaient-ils, plus durable. On
sent l'hostilité que lui porte un Mangourit, secrétaire de
l'ambassade de Madrid, hostile à l'influence diplomatique
des militaires [1].

Lors des offensives sur le Rhin et en Italie, les armées
avaient été accompagnées ou précédées d'agents politiques
chargés de fournir des renseignements, de préparer les voies
et d'amorcer des négociations éventuelles. Dans ces conditions, un Allemand, Zwanziger, avait eu l'occasion de venir
à Paris ; Clarke et Carnot l'avaient reçu ; ainsi était né ce
qu'on eût appelé, naguère, le secret de Carnot.

Sans informer Reubell, ni le ministre Delacroix, qu'il
voulait faire remplacer, Carnot envoya Zwanziger à Vienne
porter des propositions de paix à l'Autriche. Le projet
avorta, car les conditions envisagées, assez dures pour

l'Autriche, ne correspondaient plus à une situation militaire affaiblie. Mais l'entreprise fut un précédent que répéta Carnot, dans des conditions plus officielles, avec la mission de Clarke [2].

Le directeur du Cabinet topographique, tout dévoué à Carnot, au point de l'appeler son « bienfaiteur » dans la plupart de ses lettres, fut proposé par Carnot et désigné par le Directoire, le 16 novembre 1796, pour se rendre à Vienne en qualité de négociateur extraordinaire. Il devait proposer un armistice général et savoir si la République pourrait traiter avec l'Empereur seul, et sur quelles bases. S'il était revêtu d'une mission officielle par la collectivité directoriale, il n'en restait pas moins l'agent personnel de Carnot, en correspondance particulière avec lui, couverte au besoin par un chiffre spécial. C'est le prolongement du secret de Carnot [3].

A peine fut-il nommé que la presse l'attaqua. Un article de *La Gazette nationale*, reproduit par *L'Ami des Lois*, désormais violemment hostile à Carnot, le présentait comme l'adversaire de Bonaparte. Ce fut le point de départ d'une campagne venimeuse, menée pour dresser Bonaparte contre Carnot et contre les Modérés et pour exploiter le prestige de Bonaparte au détriment du Directeur et de ses amis, réels ou supposés. On en vint à écrire, au début de janvier, que le principal objet de la mission de Clarke était de « surveiller Bonaparte et de saisir la première circonstance favorable pour le faire arrêter ».

Tout n'était pas absolument inexact dans cette accusation. Il se trouvait que Clarke avait été chargé, subsidiairement et après coup, de renseigner le Directoire sur « la situation morale, politique et militaire des armées françaises en Italie et en Allemagne », et de fournir des notes sur « la moralité et les talents » des principaux chefs. Non seulement cette mission était secondaire, mais ce n'est pas Carnot qui en avait pris l'initiative : elle appartenait à La Revellière [4].

Peu importe, l'antagonisme entre Carnot et Bonaparte tenait plus à la situation qu'aux dispositions personnelles : Carnot et le Directoire voulaient un armistice général, immédiat, définitif, pendant lequel une négociation d'ensemble préparerait la paix. Un tel projet contrariait les desseins de Bonaparte, tout autant que l'arrêté qui avait prescrit naguère la division de l'armée d'Italie. Déjà l'oppoistion s'était affirmée à propos de la politique italienne, à Turin comme à Milan. Nécessairement l'un ou l'autre devrait céder, Bonaparte ou le gouvernement.

D'étranges informations étaient publiées, tantôt l'on affirmait l'arrivée de Clarke à Vienne et ses discussions avec le ministre Thugut, tantôt on déplorait que Clarke eût réussi à dresser Berthier et l'état-major contre Bonaparte, en même temps qu'il promettait la restitution de la Lombardie à l'Autriche : « Quelle trahison ! » Au même moment, les patriotes lombards déclaraient que le Directoire les autorisait à former une « république démocratique à l'exemple de celle de la France [5] ».

En fait, Clarke, loin de vouloir « espionner » Bonaparte, tenta de gagner Vienne directement, sans même avoir vu le général en chef ; ce fut l'Autriche qui ne se prêta pas à ce dessein et l'amena auprès de Bonaparte, où l'opposition des deux politiques, celle du Directoire et celle du général de l'armée d'Italie, éclata dès le premier jour.

Au moment où Clarke rencontra Bonaparte, le 29 novembre, Carnot écrivait au vainqueur d'Arcole pour le féliciter, et il saisissait cette occasion pour insister sur la nécessité de la paix [6]. Cette nécessité était ressentie par tout le Directoire, qui devint de plus en plus pressant. Carnot fut pourtant pris à partie personnellement parce que Clarke était son agent, et l'on continua de les accuser tous deux de saper l'œuvre de Bonaparte. Carnot en vint donc à se justifier auprès du général, sollicitant un témoignage dont il pût se servir pour mettre fin à ces attaques irritantes.

« Il me suffira, je pense, écrivait Carnot le 29 décembre, de vous assurer que tout ceci est une affaire d'intrigue et de cabale, que vous, Bonaparte, votre femme et tout ce qui vous appartient, n'avez pas d'amis plus chauds, plus sincères, plus identifiés à vos intérêts personnels, que moi et tous les miens. » Carnot incriminait ces « énergumènes, infâmes brigands, égorgeurs », qui se réclamaient de Bonaparte et voulaient révolutionner l'Italie, et qui traitaient Carnot de royaliste. Il affirmait l'identité des vues entre son correspondant et lui-même : « Je suis certain qu'il n'y a pas deux manières de voir plus conformes qu'entre vous et moi », c'est pourquoi il terminait par une promesse d'appui mutuel dans le cadre d'une politique modérée : « Adieu, mon cher général, comptez sur moi comme je compte sur vous, avec tous les hommes sages qui aiment la République pour elle et non pour eux. Mille choses obligeantes de toute ma famille à votre chère moitié. »

Clarke était informé par Carnot de cette démarche pour « dissiper le nuage », et c'est lui qui rassurait son protecteur en lui répondant, le 7 janvier, que la lettre avait « fait grand plaisir au général [7] ».

Celui-ci tarda jusqu'au 28 janvier, où il répondit aimablement. Pourquoi ce délai ? Sans doute parce que, dans l'intervalle, la situation fut renversée, Clarke fut subordonné à Bonaparte. Il devait se « concerter entièrement avec lui sur la négociation, et ne rien proposer ni faire aucunes démarches sans que Bonaparte les ait trouvées conformes aux intérêts de la République et à la sûreté de son armée ». Un tel retournement a surpris les contemporains, blessé Clarke, réjoui Bonaparte, qui s'empressa d'écrire à Carnot : « J'ai toujours à me louer des marques d'amitié que vous m'avez données, à moi et aux miens, et je vous en conserverai toujours une vraie reconnaissance. » Nous avons là un élément de réponse à la question posée par le retournement des relations entre Clarke et Bonaparte ; il s'agissait pour Carnot de prouver que les imputations de la presse étaient calomnieuses, et il crut pouvoir en user ainsi sans inconvénient, puisqu'il estimait être d'accord avec Bonaparte sur la politique à suivre [8].

Clarke n'en pouvait croire ses yeux : « Je vous le demande, citoyen Directeur, mandait-il à Carnot, est-il possible qu'un concert parfait puisse exister entre le général Bonaparte et moi ? » Bonaparte aurait-il l'intention d'adopter la politique du Directoire ? Peut-on assurer qu'il veuille la paix ? Et le malheureux Clarke, désemparé, décida que, désormais, en cas de dissentiment entre Bonaparte et lui, il s'adresserait non au Directoire, mais à Carnot ou à Dupont. Pour souligner cet émoi, le secrétaire Perret écrivait aussi à Carnot, le même jour, dans le même sens. Carnot pansa les blessures d'amour-propre, sans rien changer au fond des choses, et Clarke prit le parti de s'accorder avec Bonaparte [9].

Finalement, l'initiative de Carnot pour conduire promptement les négociations de paix aboutissait à un échec, imputable à ses illusions sur Bonaparte.

Au même moment, Carnot venait d'essuyer un autre échec, celui de l'expédition d'Irlande.

L'animosité de Carnot contre l'Angleterre était particulièrement vive. C'était, à tous égards, le principal ennemi,

celui qui soudoyait et renouvelait les coalitions et les soulèvements, celui qui visait à la domination économique en
captant le commerce maritime, celui enfin qui confisquait
les colonies arrachées aux États continentaux, spécialement
à la France. C'est à propos de l'Angleterre qu'on saisit l'articulation de la politique extérieure de Carnot avec ses idées
économiques, et qu'on peut observer sa préoccupation
de rétablir les colonies. Depuis longtemps Carnot avait
rassemblé une documentation sur ces questions [10].

Pour frapper l'Angleterre, Carnot s'était acharné à la
conquête de la Flandre et de la Belgique, mais ce n'était
encore qu'une étape. L'essentiel serait la « descente» en
Angleterre d'un corps expéditionnaire nombreux.

Carnot n'avait jamais perdu de vue ce dessein. Au début
d'avril 1796, alors qu'il escomptait la victoire et la paix sur
le continent, il avait confié à Sandoz-Rollin : « L'Angleterre restera seule en guerre, il faudra voir alors comment
elle supportera un débarquement de 200 000 hommes
sur ses côtes.» Le tour pris par les opérations militaires
avait ajourné l'expédition, mais Carnot ne cessait de la
préparer ; il s'entourait de projets nombreux, anciens et
récents, qui affluaient de toutes parts. Il envoyait en Angleterre des espions, comme ce négociant bordelais, Berthon-
neau, que lui avait recommandé Garrau [11].

A défaut de la grande opération, Carnot envisagea l'organisation d'un débarquement assez étrange, constitué par
des bandits, déserteurs, forçats en rupture de ban, galériens
évadés et assassins de profession. L'idée paraît appartenir
à Hoche, qui ne trouvait pas d'autre moyen de purger l'Ouest
de la France. Hoche serait promu au rang de « nouveau
Duguesclin», formule adroite pour draper dans de glorieux
souvenirs un projet assez sordide [12].

Un patriote irlandais, Wolfe Tone, fit adopter un dessein
plus avouable et plus efficace : l'envoi d'un corps expéditionnaire qui soutiendrait, contre les Anglais, les *defenders*,
ou Irlandais soulevés. Les premiers entretiens entre Carnot
et Wolfe Tone remontaient à la fin de février 1796, le temps
avait passé et Tone désespérait, lorsque les préparatifs
s'étaient soudain amorcés au début de l'été. Carnot avait
pressenti Hoche avant de lui confier le commandement ;
il lui avait écrit, le 22 juin, en termes flatteurs, pour lui
demander si cette tâche lui convenait et l'assurer qu'il se
plaisait à lui ouvrir une nouvelle carrière glorieuse. Puis

W. Tone, Hoche et Carnot avaient étudié les détails de l'opération, et Carnot avait rédigé les instructions, après avoir examiné les problèmes maritimes avec l'amiral Truguet, ministre de la Marine. C'est Carnot personnellement qui avait fait adopter le projet par le Directoire et qui en avait arrêté les dispositions ; mais il avait voulu combiner des manœuvres trop distinctes et trop compliquées : l'envoi de corps francs, d'anciens Chouans, de déserteurs étrangers, le déclenchement de chouanneries dans le pays de Galles et en Cornouailles, l'envoi échelonné des divers contingents, à quoi le ministre de la Marine voulait ajouter le départ d'une flottille pour les Indes. La coordination de pareilles entreprises, intéressant deux ministres, demanda de longs mois à Hoche. A plusieurs reprises Carnot dut intervenir, faire ajourner l'expédition de l'*Ile-de-France*, presser les autorités navales, faire accorder les moyens vainement réclamés par Hoche. Finalement, le 17 décembre, il renonçait et ordonnait l'ajournement de la tentative. Il ignorait que le départ avait eu lieu deux jours auparavant. Les circonstances, pourtant favorables, puisque la flotte accomplit sa traversée, ne permirent pas à Hoche d'arriver à temps et l'entreprise échoua. Cet échec fut imputé à Carnot par la presse qui lui était hostile [13].

Par la force des choses Carnot était ramené aux problèmes continentaux : là encore, des déboires l'attendaient.

Il s'agissait de préparer la reprise des opérations en Allemagne. Pour y parvenir plus promptement et dans de meilleures conditions, il eût fallu conserver quelques têtes de pont sur la rive droite du Rhin. Lors de la retraite de Moreau, Carnot lui avait prescrit de s'accrocher à Huningue et à Kehl et d'en assurer la défense « jusqu'à la dernière extrémité » en renforçant cette défensive par des menaces contre l'ennemi. Beurnonville, que Carnot avait nommé à la place de Jourdan, recevait l'ordre d'appuyer l'armée de Rhin-et-Moselle.

En dépit des objurgations, Beurnonville ne fit rien, il était incapable et, par surcroît, en mauvais termes avec Moreau. C'était une erreur que de lui avoir confié une fonction si importante, Carnot en convint implicitement lorsqu'il confia à Moreau le commandement supérieur des deux armées du Rhin, le 25 décembre 1796.

Moreau lui-même était très circonspect, sinon timoré, on avait même lieu de suspecter son civisme. Il se montra passif, ne prit aucune des dispositions menaçantes qu'on lui avait commandées. Les Autrichiens purent mettre le siège sans obstacles et bloquer Kehl, qui, désormais, était condamné. Ce fut seulement quand l'ennemi ouvrit la tranchée que Moreau fit une sortie, mais il avouait qu'on pouvait se flatter tout au plus de gagner du temps. C'est dans une impossible négociation avec l'ennemi que le général tenta de trouver une issue honorable, il fallut que Carnot le lui interdît expressément. Il fut aussi sommé d'utiliser les ressources énormes fournies par les deux armées du Rhin, et Carnot lui dicta les mouvements offensifs qui eussent permis de dégager Kehl. En vain, la place tomba le 2 février 1797.

Ce troisième échec fut âprement reproché à Carnot, sur le moment et après le 18 Fructidor. A tort, on l'accusait de ne pas avoir mis tout en œuvre pour sauver Kehl. Mais, quand on lui faisait grief d'avoir soutenu, vanté et félicité Moreau, il lui était difficile de se justifier. Moreau lui-même convint, plus tard, qu'il eût pu conserver Kehl « s'il y avait eu plus d'ensemble dans les opérations des deux armées [14] ».

Au moment même où Moreau perdait Kehl, Bonaparte avait pris Mantoue ; plus que jamais le sort de la guerre et des négociations appartenait au chef de l'armée d'Italie. Si Carnot et le Directoire tout entier se trouvaient dans l'impossibilité de lui imposer leur volonté, du moins l'exprimèrent-ils, et l'on peut suivre la politique italienne de Carnot.

Il s'agissait alors de régler le sort de Pie VI. Le 3 février, le Directoire conseillait à Bonaparte de « détruire le centre d'unité de la religion romaine, ennemie irréconciliable de la République », à la condition que ce fût sans priver la France des ressources qu'on pouvait arracher au pape, et aussi sans rallumer « le flambeau du fanatisme en Italie ». Carnot ne signa pas cette lettre, il n'en fallut pas plus pour que La Revellière, promoteur de ces mesures sectaires, l'accusât d'être favorable au pape et au catholicisme.

Sans doute Carnot avait-il tenté, au mois de mai, de résoudre la question religieuse en France avec l'appui du pape. Sans doute avait-il refusé de s'associer au renvoi du négociateur pontifical, mais il avait écrit à Bonaparte, le 30 novembre, que, si le pape se montrait intraitable, il faudrait « briser le trône de la sottise ».

L'opinion de Carnot, sur cette question, correspondait à la note remise par Clarke à Bonaparte en décembre : « Nous avons manqué notre révolution de religion. On est redevenu catholique romain en France, et nous en sommes peut-être au point d'avoir besoin du pape lui-même pour faire seconder chez nous la Révolution par les prêtres et, par conséquent, par les campagnes qu'ils sont parvenus à gouverner de nouveau.» Mais, avec le temps, les lumières triompheraient : « Il faut trente années de liberté de la presse en Italie et en France... pour abattre la puissance spirituelle de l'évêque de Rome. »

En fait, Bonaparte put agir à sa guise, et c'est ainsi qu'il conclut, aux applaudissements de Clarke, le traité de Tolentino, le 17 février 1797.

Dans l'affaire de Naples, Carnot avait pu agir davantage, les négociations ayant lieu à Paris. Il s'était montré favorable à la paix et hostile aux prétentions de ses collègues. Il voulait en effet renforcer la sécurité de Bonaparte et ôter des escales à l'Angleterre. L'envoyé de Naples sut exploiter ces bonnes dispositions pour obtenir des conditions favorables.

En somme, Carnot pressait la conclusion de la paix, avec un succès inégal, dans toute l'Italie, et s'appliquait à éviter la création de républiques qui eussent exigé l'appui de la France, donc, dans un avenir plus ou moins proche, la reprise de la guerre. Sur ce point, il se heurtait non seulement à ses collègues, mais à Bonaparte. Il tentait aussi de réaliser quelques trocs territoriaux, à la mode de l'Ancien Régime, pour faire rendre la Louisiane à la France, l'Espagne étant indemnisée par la Sardaigne, et le roi de Sardaigne par le Mantouan. Non seulement les Directeurs et Bonaparte firent la sourde oreille, mais Clarke lui-même désavoua les projets de son cher bienfaiteur [15].

À vrai dire, l'essentiel restait en suspens tant que l'Autriche n'était pas amenée à traiter. C'est pourquoi Carnot renforça l'action militaire et diplomatique.

Bonaparte menait l'une et l'autre en Italie, il fournissait donc nécessairement la base de tous les projets : les plans de 1797 sont caractérisés par la résolution d'exploiter à fond les succès de l'armée d'Italie. Tout est subordonné à cette idée maîtresse, notamment la campagne au-delà du Rhin. Pour passer à la réalisation, il fallait remettre les armées en état.

Celle d'Italie n'avait cessé de grandir, grâce aux renforts que Carnot avait fait acheminer. On en était venu à placer plus de 100 000 hommes en Italie, tandis que l'armée de

Sambre-et-Meuse n'en avait plus que 55 000, et celle de Rhin-et-Moselle 75 000. Pourtant il y avait eu peu de pertes. « La France n'a point eu de guerre à soutenir qui ait été moins meurtrière », disait le Directoire. Mais la désertion avait continué. Le Directoire prescrivit le rappel de tous les militaires absents et la punition rigoureuse des réfractaires, en ménageant ceux des régions mal pacifiées. Ces mesures procurèrent une notable amélioration : environ 80 000 hommes se trouvaient en avril dans chacune des armées du Rhin. Mais les ressources continuaient d'être réduites et l'on comptait vivre sur l'ennemi [16].

Le plan de campagne comportait désormais un raid sur Rome et une action décisive contre les forces autrichiennes. Une offensive outre-Rhin favoriserait ces opérations en retenant le plus d'Autrichiens possible en Allemagne.

Cette fois Carnot renonça à l'offensive simultanée des deux armées du Rhin. L'armée de Rhin-et-Moselle, commandée par Hoche à partir de février, couvrirait la frontière, Moreau conduirait ses troupes en Allemagne et soutiendrait directement Bonaparte. Carnot supposait alors que celui-ci, franchissant le Tyrol, passerait en Bavière, Moreau l'appuierait dans sa marche sur Vienne. Tout fut modifié quand l'archiduc Charles se rendit en Italie avec une partie de ses troupes.

Moreau devait déclencher son offensive fin mars ou début avril, il tarda et s'appliqua même à refréner l'ardeur de Hoche.

Bonaparte, tenu au courant, s'impatientait. En outre, il s'appliquait à supplanter Hoche et Moreau : « Si le prince Charles, écrivait-il à Carnot, commande les deux armées du Rhin et d'Italie, il faut nécessairement, lorsque nous serons en Allemagne, qu'il y ait chez nous unité de commandement. »

On n'en était pas encore là ! Moreau s'attardait. Carnot finit par ordonner, le 31 mars, le franchissement du Rhin par Hoche. Celui-ci accueillit cet ordre avec empressement et proposa de marcher directement vers le Danube pour frapper l'Autriche et la vaincre. Ainsi pourrait-il rivaliser avec Bonaparte. Carnot accepta, en précisant, le 8 avril, que Hoche devrait établir des communications avec Bonaparte pour agir de concert avec lui. Carnot redoutait de voir celui-ci le placer devant le fait accompli, comme le prouve une curieuse lettre de Clarke démentant, en termes inquiétants, les bruits d'armistice qui couraient déjà bien que, le 15 mars, le Directoire eût révoqué les pouvoirs de Clarke concernant la conclusion d'un armistice général [17].

Carnot avait fait savoir à Bonaparte, le 1er avril, que l'armée de Sambre-et-Meuse se mettait en route, et il abordait les conditions de la paix, en acceptant cette fois la création de républiques italienne, lombarde et cispadane. Ainsi cédait-il de plus en plus au programme italien de Bonaparte, se persuadant toutefois que les États nouveaux se mettraient en mesure de défendre eux-mêmes leur indépendance. Le Directoire tout entier adoptait ses vues. Le ton de la correspondance entre Carnot et Bonaparte demeurait très cordial, l'un et l'autre associaient leur amitié et leur famille aux politesses qui suivaient les discussions diplomatiques et militaires.

Peu après, sur les instances de Desaix, le 13 avril, Moreau était à son tour entré en campagne. Alors Carnot confia la marche sur le Danube à Moreau, et non plus à Hoche. Quatre jours plus tard, Bonaparte s'étant adressé à l'archiduc, le Directoire l'autorisa à signer des préliminaires, sans d'ailleurs lui en dicter les bases. C'est donc à tort qu'on a prétendu que Bonaparte avait agi sans pouvoirs [18].

Le 20 avril, Moreau reprenait Kehl et Hoche culbutait les Autrichiens. Soudain, un courrier d'Italie leur annonça que Bonaparte avait signé un armistice général.

Carnot se montra disposé à la ratification immédiate des préliminaires de paix de Léoben, bien que la frontière du Rhin ne fût pas garantie. Il ne s'était jamais vraiment attaché à la conquête de la rive gauche ; le 13 avril il avait déclaré à Hoche qu'il ne fallait pas songer à l'annexer, il s'en expliqua dans une lettre à Clarke, le 5 mai : « Je crois qu'il sera inutile de rien stipuler dans le traité sur la limite du Rhin.... Vous savez d'ailleurs les inconvénients que je [lui] trouve. » Le même jour, il félicita Bonaparte [19].

Le 30 avril, le Directoire dut décider s'il accepterait ou non les préliminaires de paix. La discussion fut violente. Carnot fit valoir la précarité de la situation de Bonaparte, il en déduisit la nécessité d'accorder des satisfactions à l'empereur.

« Comment ! Qu'entends-je ? s'écria La Revellière, mais où sommes-nous donc ? Quoi, ici, dans cette enceinte, un membre du Directoire, son président, vient nous parler en faveur des intérêts de l'empereur ! »

Barras et Reubell appuyèrent La Revellière. Reubell s'écria :

« C'est toi qui as mis la République dans l'état où elle est..., tu es devenu le point de réunion de tous les contre-révolutionnaires. Nous avons eu le malheur de nous en rapporter à toi de la direction des armées, et tu as abusé de ta position pour trahir les patriotes [20]. »

Malgré tout, les préliminaires furent ratifiés, car l'opinion n'aurait pas admis un refus.

Il s'agissait maintenant d'obtenir de l'empereur une garantie en faveur de la république lombarde, puis d'envisager des trocs de territoires pour récupérer nos colonies et celles de nos alliés, enfin de terminer la guerre contre l'Angleterre. Mais ni Clarke, ni Carnot, n'eurent à trancher ces questions.

Si Léoben ne fut pas pour la France, comme on l'espérait, le signal de la paix générale, ce n'en fut pas moins, pour Carnot, celui de la fin d'une grande époque — celle où il fut organisateur de la victoire. Désormais il ne pourrait plus faire excuser sa politique intérieure par son rôle militaire, la raison qui l'avait fait appeler était caduque : on pouvait désormais se passer de lui.

Ne s'en était-on pas aussi passé pendant la guerre qui finissait ? Depuis qu'il était Directeur, depuis que Bonaparte était général en chef, Carnot n'était plus vraiment maître de la conduite des opérations. Les succès avaient été remportés en Italie, où Bonaparte agissait à sa guise, et non sur le Rhin, où Carnot intervenait. Bonaparte avait promptement obtenu carte blanche ; loin de jalouser son génie, Carnot s'était montré amical et confiant. Du coup, il avait perdu non seulement la direction de la campagne d'Italie, mais celle des négociations.

Quant aux autres généraux, ils en avaient pris à leur aise avec les ordres de Carnot. Ils pouvaient en appeler à un autre Directeur, ou au Corps législatif, ou à la presse, ou même aux électeurs. L'autorité de Carnot était limitée de toutes parts, surtout depuis son changement d'orientation politique, car il avait contre lui une partie considérable du personnel politique et de l'opinion.

Cette désobéissance des généraux, jointe à des choix mal-

heureux et au manque de ressources — sinon de patriotisme — expliquait pour une part les échecs. Ils prove-
naient aussi de l'adversaire, qui s'était adapté à la guerre
révolutionnaire et qui avait au moins un excellent général,
l'archiduc Charles.

Carnot lui-même n'avait plus la même fermeté, la même
assurance, la même opiniâtreté. Les armées opéraient, de
plus en plus, dans des régions qu'il ne connaissait pas. Il lui
fallait s'en rapporter de plus en plus aux exécutants. Les
généraux ne lui fournissaient plus ces projets et ces plans
qu'ils se plaisaient à envoyer, en 1793 et 1794, pour se faire
connaître, ou pour sortir de prison. Désormais, ils travaillaient pour eux. Carnot leur laissait prendre avec ses prescriptions d'étranges libertés. C'est que le Directeur ne pouvait parler le même langage que le membre du Comité de
Salut public [21].

CHAPITRE VII

DE LA PRÉSIDENCE A LA DÉPORTATION

L A RUPTURE de Carnot avec les démocrates s'était accomplie malgré les objurgations de plusieurs de ses amis, malgré le danger royaliste dont ils lui signalaient la gravité. A plusieurs reprises, *L'Ami des Lois* avait tenté de ramener le transfuge, son insuccès l'avait rendu d'autant plus violent dans ses attaques : pour lui, Carnot était un traître qui passait dans le camp adverse. Or le drame de Carnot fut qu'il resta entre les deux camps.

Carnot ne fut pas seul à en faire les frais, non plus que les déportés du coup d'État de fructidor, ni la multitude des fonctionnaires cassés ou suspendus, ni toutes les victimes de la « guillotine sèche » qui sévit dans la suite : ce fut le régime même qui fut discrédité. L'Empire est né de cette erreur, et, avec lui, les longs et profonds bouleversements de l'Europe.

A cette époque, les partis extrêmes étaient les seuls qui eussent des chefs, une certaine discipline, un programme, qui fussent, en un mot, des partis. Le royalisme était mené par les émigrés, soutenus par une partie des prêtres réfractaires ; pourtant ce n'était là ni toute la noblesse, ni tout le clergé ; il était possible de creuser les divisions, de saisir les meneurs et d'apaiser leurs troupes. La gauche n'était pas davantage unie ; elle oubliait ses différends devant la menace royaliste ; elle se fût divisée avec l'affaiblissement de cette menace elle-même. Mais il n'existait pas de troisième force. Les débuts du régime avaient été marqués par les hésitations et les dissentiments des gouvernants, par l'incurie dans l'administration, la misère dans le pays.

C'était ce qui avait découragé la masse et l'avait rendue indifférente aux questions politiques. Les modérés en religion, tolérants par tactique, comme Carnot, étaient peu nombreux et facilement débordés par les partisans de l'indépendance totale de l'Église.

Aux points de vue économique, financier, social, le retour à la liberté avait déclenché une crise profonde dès la chute de Robespierre ; elle n'était pas encore terminée. La vie chère, la misère, contrastant avec le luxe des nouveaux riches et les artifices de péréquation en faveur des politiques, députés, ministres et Directeurs, l'insécurité, les impôts d'exception avaient provoqué un profond mécontentement. Les uns en concluaient que les méthodes suivies étaient condamnées, les autres prétendaient qu'il eût fallu les appliquer plus énergiquement.

Le régime manquait de force, les divisions régnaient partout. Ces débuts de l'histoire constitutionnelle et parlementaire française sont tâtonnants et maladroits. La majorité modérée était dépourvue de cohésion et d'organisation. Elle avait pourtant une puissance évidente due à sa présence au pouvoir. Les Directeurs eux-mêmes n'étaient ni démocrates, ni royalistes, sauf Barthélemy, encore était-ce un impuissant, mais ils ne surent ni arrêter une politique efficace, ni s'accorder avec les députés centristes. Même la presse affaiblit le régime, elle appartenait pourtant, dans son ensemble, à ce juste milieu.

Le prestige personnel de Carnot baissait considérablement. La réputation que lui avaient faite les victoires s'effaçait avec les échecs ; ses ennemis en profitèrent pour contester ses talents stratégiques et son rôle militaire en l'an II. A tous égards, il se trouvait dans une situation difficile.

Pour comble de malheur, il se laissa manœuvrer par des royalistes camouflés, notamment par le général Willot. Ce personnage avait été chargé de pacifier le Midi, infesté de royalistes, mais aussi de Jacobins, les uns et les autres également fanatiques.

« Tu n'as pas idée de ce pays-là, déclarait Carnot à Thibaudeau, il ne ressemble à aucun autre..., il n'y a pas de moyen terme. A Dijon ou à Poitiers, on raisonne, on s'explique ; à Marseille on commence par le poignard. Jourdan, Isnard, des hommes qui ont de l'éducation,... quand ils parlent, l'écume leur vient à la bouche, les yeux leur sortent de la tête. Juge maintenant, d'après les représentants, ce que peuvent être les représentés [1]. »

Malheureusement Willot n'était pas fait pour pacifier.

« Haineux, passionné, il était bon pour écraser un parti,
non pour tenter une juste balance », disait Thibaudeau.
Auparavant, les généraux Châteauneuf-Randon et Puget-
Barbantane avaient été accusés de soutenir les Jacobins,
terroristes impénitents. Carnot les avait révoqués en
juillet 1796. Puget avait rédigé une justification se terminant par ces mots prophétiques : « Gouvernants, tenez
au moins un juste équilibre, autrement vos erreurs seraient
bientôt funestes à vous-mêmes ². »

Willot prit le contre-pied de cette politique : « La classe
qui me paraît en ce moment la seule dangereuse, écrivait-il
le 19 août 1796, est celle de ces prétendus patriotes qui
jettent la terreur parmi tout le reste des habitants qu'ils
qualifient de chouans, papistes, honnêtes gens ³.... » Willot
voulait épurer les autorités et rétablir l'ordre au moyen des
troupes, mais sans secousses, patiemment. Ses protestations
d'impartialité trompèrent Carnot, qui le soutint énergiquement ; Willot put se flatter bientôt de « l'attachement
particulier » dont Carnot l'honorait, et il en abusa, sollicitant « l'approbation particulière » du Directeur. Carnot fut
ainsi mêlé à une lutte farouche, dans laquelle les démocrates
du Midi étaient soutenus par leurs amis dans la presse et à
l'Assemblée, tandis que Willot faisait le jeu des royalistes,
de telle sorte que Carnot ne pouvait être que dupe ou traître.

Le complot de Babeuf survint à propos pour amener
Willot à faire de ses ennemis des Babouvistes, et il ajoutait
que le parti royaliste était « encore pour lui une chimère ⁴ ».

Ce conflit aurait pu avoir des conséquences plus graves si
Carnot n'avait pas été dans les meilleurs termes avec Bonaparte, car l'opposition éclata entre Willot et le général en
chef de l'armée d'Italie. Carnot se porta garant, auprès de
Bonaparte, du républicanisme de Willot ⁵.

Willot, ses troupes et l'état de siège de nombreuses communes n'empêchèrent pas les scènes de guerre civile de se
multiplier. Carnot fournissait des renforts. Willot en vint à
proposer une mise en état de siège générale. Finalement,
Willot fut élu au Corps législatif, en 1797. Carnot consulta
Bonaparte pour lui donner un successeur. Il dut reconnaître
qu'il avait été joué, car Willot devint l'un des meneurs
royalistes aux Cinq-Cents. Détrompé un peu tard, Carnot
lui écrivit une lettre de reproches et lui interdit de venir le
voir ⁶.

Cette affaire résume assez bien l'évolution de la politique

et de la pensée de Carnot, depuis les derniers mois de 1796
jusqu'au coup d'État du 18 Fructidor. Elle contribua à le
brouiller avec ses collègues au Directoire, notamment avec
Barras.

Sur le plan national la grande affaire était la préparation
des élections de 1797. Elles ajouteraient en effet un nouveau
tiers à celui qui avait été élu au début du Directoire ; la
majorité pouvait donc changer. La tactique des royalistes
fut de faire élire, par tous les moyens, des candidats qui leur
fussent favorables. Dès le mois d'août 1796, Hoche avait
dénoncé la manœuvre et fourni des preuves au Directoire ;
puis Bonaparte avait intercepté une correspondance royaliste que *L'Ami des Lois* publia en décembre ; enfin l'un des
indicateurs qui avaient livré Babeuf fit connaître, en janvier, la conspiration royaliste. On procéda à l'arrestation et
au procès de trois des principaux agents de Louis XVIII.
Cette fois encore Carnot avait favorisé l'action de la police
et il crut pouvoir se flatter de faire triompher la politique
du juste milieu [7]. A vrai dire, les sanctions n'étaient pas
comparables, autant on s'était montré implacable contre
Babeuf et ses amis, autant on fut indulgent contre les
agents royalistes. Carnot, qui avait stimulé les poursuites
dans le premier cas, se montra passif dans le second. Le
Directoire fut habile, a-t-on affirmé ; il garda pour lui les
renseignements fournis par Duverne, l'un des inculpés,
sur la propagande royaliste [8]. Il eût été plus efficace de
déjouer l'entreprise avant son succès, il eût été plus sûr pour
l'avenir du régime de n'avoir pas à casser des élections.
L'arrestation des principaux agents avait porté un coup à
l'organisation royaliste ; les élections devaient avoir lieu le
31 mars ; or, le 31 janvier, le réseau royaliste n'existait que
sur le papier, sauf dans les régions confiées à Mallet et à
Bourmont. Ce fut dans cet intervalle, le Directoire étant
averti, que le retard fut rattrapé par ses ennemis [9]. Carnot,
qui ne voulait pas de mesure anticonstitutionnelle, ne fut ni
plus clairvoyant ni plus actif que ceux de ses collègues qui
songèrent au coup d'État [10].

Au lendemain des élections, Reubell proposa de les faire
annuler. Une tumultueuse séance eut lieu au Directoire
le 4 avril 1797. Carnot s'opposa catégoriquement au dessein
de Reubell. Il inaugurait ainsi la doctrine qu'il défendit
constamment, jusqu'au coup d'État, et d'après laquelle la
souveraineté du peuple devait être respectée dans la per-

sonne de ses représentants, au prix même de la subordination du Directoire. C'était en somme la doctrine du régime
parlementaire, comportant le renvoi des ministres condamnés par la majorité des députés, comme un proche avenir
devait le prouver. Mais Carnot n'était pas un doctrinaire ;
s'il adopta cette attitude, c'est « qu'il s'aperçut que les deux
Conseils, dans leur majorité, seraient constitutionnels »,
comme l'explique La Revellière dans ses mémoires [11].

De cette conviction, il existe une preuve, c'est la lettre
qu'il écrivit à Garrau le 6 mai : « Nous ne pouvons douter,
reconnaissait-il, que l'intrigue ne se soit glissée dans la
majeure partie des élections..., mais je suis, comme toi, bien
convaincu que la contre-révolution devient chaque jour
moins à craindre. On trouve un grand nombre de personnes
qui regrettent l'Ancien Régime, mais infiniment peu qui
veuillent courir les chances nécessaires pour tenter de le
ramener. La paix, d'ailleurs, a ramené au système républicain presque tous ceux qui n'avaient alors pas osé se prononcer, et nous ne doutons nullement que le nouveau tiers
qui va arriver au Corps législatif ne se réunisse de bonne foi
aux deux autres et au gouvernement, qui sentent aujour-
d'hui plus que jamais la nécessité de faire cause commune
et de marcher ensemble [12]. »

C'était là toute la question !... La conviction de Carnot
était alors assez ferme pour résister aux appels de ses amis
et anciens collègues, tel Lacombe Saint-Michel. Elle était
également assez intransigeante pour le rendre inaccessible
aux démarches du Corps législatif, qui voyait en lui un allié.
Ainsi, le 21 mai, un député de l'Aisne avait proposé un candidat commissaire cantonal, en traitant son concurrent
d'« ultra-révolutionnaire ». Ce fut celui-ci qui fut choisi. Il
en fut de même dans l'Aube où trois députés proposaient
dix candidats.

En revanche Carnot accueillit favorablement la demande
de Vaublanc qui recommandait le général Hédouville pour
Saint-Domingue [13].

Le tirage au sort du Directeur qui devait partir était un
acte presque aussi important que les élections. Il pouvait
en effet, selon la personnalité du sortant et celle du nouvel
élu, retourner la majorité du gouvernement. Le Corps législatif décida que ce tirage serait fait en audience publique.
Le Directoire s'indigna des arrière-pensées injurieuses que
cette loi supposait et répondit qu'elle était contraire à la

constitution. Les Cinq-Cents insistèrent et ce fut Carnot qui appuya leur demande, au nom « de l'heureuse harmonie » entre les représentants et le Directoire, mais surtout, comme le remarqua La Revellière, parce qu'un refus eût été dangereux [14].

Le sort tomba sur Letourneur; Carnot était donc maintenu; l'opinion s'en réjouit à cause de ses talents militaires et aussi parce qu'il était incorruptible. Mais il perdait le seul de ses collègues qui lui fût attaché et qui votât ordinairement avec lui : « Voilà donc un instrument de moins entre les mains de Carnot », déclarait un journal. La position de Carnot ne pouvait être rétablie que par l'élection d'un nouveau Directeur qui lui fût aussi favorable, Cochon de Lapparent, par exemple; mais celui-ci fut rejeté par les royalistes du club de Clichy, et ce fut Barthélemy qui passa, le 26 mai 1797.

Carnot, depuis le départ de Letourneur, présidait de nouveau le Directoire; à ce titre, il reçut la première visite de Barthélemy. Les deux hommes ne s'accordèrent pas; Carnot l'avait bien pressenti et laissé entendre à Sandoz-Rollin. Dès lors, Carnot était « seul de son bord » au Directoire, mais ses collègues n'étaient pas encore liés les uns aux autres [15].

*_**

La situation du régime et celle de Carnot étaient désormais également critiques, entre les démocrates, résolus au coup d'État, et les royalistes, décidés à mener le Corps législatif et la politique tout entière, pour aboutir à une restauration. La violence fournissait la solution apparemment la plus facile, mais, en fait, la plus dangereuse, car elle aboutissait à faire de la force l'arbitre de la situation, c'est-à-dire au césarisme.

Or il était possible de manœuvrer. Les royalistes étaient divisés : champions du coup de force, partisans des méthodes légales, absolutistes, constitutionnelles, sans parler de rivalités qui opposaient les hommes les uns aux autres, à Paris comme dans l'émigration. De plus, il y avait des modérés, disposés à servir une république pacifique et assurant l'ordre, la sécurité, sinon la prospérité. Ce furent ceux-ci qui tentèrent d'éviter la rupture entre les Conseils et le Directoire et qui se tournèrent vers Carnot. Celui-ci était le seul intermédiaire possible, mais, comme l'a écrit un contemporain, « en cela son caractère n'était point faux, mais sa position était fausse [16]».

Les démarches auprès de Carnot furent très nombreuses. Elles n'émanèrent pas seulement des modérés. Elles eurent lieu dans des conditions telles qu'elles sont restées mal connues, aussi bien en ce qui touche leur nature que la date où elles eurent lieu.

Beffroy de Reigny, qui avait déjà commis tant de maladresses, dans des sens divers, introduisit Portalis et Tronson-Ducoudray. Thibaudeau a déclaré qu'il vint souvent voir Carnot. Willot lui-même vint pendant quelque temps. Il y eut aussi Mathieu Dumas, ami du ministre de la Guerre Petiet, avec qui il travaillait à une revision des lois militaires et qui déclarait suivre « cette ligne moyenne, toute et franchement républicaine, également éloignée des partis extrêmes et du machiavélisme métaphysique [17]».

Carnot reprochait aux Conseils de ne pas voter les crédits nécessaires et se réservait [18].

Au début de juin, des attaques violentes furent lancées par quelques-uns des députés, notamment par Vaublanc, à propos de Saint-Domingue. Or Vaublanc avait écrit récemment à Carnot sur ce sujet. Carnot aida à trouver un compromis et se flatta d'avoir obtenu un apaisement à la première escarmouche [19].

Son attitude parmi ses collègues soulignait ce désir d'apaisement. Carnot ne signait pas les arrêtés de radiation d'émigrés, non plus que les dénonciations contre les prêtres. De plus, sur certaines questions importantes, il semblait en passe de constituer une majorité en s'appuyant sur La Revellière et Barthélemy, par exemple pour ratifier la loi qui rapportait des mesures d'exception établies par la Convention, le 3 brumaire an IV, ou encore des arrêtés et dispositions concernant la trésorerie et la gendarmerie. Il y avait là une possibilité qui inquiétait les royalistes et qu'ils voulurent ruiner en attaquant Carnot comme ancien terroriste [20].

Les difficultés vinrent d'un autre côté; La Revellière et Carnot se détestaient, leur politique religieuse était en opposition. La Revellière se tourna vers Barras et Reubell, et ils tinrent tous trois, à partir du 29 juin, des séances secrètes. La situation devenait désespérée. C'est à ce moment, le 1er juillet, que Mathieu Dumas fit appel à Carnot « pour affirmer le gouvernement constitutionnel par la confiance », et que Carnot répondit, avec une amertume révélant ses nouvelles dispositions d'esprit : « Je ne puis vous peindre ma douleur : l'anarchie et le royalisme se disputent à qui se baignera dans le sang des républicains ; partout ils tombent sous les poignards du fanatisme, des émigrés, du babouvisme. Aucun moyen de répression au-dedans, plus d'espoir de paix à l'extérieur, les ennemis travaillent avec rage, les amis s'endorment, la République croule, le chaos arrive. »

Il sut pourtant trouver d'énergiques accents pour proclamer sa politique du juste milieu, le 14 juillet, en qualité de président du Directoire [21]. Il se crut sur le point de réconcilier la majorité du Corps législatif avec le Directoire, mais ce fut une vraie journée des dupes quand il proposa, le 16 juillet, le changement de plusieurs ministres.

A lire le compte rendu des séances, le débat entre les Directeurs aurait été doctrinal : Carnot proposa le renvoi de quatre ministres, au nom du « vœu de la majorité du Corps législatif » ; Reubell lui répliqua que ce vœu n'avait jamais été exprimé et ne pouvait pas l'être, qu'une telle intrusion du législatif dans l'exécutif provoquerait une véritable anarchie. A quoi Carnot riposta qu'il était « impossible de faire marcher la constitution » sans le ralliement du Directoire à la majorité du Corps législatif. C'était le prolongement de la contestation sur l'autorité de la souveraineté nationale et sur l'interprétation de la constitution, problème qui devait tenir tant de place dans l'histoire politique du XIXᵉ siècle. Déjà La Kevellière signalait l'inconvénient du régime parlementaire : l'instabilité ministérielle, la « versatilité dans les maximes du gouvernement ».

La presse révéla des manœuvres de coulisse, confirmées depuis par les mémoires. Les Constitutionnels du Corps législatif voulaient faire partir les ministres Merlin, Truguet, Ramel et Delacroix. Ils firent sonder plusieurs Directeurs. Barthélemy, Carnot étaient favorables, il en fallait un troisième pour assurer la majorité. On envoya vers Barras un « homme de plaisir » comme lui, l'amiral Villaret-Joyeuse, et on crut pouvoir compter sur lui. Il est curieux qu'on ait arrêté une manœuvre de cette importance sur la parole d'un Barras. C'est lui qui retourna l'opération contre ses auteurs ; il repoussa « avec indignation toute espèce d'influence » du législatif sur l'exécutif, et demanda la discussion immédiate du sort des ministres, même de ceux qui n'étaient pas en cause. Ainsi Bénézech, ministre de l'Intérieur, Cochon, ministre de la Police, et Petiet, ministre de la Guerre — tous amis de Carnot et des modérés — furent révoqués en compagnie de Truguet et de Delacroix. Il fallut aussitôt les remplacer. Carnot demanda un délai de vingt-quatre heures, qui lui fut refusé, non sans ironie. Alors furent nommés de nouveaux ministres, acquis à la majorité directoriale et parmi lesquels on trouvait Hoche à la Guerre et Talleyrand aux Affaires étrangères [22]. L'opération avait été conduite magistralement, à peine avait-elle duré vingt minutes. Les Constitutionnels étaient bafoués, pour la plus grande joie non seulement des démocrates, mais des royalistes, qui se félicitaient en outre de la nomination de Talleyrand. C'était une « injure à la nation, profondément ressentie par tous les vrais républicains..., une véritable calamité », écrivait Mathieu Dumas à Moreau. Tel devait être le sentiment de Carnot, privé de ses appuis, ne disposant plus à son gré du ministère de la Guerre et obligé de subir Talleyrand qu'il méprisait : « Il y a dans l'obséquiosité de cet homme quelque chose qui est au-dessous de la bête même », disait Carnot, d'après Rousselin de Saint-Albin ; et, encore : « Il amène avec lui tous les vices de l'Ancien Régime, sans qu'il ait pu prendre une des vertus du nouveau. » Hoche ne lui inspirait pas une telle répulsion, or ce fut lui qui se prêta à une tentative de coup de force [23].

**

Un député annonça, le 18 juillet, que des troupes arrivaient à Paris après avoir violé les limites de la zone où il était interdit — par précaution — de les faire circuler. L'émoi fut immense, surtout quand la réalité du fait fut démontrée. Carnot se trouva de nouveau dans une étrange situation, puisqu'il était tout ensemble président du Directoire et chargé des questions militaires. Il déclara ne pas être au courant et voulut rejeter l'incident sur « la simple inadvertance d'un commissaire des guerres » chargé d'acheminer les troupes qui devaient se porter de l'armée de Sambre-et-Meuse vers Brest pour une nouvelle expédition d'Irlande [24].

Comment supposer que Hoche violerait le périmètre constitutionnel, lui à qui on l'avait spécialement signalé antérieurement [25] ? Carnot s'informa, Hoche fit savoir qu'il n'avait pas connaissance du détail de la route suivie. En fait, il préparait la marche sur Paris, concertée avec la majorité du Directoire et avec le ministre de la Marine.

C'était là le complot et la raison de sa nomination au ministère de la Guerre. Carnot pouvait faire de lui-même le rapprochement qui s'imposait ; d'autres l'avaient même fait pour lui et en avaient tiré les conséquences. Ils lui proposèrent de mettre en accusation Barras, Reubell et La Revellière, et de confier à Pichegru le commandement de la garnison de Paris.

Carnot refusa. Il venait d'apprendre, le 20 juillet précisément, ainsi que tous ses collègues, la trahison de Pichegru, prouvée par les papiers d'Antraigues saisis par Bonaparte. Or il ne voulait pas renverser la République. Il voulut donc rendre responsable un subalterne et ramener l'affaire à un mince incident, traitant de « contes absurdes » les bruits d'envoi de troupes à Paris : « Ce qui m'étonne, c'est que de pareilles sottises trouvent toujours quelqu'un qui veuille les croire [26]. »

Le lendemain, à l'audience du Directoire, Carnot fit de durs reproches à Hoche sans que Barras intervînt ; ce fut La Revellière qui mit fin à cette scène pénible.

La menace n'était pas conjurée. Carnot accepta de justifier Hoche, mais il exigea que toutes les troupes en mouvement fussent renvoyées à l'armée de Sambre-et-Meuse, ses trois collègues s'y refusèrent, persistant dans l'envoi des forces pour l'Ouest. Les Cinq-Cents restèrent inquiets [27].

Hoche, en effet, malgré sa déconvenue, malgré sa démission du ministère de la Guerre, restait indécis et songeait à renouveler son coup. Ses troupes se livrèrent à d'étranges allées et venues, sur les routes entre Mézières et Chartres. Il les renvoyait à Charleville, le 22 juillet, les ramenait dans la Marne, le 24. Elles arrivaient à Épernay le 28. Le 23, il avait sollicité les ordres du Directoire ; le 26, il avait détaché un officier vers Barras ; le 28, il écrivait à Schérer, le nouveau ministre de la Guerre : « Si un dernier sacrifice de ma part peut encore servir la patrie, croyez que je ferai plutôt celui de mon repos particulier... », et il préparait une marche de Reims à Beauvais. Le lendemain, il lui mandait que les troupes ne marcheraient pas, car il leur avait fait savoir son refus d'embarquer, mais, le soir, à sept heures, il demandait s'il fallait de nouveau se diriger vers l'Ouest. Le 5 août, il maugréait : l'expédition d'Irlande n'aurait pas lieu, on voulait lui « fermer la bouche sous prétexte de secrets d'État » ; et, le 6, il écrivait qu'on voulait « à toutes forces que nous marchions vers l'intérieur ».

Un ami de Pichegru, le général Salme, qui était sous les ordres de Hoche, s'est flatté d'avoir décidé celui-ci à révoquer ses ordres : « Hoche semblait regretter de ne pouvoir exécuter son projet, en taxant les Directeurs de lâches. » Le ministre de la Guerre invita Hoche à dîner, Hoche se méfiait. Il dit pourtant à ses officiers : « Peut-être aurons-nous à assurer la tranquillité intérieure. » Il confiait encore à un ami : « Tous les partis ont été trop loin..., les républicains doivent compter... sur la constance des armées qui ne veulent plus de révolution et qui maintiendront la constitution. » Certaines unités voulaient marcher sur Paris pour se venger des Conseils qui les laissaient manquer de tout.

Ainsi se dessinait le césarisme : « C'est le moyen de mettre tous les partis d'accord en nous préparant au joug du gouvernement militaire [28]. »

En effet Bonaparte avait lancé sa fameuse proclamation du 14 juillet, menaçant d'envoyer ses troupes à Paris si la République était mise en danger. Car Bonaparte avait été violemment pris à partie par les membres les plus ardents du nouveau tiers. Dans ces conditions, qu'étaient devenues les relations de Carnot et de Bonaparte ?

Officiellement, Carnot lui avait écrit, au nom du Directoire, pour lui manifester hautement sa satisfaction et approuver sa conduite à l'égard de Venise et de Gênes. Mais, personnellement, Carnot n'appréciait guère le coup de force contre Venise : « Nous aurions bien voulu éloigner ce malheureux incident, mais les services de Bonaparte nous ont subjugué. »

Non moins officiellement, Bonaparte conseillait au Directoire de sévir contre les royalistes. Sur ce point, Carnot lui écrivit personnellement, le 17 août, en des termes qui méritent d'être retenus :

« Je ne vous entretiendrai pas, mon cher général, des prétendus dangers que court en ce moment la République. Si ces dangers ne sont pas nuls, ils sont du moins centuplés par la peur. La peur fait prendre, de part et d'autre, des mesures extravagantes, et c'est dans ces mesures qu'est le véritable péril pour les spectateurs. Il y a de quoi rire de ces terreurs, paniques et réciproques. On peut dire que les deux factions ont le cauchemar ; chacune d'elles s'arme pour combattre des moulins à vent. La seule chose à craindre, c'est que, lorsqu'elles seront armées sans savoir pourquoi, elles ne se trouvent en présence et ne se battent réellement ;

mais on commence à s'éclairer ; la peur a fait le mal, la peur en sera le remède.

« J'ai vu plusieurs fois votre aide de camp La Valette, pour lequel vous m'avez écrit. C'est un homme d'esprit qui m'a paru fort sage, et je serais fort aise s'il m'est possible de faire quelque chose pour lui.

« Ce qui, à travers l'exaltation et les folies de nos Don Quichottes, fixe l'attention des hommes raisonnables qui veulent enfin un terme aux maux de leur patrie, c'est l'expectative de la paix.

« Tous, mon cher général, ont les yeux fixés sur vous. Vous tenez le sort de la France entière dans vos mains. Signez la paix, et vous le faites changer de face comme par enchantement. Dussiez-vous le faire sur les seules bases du traité préliminaire de Léoben, concluez-la ; elle sera encore superbe, elle le sera aussi pour l'empereur à la vérité, mais que nous importe : la paix pourrait-elle être solide s'il était trop lésé ?... Et alors, mon cher général, venez jouir des bénédictions du peuple français tout entier qui vous appellera son bienfaiteur. Venez étonner les Parisiens par votre modération et votre philosophie. On vous prête mille projets plus absurdes les uns que les autres. On ne veut pas croire qu'un homme qui a fait de si grandes choses puisse se réduire à vivre en simple citoyen. Quant à moi, je crois qu'il n'y a que Bonaparte redevenu simple citoyen qui puisse laisser voir dans toute sa grandeur le général Bonaparte.

« Croyez-moi, mon cher général, le plus sûr de vos amis [29]. »

Cette dernière lettre est révélatrice, surtout si on la rapproche de celle que Bonaparte envoya en réponse. « Dites à Carnot, mandait-il à La Valette, que je ne crois pas aux bruits qu'on répand sur lui ; témoignez-lui une réciprocité de sentiments de tout ce qu'il me dit ; dites-lui, comme une opinion qui vient de vous, qu'à la première occasion je me retirerai des affaires ; que, si elle tarde, je donnerai ma démission ; saisissez bien l'effet que cela fera sur lui. » Lorsqu'on trouva ces lettres, après le 18 Fructidor, on s'étonna que le général marquât une telle confiance à ce seul Directeur. D'autre part, Joséphine envoyait ses amitiés et des cadeaux à la femme de Carnot [30].

Celui-ci crut pouvoir persister dans la ligne moyenne qu'il avait adoptée. Il prononça un discours hostile aux royalistes le 10 août [31]. Ainsi fut-il de plus en plus isolé. Les uns après les autres, ses anciens amis se détachaient de lui. Coffin, ce commissaire du Pas-de-Calais dont la nomination avait fait tant de bruit, vint lui signaler les dangers de cette politique, en vain, aussi démissionna-t-il.

La crise mettait en cause la politique extérieure, Carnot fut accusé de pactiser avec des austrophiles et des anglophiles. Au vrai, il voulait la paix, c'est pourquoi il avait accepté de voir l'envoyé secret de l'Autriche, mais sans rien décider, c'est pourquoi il avait approuvé Léoben, les dispositions favorables à l'Empereur lui paraissant un gage de durée.

Du côté de l'Angleterre, Carnot préparait toujours une descente militaire. Il espéra pourtant la paix lors des négociations qui s'ouvrirent à Lille dans l'été 1797. Son ancien collègue Letourneur était l'un des négociateurs et il consulta Carnot, l'Angleterre était au courant de cette correspondance. Carnot semble avoir conseillé de céder sur un point litigieux, la restitution par l'Angleterre des colonies néerlandaises.

Carnot se brouilla mortellement avec ses collègues. Il y eut quelques scènes tumultueuses au Directoire. Ainsi, dans la nuit du 14 au 15 août, à propos des risques de voir reprendre la guerre en Autriche, comme l'indiquait Bonaparte, une altercation éclata entre Carnot et Barras. Celui-ci le traita de « vil scélérat » et d'« infâme brigand » qui vendait la République. Barras et Carnot en venaient aux mains, ils faillirent se battre en duel.

Carnot ne signait plus guère, pas même les arrêtés concernant le personnel militaire ; sa correspondance devenait presque nulle ; il ne prenait plus part aux délibérations et sortait à tout instant de la salle. Mais il restait insensible aux avertissements qui affluaient, même à ceux de son frère, commissaire à Chalon-sur-Saône. Carnot espérait que La Revellière se refuserait au coup de force, et, pour lui être agréable, il faisait poursuivre le fameux Malo, qui avait insulté La Revellière [32].

* *

Le récit du coup d'État est trop connu pour le répéter une fois de plus. Carnot avait éloigné sa famille ; lui-même se tenait prêt à fuir au cas où l'on voudrait l'arrêter. Dans la soirée du 4 septembre — 18 fructidor — on vint l'avertir que des troupes étaient rassemblées dans le jardin du palais, son entourage lui proposa de recourir à la force : « Nous étions trois frères réunis, le Directeur, le général Carnot et moi, Joseph [le futur conseiller], armés chacun d'un pistolet. Nous fussions entrés dans la salle des délibérations et chacun de nous aurait brûlé la cervelle à un de ses trois Directeurs. » Carnot préféra se cacher. C'est à 8 h. 30 qu'on l'avait informé de la présence des troupes, il apprêta alors ses armes et se coucha tout habillé. Vers 1 heure du matin, Feulint l'avertit qu'on venait pour l'arrêter, La Revellière, nouveau président, en avait donné l'ordre. Feulint amusa un instant les envoyés du triumvirat pendant que Carnot fuyait par une porte dérobée. Carnot se rendit chez des amis, les Devaines, puis, chez les Oudot, des Bourguignons. Quelques jours plus tard, le 21 septembre, il quitta Paris, déguisé en cocher, dans la voiture d'un capitaine du Génie de ses amis.

On fit courir le bruit de la mort de Carnot. Le ministre de la Police aurait même demandé à Reubell si c'était exact, à quoi celui-ci aurait répliqué : « Ce n'est pas un jour comme aujourd'hui qu'il est permis à un ministre de la Police de s'enivrer. » On rechercha Carnot, notamment dans la propriété des Dupont, près de Saint-Omer. Feulint fut mis en non-activité et Joseph Carnot fut révoqué. La famille entière était suspecte et fut étroitement solidaire dans cette rude épreuve. Du moins Carnot avait-il échappé à la déportation [33].

Pour la seconde fois, Carnot avait occupé les plus hautes fonctions ; pour la seconde fois, il les avait perdues. Dans les deux cas, il avait pourtant montré de remarquables qualités de travail, d'organisation et de commandement. Sa chute, dans les deux cas, n'était pas celle d'un homme politique, elle était liée à la chute d'un système, au renvoi d'un personnel nombreux, à de profondes transformations.

Pourtant, la conduite de Carnot fut bien différente au 18 Fructidor de ce qu'elle avait été au 9 Thermidor. Alors qu'il avait favorisé la chute de Robespierre, il était demeuré passif en fructidor. On admettra difficilement qu'il fut guidé par des motifs de doctrine, car il était plus homme d'action que théoricien. On croira plutôt qu'il se sentait moins indispensable puisque la situation militaire était améliorée, mais la guerre n'était pas encore finie et des négociations décisives étaient en cours. Il semble surtout que Carnot n'ait pu agir avec les parlementaires en utilisant leurs moyens. Il n'était ni chef de parti, ni lié à un parti, ni pourvu d'une clientèle politique. Dans la connaissance et le maniement des hommes, il manquait à la fois de clairvoyance et d'entregent ; il était plus autoritaire que manœuvrier. D'autre part, dans l'exercice de l'autorité, il ne s'entendait bien qu'avec des collaborateurs déférents : un Prieur, un Letourneur. Il se butait et rompait quand il rencontrait des personnalités intransigeantes, un Robespierre, un Reubell. Lui qui n'avait exercé que des fonctions collégiales, il ne se sentait à l'aise que s'il travaillait seul, ou à la tête de subordonnés.

Il ne lutta pas pour conserver un pouvoir qu'il devait partager et qui lui échappait.

Son refus d'être fructidorien ou antifructidorien le plaçait d'ailleurs dans une position singulière, exceptionnelle, et qui ne manquait pas de grandeur. Ce genre d'attitude ne lui déplaisait pas, il le montra à diverses reprises.

Il n'en reste pas moins que les défauts et, à certains égards, les qualités de Carnot homme d'État ont déjoué les projets royalistes en retenant les royalistes constitutionnels dans les formes légales, en les amenant même à renoncer à la mise en accusation de Hoche et du triumvirat. Il est vrai que, du même coup, se terminait la période ascendante de la carrière de Carnot, si l'on juge qu'un Directeur était plus qu'un membre du Comité de Salut public, ce qui est indéniable en droit. Une certaine aigreur gagna Carnot et aussi une certaine incapacité à se cantonner dans des postes moindres. On ne tarda pas à s'en apercevoir.

CHAPITRE VIII

UN EXILÉ ACCUSATEUR

CARNOT n'avait jamais quitté la France, il s'était montré très dur pour les émigrés, et voici qu'il allait croiser leurs routes, car la Suisse était farcie d'émigrés, de réfugiés, d'agents secrets de toute sortes.

La Suisse le dépaysait moins que tout autre pays. Il pouvait même espérer qu'elle accueillerait volontiers celui qui, dès le premier jour, avait voulu lui épargner la guerre et faire respecter sa neutralité. D'abord en 1792, lors de sa mission à l'armée du Rhin, quand il s'était avancé jusqu'à Porrentruy. Naguère, Directeur, il avait assuré aux envoyés de Genève la bonne volonté du gouvernement français. Notre représentant dans cette ville, Desportes — dont les dispositions changèrent avec les circonstances — félicitait alors ces envoyés : « On est enchanté ici de l'intérêt que le citoyen Carnot a exprimé pour votre patrie....» Mais ni Desportes ni les magistrats de Genève n'abritèrent le fugitif; l'un craignait ses chefs, et les autres craignaient la France [1].

Ce fut chez une dame Raffinesque, blanchisseuse à Plainpalais, qu'il s'abrita. Elle lui était peut-être apparentée — il l'appelle sa cousine dans ses lettres —, elle remplaça ainsi sa famille [2].

Non seulement Carnot avait dû quitter tous les siens, mais il ne pouvait guère leur écrire ; il dut même se prêter à la rupture de son mariage pour que tous les biens de la communauté ne fussent pas saisis.

Les scellés avaient été apposés sur l'appartement. Ils furent levés le 16 octobre, les « hardes » de la citoyenne Carnot furent remises à son fondé de pouvoir Collignon, le reste fut conservé provisoirement, sauf la bibliothèque qui fut versée aux archives du Directoire. La cave fut vendue aux enchères, le 3 janvier 1798, pour mille six cent cinquante francs environ, car elle n'avait pas été entretenue avec soin ; nombre de bouteilles étaient endommagées ou brisées.

Les triumvirs se moquaient bien de ces détails. C'est la correspondance qui les intéressait, ils y cherchaient des informations sur le rôle personnel de leur ex-collègue, peut-être des pièces secrètes, des lettres de Bonaparte, de Letourneur, devenu négociateur à Lille pour la paix avec l'Angleterre. Leur butin fut maigre, il ne permettait pas même de justifier les mesures qui frappaient Carnot.

Les biens de Carnot devaient être mis sous séquestre. Quels étaient-ils ? C'est là un point important, comme nous le montreront ses relations ultérieures avec Napoléon, et c'est encore un point obscur.

Conformément à la loi du 4 vendémiaire an IV, Carnot a rendu compte de l'état de sa fortune, le 29 septembre 1795.

Il ne possédait alors que ce qu'il avait à la veille de la Révolution, quelques vignes en Bourgogne, rapportant bon an mal an 600 à 700 livres. Il n'avait pas reçu les 30 000 livres de dot de sa femme, mais seulement un intérêt annuel de 15 000 livres — en assignats. Quant aux meubles, effets et argent, il les évaluait aux environs de 4 000 livres.

Le passage au Directoire avait permis à Carnot d'épargner assez pour acquérir — en s'endettant, paraît-il — un bien national. C'était la ferme du Forestil, sise près de Montdidier. Il y avait là une maison, des grange, étable, pigeonnier, jardin et vigne, s'étendant sur trois journaux, les terres comprenaient 316 journaux de terres labourables et 24 journaux de bois. Ce domaine avait été vendu deux cent mille livres en 1792.

La fortune de Carnot demeurait donc médiocre, mais elle risquait d'être séquestrée. Pour limiter les pertes, Mme Carnot demanda la dissolution de la communauté conjugale, le divorce fut prononcé le 17 juillet 1799 [3].

La fausse nouvelle de la mise à mort de Lazare était parvenue à Claude, son père, qui vivait toujours à Nolay. Il en fut si affecté qu'il s'éteignit peu après, le 19 novembre 1797. Il laissait une succession modeste dont rien ne pouvait légalement revenir à Carnot. Les autres héritiers voulurent tourner la loi en attribuant un lot à Sadi, fils de Lazare, mais ils ne purent éviter le séquestre. Ce lot était estimé, comme les autres, à un peu plus de 7 000 livres en immeubles et 330 livres en argent, soit 7 600 livres au total [4].

D'autres soucis, plus immédiats, vinrent troubler Carnot

dans sa retraite. Le 15 novembre, Desportes avait dénoncé aux autorités de Genève la présence de Carnot reconnu en dépit de la grosse perruque masquant sa calvitie. Desportes revint à la charge le lendemain, précisant l'emplacement de la maison, à Plainpalais, où devait se trouver Carnot. C'était pour lui le moyen de garder son poste, car le dénonciateur de Carnot, un démocrate, accusait Desportes d'être un patriote tiède et favorable à Carnot. Pourtant les recherches restèrent vaines.

Sur ces entrefaites, le 21 novembre, Bonaparte, qui se rendait à Rastadt, était arrivé à Genève. Aussitôt un Milanais lui signala la présence de l'ancien Directeur, donnant les noms de ses protecteurs supposés. Bonaparte les fit comparaître et l'un d'entre eux, Bontemps, qui se défendit mal, fut arrêté. « Carnot croit pouvoir assurer que cela n'est qu'un jeu et telle est aussi l'opinion du malheureux dans les fers », expliqua Bornes, député fructidorisé qui avait été amené de Paris précisément par Bontemps. Pourtant, dans sa *Réponse à Bailleul*, Carnot relate sans la commenter cette conduite de Bonaparte à son égard ; procédé imprudent que Feulint voulut rattraper en déclarant que la *Réponse* ne pouvait être — pour cette raison — de son frère.

Un Genevois, Des Gouttes, avait prévenu Carnot des risques qu'il courrait et lui avait remis un mot pour M. de Bonstetten. Carnot franchit le Léman, déguisé en garçon blanchisseur, pour rejoindre Bonstetten. Celui-ci était un patricien bernois, épris de la culture française, admirateur de la Révolution à ses débuts, mais non en l'an II. Il était resté libéral, en relation avec Mme de Staël. Il apprécia Carnot assez pour rechercher sa société dans la suite et même exercer sur lui une certaine influence [5].

Peu après, le 14 février 1798, le Directoire ayant ordonné l'entrée des troupes françaises en Suisse pour y appuyer une révolution démocratique et préparer l'annexion, Carnot dut chercher un autre refuge. Bonstetten lui permit d'obtenir des passeports sous des noms supposés [6].

Pendant son séjour en Suisse, Carnot avait été sollicité par des agents royalistes et anglais, bien que Pichegru eût affirmé qu'on n'en pourrait rien obtenir. Bornes avait eu avec Carnot une longue conversation, dont il envoya le compte rendu à Londres. Il confirmait qu'on ne pouvait compter sur l'ancien régicide, mais il relatait l'opinion de Carnot sur Bonaparte, et c'est là un point d'importance.

« Bonaparte paraît persuadé que, pour maintenir son crédit, il a besoin d'être toujours en activité ; avec une armée, il peut de grandes choses. » Carnot prévoyait pourtant que Bonaparte ne se limiterait pas à la carrière militaire, si éclatante fût-elle. « Il se livrera entièrement au rôle de politique, de législateur et même de réformateur.... S'il a un plan, il ne peut être qu'en opposition avec celui des Jacobins ; il sera un acheminement à l'ordre, s'il n'est pas l'ordre lui-même..., se réservant de terminer la longue tragédie de la Révolution [7]. » A notre connaissance ces paroles remarquables, transcrites dès mars 1798, n'ont pas été relevées.

Fixé à Augsbourg, puis dans un village voisin, Carnot prit connaissance des charges que Bailleul avait retenues contre lui dans son rapport sur le coup d'État. Il décida d'y répondre et fit paraître sa justification — en forme de réquisitoire — à Augsbourg, en mai 1798.

Réplique magistrale que cette *Réponse à Bailleul*, écrite avec une vigueur, une verve de pamphlétaire. On était loin de l'*Éloge de Vauban* et des discours officiels prononcés par le Directeur. Aucune affectation, aucune emphase, non plus que ces métaphores grandiloquentes dont on avait tant abusé. L'homme était là, vibrant d'indignation, interpellant ses adversaires, les défiant, les couvrant de sarcasmes, les dessinant en traits caricaturaux et féroces. Nul ne peut oublier les portraits qu'il traça de ses trois anciens collègues. La puissance du ressentiment lui dicta des traits terribles, où les défauts physiques étaient moqués, autant que les tares et les vices.

L'argumentation, serrée, frappait d'autant plus que les accusations de Bailleul étaient vagues et maladroites. Carnot se présentait comme l'homme de la paix extérieure et intérieure, de la liberté et de la modération, également éloigné des factions antagonistes. Nous avons déjà rencontré, à propos de son action au Directoire, les questions qu'il abordait. Mais ce qui s'ajoutait, c'était l'ardent amour de la France, doublé par la nostalgie de l'exil, et qui lui inspira une prosopopée que citèrent ensuite tous ses biographes. Carnot invoquait la France, sa famille, ses amis, le sol sur lequel il avait eu le bonheur de naître et auquel il ne cesserait d'être attaché ; il leur souhaitait la gloire et la prospérité, tandis qu'il ne demandait pour lui que le pouvoir de supporter l'injustice.

L'ouvrage eut un vif succès, car on se lassa vite en France

de la dictature du triumvirat. La police fut chargée de le traquer, elle perquisitionna chez les imprimeurs. En vain, les copies étaient reprises, imprimées en divers formats, et vendues avec précautions.

Des répliques furent lancées, sous des titres variés : *De la Tyrannie de Carnot, ou les Carnutes*, par Poultier ; *Menaces furieuses de Carnot au Peuple de Paris* par Rouet ; *Essai sur la Nature et les divers Agents de la Conspiration présente, ou Lettres d'un Représentant du Peuple sur la Réponse de Carnot à Bailleul.*

Ce succès incita même un éditeur à imaginer un *Second Mémoire de Carnot* qui fut publié à Hambourg en 1799. En revanche Joseph Carnot avait fait imprimer, sous le titre de *Réflexions sur la Réponse de Carnot à Bailleul*, les passages les plus importants de cet ouvrage. De son côté Feulint avait composé une *Histoire du Directoire constitutionnel*, mais elle parut en retard, après le 18 Brumaire. Fort heureusement, car cela permit à son auteur d'y ajouter quelques compliments à Bonaparte, pour tenter de réhabiliter la famille et de regagner les fonctions perdues [8].

Après la chute du triumvirat, il avait déjà semblé possible de tenter d'obtenir la levée des sanctions qui frappaient Carnot. Son frère Joseph parle d'une pétition adressée au Corps législatif et que Lacuée aurait empêché de remettre. De son côté, Lomet incrimine violemment le même Lacuée. Après le 18 Brumaire, Feulint voulut aller solliciter le Premier Consul ; Lacuée s'y serait encore opposé. Un dissentiment se dessinait entre Feulint et Lacuée, et plus largement entre ceux qui avaient été victimes du 18 Fructidor et ceux qui étaient restés en fonctions [9].

Il n'en reste pas moins que Lacuée avait, le premier, élevé publiquement la voix en faveur de Carnot, après le coup d'État du 18 Fructidor. Il avait affirmé le républicanisme de Carnot, dès novembre 1797.

La disparition de toute correspondance de Carnot, pendant son exil, au long des années 1798 et 1799, ne permet ni de connaître sa pensée sur les avatars de la France, ni son action éventuelle pendant que le régime se discréditait, qu'une deuxième coalition ruinait les victoires et les traités de paix qui avaient mis un terme à la première, ni enfin de savoir comment il accueillit la nouvelle du coup d'État de Bonaparte.

Du moins Feulint saisit-il l'occasion avec une promptitude qui fait honneur à sa perspicacité. Dès le 23 octobre 1799, bien avant le coup d'État, il avait fait sa cour à Bonaparte dont l' « heureux retour, si longtemps espéré, pouvait mettre enfin un terme aux malheurs de la République ». Il lui exprimait sa confiance, « bien plus fondée encore sur la connaissance personnelle que j'ai de votre correspondance, tant officielle qu'amicale, avec mon malheureux frère, lors de vos glorieux succès en Italie, que sur vos brillants et nombreux triomphes eux-mêmes... ».

Cet empressement ne pouvait recevoir sa récompense qu'après le coup d'État.... Elle tarda un peu et fut limitée. Carnot put revenir grâce à une mesure générale, prise le 26 décembre, en faveur des victimes de fructidor, mais il restait placé sous la surveillance de la police ; chacun avait une résidence assignée, celle de Carnot était Paris.

« Je me hâte, mon très cher ami, de t'annoncer mon retour à Paris, écrivait Carnot à son frère Joseph le 19 janvier 1800. Ma femme est arrivée un quart d'heure après moi. Tu juges de notre joie.... »

La vie familiale reprit donc aussitôt. Lazare et sa femme étaient provisoirement installés chez Toussaint Collignon, celui qui avait signé les inventaires lors du séquestre.

Le dénuement relatif dans lequel se trouvait l'amnistié fut peu à peu atténué. Les papiers séquestrés, les archives et les livres lui furent rendus, presque au complet, ainsi que l'argent — plus de dix mille francs —, les biens, la ferme de Forestil, et la part de l'héritage paternel. D'autre part, la dot de Mme Carnot avait été préservée. La situation n'était pas inquiétante de ce côté [10]. Carnot allait-il reprendre un rôle dans la vie publique ?

MINISTRE DE BONAPARTE

L E JOUR même de son retour, nous dit Körte, Carnot fut
appelé au Luxembourg par Bonaparte, avec qui il
eut un long entretien confidentiel.

« Vous dites, dans votre *Réponse à Bailleul*, que vous étiez
à Nyon quand j'y suis passé ; pourquoi n'êtes-vous pas venu
à moi ?

— Si vous aviez été seul, j'y serais allé, mais vous aviez
une suite qui aurait pu me reconnaître, et peut-être vous-
même n'auriez-vous pu empêcher que je fusse livré au
Directoire.

— Il est vrai, mais pourquoi ne m'avoir pas écrit au
cours de votre exil ? Pouviez douter de la part que je prenais à votre sort !

— Je m'en suis bien gardé, en raison de votre amitié
pour Barras.

— Pour Barras ?... Vous savez que c'est toujours à vous
seul que j'ai écrit personnellement. En vous seul j'avais
confiance, à vous seul j'ai confié ce qui me touchait personnellement, et ce qui touchait les miens. »

Sur-le-champ, Carnot fut nommé par le Premier Consul
lieutenant général et président du Comité des inspecteurs
aux revues.

Ainsi va la légende, accréditée par un homme qui écrivait
au contact de Carnot définitivement exilé.... La nomination
fut prononcée seulement le 7 février. Bonaparte avait quitté
le Luxembourg pour les Tuileries le jour même du retour de
Carnot, le rôle enfin de celui-ci restait incertain : nommé
inspecteur aux revues, il avait « le grade et le traitement des
généraux de division », mais il ne reçut pas de promotion
personnelle, et, s'il devint président des inspecteurs, il le dut
à la déférence de ses collègues qui avaient naguère été
sous ses ordres, tels Petiet et Villemanzy [1].

Il est probable cependant que Carnot se rendit auprès de Bonaparte pour le remercier, et l'allusion à l'épisode de Nyon a été retenue par les biographes, mais nous savons que Carnot lui-même n'avait pas accordé d'importance à cet incident. La question n'était pas là : il s'agissait de savoir la place que Carnot pouvait tenir dans la politique et dans l'œuvre du Consul.

Le retour de Carnot n'était pas resté inaperçu, surtout quand on avait su qu'il avait été presque immédiatement — le 24 janvier — libéré de la surveillance de la police. « Carnot reçoit plus de visites qu'il n'en rend, écrivait la *Gazette de France*, et personne ne doute qu'avec un titre ou sans titre il ne prenne une grande influence dans ce qui aura rapport à la guerre. »

Clarke était venu, lui qui avait conservé ses fonctions et qui était en faveur. Il apportait une lettre du général Moncey, qui félicitait, non sans grandiloquence, l'exilé revenu. Un ami anonyme publiait une *Épître à Carnot* demandant aux Consuls « de s'entourer des conseils d'un homme qui a fait triompher six ans de suite la République ; l'époque de ses revers a été celle de la proscription de cet homme de génie [2] ».

Mais la presse, prudente, ne pouvait connaître d'autre organisateur de la victoire que le Premier Consul. Sieyès, puissant encore, était hostile à Carnot, les Fructidoriens haïssaient les fructidorisés, surtout celui qui les avait fustigés dans sa fameuse *Réponse à Bailleul*, et ils occupaient des places nombreuses et considérables. Les démocrates demeuraient les adversaires de l'exécuteur de Babeuf, de l'homme du camp de Grenelle ; les royalistes et les modérés ne pardonnaient pas au membre du Comité de Salut public et au régicide. Carnot était un signe de division, d'inquiétude, de répulsion, tout autant que d'espérance. A peine savait-on quelle politique il poursuivait quand il s'était enfui ; on ignorait absolument celle qu'il préconisait à son retour.

Ses plus anciens collègues, ceux du Génie, camarades ou subordonnés, se gardaient bien de revendiquer leur illustre confrère : il s'agissait précisément alors de nommer un premier inspecteur du Génie. Marescot — ami de Carnot — fut choisi. De même, pour réorganiser l'arme, son école, ses places et ses cadres, on forma un comité, mais d'officiers du Génie « qui aient fait la guerre », comme l'exigeait Bonaparte [3].

Ceux qui comptaient, dans l'armée, c'étaient les généraux

et les états-majors d'Italie et d'Égypte, cette camarilla que jalousaient les autres, et ces généraux en chef, enrichis, infatués et pourtant avides encore. L'exemple de Bonaparte les stimulait et les encourageait plus encore qu'il ne les irritait.

Ni les militaires ni les politiques n'étaient disposés à se fier à Carnot. Il représentait une force redoutable par son passé, par ses multiples passés. C'est pourquoi Bonaparte le mit d'abord en observation, si l'on peut dire, dans un poste inattendu qui l'écartait de la direction des opérations et le confinait dans la comptabilité, les contrôles, tâche ingrate à laquelle il était mal préparé, tâche d'intendant militaire. Carnot hésita, Bonaparte fut flatteur, comme il savait l'être : « C'est un nouveau système à établir, vous seul en êtes capable.» Il emporta l'assentiment de Carnot, désormais attaché au Consulat [4].

La famille tout entière rentra en grâce : Feulint fut réintégré, le 22 février ; Collignon, six jours plus tard, devenait aussi inspecteur aux revues. Mais Carnot n'eut pas à remplir ses nouvelles fonctions : elles étaient définies par l'instruction du 23 mars ; or, le 2 avril, il était nommé ministre de la Guerre.

Dans l'intervalle il avait joué un rôle inattendu, celui de conseiller pour les nominations de préfets. Une liste de vingt-deux noms lui est due. Elle le classe politiquement avec une précision qui n'a jamais été observée et qui prend toute sa valeur si l'on évoque les nominations de fonctionnaires qu'il avait faites en 1796.

D'abord il propose d'anciens fructidorisés, ses confrères dans la disgrâce : Barbé-Marbois, Parent-Réal. Ensuite des modérés, voire des ci-devant : Amelot, ancien intendant de Bourgogne, Sers, Saint-Amour, Dubois-Fosseux, de Baert. Des officiers : Pasquet-Salaignac, Robert, le père du général Darnaudat. Un « associé à l'Institut », Dyanière, « ami de Condorcet ». Un parent de Clarke, Shée.

Il vante leurs talents, leur probité, parfois leur civisme ou leur patriotisme, ou leur esprit conciliant.

Six d'entre eux étaient du Pas-de-Calais ou de la Somme. Ils étaient presque tous de second plan.

Bien que plusieurs aient été portés sur la liste générale de propositions, deux seulement furent nommés : Desmousseaux — qui était appuyé par Lebrun —, Rioux — qui était soutenu par Lucien Bonaparte.

En somme, Carnot n'avait pas eu d'influence, mais il avait révélé son orientation politique [5].

*
* *

Carnot allait donc faire sa véritable rentrée ; pourtant, loin de se montrer empressé, il hésita, dit-on, quelque peu. La charge était accablante, il avait pu s'en rendre compte depuis son retour, notamment comme inspecteur aux revues. Les armées manquaient de tout, les administrations militaires étaient en pleine anarchie, le vol et l'indiscipline régnaient partout, et il s'agissait de faire face aux besoins de la campagne qui allait commencer aussitôt. Dans une telle situation, le ministre — en raison même d'une constitution qui le faisait nommer et révoquer par le Premier Consul — ne pouvait être que le bouc émissaire ; tous les retards, malfaçons et manques lui seraient reprochés. Bonaparte était impérieux et brusque, il allait jouer son avenir sur le champ de bataille, il lui fallait donc un organisateur impeccable et des résultats immédiats.

Or les abus étaient invétérés ; leurs puissants bénéficiaires, généraux victorieux ou fournisseurs indispensables, n'étaient pas disposés à s'incliner devant un ministre, même s'il avait été Directeur et membre du Comité de Salut public. Au contraire : n'avaient-ils pas secoué ce joug abhorré !

S'il faut en croire Hippolyte, son père commença par refuser, craignant de ne pas avoir la liberté d'action nécessaire, et ne céda que sur les instances de Lebrun, le troisième consul [6].

Carnot remplaçait Berthier, ancien chef d'état-major de l'armée d'Italie, administrateur précis, docile, prodigieusement actif, mais qui devait préparer et diriger, en attendant son maître, l'armée que Bonaparte allait faire triompher à Marengo [7].

L'arrivée de Carnot fut interprétée comme une mesure républicaine, ainsi en jugeaient le *Journal des Hommes libres*, et les généraux Coumes et Gilly ; ainsi devait l'avoir prévu et voulu Bonaparte qui avait nommé, le même jour, un royaliste — Dufrêne — directeur du Trésor. Les félicitations furent peu nombreuses, aucune ne fut adressée par les commandants d'armées, pas même par Moreau. La partie qui s'engageait allait être rude comme les jouteurs qu'elle mettait aux prises [8].

Dès son arrivée au pouvoir, Bonaparte avait défini le type

d'administration qu'il exigeait : le moins d'employés possible, la plus grande économie, la plus grande rapidité dans l'exécution des ordres. De plus, pour l'administration des forces armées, il voulait départager strictement l'action des civils et des militaires, pour accorder à ceux-ci « le mouvement et le classement des hommes qu'ils doivent faire battre » et leur laisser « le moins possible des détails de la comptabilité [9] ».

C'étaient bien là les vues de Carnot. Aidé de ses collaborateurs habituels — son beau-frère Collignon comme secrétaire général, ses amis Dupont et Lomet pour diriger le mouvement des troupes, son frère Feulint pour le seconder en tout —, il voulut imprimer une marche vigoureuse, prompte et précise, à l'expédition des affaires. Payant de sa personne, à son accoutumée, il se levait à cinq heures et travaillait seul jusqu'à huit et neuf heures. Ensuite, suivant un horaire et un calendrier stricts, il recevait les chefs de division et les officiers. Chacun devait laisser un rapport succinct — dix lignes au maximum — comportant un projet de décision, sur lequel le ministre portait, en marge, son avis. Pour surveiller de plus près l'activité, le ministre travailla avec les chefs de bureau et supprima les chefs de division. Toute l'organisation fut simplifiée, coordonnée, fondée sur des « règles invariables» que leur auteur espérait voir devenir organiques et soustraites à la volonté des ministres. Il s'efforça d'éliminer les détails et voulut «mettre fin à cette correspondance volumineuse qui, née dans le temps de la crainte, donne à l'autorité un air de doute et d'incertitude que ne doivent jamais avoir les ordres d'un ministre, et surtout d'un ministre de la Guerre [10] ».

Tout cela eût été bien, si le ministre avait trouvé la franche collaboration — ou la crainte — dans le personnel ministériel, dans les administrations militaires à l'intérieur, dans les chefs aux armées. Or tout le monde était accoutumé à pêcher en eau trouble — le personnel, au ministère, n'était-il pas resté dix mois sans recevoir son traitement ! — il avait pris des habitudes. Carnot devait s'imposer, et imposer ses méthodes ; quels étaient ses moyens ?

Il s'aperçut vite qu'un ministre était un mince personnage, entre les Consuls — et surtout le Premier — et le Conseil d'État. Le ministre devait solliciter l'assentiment des uns et des autres, adopter leurs conclusions, et surtout quêter des crédits dans un État qui manquait terriblement de trésorerie. Les quelques pieds carrés de son bureau n'étaient pas le lieu des décisions, mais bien le bureau de travail du Premier Consul, où il fallait procéder en toute hâte, après avoir fait antichambre, et où l'on se heurtait à d'autres autorités, à d'autres ambitions, à d'autres exigences. Tous les deux ou trois jours, Carnot soumettait à Bonaparte des questions nombreuses — jusqu'à trente pour une seule séance — promotions, nominations, révocations, récompenses et sanctions, levées d'hommes, solde et approvisionnement. Bonaparte entrait dans le détail le plus minutieux, le champ d'initiative et d'action indépendant du ministre était presque inexistant. Le personnel de la Guerre n'était pas celui du ministre, mais bien du Premier Consul; quant aux problèmes d'organisation, ils étaient renvoyés au Conseil d'État. Souvent les questions demeuraient à la discrétion de Bonaparte « resté chez les consuls », notait-on sur la « feuille de travail », en face de l'indication d'une question et d'un dossier. Les demandes de crédit se heurtaient d'ordinaire à un refus, à une réduction, à des ajournements [11].

Du moins, ce cap franchi, Carnot pouvait-il s'appuyer sur l'autorité de Bonaparte, mais il lui avait fallu, au préalable, jeter beaucoup de lest ; or il devait encore compter avec les « Conseils d'administration de la Guerre ».

C'était là un rouage caractéristique du régime, de ces débuts de l'ère napoléonienne, époque où le nouveau maître de la France s'initiait aux disciplines les plus diverses, exploitait la compétence et le travail des spécialistes les plus éminents et pressait l'orange avant de jeter l'écorce. C'était aussi l'instrument qui lui permettait de savoir où en était la France, ses institutions et ses ressources. Tel était l'objectif des Conseils d'administration de la Guerre : examen de « toutes les opérations de l'administration de la Guerre », avait déclaré Bonaparte à la première réunion, le 14 janvier 1800, et confrontation entre ses besoins financiers et les ressources du Trésor.

Des conseillers d'État, ceux de la section de la Guerre prenaient part régulièrement aux réunions, apportant là ce souci constructif qui donne une telle importance au Conseil d'État sous le Consulat. De hauts fonctionnaires étaient appelés en consultation. Le Premier Consul présidait les débats ; le plus souvent, les autres consuls étaient présents, mais silencieux. C'est là, notamment, que Berthier fut inférieur à sa tâche, demandant des délais, se faisant accompagner par ses chefs de service et par ses techniciens. C'est là, surtout, que l'état de désorganisation totale fut reconnu.

Le Conseil d'administration de la Guerre se tenait en principe une fois par décade : en trois mois de ministère, Berthier avait participé à neuf réunions. Carnot, en dix mois, n'eut à se rendre qu'à sept réunions : l'absence de Bonaparte provoqua une première interruption, du 5 mai au 2 août, puis les conseils s'arrêtèrent au 1er septembre, pour ne reprendre que le 4 mars 1801.

Les conseillers d'État présents n'étaient pas toujours les mêmes. Il y avait parmi eux des généraux qui reçurent des commandements ; ainsi Bernadotte vint aux deux dernières réunions et Marmont aux trois dernières. Des administrateurs remplissaient des missions : Petiet fut présent aux trois premières séances, puis partit veiller à la préparation des troupes que Bonaparte allait commander. Le seul membre qui fut toujours présent, toujours actif, fut Lacuée, président de la section de la Guerre au Conseil d'État [12].

Carnot était en excellents termes avec Lacuée ; une partie de sa famille pourtant accusait celui-ci de s'insinuer dans les bonnes grâces du Premier Consul, tant par la flatterie que par un labeur acharné, préparant ainsi le départ de Carnot pour recueillir sa succession. Carnot, au contraire, se montrait confiant au point de remettre, pendant son absence, le ministère à Lacuée. Feulint fut mortifié de pas avoir l'intérim.

Quelques grandes questions furent réglées dans ces conseils, par exemple l'organisation de l'habillement des troupes. Carnot ne voulait pas laisser les troupes gérer elles-mêmes les fonds, ni passer les commandes ; les autres membres étaient d'avis opposé ; le Premier Consul trancha dans le sens de Carnot, en décidant l'organisation d'un Directoire central à Paris, qui passerait les marchés avec les fabricants, du moins jusqu'à nouvel ordre.

Cette question, aussi bien que l'examen des marchés conclus avec les fournisseurs de guerre, évoquait les problèmes financiers. Carnot réclama des fonds, l'affaire fut renvoyée au ministre des Finances. Carnot aurait voulu obtenir du directeur du Trésor l'état quotidien des règlements et des dispositions financières prises pour faire face aux besoins. Le Premier Consul renvoya l'affaire au Conseil d'administration des Finances.

Ainsi beaucoup de décisions échappaient au ministre, soit qu'elles fussent ajournées, soit qu'elles fussent renvoyées à d'autres autorités ; par exemple un projet d'organisation des hôpitaux militaires fut renvoyé au Conseil d'État. Seules les questions urgentes étaient tranchées sur place, mais par le Premier Consul qui arbitrait les dissentiments entre son ministre et ses conseillers d'État.

Après Marengo on envisagea plus largement l'avenir, la réduction des effectifs et les questions d'organisation générale et des réformes à réaliser après « quelques années de paix ». Il faudrait remercier une centaine de généraux et d'adjudants généraux, tâche ingrate, Carnot le savait mieux que quiconque. Le Premier Consul n'avait rien dit sur ce point, mais il avait demandé « de quel droit, à la paix, un citoyen français pourra malgré lui être retenu aux drapeaux *(sic)* ». Lacuée avait rappelé que la loi de conscription établissait un service militaire de cinq ans ; seuls les hommes levés antérieurement pourraient donc être libérés. Carnot était alors intervenu pour fixer les modalités de la démobilisation : « Un trait marqué du caractère national est la soumission aux règles générales et la disposition à s'indigner des exceptions. »

Si la paix était conclue, on pourrait ramener les effectifs de 520 000 à 240 000 hommes et le budget de 400 à 200 millions environ. Ce dernier chiffre pourrait être assuré par le budget, mais l'on jugea prudent d'envisager un moyen terme, la paix n'étant pas assurée, et de rechercher le moyen d'obtenir environ 300 millions. De toute nécessité les alliés, l'Italie, l'Allemagne et la Batavie, devraient payer.

Carnot se préoccupa du vote de ce budget, son expérience récente et ancienne l'amenait à craindre des difficultés : « Si on le détaille, il sera chicané pièce à pièce, et si on ne le détaille point, on prendra de l'humeur. » Aussi Carnot proposait-il de s'en tenir aux « grosses masses, telles que soldes, masses, fournitures de campagne, le tout en 12 ou 15 articles ». Son respect du contrôle parlementaire passait après le désir d'obtenir des moyens d'action.

Ces grandes mesures furent d'ailleurs ajournées, elles aussi, et soumises au Conseil d'État. Ainsi en revenait-on sans cesse à cette institution dont Carnot n'était pas membre et qui finissait par exercer une manière de tutelle sur le ministre. Un arrêté du 25 mai confia à la section de la Guerre la plupart des grands problèmes d'organisation : recrutement, avancement, tribunaux militaires et code pénal militaire, comptabilité, habillement, équipement, etc. En somme, le ministre était cantonné dans les affaires courantes [13].

Carnot savait ce qu'il en était quand il avait accepté le poste ; il avait alors demandé des pouvoirs élargis. Ceux qu'on lui accordait ne répondaient ni à son caractère, ni à son passé, ni même aux exigences du moment. On s'en aperçut quand il s'agit de faire cesser les malversations.

* *

« Le désintéressement personnel que vous n'avez cessé de montrer m'engage à vous dévoiler certains abus qui engloutissent une partie du fruit de nos victoires. » Ainsi s'exprimait l'auteur d'un rapport conservé aux archives autrichiennes. On y voyait comment l'armée vivait sur le pays, et comment les comptables fabriquaient de toutes pièces des documents officiels, faux reçus d'achats fictifs, dont l'apparence impeccable assurait le règlement par le Trésor [14].

Le pillage était général. A l'armée d'Italie, il fallut mettre en cause les généraux, l'état-major, l'administration tout entière, spécialement les directions des hôpitaux, des charrois, des transports et des remontes. Bonaparte dut se résoudre à rappeler le commissaire ordonnateur en chef. A l'armée du Rhin, le pillage était effroyable, des contributions écrasantes étaient levées sur les habitants, des généraux menaient une vie scandaleuse parmi les filles et les éléments les plus douteux de l'armée et de la région. A l'armée de l'Ouest, Bernadotte faisait forcer les caisses publiques. En Hollande, tour à tour Brune et Augereau exploitaient le pays [15].

Remonter ce courant ? Quelle audace, quelle tâche et quels risques ! Carnot brava la difficulté et paya d'exemple ; ainsi refusa-t-il les 50 000 francs qu'un fournisseur lui proposait, suivant l'usage, à l'occasion d'un marché. Il donna les ordres les plus stricts pour interdire les trafics d'influence, pour faire examiner et connaître toutes les offres de fournisseurs afin qu'on ne puisse dire « qu'on donne la préférence à ceux qui ont plus de crédit et de faveur [16] ».

On peut admettre que l'assainissement fut réalisé dans les bureaux du ministère, encore n'oserait-on s'en porter garant. Mais aux armées ? Là Carnot se heurtait à l'autorité jalouse des généraux en chef ; il devait essuyer les plus étonnantes rebuffades, bien révélatrices du militarisme qui dominait la France.

Voici d'abord le cas le plus favorable, celui de l'armée du Rhin, commandée par Moreau, ami déclaré de Carnot. Le commissaire du gouvernement des nouveaux départements de la rive gauche du Rhin, Shée, avait signalé à Clarke la conduite scandaleuse des généraux, états-majors et conseil de guerre de Mayence.

Aussitôt, le 26 juin, Carnot fit décider par Cambacérès, en l'absence de Bonaparte parti pour l'Italie, l'envoi d'un commissaire revêtu de pouvoirs exceptionnels. Il choisit le général Pille qu'il connaissait de longue date. A peine celui-ci fut-il arrivé que Moreau lui interdit d'agir et s'en prit à Carnot : « Je vous laisse à penser combien la mission qu'on donne au général Pille est humiliante... pour moi. » Carnot dut envoyer une lettre d'apaisement. La région de Mayence passa sous le commandement d'Augereau, alors Carnot renonça à son projet et, le 12 juillet, rappela Pille. Dans l'intervalle un espion double, Nau, familier de Thuring, avait pu s'évader. Thuring lui-même, par la menace, avait exigé des certificats d'honnêteté des communes qu'il avait volées. En revanche Shée avait réuni les pièces d'un dossier qui incriminait une série de généraux, le conseil de guerre de Mayence et le contrôleur de la poste qui avait violé le secret des lettres pour aider Nau. Carnot demanda des sanctions sévères; quatre généraux furent réformés le 29 septembre, malgré Moreau qui n'accusait que Thuring, malgré Augereau qui s'était plaint à Bonaparte, le 2 août. Mais l'espion s'était évadé, le dossier d'accusation avait été mal constitué, les officiers condamnés furent réintégrés un peu plus tard. En somme, l'effet cherché n'avait pas été obtenu [17].

A l'armée de l'Ouest, ce fut bien autre chose. Bernadotte qui la commandait décida, faute de fonds, de prélever ce qui lui était nécessaire sur la caisse des receveurs généraux. L'un d'eux, celui du Finistère, s'en plaignit vivement et fut appuyé par Lucien Bonaparte, ministre de l'Intérieur. Carnot admit que l'acte était « répréhensible et même désastreux », mais il exposa aux Consuls qu'il y avait 800 000 francs de solde arriéré à l'armée de l'Ouest, et que le dénuement provoquait des rébellions. Il concluait en demandant un rappel à l'ordre, général, sans aucune sanction.

Cependant Bernadotte écrivait à Carnot que « ceux qui

ont conduit les troupes » peuvent comprendre ces nécessités. Il se plaignait, d'autre part, à Bonaparte : « Il est nécessaire que le ministre ne s'endorme pas.... Le ministre annonce deux mille habits des magasins de Rouen, il n'y en existe pas un seul. L'ordonnateur de cette place mande qu'il a tout dirigé sur Dijon, par son ordre. » Avec quelque vivacité, Bernadotte écrivait à Carnot son espoir « que le ministre daignerait s'occuper de cette armée », et la nécessité où il avait été de se pourvoir lui-même, « si j'avais attendu l'effet des ordres donnés par le ministère... », mais il terminait en affirmant qu'il ne s'en prenait pas personnellement à Carnot, « mon devoir et ma délicatesse exigent que je dise la vérité ; le Premier Consul, comme vous, aime à l'entendre ».

Carnot, loin de se formaliser, précisa qu'il disposait de trois millions par décade, transmis avec de longs retards, et qu'il ne pouvait faire mieux. Il disait à Bernadotte toute l'estime qu'il avait pour son caractère et la confiance en son talent. Il lui rappelait le temps où Bernadotte était lui-même ministre de la Guerre. Le général, loin de se montrer conciliant, répondit cavalièrement. Quand il était ministre, il devait rappeler souvent les bureaux à leurs devoirs, car ils étaient négligents, comme ceux de Carnot qui n'avertissaient pas Bernadotte des mesures intéressant l'armée de l'Ouest.

Cette fois Carnot se fâcha : « Je ne saurais approuver que vous arrêtiez l'exécution des ordres que je trouve à propos de donner. » Il blâmait les prélèvements dans les caisses, « illégalement ordonnés par vous », il avait pourtant appliqué cette méthode inégale, lui-même, aux Pyrénées ! Il affirmait que l'armée de l'Ouest recevait plus que les autres, il spécifiait aussi qu'il n'avait pas à communiquer les ordres qu'il donnait, sinon s'il le jugeait à propos.

A cette « lettre de semonce », comme on l'a qualifiée, Bernadotte riposta avec une insolence calculée, affirmant n'avoir été « que froidement affecté... des reproches immérités que vous vous êtes cru autorisé à me faire », et faisant la leçon à Carnot : « Les lois et les usages militaires, et par-dessus tout notre propre conscience, nous imposent, citoyen ministre, des obligations.... » Il rappelait en outre son caractère de conseiller d'État et de général en chef, ajoutant que, s'il était amené à recourir à des mesures extraordinaires, il en rendrait compte au Premier Consul et en donnerait avis au ministre.

Mais les pointes les plus acérées étaient dirigées contre le passé de Carnot : « Nous ne sommes plus au temps où une dénonciation et l'inimitié d'un homme puissant étaient un arrêt de mort contre un général.... Dans tous les cas, je ne puis que vous plaindre si vous ne rendez pas justice à un homme que vous avez intéressé dans vos malheurs, et qui vous a jugé avec indulgence dans votre carrière politique. »

Le lendemain, Bernadotte ajoutait encore un trait à cette lettre. Il s'opposait aux mesures que Carnot lui avait ordonné de prendre contre les insurgés : « Je n'ai pas prétendu provoquer l'autorisation de transformer les soldats en mouchards. » Dès lors, le ministre et le général communiquèrent par l'intermédiaire d'un chef d'état-major ou se contentèrent d'échanger des télégrammes. Bonaparte se garda bien de trancher le différend [18].

Carnot était donc pris entre l'insuffisance de son autorité et de ses ressources et les exigences des généraux. Pour mettre fin aux concussions, il lui aurait fallu obtenir des sanctions que Bonaparte lui-même ne pouvait infliger sans danger : « J'ai besoin d'une extrême habileté pour contenir cette foule impatiente et enorgueillie de généraux qui ambitionnent le poste brillant que j'occupe [19]. » Il aurait fallu aussi des crédits qui faisaient encore défaut. Carnot se plaignait des services financiers, plus spécialement du directeur du Trésor. Ce fut, au dire de Bonaparte, l'une des causes de son départ [20].

Pendant ce temps, les troupes manquaient de tout : vêtements, équipements, ravitaillement, solde. Il n'était chef d'armée qui ne fît le tableau le plus effrayant du dénuement de ses hommes, et c'était là un fait corroboré par tous les témoins, par les inspecteurs aux revues notamment. Masséna et Suchet, Augereau et Moreau, Bernadotte, tous étalaient leurs misères et réclamaient des fonds, des envois, des ressources. Carnot reconnaissait leurs besoins, mais continuait de penser qu'il fallait vivre sur le pays, ou plutôt que les prélèvements faits sur les pays occupés auraient dû fournir l'essentiel aux armées. Tous ses correspondants sûrs confirmaient ce qu'on savait des vols, dilapidations, brigandages divers [21].

En attendant que ces maux fussent supprimés — ce qui devait longtemps tarder — il fallait parer au plus pressé. Carnot voulut d'abord fournir aux troupes qui combattaient, mais il ne put ignorer celles qui assuraient l'ordre à l'intérieur, dans les divisions territoriales, car elles étaient guettées par les ennemis du régime, qui les provoquaient à la désertion et qui se réjouissaient des violences commises contre les habitants, car elles discréditaient le Consulat. Cette fois, les généraux n'étaient plus seuls à se plaindre, ils étaient soutenus par les préfets, par les ministres même, de l'Intérieur et de la Police, Louis Bonaparte et Fouché.

Que pouvait faire Carnot, sinon se retourner vers les Consuls pour leur dépeindre la situation, insister sur les risques, fournir des preuves ? Mais les crédits demeuraient insuffisants. Du moins s'appliqua-t-il à faire cesser les réquisitions partielles, incontrôlables, telles qu'on les pratiquait aux armées, et à faire procéder à des adjudications, par département, pour les troupes de l'intérieur. Encore fallait-il que les adjudicataires fussent payés, au moins partiellement, ce qui n'allait pas sans mal. Certains se lassaient et ne fournissaient plus, certaines unités se soulevaient. Bonaparte n'intervenait pas. Carnot était là pour régler ces difficultés [22].

* * *

Le ministère de la Guerre était aussi un ministère de l'Intérieur et de la Police. Les généraux qui commandaient les divisions territoriales devaient rendre compte de l'« esprit public » et s'appliquer à l'améliorer. Leur rôle était encore plus important dans les départements et les villes soumis à l'état de siège : ils devaient y assurer l'ordre, préparer la mise en application de la constitution, obtenir les levées d'hommes et d'argent, le tout en alliant la fermeté à l'indulgence, les sanctions aux amnisties. Encore devaient-ils s'entendre avec les préfets.

Or les généraux méprisaient les « pékins », et les préfets étaient imbus de leur importance. Lucien Bonaparte soutenait ses préfets et demandait à Carnot « de faire aimer le gouvernement en faisant respecter la liberté civile ». Carnot rédigea une circulaire dans ce sens et s'adressa directement aux généraux et aux préfets les plus acharnés. Il s'appliquait à les calmer, quitte à proposer des déplacements dans les cas les plus désespérés ; ainsi fit-il muter le général Carteaux [23].

« Vous allez dans un pays difficile.... Les Provençaux sont frondeurs et turbulents, toujours prêts à se jeter dans les extrêmes. » En ces termes, Bonaparte mettait en garde Thibaudeau, nommé préfet des Bouches-du-Rhône. C'était le cri unanime, Miot de Mélito observait sur place les brigandages, les meurtres, les fureurs sanguinaires et l'absurde intolérance.

Carnot ne l'ignorait pas, lui qui avait, pendant des mois, tenté la pacification par l'entremise du général Willot. Le choix était mauvais, on l'avait vu depuis, mais celui qui le remplaçait, en 1800, n'était pas mieux qualifié. Le général Férino était zélé, droit, honnête, mais totalement dépourvu de sens politique et de sang-froid. Il s'échauffait aisément, tonnait et prenait des mesures malheureuses. Il dénonçait les anarchistes, Antonelli, Félix Lepelletier, il malmenait les autorités civiles, puis il accordait de généreuses et imprudentes amnisties. A l'occasion, il faisait procéder à des exécutions sommaires. Lucien Bonaparte et Fouché s'inquiétèrent et demandèrent à Carnot d'intervenir. Des mois passèrent sans apporter d'amélioration notable.

Dans le Sud-Ouest, la situation était moins grave, mais elle n'évoluait pas mieux. La région était commandée par un général pourvu de pouvoirs exceptionnels, Servan, l'ancien ministre aux Pyrénées. Servan avait félicité chaleureusement Carnot quand celui-ci avait été nommé ministre : « Enfin, j'écris à un homme qui me lira avec un peu d'indulgence. » Il en avait en effet grand besoin. Dans sa division, il s'était laissé influencer par des royalistes et avait combattu les républicains. Carnot lui exprima ses regrets et son amitié, mais il le fit remplacer [24].

La levée des conscrits amena aussi quelques dissentiments entre le ministre de la Guerre et les préfets. La levée était lente : du 8 mars au 19 mai, elle fournit 15 732 hommes sur 170 000. Les préfets accordaient libéralement des dispenses — plus de quatre mille dans la 17e division ; ils acceptaient des remplaçants incapables de servir. Un officier supérieur fut chargé de veiller à la levée des conscrits dans chaque département. Carnot estimait que « le recrutement par voie de conscription était le seul qui puisse nous convenir », mais il aurait voulu éliminer la pratique des congés achetés abusivement, sinon celle du remplacement, qu'il avait toujours condamnée, mais qui s'inscrivait dans la politique consulaire.

Malgré tout, Carnot dressait un bilan favorable. Il avait maintenu les effectifs : 464 000 hommes au début de 1800, 450 000 en septembre. Malheureusement il y avait parmi eux — et même parmi les officiers — des hommes qui pouvaient « flétrir » l'armée par leur immoralité ou la compromettre par leur ignorance; on donnait trop à l'ancienneté et à la bravoure, pas assez aux « talents ». On comptait trop d'officiers âgés et incapables. Le matériel, notamment dans l'Artillerie, manquait faute de fonds, la comptabilité était inextricable, et la qualité des canons et des fusils fabriqués pendant la Révolution avait été médiocre ; grâce aux hommes de talents, elle commençait de s'améliorer. Les armes savantes souffraient d'un recrutement improvisé pendant la Révolution et qui avait introduit dans leurs cadres beaucoup trop d'officiers non sélectionnés par examen. Déjà une revision avait été entamée, qu'il importait de mener à bon terme. Le recrutement et la formation des officiers par les écoles donnaient de bons résultats, surtout grâce à l'apport de l'École polytechnique. Chemin faisant, Carnot exaltait le rôle du Génie, en paix comme en guerre, dans la défensive comme dans l'offensive. La gendarmerie et les conseils de Guerre avaient amélioré la discipline ; le nombre des poursuites pour insubordination, désertion et vol s'était fortement accru.

Tout n'était pas accompli, cependant, en matière de remise en ordre : « Les abus inévitables dans une si vaste administration ont été augmentés par les désordres de la Révolution.... Il faut la fixité du gouvernement et l'esprit de suite, au lieu de cette continuelle versatilité dans les hommes et dans les choses, qui faisaient depuis plusieurs années le malheur de la France. »

Les innovations séduisaient Carnot : il proposait la création de compagnies de «télégraphiers » dans les diverses armées, il préconisait aussi la formation d'unités de nageurs, il s'intéressait aux projets de Fulton pour la navigation sous-marine.

L'œuvre était énorme et aurait dû se poursuivre longtemps; il n'en fut rien. Mais, avant d'aborder la rupture qui interrompit l'entreprise de Carnot, il importe de noter ce qu'il fit pendant la guerre, dans la direction des opérations [25].

***

Le seul organisateur de la victoire, désormais, était Bonaparte. L'élaboration des plans de campagne, leur mise en œuvre, leurs retouches successives au gré des circonstances, la répartition des forces et des commandements

qui devaient en assurer le succès, tout revenait au Premier
Consul. Le ministre de la Guerre était un chef d'état-major
général, chargé de détailler et de répartir les ordres, d'acheminer les unités, de correspondre avec les généraux en chef,
de vérifier les résultats obtenus, de rendre compte au
Premier Consul. Ainsi avait fait Berthier, admirable chef
d'état-major ; ainsi fit Carnot, accoutumé à ce rôle.

Ce qui compliquait un peu les choses c'était ce Cabinet
historique et topographique, qu'il avait naguère créé et qui
demeurait à la disposition de Bonaparte sous le commandement de Clarke. C'était un rouage parallèle et qui remplis-
sait la même fonction. Il assurait l'indépendance totale et
l'application directe de l'autorité du Premier Consul. Mais il
permettait aux généraux d'éluder les ordres de l'un — plutôt
ceux du ministre — en se réclamant de ceux de l'autre —
le Premier Consul. Ceux-ci, d'ailleurs, n'avaient pas encore,
à beaucoup près, le caractère impérieux, indiscutable,
qu'ils revêtirent dans la suite. On en jugera aisément
d'après certains heurts aussi curieux que gênants pour
Carnot.

Au début de son ministère, la situation générale était
difficile : Masséna était aux prises avec des forces ennemies
qui le dominaient en Italie, Moreau n'avait pas encore
commencé l'offensive sur le Rhin, Bonaparte se préparait
à intervenir dans la plaine du Pô. Il fallait coordonner le
tout, c'était l'affaire de Bonaparte. Mais il fallait faire
accepter à Moreau d'appuyer Bonaparte, et à Augereau
d'appuyer Moreau. Or ces trois hommes se jalousaient et se
haïssaient. Berthier, qui préparait en Bourgogne l'armée dite
de réserve, et que Bonaparte fit triompher à Marengo, dut
négocier une manière de compromis entre Bonaparte et
Moreau. Celui-ci accepta, le 16 avril, à Bâle, de fournir des
renforts à Bonaparte dès qu'il aurait lui-même obtenu des
victoires. Précaution stratégique ? Soucis d'amour-propre ?
Les deux à la fois, mais cela réservait bien des difficultés
d'application.

Le 24 avril, Bonaparte enjoignit à Carnot d'envoyer
d'urgence les forces de Berthier en Italie. Carnot les envoya
en Suisse, leur ordonnant de passer en Italie seulement
après avoir fourni à Moreau le moyen d'obtenir ses victoires,
conformément aux arrangements de Bâle. On a dit que
Carnot s'était mépris et qu'il avait commis une grave
erreur dans la transmission des ordres. Interprétation super-

ficielle : l'esprit de Carnot était la précision même, et toute
sa correspondance le montre soucieux alors de favoriser les
victoires de Moreau. Bonaparte ne pouvait se flatter de
dicter à Moreau son plan d'action, ni la date de sa réalisation ; celui-ci lui avait fait connaître ses vues. Carnot, ami
de Moreau, pouvait plus dans ce domaine que le Premier
Consul lui-même. Et c'est pourquoi, le 24 avril précisément,
Carnot pressait Moreau, lui dépeignant la situation désespérée de Masséna. « Vous seul, mon cher général, pouvez
prévenir de si grands malheurs en attaquant avec impétuosité.... Je vous conjure donc, mon cher général, au nom du
salut de la patrie, d'ouvrir la campagne sans hésiter....
Dans les circonstances actuelles, les Consuls attendent
votre réponse avec une impatience inexprimable.... Vous
connaissez, mon cher général, ma haute estime et mon tendre
attachement pour vous. »

Moreau fut favorable à cet appel : « Vos ordres sont
exécutés, mon cher ministre, écrivait-il le 27 avril. Tout
marche et je présume que nous aborderons l'ennemi dans
quelques jours.... Comptez, mon cher ministre, sur notre
dévouement et soyez sûr que notre marche sera aussi
rapide que possible..., personne ne vous estime et ne vous
aime plus que moi. » Le même jour, Moreau rassurait aussi
le Premier Consul et lui affirmait son attachement.

La victoire répondit à ces promesses et Moreau entretint
bientôt Bonaparte des possibilités d'un armistice. Mauvaise
nouvelle pour le Premier Consul, la gloire de Moreau devenait encombrante ; d'ailleurs, Bonaparte avait déjà décidé
de lui demander les renforts promis ; un arrêté des Consuls
réclamait, le 5 mai, l'envoi de 20 000 hommes en Italie.
Moreau s'exécuterait-il, et dans quels délais ? Carnot fut
chargé d'obtenir un résultat favorable et prompt.

Le 6 mai, Bonaparte et Carnot quittèrent Paris, l'un pour
Genève et l'Italie, l'autre pour l'armée du Rhin. Et l'on
disait, dans le public, que chacun allait diriger les opérations
et que la victoire et la paix ne tarderaient pas. Ce parallé-
lisme ne pouvait plaire à Bonaparte.

Carnot voyagea jour et nuit et parvint à Biberach le 10 au
matin. Il obtint de Moreau le renfort désiré, mais non sans
peine : « Ma présence a été très utile, écrivait-il à Lacuée,
pour dissiper les préventions qu'on avait cherché à faire
naître dans son esprit contre le gouvernement.... Je devais
m'attendre à faire beaucoup de peine au général en chef,

l'arrêter dans le cours de ses plus brillantes victoires..., il a acquiescé après m'avoir représenté les inconvénients qui pouvaient en résulter pour l'armée du Rhin.... » Il est vrai que les victoires de Moreau plaçaient la demande des renforts dans le cas prévu par l'accord de Bâle.

Le 15 mai, à six heures du matin, Carnot arrivait à Genève, où il retrouva Bonaparte, et lui rendit compte de sa mission. Il voulait « produire sur son esprit un effet réciproque et semblable » à celui qu'il avait obtenu sur Moreau. Il notait les besoins de l'armée de Bonaparte et les signalait aussitôt à Lacuée. Puis il regagnait Paris en passant par Chalon-sur-Saône et par Dijon, où il avait demandé à ses frères de se réunir. Il avait reçu 24 000 francs pour ses frais de voyage, il n'avait dépensé que 13 800 francs et il rendit le reste, ce qui n'était guère l'habitude.

A peine arrivé, le 21 mai, Carnot écrivait à Bonaparte pour lui signaler que les généraux Pérignon et Grouchy avaient eu un entretien avec le général autrichien Bellegarde, qui souhaitait l'ouverture de négociations secrètes. Carnot soumettait cette information à Bonaparte sans autre commentaire, « bien convaincu, déclarait-il, qu'une paix honorable est l'objet de vos vœux les plus ardents et de votre sollicitude ». Le Premier Consul répondit aimablement mais évasivement ; il songeait à remporter une victoire avant de négocier. Pour plus de sécurité, Carnot recommandait à Moreau, le 31 mai, d'attirer « toutes les forces et l'attention de l'ennemi ».

Mission ingrate. Moreau, affaibli, devait affronter l'ennemi en évitant d'engager une lutte incertaine. Ses officiers s'en irritaient ; le général Leclerc écrivait, le 4 juin, à son « beau-frère Bonaparte » pour dénoncer « cette manière lente et indécise de faire la guerre » ; il déplorait le manque d'autorité de son chef et ajoutait, pour mieux brouiller les deux hommes : « Votre gloire offusque Moreau, il répète souvent qu'à l'armée d'Italie on faisait la guerre comme des écoliers, et que la guerre savante est celle qu'il fait. On parle souvent de la *faction italique*.... »

La crise était si grave que Carnot devait exhorter Moreau d'user de son autorité : « J'ai même appris que les généraux se permettaient de modifier vos ordres eux-mêmes. » Le chef d'état-major de Moreau déclarait que le manque de ressources paralysait l'administration des transports d'artillerie qui refusait tout service, cependant que Bonaparte réclamait des munitions. Les généraux demandaient à quitter leur poste, Leclerc écrivait à son beau-frère : « Moreau ne vous aime pas, sa haine va jusqu'à ne me jamais fournir l'occasion de me distinguer. » Baraguey d'Hilliers dénonçait l'imposture des rapports officiels de son général Cependant Moreau assurait Bonaparte de son dévouement, mais il le félicita assez froidement au lendemain de Marengo.

Au début de juillet, il s'agit de confier à Moreau le commandement supérieur des armées d'Augereau et de Brune, en plus de l'armée du Rhin. Moreau s'en défendit ; il ne donna la vraie raison qu'au seul Carnot, et confidentiellement : ces armées « ne serviront qu'à... me priver de ressources que je pourrais tirer, commandées... par des officiers généraux qui me détestent très cordialement, vous ne l'ignorez pas ».

C'est juste à ce moment que l'affaire de Mayence et la mission du général Pille refroidit momentanément ses sentiments à l'égard de Carnot.

Les relations de Moreau avec Augereau furent assez singulières : Moreau lui indiquait, « par manière d'avis, les mouvements qui se coordonneraient de la manière la plus utile avec ceux que le gouvernement prescrirait à l'armée du Rhin ».

Carnot s'appliquait à mettre Moreau « en garde contre les intrigants qui essaieraient d'altérer une réciprocité de sentiments » favorables entre Moreau et Bonaparte, et à subordonner Augereau.

Dans sa *Réponse à Bailleul*, Carnot avait traité Augereau de « fier coquin », nul n'avait pu l'oublier. Leurs rapports furent hostiles dès le premier jour. Carnot soumit pourtant à l'agrément du général le projet d'organisation de l'entretien et de la solde des troupes par le gouvernement batave, qu'il avait trouvé en arrivant au ministère. Augereau le remercia de cette confiance, mais condamna ce projet « onéreux » et « humiliant », et il écrivit à Bonaparte pour en souligner les inconvénients.

Quelques jours plus tard il se plaignit vivement qu'on lui envoyât un renfort d'anciens prisonniers de guerre, inutilisables contre les Autrichiens.

En juillet, quand il fallut se soumettre à Moreau, Augereau devint rétif. Il réclama des renforts, se plaignit des marches et contremarches qui lui étaient prescrites. Il refusa d'exécuter des ordres de Carnot, peu clairs, sinon contradictoires, et s'en expliqua nettement à Bonaparte, déclarant qu'il attendait désormais des ordres directs du Premier Consul : « l'obéissance eût été un crime ».

Enfin, le 15 août, il félicita ironiquement Carnot d'être entré dans ses vues en lui envoyant un contrordre. Et il adressait le même jour une lettre étonnante à Bonaparte.

« Citoyen Consul, j'ai lieu de penser que vous ne doutez pas de mon inviolable attachement pour vous. Il m'impose le devoir de vous dévoiler mes sentiments. Je suis mécontent de Carnot, et révolté de sa correspondance. Si je ne lui ai pas témoigné à lui-même, c'est uniquement par considération pour vous, mais ma prudence et ma patience commencent à m'abandonner, et je serai forcé de quitter le commandement si j'ai toujours à redouter des pièges ou à éprouver des contrariétés. Cet homme n'est ni mon ami, ni le vôtre, je le déteste autant qu'il peut me haïr, et je ne peux pas voir tranquillement entre les mains de mon ennemi les moyens de compromettre ma réputation et le sort de l'armée. Je m'abstiendrai de rompre avec lui pour ne pas vous désobliger, mais il faut que vous me permettiez de me retirer, et si, quand il sera hors du ministère, vous avez besoin de moi, vous savez que je vous suis dévoué comme à mon pays.... »

Magnifique cri de haine, qui fut suivi d'une nouvelle déclaration par laquelle Augereau affirmait attendre les ordres directs de Bonaparte, et d'une lettre non moins vive à Lannes :

« Le dégoût et l'amertume dont Carnot m'abreuve sont tels que, je te l'avoue, mon ami, si le Premier Consul ne veut pas mettre un frein aux vexations que ce ministre multiplie pour moi, je suis bien décidé à me retirer; c'est sans doute ce que Carnot désire, mais il met à bout toute ma constance, et, ma foi, je n'y peux plus tenir. » Il terminait en dénonçant les plans « machiavéliques » de ce « caméléon »; il affirmait qu'il était malade « du mauvais sang que cet homme [lui faisait] faire jour et nuit ».

Augereau n'était pas sans inquiétude sur les sentiments de Bonaparte à son égard, il lui répétait fréquemment son attachement et le conjurait de ne se fier qu'à de vieux amis comme lui. Bonaparte lui répondait, peu mais cordialement [26].

Le ton des relations entre Bernadotte et Carnot était tel, nous l'avons vu, que le rôle du ministre était devenu pratiquement intenable. Encore n'avons-nous noté que les traits les plus forts, concernant l'affaire des caisses forcées.

Bonaparte, d'autre part, refusait à Carnot des décisions que celui-ci sollicitait personnellement. Par exemple, une promotion pour Prieur de la Côte-d'Or, une pension à la veuve du général Houchard, des projets sur la réorganisation du Génie [27].

Ainsi soumis aux directives du Premier Consul et en butte à l'hostilité ou à la fierté ombrageuse des généraux, Carnot dut-il limiter son action et bientôt même renoncer à la poursuivre. Peu à peu il allait glisser dans l'opposition.

CHAPITRE X

JE VOTERAI CONTRE L'EMPIRE

LE 29 AOUT 1800, pour des raisons de santé, Carnot donnait sa démission ; dans une note personnelle, il expliquait sa décision par son « inflexibilité » — il s'agissait là autant des idées que du caractère ; or, depuis Marengo, Bonaparte ne tolérait plus les gens inflexibles.

La victoire avait d'abord semblé resserrer les liens entre les deux hommes. « J'espère, mon cher ministre, que vous êtes content de nous », jamais Bonaparte n'avait usé d'un ton aussi cordial avec Carnot. Et celui-ci avait envoyé ses félicitations chaleureuses, lui disant « la joie de tous les cœurs français et la sienne ». Il écrivait à Dupont : « Bonaparte peut dire, à plus juste titre que César, *veni, vidi, vici.* Qu'il revienne promptement, sa moisson de lauriers est faite, mais qu'il n'oublie pas la petite branche d'olivier [1]. »

Mais quand Bonaparte fut de retour, Fouché lui dénonça les agissements de Lucien et de Talleyrand ; d'autre part Lucien dénonçait Talleyrand, et tous parlaient de Carnot. Il fallut élucider l'affaire, et elle ne le fut que très imparfaitement.

Au départ de Bonaparte on avait envisagé, dans quelques cercles, l'éventualité de sa mort au combat.

Dans la suite, les nouvelles tardèrent et, bientôt, le bruit d'une défaite fut même propagé. Miot et Stanislas de Girardin ont raconté l'inquiétude de Joseph Bonaparte et la conversation qu'ils eurent avec lui, le 30 ou 31 mai. Sieyès avait réuni les membres des Commissions législatives formées le 19 brumaire, à l'occasion du coup d'État, et avait envisagé la décision à prendre en cas de mort du Premier Consul. Tous avaient jugé que le mieux serait de confier le pouvoir à Carnot. En revanche, Joseph redoutait de voir Carnot ramener les anciens Conventionnels et disgracier la famille Bonaparte ; il avait cherché à susciter un rival à

Carnot, mais il demeurait hésitant. Rœderer reconnut le fait quand Bonaparte lui en parla; celui-ci ne semblait pas irrité : « Carnot vaudrait peut-être plus qu'un autre, si Carnot était du goût de tout le monde. » Fouché, au contraire, affirme que Bonaparte ne pardonna pas, bien que Fouché eût déclaré que Carnot n'était pas même au courant de ces intrigues. Le bruit fit son chemin puisque le cabinet anglais en fut informé [2].

Peut-être aussi Bonaparte fut-il mécontent du soin que mit Carnot à faire publier une relation de Marengo due au général Dupont et qui ne s'accordait pas avec celle de Berthier [3].

Peut-être encore était-il irrité que certains voulussent attribuer une part des victoires à l'action de Carnot ? Il avait déclaré en effet, après une discussion, que « Carnot n'était pas un homme aussi distingué qu'on avait bien voulu le prétendre [4] ».

Carnot restait lié à son passé. Il avait contre lui les hommes de fructidor qui l'avaient banni. Il soutenait les fructidorisés; l'un d'eux a déclaré que Carnot lui avait écrit pour lui offrir des secours et qu'il avait réuni les anciens proscrits qui se trouvaient à Paris et les avait placés, soit dans les administrations militaires, soit dans celle des hôpitaux, soit dans les bureaux de la Guerre.

A l'appui de ces dires, bien tardifs, on peut relever des démarches faites par Carnot en faveur du fils de Tronson-Ducoudray, et en faveur de gens patronnés par Siméon, Paradis, Barbé-Marbois. On peut aussi mentionner l'appui qu'il accorda à Vaublanc pour le faire entrer au Tribunat, les promesses données à Grisel pour un avancement, et la réintégration d'un capitaine de gendarmerie, Beffroy, réformé après fructidor, parce que parent de Beffroy de Reigny. Celui-ci même fut proposé comme tribun ou législateur. Beffroy, de son propre aveu, mit un zèle indiscret à recommander une multitude de solliciteurs à Carnot et il finit par l'aigrir [5].

« Le sens dans lequel Carnot inclinait provoqua des récriminations et des craintes, et les généraux qui ont figuré au 18 fructidor attendent à chaque instant l'avis de leur non-activité », écrivait le général Dugua, préfet du Calvados, à Bourrienne. Il y eut même quelques démarches des hommes de 1793 et de 1794, une lettre fière de Bouchotte qui en appelait à l'équité de Carnot pour obtenir une promotion, une autre de Gillet, par l'entremise d'Oudot, en faveur de Saint-Cyr-Nugues, ancien chef de bureau au Comité de Salut public [6].

C'était assez pour montrer que Carnot n'appartenait ni au clan des Brumairiens, ni à celui des partisans du pouvoir personnel. Toutefois Bonaparte refusa la démission de Carnot, le 1er septembre, en termes flatteurs — à peu près ceux dont il avait usé envers Gaudin dans une circonstance analogue.

Mais, le 8 octobre, Carnot insista fortement : « Je vous donne de nouveau ma démission ; veuillez bien, Citoyens Consuls, ne plus différer à l'accepter. » Cette démission fut acceptée sur-le-champ et officiellement annoncée, dans les termes les plus singuliers : « Pendant l'absence du général Berthier, nommé ministre de la Guerre, le citoyen Lacuée, conseiller d'État, sera chargé du portefeuille de ce département. »

Fouché a écrit qu'il avait été chargé par Bonaparte de demander cette démission à Carnot. On faisait grief à celui-ci de défendre les libertés publiques, de reprocher au gouvernement les faveurs accordées aux royalistes et la pompe royale qui entourait le Premier Consul. C'était au lendemain d'un attentat contre Bonaparte et l'on poursuivait les hommes de la Révolution.

Carnot avait déjà renoncé aux fonctions d'inspecteur général aux revues ; il renouvela sa démission de ce poste, le 19 octobre.

« Quoique j'aie jugé à propos de donner ma démission, je m'inquiète peu de dissuader ceux qui assurent que j'ai été disgracié. » Un mot de Mathieu Dumas explique ce qui s'était passé : « Connaissant votre caractère, vos principes d'administration et votre indépendance de cœur et d'esprit, je n'ai point été surpris de votre détermination [7]. »

Ce qui souligne la tension entre Carnot et Bonaparte, c'est le soin extrême que Carnot prit à dresser et à présenter le compte rendu de son activité au ministère. Il s'entoura des conseils de Feulint et de Collignon, renonça à publier son rapport et le réduisit à un compte financier, car, spécifiait-il, « si les ordres qu'a dû faire exécuter le ministre s'étaient trouvés parfois en opposition avec son propre système administratif, on voit aisément la teinte défavorable qu'il pourrait donner aux premiers ».

Clarke avait accepté de transmettre ce rapport à Maret qui

le présenterait au Premier Consul, mais, quand il lut la déclaration de Carnot, il insista pour la faire supprimer, car elle
servirait « à de certains personnages occupés à indisposer
contre vous le gouvernement ».

Quelques jours plus tôt, le 9 février 1801, Clarke avait
écrit à « son cher bienfaiteur » le bon souvenir que Bonaparte
conservait du travail de Carnot au ministère ; « il en parle
comme j'en parlerais moi-même, et s'il y a un *mais* à la suite
de cet éloge, votre frère, qui a trouvé je ne sais comment
le moyen d'en être instruit, sait que, malgré les apparences,
il ne doit pas tomber sur vous, je le sais aussi. Ce sera à lui
à vous en instruire. »

Des incidents avaient éclaté : un employé révoqué pour
les irrégularités de ses opérations avait soulevé une affaire
de fournitures, le ministre des Finances avait remis en
question un règlement fait par Carnot. Collignon fournit
toutes les pièces qui disculpaient l'ancien ministre, mais
l'alerte avait été vive.

Ainsi Carnot quittait le ministère sans le moindre mot de
satisfaction de la part de Bonaparte. Celui-ci avait même
refusé, le 20 octobre, de nommer Carnot général de division,
comme Lacuée l'avait demandé, en termes pressants et déli-
cats, à l'insu de l'intéressé [8].

* *

Le thème de la retraite champêtre, studieuse et digne,
revint désormais dans toutes les correspondances, sous la
plume de Carnot et sous celle de ses amis. Prieur de la Côte-
d'Or écrivait le 7 novembre : « Ma pensée va souvent te
chercher dans ta retraite, mon cher Carnot. Je t'y vois...,
entouré de tes proches, donnant déjà des soins à l'éducation
de ton fils, consacrant quelques méditations aux sciences,
et peut-être, dans un autre genre, traçant de ta plume expé-
rimentée quelques leçons utiles à ton pays. » Carnot répondait de la même encre qu'il préférait la vie paisible aux
tracas et aux intrigues de la capitale, que sa femme partageait ce goût, et qu'ils s'étaient fixés définitivement à
Saint-Omer [9].

La vie familiale fut égayée par la naissance d'un second
fils, Hippolyte, le futur biographe de Lazare. C'était un
compagnon pour l'aîné, Sadi, dont la solitude avait été
tempérée par le séjour de ses jeunes cousins [10].

Carnot songeait aussi à ses travaux scientifiques. Il avait

publié naguère, en 1797, ses *Réflexions sur la Métaphysique du Calcul infinitésimal*, aussitôt traduites en espagnol, rééditées bientôt à Bâle ; puis sa *Lettre au citoyen Bossut sur la Trigonométrie*, en 1800. Il y ajouta une étude *De la Corrélation des Figures de Géométrie*, en 1801 ; et enfin il préparait une *Géométrie de Position*, et un exposé des principes fondamentaux *De l'Équilibre et du Mouvement*, qui parurent en 1803.

Ces titres scientifiques justifiaient surabondamment son appartenance à l'Institut, et pourtant il venait d'en être réélu membre, après avoir été rayé.

La première élection remontait au Directoire. Carnot n'avait pas voulu être placé dans la première formation de l'Institut qu'il avait contribué à organiser. Il avait été nommé à la première place vacante, dans la section de mécanique, de préférence à Bréguet. Mais il avait été rayé lors de sa proscription, en fructidor. Son retour avait posé un problème d'autant plus irritant que son cas n'était pas le seul. Les membres de l'Institut étaient-ils réintégrés d'office ? Devaient-ils être réélus ? La première thèse affirmait l'indépendance de l'institution, la seconde cédait aux circonstances. De plus, Bonaparte avait remplacé Carnot à l'Institut ; faudrait-il annuler son élection pour raison de non-vacance du fauteuil ? Enfin l'Institut comptait dans ses rangs des Thermidoriens impénitents, La Revellière lui-même. Les avis se heurtèrent sourdement, mais âprement. Un membre défendait tumultueusement Carnot : les déportés, disait-il, n'avaient pas cessé d'appartenir à la compagnie. Cette campagne de Delisle de Sales plaça ses confrères dans une situation bien désagréable. Le dissentiment risquait de s'éterniser. Survint le décès d'un membre de la classe des Sciences, Carnot fut élu à sa place, le 26 mars 1800. Ainsi se dessinait un compromis que Carnot ne voulut pas ruiner en refusant l'élection [11].

Une année se passa donc dans la vie familiale et les travaux scientifiques.

Pourtant Carnot gardait quelque amertume. Lors d'un voyage rapide à Paris, le Premier Consul lui avait paru distant, et Carnot n'avait pas accepté l'invitation qu'il avait reçue pour la Malmaison. Mais il n'avait pas voulu se tenir à l'écart : « Je suis loin d'être indifférent sur les affaires publiques et le succès du gouvernement », avait-il écrit à Bonaparte.

Un peu plus tard, félicitant son frère, maire de Nolay, d'avoir été porté sur la liste de notabilités nationales, il regrettait que son frère de Chalon eût été écarté : « Quand une fois une famille a déjà éprouvé tant d'injustices et de persécutions, on ne doit s'étonner de rien. » Il faisait allusion aux tracas de Feulint. Celui-ci, malade, avait été désigné pour Saint-Domingue, et sommé de s'y rendre. Carnot avait vainement tenté de le tirer d'affaire. Il était aigri et supportait malaisément l'interruption de son activité politique.

* * *

Lazare fut nommé membre de l'une des assemblées du Consulat, le Tribunat, le 21 mars 1802. Le Sénat avait porté au Tribunat les deux anciens ministres : Lucien Bonaparte et Carnot, mais cette mesure ne rallia pas Carnot aux tendances du régime. Il accepta pourtant, car il songeait aux siens, il le déclarait à son frère de Nolay : « Je désire de tout mon cœur pouvoir y être utile à ma famille. Mais ce sera beaucoup, si je parviens à empêcher qu'on lui fasse du mal [12]. »

Tribun, Carnot se trouvait parmi les idéologues, au centre de l'opposition, mais au lendemain d'une épuration qui devait servir d'avertissement. Carnot, pourtant, combattit toutes les mesures qui conduisaient Bonaparte au pouvoir personnel et la France à la monarchie.

D'abord il prit position contre la création d'une Légion d'honneur, phalange dévouée personnellement au Premier Consul et non pas distinction honorifique. Son opposition fut inefficace et passa inaperçue.

Quand il s'agit du consulat à vie, la mesure étant plus importante, Carnot voulut la combattre plus ostensiblement. Le registre des signatures, où l'on devait porter son avis par oui ou par non, était au pied de la tribune. Carnot siégeait sur les gradins supérieurs. Il descendit pour signer et fut bientôt rejoint par ses collègues, désireux d'éviter un éclat dont le Tribunat tout entier pourrait souffrir. « Chacun le veut empêcher par des procédés différents.... L'un par la menace, l'autre par la prière ; celui-ci le tient par son habit, l'autre veut arrêter son bras, un autre lui retirer sa plume. » Carnot passa outre et inscrivit : « Je sais que je signe ma condamnation. NON. »

Les tribuns atterrés se concertèrent, Lucien les tira d'embarras en faisant ouvrir un nouveau registre. Cette fois, Carnot accepta de signer purement et simplement son vote négatif sans le moindre commentaire [13].

Pour l'établissement de l'Empire Carnot, seul, fut assez courageux pour affirmer publiquement son opposition. Cette fois, il tint à s'en expliquer par un discours. Le 4 avril 1804, la proposition étant déposée, Fabre de l'Aude, président, tenta d'écarter Carnot en lui faisant remarquer qu'il n'était pas inscrit pour prendre la parole. Carnot se fit inscrire sur-le-champ. Le lendemain, il prononça un discours qui lui rendit soudain toute sa célébrité :

« Je suis bien loin de vouloir atténuer les louanges données au Premier Consul : ne dussions-nous à Bonaparte que le Code civil, son nom mériterait de passer à la postérité. Mais... si un citoyen a restauré la liberté politique,... sera-ce une récompense à lui offrir que le sacrifice de cette même liberté ?

« Du moment qu'il fut proposé au peuple français de voter sur la question du consulat à vie... on vit se succéder une foule d'institutions évidemment monarchiques ; mais à chacune d'elles on s'empressa de rassurer les esprits inquiets sur le sort de la liberté, en leur protestant que ces institutions n'étaient imaginées qu'afin de lui procurer la plus haute protection.

« Aujourd'hui se découvre enfin d'une manière positive le terme de tant de mesures préliminaires.

« Je voterai contre le rétablissement de la monarchie.

« J'observerai que le gouvernement d'un seul n'est rien moins qu'un gage assuré de stabilité et de tranquillité.

« Nous n'avons pu établir parmi nous le régime républicain, quoique nous l'ayons essayé sous diverses formes plus ou moins démocratiques. Mais il faut observer que, de toutes les constitutions qui ont été successivement essayées sans succès, il n'en est aucune qui ne fût née au sein des factions, et qui ne fût l'ouvrage de circonstances aussi impérieuses que fugitives : voilà pourquoi toutes ont été vicieuses. Mais, depuis le 18 Brumaire, il s'est trouvé une époque, unique dans les annales du monde, pour méditer à l'abri des orages, pour fonder la liberté sur des bases solides.

« Tout ce qui a été dit jusqu'ici sur le pouvoir absolu prouve seulement la nécessité d'une dictature momentanée dans les crises de l'État, mais non celle d'un pouvoir permanent et inamovible.

« Une république fut organisée dans le calme et subsiste, pleine de sagesse et de vigueur : les États-Unis, et chaque jour leur prospérité reçoit des accroissements qui étonnent les autres nations. Il est moins difficile de former une république sans anarchie qu'une monarchie sans despotisme.

« Jusqu'ici on n'a rien inventé pour pouvoir tempérer le pouvoir suprême, que ce qu'on nomme des Corps intermédiaires ou privilégiés. Serait-ce donc d'une nouvelle noblesse qu'on voudrait parler ? »

Carnot distribua à ses amis des exemplaires de ce discours et lui fit ainsi franchir l'enceinte du Tribunat.

Brusquement Carnot apparut comme le champion de la république : « Je reçois de partout des lettres de félicitations, qu'assurément je n'ai ni mendiées ni commandées. Je suis étonné moi-même du succès prodigieux qu'a obtenu ce discours dans une ville comme celle-ci, depuis longtemps accoutumée à plier sans résistance à toutes les volontés du maître [14]. »

Encore Carnot ne sut-il pas toute la portée de son discours. On en fit circuler des copies, parfois accompagnées d'une prétendue lettre de Bonaparte à Réal, saluant dans ce texte « la noble franchise et ce sentiment de la liberté qui caractérise tout bon citoyen », vantant le régime consulaire et flétrissant les « ambitieux » et les « stipendiés » qui avaient voulu établir l'Empire [15].

Mieux encore. A l'École d'Artillerie et du Génie, une adresse au Premier Consul sur la création de l'Empire fut soumise à la signature des élèves. Quarante-trois de ceux-ci refusèrent de signer et cinq d'entre eux réclamèrent contre l'unanimité de l'acceptation que le général avait voulu déclarer. Le général les accueillit « avec l'indignation » que méritait un pareil acte d'insubordination, et les cinq députés furent envoyés en prison. Alors tous les élèves s'exécutèrent [16].

Ainsi les armes savantes, les talents vibraient à l'unisson de Carnot.

Pourtant, par la suite, le régime impérial fut accepté loyalement par Carnot. N'avait-il pas déclaré dans son discours : « Je fis toujours profession d'être soumis aux lois existantes » ? Il appartint au Tribunat tout le temps que celui-ci exista ; comme tribun, il accepta d'être chevalier de cette Légion d'honneur, qu'il avait combattue ; il signa la formule du serment de fidélité au régime que prêtaient les membres de la Légion d'honneur [17].

Apparemment, rien n'était changé. En fait Carnot, de nouveau, avait brisé sa carrière. Un incident révèle à quel point il était devenu le symbole de l'opposition. On arrêta un étudiant en droit, nommé Berthois, accusé de vouloir assassiner l'Empereur.

« Avez-vous fait part de votre projet à quelqu'un ?

— A un seul homme, celui qui m'a fait prendre, Carnot. »

On trouva une lettre et des notes adressées par Berthois à Carnot : « Comptez-y, Carnot, comptez-y, comptez-y, à Dieu jusqu'au revoir. — Émile. »

Le malheureux avait été rebuté par Carnot, mais c'est vers lui qu'il s'était, d'abord, tourné [18].

Le rôle du Tribunat était des plus effacés : quelques jours après l'entrée de Carnot, il avait été divisé en trois sections indépendantes, celles de Législation, de l'Intérieur et des Finances. Carnot appartenait à la section de l'Intérieur. Par esprit d'opposition, on l'avait élu secrétaire en même temps que Lucien Bonaparte avait été nommé président ; quand celui-ci fut absent, Carnot le remplaça. Il présida notamment les débats sur l'organisation des lycées, il s'intéressa au développement des langues vivantes. En décembre, Lucien fut nommé sénateur et Carnot cessa d'être secrétaire ; dès lors ses interventions devinrent exceptionnelles. On note simplement qu'en 1806 il appuya le projet de création d'un Corps enseignant disposant du monopole universitaire. Il fit partie, à la même époque, d'une commission chargée d'étudier la conservation des édifices militaires. Enfin, il se prononça contre le droit des fonctionnaires à remplir des mandats législatifs.

C'est tout ce qui subsiste de son activité jusqu'à la suppression du Tribunat en août 1807. Alors Carnot, qui appartenait au groupe des tribuns dont le mandat s'achevait, fut rendu à la vie privée. L'Empereur ne lui confia aucune fonction, et lui ne voulut pas en solliciter [19].

CHAPITRE XI

RÉCONCILIATION AVEC NAPOLÉON

L E 7 MARS 1807, à un ami suisse qui demandait son appui
Carnot répondait : « Il faudrait au moins que vous
fussiez soutenu par quelque personnage puissant, et
je ne suis rien moins. Je n'ai conservé aucune relation avec
les hommes qui occupent aujourd'hui les premiers emplois
de l'État, et je suis entièrement isolé.... »

Carnot s'était retiré de nouveau. Il vivait en famille et se
consacrait aux travaux scientifiques. Le public venait le
voir à l'Institut. C'est là que Brougham avait voulut le
rencontrer, c'est là que Wilhelm Doron admirait — a-t-il
écrit — la haute stature, le masque pâle, les yeux étincelants
d'intelligence et de vie intérieure de ce pur républicain,
intègre et irréductible, ennemi de tout tyran, fût-il Napoléon[1].

Son traitement de tribun — 15 000 francs par an — lui
avait permis de mener une vie aisée et simple. La suppression du Tribunat lui avait ôté cette ressource, mais il avait
une fortune suffisante.

Il était installé à Presles, auprès de La Ferté-Alais, dans
une modeste propriété qu'il avait fait aménager et où certains de ses descendants conservent aujourd'hui sa mémoire,
ses livres, des documents et des souvenirs.

Partagé entre l'éducation de ses enfants et ses travaux
scientifiques, il demeurait à l'écart de la vie politique et
militaire. Tantôt à Presles, tantôt à Paris, les Carnot menaient
une vie bourgeoise et studieuse.

Carnot était assidu aux séances de l'Institut, il fut même
président de sa section. A maintes reprises il fut amené à
présenter des rapports sur des inventions et découvertes,
tantôt un chauffage central, tantôt un moteur à explosion,
tantôt un sous-marin. Carnot s'exaltait à l'idée de la conquête
des profondeurs marines après celle des airs.

A Paris, Lazare aimait à travailler dans sa bibliothèque
— plus de 1 000 volumes étaient distribués dans un vaste

meuble en bois peint. Carnot s'installait à son bureau d'acajou. Au salon, sa femme se tenait sur la chaise longue, occupée
à quelque ouvrage de tapisserie, sa santé étant médiocre
depuis longtemps. Mais ce salon recevait des amis, il y avait
un canapé, plusieurs bergères et fauteuils. On faisait parfois
de la musique sur le piano forte d'Érard, ou sur la harpe.
Garnie de deux guéridons, d'encoignures d'acajou, d'un
« bonheur du jour », éclairée par des candélabres de bronze,
la pièce avait une tenue bien adaptée aux maîtres de la
maison. Ceux-ci, pour sortir, disposaient d'un cheval et
d'un cabriolet.

A Presles il y avait une bibliothèque, mais beaucoup moins
importante, un salon, de nombreuses chambres — 17 mate-
las —, un cabriolet, un bateau, deux cygnes sur la pièce
d'eau, deux vaches et dix-sept volailles dans les dépen-
dances. C'était la résidence d'été [2].

Deux domestiques : un homme et une cuisinière, Joséphine Brios, attachée à la famille au point de lui confier
ses gages, moyennant un intérêt de 5 p. 100. Elle était
originaire d'Hesdin, et servit Mme Carnot pendant douze
ans, d'abord comme femme de chambre, puis comme cuisinière. Elle lui fut très attachée et aida à élever Sadi et
Hippolyte « qui l'aimaient beaucoup ». Carnot la garda à
son service après la mort de sa femme.

A Presles, il y avait aussi des fermiers et un garde pour
le bois.

Quelques notes donnent une idée des dépenses :
6 200 francs pour le ménage, pour trois mois. « Le 9 mai 1811,
j'ai acheté chez M. Lepage, armurier de l'Empereur, une
paire de pistolets de la manufacture de Versailles : 120 francs.
Ils ne sont pas neufs, mais ils sont très bons.... Le 10 mai, j'ai
acheté chez M. Jardin, opticien, une planchette, un grapho-
mètre, un niveau d'eau et une chaîne d'arpenteur avec les
piquets pour la somme de 152 francs dont j'ai payé tout de
suite 140 francs. » C'était peut-être pour faire le lever topographique de Presles. « Le 21 juin, j'ai acheté de la bougie
qui avait été allumée, elle m'a coûté 56 sous la livre, la neuve
coûte 3 francs 15, mais la livre n'est que de 14 onces, au lieu
que celle que j'ai achetée en a 15. »

« Le 23 juin, j'ai acheté une petite montre d'or, pour
120 francs, pour ma femme. »

En 1812, ce sont des achats utilitaires : « un habit veste,
et le pantalon gros bleu, beau drap de femme, qui m'a coûté

60 francs, y compris le gilet d'hiver de 8 francs, et une paire de demi-guêtres de 4 francs. La veille, j'avais acheté douze paires de bas, deux paires de souliers et trois caleçons, le tout 60 francs. »

Le fils aîné, Sadi, avait suivi les cours du lycée Charlemagne ; il entra à Polytechnique le 12 octobre 1811 ; son père paya 1 024 francs, dont 200 pour le quartier de pension et le reste pour le trousseau.

Hippolyte était en pension, ce qui coûtait 1 000 francs par an ; il s'orientait aussi vers la carrière militaire, vers l'École de Saint-Cyr [3].

La famille se tournait vers les fonctions publiques. Carnot félicitait son frère de Nolay qui avait placé l'un de ses fils à l'entrepôt de la ville de Beaune et qui envisageait de faire entrer l'autre dans l'administration aux Eaux et Forêts : « C'est encore un état très convenable et recherché par les personnes bien élevées et faites pour vivre dans une bonne société. »

Ainsi, très bourgeoisement, la carrière et la vie sociale de Carnot se poursuivaient bien loin de la politique et des remous consécutifs à la Révolution.

***

Pourtant tout cela avait failli s'effondrer. Au début de 1809, les Anglais s'étaient emparés de Cayenne et de la Martinique, et ils avaient pris les vaisseaux français.

Or Carnot avait placé toute sa fortune, et même davantage, chez un armateur dont les vaisseaux figuraient parmi les prises. C'était la ruine [4].

Cet épisode eut de profonds retentissements dans la carrière de Carnot ; il est pourtant obscur, d'autant que les commentaires, flatteurs ou calomnieux, ont été multipliés à l'époque même et dans la suite.

La situation financière de Carnot était rétablie depuis son retour de proscription. Elle s'était améliorée par les héritages provoqués par la mort de sa belle-mère, le 11 mai 1807, puis de son beau-père, le 24 juin 1808. Celui-ci laissait près d'un million, en terres, bois, prés et fermes. Lazare et Feulint reçurent chacun plus de 320 000 francs. Il est vrai que le partage de la succession ne fut accompli que le 4 janvier 1810, mais l'attribution ne pouvait laisser le moindre doute. Carnot disposait donc d'une large aisance [5].

D'après les notes de son frère le conseiller, « il eut le

malheur de se laisser leurrer par un homme qui avait pris sa confiance ». Il s'agissait, selon Clarke, « d'une spéculation de commerce aux colonies » qui portait sur 125 000 francs, soit à peu près toute la fortune de Carnot, écrivait Clarke, ou même beaucoup plus que son avoir personnel, selon le conseiller. C'est là le premier point obscur. Carnot avait-il investi le reste de son avoir à Presles ? Se refusait-il à escompter la succession qui devait lui revenir ? Avait-il d'autres engagements [6] ?

La suite n'est pas beaucoup plus claire. Des mémorialistes, la duchesse d'Abrantès, le baron Méneval, ont affirmé qu'il s'inquiéta et s'adressa à l'Empereur, par l'intermédiaire de Collignon, qui avait des relations avec Méneval, pour demander un prêt. Or Carnot a maintes fois répété qu'il n'avait rien sollicité [7].

Les faits ne s'éclairent un peu qu'avec la lettre de Napoléon, écrite à Schœnbrunn le 17 juin 1809. L'Empereur s'adressait à Clarke et répondait « à la lettre relative au sieur Carnot et à la connaissance qu'il vous a donnée de l'état de ses finances ». Il demandait l'indication de la somme nécessaire pour le tirer d'embarras, et ajoutait qu'il ne ferait « point de difficultés de l'employer selon son désir [8] ».

Clarke informa l'intéressé, qui consulta sa famille. Celle-ci envisagea une nomination de sénateur, une promotion dans l'ordre de la Légion d'honneur, mais Carnot ne retint pas ces propositions, « parce qu'elles pourraient être indiscrètes ». Il demanda « le traitement de général de division à partir du jour où il [avait] quitté le ministère, et ensuite une retraite de 6 000 francs, ce qui est le maximum de ce grade ». Clarke pensait même que Carnot pouvait être remis en activité[9].

L'aide sous forme de retraite avait été suggérée par Napoléon ; « comme ministre de la guerre, il a droit à une retraite », avait-il écrit. Effectivement, Lajard avait reçu à ce titre une retraite de 6 000 francs, le 2 février 1809. Carnot fut mieux traité : il eut une pension de 10 000 francs, avec rappel depuis le 16 vendémiaire an IX (8 octobre 1800). Il allait donc toucher 90 000 francs, sans parler des annuités à venir. L'année suivante, il déclarait disposer d'un revenu de 17 000 francs [10].

Si ses difficultés financières étaient réglées, la position politique de Carnot était profondément modifiée, ce qui est, pour l'Histoire, encore plus important.

A ses parents et amis, Carnot vantait les « impressions flatteuses », la bienveillance, la grâce de l'Empereur. Il voulait lui « témoigner sa reconnaissance ».

Dès que Napoléon eut regagné Paris, Carnot alla le remercier. Son frère, le conseiller, fit une démarche préalable, le 12 septembre, à Fontainebleau, exprimant « la reconnaissance de la famille ». Puis, le 30 septembre, Carnot lui-même fut reçu. Napoléon se montra aimable, consacra une heure à l'entretenir « de la chose publique, des armées, de la politique ». Il lui accorda aussi une pension pour Feulint, et lui promit de lui donner, quand il le souhaiterait, le poste qu'il pourrait désirer. Cette audience fut remarquée et commentée. Carnot reçut les félicitations de ses amis et de ses proches.

Dans ses réponses, Carnot insistait sur la spontanéité du geste de l'Empereur et sur la sécurité que cette pension lui valait, pour lui, pour ses enfants, pour sa famille. Mais chacun se demandait quel poste Carnot allait remplir. Or ni l'Empereur ni son ancien ministre ne se soucièrent de fixer un choix ; ce fut simplement un petit travail que Napoléon fit proposer à Carnot et qui ramenait celui-ci aux problèmes de fortifications.

* ***

Il s'agissait de composer un manuel pour les élèves de l'École de Metz. On y placerait les ordonnances sur les places, les sanctions frappant les défaillances des gouverneurs ; le tout serait illustré de récits historiques, « quelquefois amusants », notait l'Empereur, et devrait exciter l'enthousiasme des jeunes. Ainsi les places fortes seraient-elles désormais défendues jusqu'à la dernière extrémité. « C'est un travail complet à faire, et je crois que Carnot, ou tout autre de cette classe, serait très propre à s'en charger ; j'attache une grande importance à cet ouvrage, et celui qui le fera bien méritera bien de moi. »

Carnot composa le traité. Le sujet lui en était si familier que l'ouvrage était achevé au début de 1810. Carnot fit demander quand il pourrait en faire hommage à l'Empereur[11]. On lui répondit de le remettre par l'intermédiaire du ministre de la Guerre. Il y joignit donc une lettre, exposant son dessein, notamment son désir d'inspirer aux jeunes militaires « les sentiments d'honneur et de dévouement à votre personne qui doivent les animer. J'ai moi-même été guidé dans mon travail par celui de ma profonde reconnaissance envers vous [12] ».

Pourtant, Napoléon n'envoya pas de lettre de satisfaction. Les exemplaires, imprimés aux frais de Carnot, déposés au dépôt des Fortifications, y restèrent. Ils ne furent pas distribués aux élèves de l'École de Metz. Carnot s'en plaignit au ministre de la Guerre, car on allait ainsi empêcher la destruction des « faux principes » qui étaient toujours enseignés [13].

Cette cruelle déception tenait aux dispositions du Corps du Génie, toujours hostile au système de Montalembert. La doctrine du Corps n'avait pas été modifiée par les guerres, le comité des Fortifications avait décidé, en octobre 1809, de s'en tenir à Vauban perfectionné par Cormontaigne. Carnot s'en prenait encore à Fourcroy, avec toute l'amertume de ses anciens écrits, et célébrait Montalembert, tout en modifiant un peu ses vues. Il considérait les casemates comme un progrès décisif — ce que la suite a confirmé —, mais il substituait aux feux directs — canon, mousqueterie — les feux verticaux par mortiers et pierriers, ce qui fut très contesté et parut condamné par les expériences.

Carnot vivait sur de vieux souvenirs. Il se réclamait toujours de Montecuculli et de Vauban, il ne citait pas les guerres révolutionnaires, sinon le siège de Gênes, en 1800.

De plus, à la façon de Montalembert, il condamnait toutes les places existantes, les discréditait et voulait les faire reconstruire. Déjà il s'était heurté à une opposition résolue dans ses projets sur le Génie, à la fin de son ministère de la Guerre, sous le Consulat. Il rencontra les mêmes critiques, qu'il rendit avec fermeté. Favart lui ayant soumis un *Abrégé de Fortifications*, Carnot refusa de le patronner : « Ce sont les principes de Cormontaigne, ceux mêmes du Comité de Fortification, mais non pas les miens », ni ceux de Vauban, ajoutait-il ailleurs, devançant ainsi d'un siècle les remarquables travaux historiques du général Lazard.

L'ouvrage fut réédité en 1811 et 1812. Il fut traduit en allemand, en 1811, et en anglais, en 1814. Les critiques furent nombreuses, bien que l'idée des casemates ait souvent été favorablement accueillie [14]. A bien des égards, ce n'était pas ce qu'attendait Napoléon.

L'auteur n'avait jamais été un pur géomètre et, loin de juger que l'art de fortifier tenait aux seules règles de l'architecture et de la balistique, il avait toujours affirmé la prépondérance du facteur humain. Que pouvait-il écrire à ce propos, après la Révolution et au temps où l'Empire était devenu absolu ?

« Il faut qu'une grande passion soit l'âme d'un grand ensemble. » Carnot, devenu romantique, évoquait toutes les grandes passions, l'honneur et la piété, l'amour de la gloire, l'apostolat religieux, l'attachement au chef, la fidélité au prince, mais aussi l'amour de la patrie et la haine de la tyrannie. C'était affaire d'époques et de circonstances. L'essentiel était cette conviction fanatique, cette « impulsion d'un sentiment qui ne se définit pas, mais qui est l'unique principe de ce qui se fait de beau et de grand dans le monde ». Qu'était donc devenu le rationalisme chez ce chantre de l'enthousiasme ?

Le problème fondamental, celui de la barbarie des guerres, objet des méditations de Carnot, et de bien des Français, depuis tant d'années, était effleuré. Convenait-il de limiter les efforts et les destructions ? Ou bien la guerre devrait-elle être totale ? Carnot avait encore à l'esprit le dialogue pathétique de Guibert et d'Arçon, à la veille de la Révolution. A cette époque, il avait pris position contre le capitaine génial, chef irrésistible et novateur, dont on célébrait par avance les victoires fulgurantes. Et depuis on s'était acheminé vers la guerre totale, déchaînant les passions cruelles, et l'on avait rencontré le général génial ; c'est lui qui gouvernait la France et tenait l'Europe sous sa botte. Carnot continuait de condamner les « guerres à mort qui n'ont plus lieu que chez les sauvages », mais il professait que la place forte ne pouvait précisément assurer la sécurité du pays que par une résistance à mort. Là il ne saurait être question, ni d'humanité ni de limites dans la durée de la résistance. Les horreurs mêmes auxquelles aboutissait un assaut, et la prise de vive force, ne sauraient retenir la résistance. C'eût été céder à des « discours empoisonnés » ; un gouverneur devait avoir le courage plus fier. Et Carnot traçait un magnifique portrait du gouverneur, tout comme jadis il avait exalté l'ingénieur. Songeait-il déjà qu'un tel poste pourrait lui être confié ?

Quant aux soldats, loin d'être guidés par cette discipline raisonnée que Carnot avait prônée à la Législative, ils connaîtront la grandeur de la servitude militaire. Ou plutôt ils créeront cette grandeur par l'adhésion de leur intelligence aux ordres qui leur seront donnés : « Parmi les Français, l'obéissance n'est point aveugle, elle n'en est que plus héroïque ; l'intelligence, loin de la contrarier, lui sert à mieux exécuter les ordres. » Mais non à les critiquer, car, sur ce point, ils font « abnégation de [leurs] propres lumières ».

Ces indications, aussi précieuses pour l'historien des idées de Carnot que conformes à la volonté de l'Empereur, ne suffisaient pas à racheter les hérésies du fortificateur. Non plus que certaines assertions en faveur des armes blanches, préférées aux armes à feu.

Le refus de Napoléon, qui n'utilisa pas l'ouvrage de Carnot, a fait croire que celui-ci n'eut pas d'effet en France. C'est là une conclusion excessive. Le Comité des Fortifications fit des emprunts à Carnot, certaines de ses pensées passèrent dans les instructions et dans les circulaires impériales. Sans parler des textes du 24 décembre 1811, la grande instruction de 1813, élaborée au Comité, reprit une partie considérable des pages de Carnot sur les phases de la résistance. Ainsi les consignes qui furent données aux troupes qui tenaient les forteresses, au moment où le déclin de l'Empire remettait la patrie en danger, émanèrent de l'organisateur de la victoire [15].

D'ailleurs, même en France, Carnot reçut des félicitations. Elles venaient de correspondants fort inégalement qualifiés : Pastoret, le maréchal Serurier, Daru, le maréchal Mac Donald, le duc d'Abrantès, le comte Kalckreut, le prince d'Essling, Berthollet, Eugène Napoléon, le duc de Cadore, la princesse Elisa. Le plus flatteur, mais aussi le plus tardif — 16 janvier 1815 —, fut le futur Louis-Philippe : « C'est un livre bien utile et déjà célèbre, l'ouvrage d'un militaire très distingué par ses services, très savant dans la théorie et d'une habileté reconnue dans l'application de l'art suivant les localités et les circonstances [16]. »

Napoléon resta défavorable. Carnot lui soumit « d'anciennes réflexions » sur les fortifications, le 8 août 1811. « Il serait digne d'un règne signalé par tant de créations extraordinaires qu'il fût aussi l'époque d'une grande amélioration dans l'art de construire et de défendre les places. Votre Majesté a sur les autres souverains l'avantage de pouvoir juger par elle-même en pareille matière.... » Napoléon soumit ces idées au premier inspecteur du Génie, le général Chasseloup-Laubat.

Celui-ci fut très dur. Carnot ne tenait pas compte des progrès de l'artillerie, il supprimait les flanquements et reculait ainsi au-delà de Vauban ; il préconisait l'arme blanche et comptait sur les feux verticaux de mortiers. Seules les casemates méritaient les éloges qu'il lui faisait à l'instar de Montalembert.

« Si l'auteur avait vu des brèches praticables faites à de bons revêtements terrassés par les seuls boulets perdus de batteries à ricochet, il aurait moins de confiance.... C'est en outrant des propriétés utiles, c'est en confondant les temps et en s'arrêtant trop peu aux changements qu'a apportés, même dans le moral des hommes, la différence des armes anciennes et des nôtres, qu'on parvient à des résultats extraordinaires.... Une imagination non tempérée par l'expérience de la guerre conduit à des erreurs.... Il est difficile qu'un homme nourri dans l'art de fortifier puisse pousser plus loin le paradoxe [17]. »

En dépit de ses déboires, Carnot comptait pourtant sur les promesses reçues ; il les rappelait :

« Sire. Je n'oublierai jamais les paroles que Votre Majesté m'adressa en terminant l'audience qu'elle voulut bien m'accorder à son retour d'Allemagne : demandez-moi ce que vous voudrez, quand vous voudrez et comme vous le voudrez. Votre Majesté m'avait déjà mis au-dessus des besoins et je n'étais occupé que des moyens de lui en témoigner ma reconnaissance. Je n'ai pu lui en donner qu'une faible marque en rédigeant l'ouvrage composé par ses ordres sur la défense des places et où j'ai fait un effort pour inspirer aux militaires les sentiments de l'honneur et du dévouement dus à votre personne.... Mais maintenant, Sire, je sens que j'ai besoin de l'accomplissement de vos promesses généreuses. Le sort de mes enfants est précaire, et l'aisance dans laquelle vos bontés les ont mis ne durera pas plus que moi, si Votre Majesté n'étend pas à eux sa bienveillance. Je lui soumets donc le désir que j'aurai que leur existence fût assurée par une médiocre dotation qui leur fût personnelle. Ils sont deux et se destinent à votre service dans le métier des armes ; il me tarde qu'ils aient atteint l'âge compétent pour être admis dans les écoles militaires. Je ne souhaite point pour eux de grandes fortunes, mais qu'en travaillant à se rendre dignes de vos regards ils puissent s'acquitter par leur zèle de ce que vous aurez bien voulu faire pour eux.

« Votre Majesté voulut aussi m'accorder une pension pour mon frère, ancien officier général, père de famille et sans fortune, mais le temps écoulé depuis cette époque a été rempli par des événements si grands, et qui intéressent si fort le bonheur personnel de Votre Majesté, que cette affaire de détail a pu être oubliée. Je prends donc, avec confiance, la liberté de la rappeler à Votre Majesté, la suppliant de vouloir bien en ordonner l'exécution. »

Cette demande avait été faite le 21 juin 1810; or dans ses lettres à ses parents et amis, en automne, Carnot se disait rassuré pour ses enfants; avait-il obtenu satisfaction [18] ?

Le retour en grâce aurait pu être couronné avec plus d'éclat et de ressources : Carnot fut élu candidat au Sénat dans la Côte-d'Or, pour lutter contre la candidature d'un ci-devant [19]. Napoléon allait-il le nommer sénateur ? C'était le moment de lui rappeler ses promesses. Canot lui écrivit de nouveau :

« Sire, je viens d'être nommé candidat au Sénat conservateur par le collège électoral du département de la Côte-d'Or, qui est le lieu de ma naissance. Je dois certainement cette marque flatteuse de la considération et de l'estime de mes compatriotes à la généreuse bienveillance dont Votre Majesté m'a nouvellement honoré. Je la prie donc de se rappeler tout ce qu'elle m'a témoigné de bonté, et d'y mettre le sceau en confirmant le suffrage des habitants d'un pays qui a toujours été particulièrement dévoué à votre gloire, et qui, dans tous les temps, a fourni tant aux armées que dans les autres classes de citoyens des hommes d'un courage et d'un talent distingués. Ce sera, Sire, combler tout à la fois mes vœux et les devoirs sacrés que vous avez déjà imposés à ma reconnaissance.

« Je suis, avec le plus profond respect, et le plus parfait dévouement, de Votre Majesté le plus obéissant et fidèle sujet. »

Napoléon ne jugea pas à propos d'accéder à cette requête. Le public ignora tout. Carnot n'avait toujours aucune fonction publique et pouvait continuer de passer pour un opposant.

CHAPITRE XII

DE L'EMPEREUR AU ROI

« JE REÇOIS, mon cher Tiffet, tes félicitations avec autant plus de plaisir que les grandes opérations, auxquelles tu présumes que je dois coopérer, n'exigeront de moi aucun déplacement, ni fatigue : ce ne sont pas, mon cher ami, des hommes de soixante ans qu'il faut à l'Empereur.... » Le même Carnot, qui s'exprimait en ces termes le 20 avril 1813, offrit pourtant ses services à Napoléon le 20 janvier 1814.

Il est vrai que l'été avait ruiné les espérances qui étaient encore permises au printemps. La jeune armée, improvisée après les désastres de Russie, était dominée par une coalition sans cesse plus nombreuse, les occasions de négocier en renonçant à dominer l'Europe étaient manquées, et l'année 1814 ramenait la menace oubliée de l'invasion : la patrie était en danger ! Avec elle, c'étaient les principes, et aussi les hommes de la Révolution, qui étaient menacés. Certains s'en réjouissaient, d'autres en prenaient leur parti, les plus avisés cherchaient à sauver ce qui pouvait l'être, la plupart s'apprêtaient à abandonner Napoléon. C'était pour rallier les hésitants — il le déclara nettement — que Carnot reprenait le service; tous ceux qui attachaient quelque prix à l'exemple de l'organisateur de la victoire, si longtemps hostile à l'Empire, seraient ainsi convaincus que l'union sous les aigles était le moyen de sauver la Révolution. C'était aussi pour amener Napoléon à faire une paix durable et à regagner « l'amour d'un grand peuple » en assouplissant son régime [1]. En somme, Carnot était une force qui, pour s'exercer, choisissait son point d'appui ; ce point était-il solide ? Était-ce le moment de se solidariser avec un régime chancelant ?

Il faut rappeler la confiance de Carnot dans la puissance de résistance des places fortes pour comprendre son espoir et son geste. Il faut compter aussi avec son patriotisme, son attachement au sol de la patrie. Le passé enfin le poussait à l'action, il croyait pouvoir tenir de nouveau ce rôle de défenseur des frontières qui l'avait illustré.

Rien enfin ne le retenait plus à l'arrière : sa femme venait de mourir, son fils Sadi était entré à Polytechnique, et le plus jeune, Hippolyte, était en pension.

Napoléon accepta sur-le-champ ces offres, mais sans leur donner une publicité qui seule eût correspondu aux mobiles de Carnot. L'Empereur ne voulait rien céder au libéralisme, il venait de le proclamer brutalement au Corps législatif. Ainsi le geste de Carnot demeura-t-il ignoré ; plus tard, sa lettre fut publiée et, au dire d'un de ses amis, elle « a couru le monde ».

Le poste confié à ce chef qui n'avait pas combattu depuis Wattignies fut celui de gouverneur général d'Anvers. N'était-ce pas ce qui convenait à l'auteur de *La Défense des Places fortes* ? Il allait fournir des exemples vivants à l'appui de ses écrits, en même temps qu'il bénéficierait d'une large indépendance à l'égard de tant de chefs, devenus ducs et maréchaux après avoir servi sous ses ordres.

Au dire de l'Empereur, Anvers était une « place de premier ordre », capable d'épauler le camp retranché qui protégeait la Belgique et la France. Il était douteux que l'ennemi osât en faire le siège ; il tenterait plutôt de masquer la position pour la contourner.

Malheureusement la situation était déjà compromise ; le corps d'armée du général Maison, qui devait contenir l'ennemi, avait été bousculé et s'était replié sur Louvain, tandis que le camp retranché était tenu en respect. L'Empereur croyait encore qu'il s'agissait d'un échec passager et, en même temps qu'il nommait Carnot, il ordonnait à Maison de revenir à Anvers [2].

Le nouveau gouverneur se rendit à son poste en toute hâte, au risque de se faire prendre par les partis ennemis qui sillonnaient la région. Il prit possession de ses fonctions le 2 février [3].

La ville avait été renforcée depuis 1810, après le débarquement anglais, au moment où Napoléon avait songé à s'appuyer sur les forteresses. On avait remis l'enceinte en état ; on avait commencé de nouveaux ouvrages extérieurs ; certains étaient achevés, d'autres étaient encore en construction, tandis que plusieurs n'étaient pas commencés. La citadelle était en mauvais état. Enfin le port et les établissements maritimes, aménagés après l'organisation de l'enceinte, non seulement n'étaient pas protégés, mais gênaient la défense. Le nouveau gouverneur se mit aussitôt à la tâche [4].

Hippolyte Carnot s'est plu à montrer son père appliquant méthodiquement tous les principes de *La Défense des Places fortes*. Nous n'insisterons pas sur ce point, où il n'y a rien de neuf à dire, d'autant qu'il n'y eut — comme Napoléon l'avait prévu — ni siège, ni assaut, ni grands combats. Les circonstances posèrent plutôt des problèmes d'autorité et d'organisation concernant les chefs militaires et la population civile.

Depuis un peu plus de deux mois, la ville avait pour gouverneur le général Lebrun, duc de Plaisance, fils de l'architrésorier. C'était un chef énergique, cassant même, et qui avait fait renforcer la position. Mais il s'était heurté à des résistances : un conflit s'était produit entre le commandant de la place et le gouverneur; les autorités maritimes occupaient les locaux de la citadelle et ne se prêtaient pas à une remise en état de celle-ci.

Carnot donna au commandant de la place la plénitude des attributions qui lui revenaient. Il se garda d'empiéter sur les pouvoirs du préfet maritime, Kersaint, qui était plutôt timoré qu'envahissant. Enfin il coordonna l'action de l'escadre commandée par l'amiral Missiessy, avec celle des troupes de terre. Il y parvint en créant un Conseil de défense, où chacun avait sa place et son initiative, mais où tous devaient s'incliner devant les décisions du Conseil, dans lequel le gouverneur avait l'autorité suprême. *A fortiori*, dans cette ville en état de siège, les autorités civiles, préfet et maire, devaient obéir. Mais Carnot ne brusqua ni les uns ni les autres [5].

La plupart des troupes couvraient la ville en occupant les environs, avec plus de 6 000 hommes. Dans la place même se trouvaient environ 3 700 hommes. Le meilleur de ces forces était constitué par la 1re division de la garde impériale que commandait le général Roguet. Le plus grand nombre, en revanche, étaient des conscrits sans aucune formation et sans désir de combattre. Belges, ils attendaient la libération de leur pays par les coalisés. De sorte que la puissance des troupes ne correspondait pas à leurs effectifs. Il y avait plus de 18 000 hommes, si l'on tenait compte des garnisons installées hors du camp retranché, dans toute la région. Mais, hormis la division de la garde, on ne pouvait compter que sur la marine. Celle-ci disposait d'un peu plus de 2 000 hommes, de diverses formations, notamment des artilleurs dont on avait le plus grand besoin. Les marins n'étaient pas assez nombreux pour fournir aux besoins de l'escadre. Il y avait dans le port dix-sept à dix-huit gros vaisseaux, dont sept étaient désarmés, et une flottille de canonnières. Le gouverneur pouvait les associer à la défense de la place ; déjà le duc de Plaisance en avait donné l'exemple.

Le gouverneur d'Anvers était placé sous les ordres du général Maison, commandant le Corps d'armée. Mais celui-ci ne put porter ses forces jusqu'au camp ; les communications furent bientôt très relâchées, Carnot fut vraiment son propre maître.

Déjà l'ennemi avait resserré sa pression ; peu à peu les troupes se repliaient sur la place, le canon adverse était à bonne portée et le préfet maritime s'attendait à une tentative de destruction de la flotte et des établissements maritimes.

L'événement se produisit au moment où Carnot, pour la première fois visitait les retranchements. Le bombardement se prolongea trois jours, faisant pleuvoir mille cinquante bombes et huit cents boulets rouges sur le bassin et dans les parages.

La population fut consternée ; le bombardement annonçait-il un plan de destruction ? Les Anversois étaient moins hostiles à l'occupation française que la plupart de leurs compatriotes. Napoléon avait fait de grands travaux dans leur port ; il voulait le doter d'un commerce puissant, mais la guerre avait nui à ce commerce. Anvers, comme toute la Belgique, souhaitait la paix et la fin de la domination napoléonienne. On pouvait craindre que le bombardement ne provoquât un mouvement pour la capitulation. Carnot fit preuve de fermeté aussi bien que de souplesse ; il fut puissamment aidé par l'ennemi, qui ne bombarda pas la ville et interrompit même son feu après trois jours.

Il y eut bien quelques tentatives pour provoquer un soulèvement des civils comme des conscrits, mais elles furent bientôt abandonnées.

Le gouverneur renvoya les personnes étrangères à la ville, renforça les approvisionnements, promit de nourrir treize mille pauvres, épargna deux faubourgs que son prédécesseur avait ordonné d'abattre et qui lui parurent pouvoir subsister sans inconvénients. Il améliora l'habillement, la nourriture et le chauffage des soldats, ce qui supprima tout prétexte au pillage. Il parvint à loger, dans la ville, en réquisitionnant locaux et lits, les Corps qui s'étaient repliés. Les suspects furent éloignés, parfois brutalement et sans discrimination, ce qui amena les protestations du maire. Mais Carnot maintint ses ordres et rien ne bougea.

Le plus difficile était de financer cette politique. Il fallut réclamer la rentrée des contributions et imposer d'office les plus riches. Les résultats restèrent tardifs et insuffisants, en dépit de l'emprisonnement des récalcitrants dans la citadelle, puis sur les navires. Carnot préleva, dans les magasins de la marine, du cuivre et du bronze pour frapper des pièces de monnaie qui améliorèrent un peu la situation.

Sur le plan militaire, la prise de fonctions était aussi un succès. Le bombardement avait fait très peu de dégâts et aussi très peu de victimes. Les artilleurs de la marine, servant les pièces terrestres, avaient riposté efficacement. L'affaire avait stimulé la garnison tout entière, les travaux avaient avancé plus vite, l'organisation s'était affermie sans peine, tout le monde était aux aguets. D'autant plus que les Anglais tentèrent de débarquer par ruse, dans la nuit du 6 au 7 février.

La presse parisienne mentionnait les succès de Carnot à Anvers [6]. Bülow tenta, le 11 février, d'entraîner Carnot dans la lutte contre Napoléon, présentée comme une lutte de libération des Français. « Que Votre Excellence, dont les talents comme militaire et comme homme de cabinet sont également connus..., se mette à la tête d'un peuple qui veut briser ses fers. » Carnot s'y refusa, affirmant son loyalisme à l'égard de Napoléon, et il présenta les victoires de Sézanne et de Champaubert comme le présage d'une campagne décisive. Ce fut l'occasion d'une manifestation éclatante, destinée à soutenir le moral des troupes et contenir celui des civils. Il y eut, le 16 février, *Te Deum*, revue solennelle, dîner d'honneur, spectacle et salves d'artillerie. Au théâtre, les spectateurs acclamèrent Napoléon et le gouverneur : « Vive l'Empereur ! Vive Carnot ! »

Carnot n'était pas dupe de cette mise en scène. Pour savoir exactement comment évoluait la situation, il envoya un agent en mission secrète. Celui-ci quitta Anvers précisément le 16 février ; il revint dix jours plus tard, ayant visité

Ypres, Furnes, Dunkerque et Saint-Omer. Il disait la joie des Belges, libérés par les cosaques, et l'angoisse des Français envahis [7].

Ces nouvelles filtraient dans la population et dans les troupes. Elles encourageaient, chez les civils, la résistance aux contributions et aux emprunts; chez les militaires, l'apathie et la désertion. La surveillance se relâcha aux portes de la ville; on entrait, on sortait à volonté. Les recrues belges, et surtout flamandes, abandonnaient leurs unités; la garde elle-même regimbait, se plaignait du retard de la solde, de l'insuffisance de la nourriture. L'absence d'opérations, l'absence de courrier, les bruits colportés, tout était déprimant. Comme écrivait Roguet, « tout ce qui vient n'est pas, pour les esprits faibles, fort tranquillisant; il serait à désirer qu'on nous fît connaître les victoires de l'Empereur ». A défaut, Carnot s'efforça de galvaniser les énergies. Il contrôlait la presse et tentait de la rendre optimiste, mais il n'avait plus de victoires à célébrer.

Pour tenir les troupes en haleine, cet homme de soixante ans, chaque jour ou presque, montait à cheval. Il parcourait les quartiers de la ville et les fortifications. De temps à autre il prescrivait des sorties. Le 27 février, il avait tenté de capturer un Corps saxon; le coup avait manqué de peu; on avait pu prendre la caisse, les armes et les bagages. Une semaine plus tard, Carnot eut un moment d'espoir : le général Maison essayait de nouveau de se porter sur Anvers. Carnot, le 7 mars, envoya 4 000 hommes au-devant de lui, sous prétexte d'aller chercher du ravitaillement. Mais la jonction n'eut pas lieu : Maison ne put forcer l'adversaire, il recula, et les hommes de Carnot regagnèrent Anvers.

D'autres sorties, plus modestes, furent réalisées avec succès; la marine prêtait l'appui de ses canons. Malheureusement les résultats étaient limités. D'autre part on déplorait la multiplication des malades : le 17 mars, il ne restait guère plus de 4 700 hommes pour assurer le service; on avait compté 480 morts à l'hôpital depuis le début de janvier.

Cependant Carnot avait une confiance rayonnante qui lui faisait écrire, le 25 mars, au ministre de la Guerre une lettre étonnante : « Notre situation est très bonne.... Je tiens l'ennemi en échec, j'ai des vivres pour plus de trois mois. La place est dans le meilleur état de défense.... Elle est la plus heureuse de toute la Belgique, peut-être même de toute la France [8].... »

Effectivement en France la situation était désespérée. Peut-être l'eût-elle été moins s'il n'y avait eu tant de forces dispersées dans les places ? L'Empereur prescrivit au général Maison de rassembler toutes les troupes d'Anvers pour renforcer son Corps d'armée, en ne laissant dans la place que les marins. Maison en informa Carnot, le 26 mars.

Le gouverneur fut atterré : « Ces ordres équivalent à celui de rendre la place », écrivait-il à Maison. Et il ajoutait, dans une nouvelle lettre au ministre : « Quand j'ai offert mes services à l'Empereur, j'ai bien voulu lui sacrifier ma vie, mais non mon honneur. » A la suite de ces protestations, Maison laissa à Carnot deux bataillons d'infanterie et une compagnie d'artillerie. L'effectif tomba de 20 000 hommes à 11 900 pour la région, et de 12 000 à 5 000 pour la ville ; encore aurait-il fallu défalquer les 1 885 malades. D'autre part, le manque d'argent devenait de plus en plus gênant et l'on commençait à rationner les vivres. Anvers était à la merci de l'adversaire [9].

C'est dans cette conjoncture que l'on apprit la fin de la campagne de France. Les premières nouvelles, et les premières invitations à capituler, furent apportées par un parlementaire anglais, le 27 mars. Quelques jours plus tard arrivait un voyageur qui avait quitté Paris le 4 mars, et qui était passé à Lille le 28 ; il confirma que tout était perdu et que la paix était sur le point d'être conclue. Le 4 avril, un nouveau parlementaire anglais annonçait que les Alliés étaient entrés dans Paris. Cette nouvelle accablante fut confirmée par un parlementaire prussien, puis par un suédois. Celui-ci annonçait que le Sénat offrait la couronne à Louis XVIII, moyennant une constitution libérale « répondant parfaitement aux principes que vous connaissez ». Les uns et les autres demandaient au gouverneur de cesser le feu, voire même de se ranger au côté des Alliés. Carnot s'y refusa, en des termes qui annonçaient son ralliement : « C'est au nom du gouvernement français que je commande dans la place d'Anvers.... Aussitôt que ce gouvernement sera définitivement et incontestablement établi sur ses nouvelles bases, je m'empresserai d'exécuter ses ordres [10]. »

Le 11 avril, coup sur coup, trois courriers arrivèrent de Paris, apportant des journaux et des nouvelles ; c'étaient les premiers depuis février. Ils confirmèrent la présence des Alliés à Paris, la chute de Napoléon, l'armistice, le projet de constitution élaboré par le Sénat, mais ils n'étaient porteurs d'aucune dépêche officielle.

La plus grande effervescence régna dans la ville. Les uns songeaient à poser les armes pour reconnaître le gouvernement provisoire, d'autres « affectaient, écrit Carnot, une incrédulité extraordinaire et vraiment surprenante ».

D'accord avec le préfet du département, Carnot maintint son expectative : « De grands événements viennent de se passer. Nous en ignorons encore les résultats. Jusqu'à ce qu'ils nous soient authentiquement et légalement connus, les autorités qui représentent le gouvernement français à Anvers continueront d'y faire respecter et exécuter les lois [11]. »

Une telle situation ne pouvait se prolonger sans danger, car la population s'énervait et les autorités cherchaient chacune leur voie dans un sens différent. S'agissait-il d'obéir au Sénat, à la régente Marie-Louise, aux Alliés ou à Louis XVIII ? Les troupes enfin, apprenant que les nouveaux pouvoirs avaient prescrit la démobilisation, se débandaient.

Le 12, Ferrandin-Gazan, aide de camp du nouveau ministre de la Guerre, demanda à être reçu par le gouverneur. Il apportait des lettres officielles et il était accompagné par un capitaine anglais.

La principale lettre, écrite le 7 avril, annonçait la déchéance de Napoléon et de sa famille, et la formation d'un gouvernement provisoire ; elle demandait l'adhésion du gouverneur d'Anvers et de ses troupes, et annonçait des instructions. L'acte d'adhésion ferait cesser immédiatement les hostilités.

Le nouveau ministre de la Guerre était le général Dupont, qui avait collaboré naguère avec Carnot et qui depuis avait été rendu responsable de la capitulation de l'armée française en Espagne, à Baylen. Il avait écrit une lettre personnelle à Carnot, très cordiale, lui confirmant l'abdication pure et simple de l'Empereur, le refus de la régence, et lui annonçant la nouvelle constitution.

Ferrandin-Gazan était arrivé à trois heures ; à six heures, le Conseil de défense était saisi de la situation et mis en possession des pièces. L'unanimité se fit aussitôt sur l'adhésion au nouveau gouvernement. Carnot tenait tant à cette unité d'action qu'il mit aux arrêts et remplaça dans son poste le colonel d'un régiment qui avait pris sur lui d'envoyer son serment de fidélité à Louis XVIII [12].

Le soir même, Carnot rédigea l'acte d'adhésion et fit imprimer une proclamation. Le lendemain matin, les officiers étaient réunis pour être mis au courant de la décision, quand les membres du Conseil de défense se rendirent chez le gouverneur pour lui présenter des objections. L'abdication de l'Empereur n'était pas prouvée par un acte formel ; l'une des lettres parlait d'abdication, l'autre de déchéance, les décisions du Sénat et du Corps législatif semblaient avoir été prises par une minorité, qui ne pouvait agir librement dans une ville occupée par l'ennemi. Outre ces motifs ouvertement allégués, il y avait la cocarde blanche que portait Ferrandin-Gazan, et qui avait provoqué l'indignation d'une partie de la garnison, et l'arrêt du 4 avril, invitant les troupes à la désertion.

Les éléments bonapartistes avaient présenté les objections. Carnot en avait reconnu la valeur, et même, peu après, en était venu à l'indignation. Sa première réponse, en date du 13, était mesurée et calme : il attendait des preuves complémentaires. Une deuxième lettre à Dupont, écrite le 15, rappelait, par sa violence, les épîtres de Carnot à Pache : « On veut donc la guerre civile, on veut donc que l'ennemi se rende maître de toutes nos places, et, parce que la ville de Paris a été forcée de recevoir la loi du vainqueur, il faut que la France la reçoive ! Il est évident que le gouvernement provisoire ne fait que transmettre les ordres de l'Empereur de Russie.... Quoi ! Vous ne nous permettez pas seulement de sauver notre honneur ! Vous devenez vous-même fauteur de désertion, provocateur de la plus monstrueuse anarchie ! Les leçons de 1792 et de 1793 sont donc perdues pour les nombreux chefs de l'État : ils cherchent à surprendre notre adhésion en nous affirmant que Napoléon vient d'abdiquer, et aujourd'hui ils annoncent le contraire [13]....»

Cette explosion s'explique par la situation critique d'Anvers. Dès le 12 avril, le préfet avait envoyé son adhésion ; le 13, il avait envoyé celle des fonctionnaires civils. L'attitude du commissaire général de police incita Carnot à lui faire quitter immédiatement la place.

D'autre part, des dissentiments éclataient entre les chefs militaires, où se trouvaient d'anciens révolutionnaires et d'anciens émigrés. L'amiral Missiessy avait appris que son frère avait été fort bien reçu par le comte d'Artois ; il voulut précipiter son adhésion et fit savoir à son frère qu'il avait inutilement tenté de décider le Conseil de défense. L'aide de camp de Carnot publiait un article, dans le *Journal du Département des Deux-Nèthes*, en l'honneur du prince Eugène ; le propre secrétaire de Carnot lui répondait, dans le même journal, en observant que Paris n'était pas l'Empire, et qu'il fallait attendre l'adhésion générale de la France.

Les troupes se divisaient : les uns manifestaient en l'honneur de l'Empereur, les autres voulaient quitter les armes, les effectifs fondaient [14].

On comprend l'humeur de Carnot, et la hantise de la guerre civile, qui ne devait pas le quitter pendant longtemps. Toutefois Ferrandin-Gazan, dès le 13, avait été tancé par Carnot, qui lui avait tout bonnement déclaré qu'il aurait mérité d'être fusillé comme porteur de fausses nouvelles. Le malheureux ne fut pas mieux reçu dans les autres places où il se présenta. En vain écrivit-il à Carnot pour se plaindre de la « trame infernale » qui avait été ourdie pour le déconsidérer. En somme, l'armée se prononçait contre la cocarde blanche : le régime des Bourbons lui ôterait inévitablement son prestige, son pouvoir, ses ressources mêmes. Et Carnot, pourtant hostile au gouvernement militaire, ne pouvait envisager sans appréhension l'avènement du frère de Louis XVI. La situation d'Anvers était un raccourci de celle de la France, Carnot y tenait la place du Sénat.

Sur ces entrefaites, des précisions nouvelles parvinrent au gouverneur. Le général Maison lui faisait savoir qu'il avait envoyé son adhésion, comme la France entière. Les journaux arrivaient, la correspondance officielle aussi des divers ministères. *Le Courrier de Belgique* affirmait que « le gouverneur Carnot ne voudra pas se compromettre en persistant à se défendre mal à propos.... Les suites ne pourraient retomber que sur sa personne ».

Le 16 avril, Carnot obligea les membres du Conseil de défense à faire connaître par écrit leur opinion concernant leur adhésion et l'attitude à prendre à l'égard des troupes : devaient-elles être mises en demeure de suivre leurs chefs ? Ou seraient-elles invitées à se prononcer ? Tous furent d'avis d'adhérer, non sans conditions : l'un refusait de rendre la place, trois autres n'obéiraient à Louis XVIII que lorsque celui-ci aurait accepté la constitution ; les généraux de la garde ne s'inclinaient qu'après avoir appris que les généraux Maison et Roguet l'avaient fait avant eux, l'amiral Missiessy refusait de remettre son acte à Carnot; il l'envoyait au ministre de la Marine.

La plupart estimaient que les troupes devaient obéir, comme Carnot lui-même qui jugeait depuis longtemps que la force armée est essentiellement obéissante.... Où étaient les espérances d'antan ?

Après quoi Carnot fit savoir qu'il se réservait de décider à son heure, et il imposa sa volonté en dépit des plus vives protestations [15].

Cependant il acceptait, le 16 avril, de conclure un armistice avec le général anglais. Puis il annonçait l'adhésion de toute la garnison, le 17 avril, et il la faisait célébrer avec éclat. Une proclamation fit savoir que Napoléon avait « abandonné » ses troupes et qu'il avait enfin renoncé « à un pouvoir dont il [avait] si longtemps abusé »; chacun était donc délié du serment de fidélité. Le 19 avril à midi, des salves d'artillerie, tant de la forteresse que de la flotte, furent tirées « en réjouissance », selon les termes de Carnot, pour annoncer que la garnison reconnaissait Louis XVIII; le drapeau blanc flottait sur les vaisseaux, la cocarde blanche était arborée par les troupes. Carnot insista pour que tous en fussent pourvus, mais il toléra cependant que des troupes fussent à la parade sans cocarde, faute d'argent, disait-on. Carnot n'était pas dupe de ce prétexte qui lui avait été fourni par le général Flamand, commandant d'une unité de la garde impériale.

Le 24 avril il y eut une revue et un défilé des troupes; l'adhésion s'était accomplie sans incidents graves, ce qui n'avait pas été le cas partout, à beaucoup près. Le soir, Carnot se rendait au théâtre et il était acclamé.

Il ne restait plus qu'à obtenir l'adhésion de la garnison de Berg-op-Zoom, qui dépendait aussi d'Anvers; elle était acquise quatre jours plus tard.

Carnot adressa une dernière proclamation pour prendre congé des Anversois. Ils répondirent en témoignant que le gouverneur avait été « affable, impartial, sévère à la vérité, mais juste », et en assurant Carnot qu'il emportait « l'estime, la reconnaissance de presque tous les habitants ». Déjà le maire d'Anvers avait dit à Paris les mérites de Carnot. La population des faubourgs épargnés avait tenu à adresser des remerciements spéciaux ; elle éleva plus tard un monument en l'honneur de Carnot.

La remise de la place à l'ennemi ne fut pas effectuée par

Carnot; il avait obtenu d'être dispensé de ce geste. Cependant le général anglais Graham l'avait félicité, avec le plus grand tact, pour sa prudence.

Il restait à faire admettre par le nouveau gouvernement les motifs qui avaient si longtemps différé le ralliement. Carnot écrivit, le 17 avril, deux lettres d'explications au ministre de la Guerre; une troisième suivit le 19; il écrivit une lettre analogue au général Maison [16]. Enfin il rédigea un *Précis des Événements* à l'intention du ministre et du gouvernement.

Dupont fit savoir que non seulement il approuvait Carnot, mais que Monsieur avait vu « avec satisfaction la conduite prudente et ferme » du gouverneur dans des « circonstances difficiles [17] ».

Ainsi, venu à Anvers pour défendre Napoléon, Carnot quittait la place en se mettant au service des Bourbons. *Le Journal des Deux-Nèthes* publiait des articles en l'honneur de Louis XVIII, les monnaies obsidionales étaient frappées au chiffre de Louis XVIII. Le bruit courait que le nouveau régime allait rendre à Carnot ses anciennes fonctions d'inspecteur aux revues.

Déjà certains amis de Carnot admiraient sa subtilité; ils pensaient que celui qui avait défendu Anvers et qui en avait conservé la garnison au roi serait bien en cour : « Je ne désespère pas que ce marchepied ne serve bientôt, dans l'ordre des choses qui se prépare, à vous y faire éminemment placer [18]. »

Carnot se gardait bien de telles illusions et attendait un ordre, ou une autorisation de Dupont, pour se rendre à Paris où se trouvait le roi.

CHAPITRE XIII

CARNOT ET LOUIS XVIII

D E GRAND matin, pour éviter toute manifestation,
Carnot avait quitté Anvers, le 3 mai. Il s'était dirigé
sur Dunkerque, par Nieuport et Furnes, ces anciens
objectifs des armées révolutionnaires qu'il stimulait jadis.
Il se considérait au service du nouveau gouvernement et
priait le ministre de le rappeler au plus tôt à Paris. Il attendit
la réponse à Dunkerque.

Tout, autour de lui, témoignait de la défaite et du désarroi ;
les occupants, les émigrés qui affluaient, l'inquiétude qui
avait gagné les autorités, l'âpreté qui opposait les clans
politiques. Pourtant c'était la paix, tant attendue. Elle
autorisait bien des espérances, surtout au lendemain de la
déclaration que le roi venait de faire à Saint-Ouen, lors de
son arrivée, et qui promettait un régime libéral, éloigné de
toute vengeance et de toute réaction.

Le 8 mai, Carnot reçut l'autorisation de se rendre à Paris
par congé ; il s'achemina aussitôt et arriva le 12 au soir [1].

Le lendemain matin, il visita le ministre de la Guerre et le
gouverneur de la place de Paris. Après quoi il se rendit aux
Tuileries. Il portait la croix de Saint-Louis, qu'il avait
obtenue sous Louis XVI.

Le comte d'Artois se montra léger, le duc de Berry fit
une allusion à la défense d'Anvers, le roi fut très froid.
Carnot jugea qu'il ne devait plus revenir au Château. Ce
n'était pas une disgrâce ; il conservait son grade, sa solde
d'activité ; il espérait pouvoir y joindre sa pension, mais il
n'avait plus d'emploi. Ses amis le croyaient assez bien en
cour pour solliciter son appui. Prieur de la Côte-d'Or lui
demandait le moyen de rentrer dans le Génie et d'obtenir
la Légion d'honneur et la croix de Saint-Louis : « A l'égard
de mes sentiments pour le roi, ajoutait-il, j'espère que ma
moralité garantit la fidélité que je lui dois et lui voue avec

sincérité. » Un autre écrivait : « On m'assure que vous jouissez de la considération qui vous est due à tant de titres. » Cette impression était renforcée par la réintégration de Feulint dans les cadres et par sa nomination dans la Légion d'honneur[2]. Ainsi les positions étaient beaucoup moins tranchées qu'on pourrait le supposer, le ralliement de Carnot paraissait, aux yeux de ses amis, devoir assurer son influence.

La Charte, le 4 juin, consolida cet apaisement. Un article intéressait directement Carnot — le onzième —, proscrivant « toutes les recherches des opinions et votes émis jusqu'à la Restauration ».

On pouvait croire que Carnot et la France allaient couler des jours tranquilles. Il en alla tout autrement....

**
*

Au début d'octobre, l'opinion fut soudain saisie et violemment partagée par la publication d'un ouvrage polémique, vif dans le ton, jusqu'à la provocation, et qui était une mise en garde au roi, il portait le nom de Carnot.

Mais celui-ci désavoua publiquement, dans la presse, la publication de ce *Mémoire au Roi*, et l'éditeur avoua avoir agi à son insu.

Ainsi l'énigme se mêlait au scandale.

Carnot avait en effet écrit cet ouvrage pour combattre l'influence néfaste des émigrés rentrés, leurs campagnes contre les acquéreurs de biens nationaux, contre les révolutionnaires marquants, spécialement ceux qu'ils appelaient les *votants*, c'est-à-dire les régicides, contre leur action cléricale et autoritaire. Il s'était ému quand il avait vu que le gouvernement, éliminant cinquante-trois sénateurs et épurant la plupart des fonctionnaires, allait abandonner la Charte pour satisfaire les ultras. Non pas qu'il eût peur pour lui — bien qu'il eût déjà, à diverses reprises, redouté pour les siens les effets d'une disgrâce —, mais parce qu'il restait foncièrement attaché aux conquêtes de la Révolution, hostile à tout privilège nobiliaire ou clérical, et confiant dans les progrès par la raison. Enfin, et surtout, il voulait conjurer les divisions qu'une telle politique ne manquerait pas de renouveler ; peut-être même ressusciterait-elle la guerre civile. Carnot en avait eu l'impression à Anvers et l'avait écrit, avec quelle vivacité, au ministre de la Guerre.

Toutefois, pour éviter un éclat inutile, Carnot avait résolu de garder l'anonymat ; il s'adressait à ses concitoyens et non au roi. Mais la police avait vu une épreuve de l'ouvrage et l'avait interdit. Carnot avait alors décidé de se faire connaître à Beugnot, le directeur de la Police.

Ce fut peu avant le 20 juillet que Carnot eut un entretien avec Beugnot.

Au cours de la conversation, il lui exposa les raisons pour lesquelles il n'avait pas signé, mais ajouta qu'il espérait toucher le gouvernement. Beugnot lui répondit : « Eh bien, il y a un moyen d'arranger cette affaire sans retard, donnez-moi votre parole de ne pas le livrer de nouveau à l'impression, et je me charge de donner communication de l'écrit au roi et de lui expliquer les motifs qui vous avaient engagé à le composer. En conséquence, faites-m'en faire une copie manuscrite, envoyez-la-moi, et qu'il n'en soit plus question. » Ainsi l'écrit devenait-il un mémoire au roi.

Il convenait d'adoucir quelques expressions, si vraiment le but était de convaincre le roi et non de le heurter. Carnot y travaillait quand il apprit qu'un exemplaire imprimé était entre les mains de Beugnot et avait été lu au Conseil des ministres ; il lui écrivit alors, le 20 juillet, qu'une copie épurée ne lui paraissait plus nécessaire. Beugnot n'en convint pas. Dans ces conditions, dès le 22, Carnot lui remit le texte accompagné d'une lettre explicative.

Peu après, Carnot revit Beugnot. Le roi n'avait pas lu le mémoire, mais il avait pris connaissance de la lettre. Elle était, avait-il déclaré, d'un bon citoyen. M. Carnot pouvait aller tranquillement à la campagne, l'affaire était réglée. Carnot quitta Paris.

La lettre explicative mérite d'être rappelée ; elle donne les idées maîtresses et les intentions de Carnot.

      « Monsieur le Comte,

« Le but que je me suis proposé dans l'écrit dont Votre Excellence me demande la copie pour la mettre sous les yeux du Roi, et que j'ai l'honneur de vous adresser, a été d'instruire Sa Majesté de l'inquiétude générale qui règne dans les esprits et de lui en faire connaître la véritable cause.

« Votre Excellence n'est sans doute pas à s'apercevoir que cette inquiétude est le résultat nécessaire de la crainte très naturelle de voir renaître de leurs cendres nos discordes civiles.

« L'enthousiasme qui eut lieu dans toutes les classes de

la société, l'élan de tous les cœurs vers le Roi, lors de sa rentrée en France, semblaient être de sûrs garants de la réunion de tous les esprits.

« Monsieur le comte d'Artois avait préparé cet heureux événement par l'assurance qu'il avait donnée au nom du Roi que tout était oublié, que Sa Majesté ne voulait voir que des enfants dans tous les Français, que toutes les places, tous les honneurs seraient conservés à ceux qui en jouissaient.

« Sa Majesté avait elle-même confirmé ces promesses par son ordonnance du 2 mai : tous les Français crurent que l'on pouvait compter sur un oubli généreux qui leur avait été si solennellement promis ; aussi la joie publique ne fut-elle altérée par aucun nuage.

« Comment arrive-t-il donc qu'une inquiétude générale ait succédé à d'aussi heureuses dispositions ? C'est que ceux qui ont pris une part plus ou moins active à la Révolution se voient, par suite des mesures déjà prises, menacés d'être dépouillés de leurs emplois, d'être rangés dans une classe proscrite, de n'être plus considérés sur leur sol natal, eux et leurs familles, que comme de véritables ilotes.

« La proscription n'a pesé jusqu'à présent que sur les Conventionnels que l'on nomme *votants*, et sur les personnes qui leur tiennent par des liens d'amitié ou de parenté. Mais, dès que c'est le vote qu'ils ont émis qui les fait proscrire, la proscription s'étendra nécessairement bientôt sur ceux qui ont provoqué le vote par leurs adresses, ou ceux qui l'auront confirmé par leur adhésion ; et ceux-ci composent au moins les trois quarts et demi des Français.

« Il y a peu de communes qui n'aient fait des adresses en ce sens, soit pour provoquer le vote tel qu'il a été émis, soit pour en féliciter la Convention.

« Toutes ces adresses étaient signées individuellement, toutes étaient menaçantes, toutes s'exprimaient dans des termes plus ou moins violents ; et ces adresses existent, elles furent imprimées dans les papiers publics.

« Les signataires d'adresses, leurs enfants, leurs proches peuvent donc avoir des craintes fondées sur le sort qui les attend, et, jusqu'à ce que ces craintes aient cessé, la fermentation ne peut être calmée.

« Or ces craintes ne peuvent cesser, Monsieur le Comte, vous devez en être convaincu, que par la réalisation non douteuse des promesses faites par le Roi, promesses au surplus qui auraient été dictées par une bonne politique, lors même qu'elles n'auraient pas été dans le cœur de Sa Majesté. L'oubli seul du passé pouvait, en effet, concilier tous les intérêts, réunir tous les Français dans l'amour du Roi.

« Comme bon Français moi-même, j'ai dû chercher le moyen de faire parvenir la vérité jusqu'au Trône ; il ne dépend que du Roi de ramener la sécurité dans les esprits, il lui suffira d'assurer le maintien de sa parole sacrée. Sa Majesté verra dans l'instant même se réaliser le vœu de son cœur, tous les Français s'empresseront de lui manifester leur amour et de se dévouer à son service [3]. »

Cette lettre fut bien accueillie. Carnot reçut même, le 1er septembre, une distinction :

« M. Carnot, lieutenant général, ex-gouverneur d'Anvers,

« Sa Majesté, pleine de confiance dans votre fidélité et dans votre dévouement à sa personne, vous autorise à porter la décoration du Lis [4]. »

Tout changea soudain.

Le 30 septembre, sur les dix heures du soir, Feulint reçut une lettre de Gouget-Deslandres l'avertissant qu'on imprimait le mémoire de Carnot, chez un imprimeur dont il donnait l'adresse afin de prendre « telle mesure qui lui conviendra contre cet abus de confiance [5] ».

Feulint avertit Beugnot et Carnot. Celui-ci, fidèle à sa promesse, décida de désavouer toute publication éventuelle. Il semblait suspecter les intentions de Beugnot. Lui et ses proches ont longtemps cru que le directeur de la Police favorisait sous-main ce qu'il interdisait officiellement [6]. Les papiers Beugnot et les abondantes notes de police n'appuient par cette accusation, mais donnent l'impression d'une maladresse et d'une inefficacité exceptionnelles.

Il n'est question que du mémoire de Carnot, et que de son imprimeur supposé, dans une longue suite de bulletins et de correspondances, à partir du 25 juillet. Les indications sont confuses et mêlent curieusement le vrai et le faux, attribuant à Carnot le meilleur et le pire, ajoutant que le roi et le directeur de la Police seraient au courant d'un écrit « de la plus haute conception », mais qu'il y aurait d'autre part une apologie du régicide. Beugnot affirmait que l'imprimé aurait peu de retentissement, car des copies manuscrites avaient déjà circulé.

Il ne s'était même pas aperçu que le journal *Le Censeur* avait publié toute une partie du mémoire, dans son numéro 11, en septembre ! Il avait reçu, avec quelques

soupçons, la visite de Joseph Carnot, le conseiller à la Cour
de cassation, et de Feulint, venus affirmer la loyauté de
leur frère. Il avait ensuite fait arrêter et déférer au procureur général six libraires, pour attentat à la majesté royale.
Ils avaient imprimé divers libelles. Beugnot voulait croire
que l'un ou l'autre était ainsi responsable du mémoire de
Carnot. Alors que le public était largement pourvu de cet
ouvrage, Beugnot mit des mois pour en saisir quelques
exemplaires. D'un air sentencieux, il dénonçait tour à tour
Carnot et Grégoire, Guinguené, Sicart et l'Institut [7].
L'affaire était si mal engagée que les magistrats abandon-
nèrent les poursuites. On avait cru habile de rattacher le
mémoire de Carnot à des écrits plus violents, dus à des
auteurs compromis, comme Méhée. L'enquête établit que
Carnot était étranger à la publication, qu'on ne savait rien
sur les éditeurs et imprimeurs, et qu'il n'y avait aucune
relation entre le *Mémoire au Roi* et les autres libelles. Le
chancelier ne cacha pas son irritation [8].

Cet échec ne fut pas étranger à la disgrâce de Beugnot.

Pendant ce temps, l'ouvrage circulait et soulevait des
commentaires passionnés. Dans quelle mesure apportait-il
la pensée et les paroles mêmes de Carnot ? Question importante, posée à l'époque même, souvent répétée depuis, et
jusqu'alors demeurée sans réponse.

Il subsiste au moins un exemplaire du premier état de ce
fameux mémoire. Il portait alors un titre peu fait pour
attirer l'attention, et il était anonyme. Le texte était un
peu plus bref que celui des imprimés qui circulèrent dans
la suite. Il commençait par une longue et dure attaque
contre les émigrés, et l'objet propre du libelle — *Étude des
Caractères d'une juste Liberté et d'un Pouvoir légitime* —
constituait la seconde partie de l'œuvre, exactement, comme
dans les éditions suivantes.

Hormis quelques modifications du plan, quelques
retouches de détail, c'était bien la pensée, l'expression
même du fameux *Mémoire au Roi*. Ce fut assurément ce
que Beugnot parvint à connaître. L'anonymat avait permis à
l'auteur de décocher quelques traits qui parurent déplacés
quand l'écrit fut soumis à Louis XVIII [9].

Alors Carnot retoucha son travail ; il prit soin de l'indiquer dans un avertissement. Le manuscrit intitulé *Mémoire
adressé au Roi en juillet 1814 par M. Carnot* a été conservé
et permet de suivre la pensée de l'auteur [10].

La Charte était ouvertement citée et approuvée, l'auteur plaçait sa confiance dans le roi et dans les élections, à la condition que la Charte fût appliquée, que le roi fût informé et que les élections fussent libres. Ainsi les erreurs commises pourraient être réparées et la fusion des partis s'accomplirait. Cette adjonction soulignait le ralliement de l'auteur, d'autant mieux qu'il déclarait que « le retour des Bourbons produisit un enthousiasme universel».

Un autre développement était introduit pour comparer la France et l'Angleterre, en soulignant l'opposition de la structure aussi bien sociale qu'économique.

Un appel aux ministres formait la conclusion et déplaçait ainsi les reproches en les détournant du roi.

Cette série d'adjonctions prouve le désir de l'auteur de limiter son opposition; il condamnait une politique, non un régime.

Les suppressions n'étaient pas moins concluantes, elles éliminaient les traits les plus acérés. Certains étaient durs jusqu'à la brutalité, comparant l'autorité royale et l'autorité paternelle. Carnot avait écrit : « Il n'y a que les rois qui n'ont jamais été pères qui puissent méconnaître cette différence.» L'allusion était cruelle. Après avoir reproché au roi sa servilité à l'égard des étrangers, Carnot avait déclaré : « Alors nos cœurs se sont resserrés, ils se sont tusi et ce morne silence annonce à Louis XVIII qu'il est roi de France, mais qu'il n'est pas roi des Français.» Il avait relevé avec la même amertume que Louis XVIII était « véritablement dans la vingtième année de son règne; on voit bien qu'il a passé ces vingt années loin du territoire des Francs.... Il ne suffit pas d'être le fils du grand Henri pour lui ressembler.» Enfin Carnot avait supprimé un passage plus long, dans lequel il comparait le roi aux juifs trafiquants et fripiers : « Il a reçu la couronne des mains de l'ennemi, comme on fait un marché qu'on est pressé de conclure, en se hâtant d'abandonner ce qui était le prix du sang français versé depuis vingt ans. »

Carnot avait aussi remplacé par une note la longue citation de la Bible qui préconisait le régicide. En somme, il ménageait le roi le plus possible, réservant les critiques aux ministres, aux courtisans, à l'entourage même du roi et aux émigrés.

C'est sous cette forme que l'écrit circula, qu'il fut copié et recopié, et qu'il fut enfin imprimé. Cependant Carnot atténua encore son opposition en supprimant une menace qui pouvait passer pour un appel à l'armée : « Les militaires entrés dans leurs foyers, avait-il écrit dans la seconde version du mémoire, sont les dépositaires de la gloire nationale, et c'est à cette gloire importune surtout qu'on en veut. Que les braves sentent donc bien que cette gloire est non seulement aujourd'hui leur seule récompense, mais encore le palladium de ce qui nous reste de liberté. »

A cela près, le texte de Carnot fut exactement publié. Tout au plus peut-on relever quelques variantes, ou quelques incorrections dans les diverses éditions. L'ouvrage, tel que le connut le public, était bien l'œuvre de Carnot, et l'effet qu'il produisit donne une idée de ce que le texte intégral eût provoqué [11].

Les contemporains furent surtout sensibles à la violence du ton et au caractère agressif de la pensée. Au contraire, avec le recul du temps, ce qui frappe aujourd'hui, c'est plutôt la lassitude de l'ancien révolutionnaire. Les Français, écrivait-il, sont « fatigués de révolutions », fatigués et déçus. « Nous crûmes avoir saisi le fantôme de la félicité nationale ; nous crûmes qu'il était possible d'obtenir une république sans anarchie, une liberté sans factions ; l'expérience nous a cruellement déçus. »

Carnot était ici le porte-parole d'une génération, celle qui avait atteint l'âge de la retraite. Les jeunes n'approuvaient pas cette résignation.

Rigomer Bazin, qui les représente assez bien, s'écriait : « Quoique, en effet, il y ait eu du découragement pour quelques-uns, le courage n'a fait que redoubler dans un million d'autres [12]. »

La Révolution n'avait pas été le règne de la liberté, observait encore Carnot, mais celui du « despotisme continuel », une lutte forcenée provoquée par la résistance opiniâtre des privilégiés, et cette lutte avait mêlé l'héroïsme à la cruauté, les traits sublimes aux désordres monstrueux. Dans cet héritage, il se tournait avec prédilection vers la défense de la patrie, la gloire militaire, unissant dans un même tribut d'éloges et une même nostalgie les fastes de la Révolution et de l'Empire.

« Cette gloire était devenue notre idole.... Un coup imprévu l'a frappé. Nous trouvons dans nos cœurs un vide semblable à celui qu'éprouve un amant qui a perdu l'objet de sa passion. »

Pourtant ni l'amertume de la déception, ni le poids de la lassitude n'amenaient Carnot à répudier cette Révolution. Il revenait au contraire à la source, à la « philosophie » des grands auteurs du XVIIIe siècle, à la « raison » qui dissipait l'obscurité des préjugés pour faire rayonner les bienfaisantes « lumières ». « La science du gouvernement » se perfectionne comme toutes les autres, par l'intelligence et la recherche, à la condition d'empêcher la « résurrection des préjugés qui rendent les peuples imbéciles » et de laisser l'opinion s'exprimer librement, surtout par la presse. C'étaient les idées que professait Carnot à la veille de la Révolution.

Comme la plupart des libéraux de 1814, Carnot unissait à ses idées, antérieures à 1789, le sentiment national exalté par la Révolution et l'Empire. Il voulait animer l'opinion par une noble et forte passion... : « l'amour de la Patrie ». Cet amour pouvait seul lier puissamment les uns aux autres tous les Français, les amener à aliéner une partie de leur liberté au profit de celle des autres, et à sacrifier leur intérêt particulier au bien commun, à renoncer aux troubles, aux violences, aux guerres intérieures, pour former une famille, une nation.

Cet idéalisme pourtant n'excluait pas des vues plus concrètes, fondées sur les intérêts matériels des individus et des groupes. L'unité devait se renforcer « par la facilité des communications intérieures », et par une économie orientée vers l'accroissement de la richesse agricole.

Carnot renonçait à rivaliser avec les Anglais pour l'industrie et le commerce, la position géographique et l'esprit national ne s'y prêtant pas. Sur ce point, il abandonnait de longs espoirs et condamnait de récentes tentatives. S'y mêlait-il inconsciemment le souvenir de sa fortune engloutie dans les spéculations commerciales ?

Cette attitude aurait pu lui assurer l'assentiment des nobles, le plus souvent propriétaires fonciers, mais ils étaient rebutés par le ton général. Elle lui valut en revanche les protestations des jeunes libéraux, mal disposés à sacrifier le commerce et l'industrie, non plus qu'à s'incliner devant l'Angleterre [13].

Le règne des lumières et le développement de l'unité nationale pouvaient se poursuivre sous Louis XVIII pour peu que la Charte fût littéralement appliquée. « Un roi ne doit-il pas aller au-delà plutôt que de rester en deçà de ce

qu'il a promis ? Et ne devriez-vous pas lui rappeler sans
cesse [vous, les ministres] ce passage sublime de la proclamation de son aïeul Henri IV, n'étant encore que roi de
Navarre : « Qui peut dire au roi de Navarre qu'il ait jamais
« manqué à sa parole ? »

Toute cette partie du message de Carnot souligne la modération de ses désirs, l'absence de préoccupations démocratiques aussi bien que mercantiles, la possibilité d'un accord
avec Louis XVIII et ses partisans clairvoyants. Il est bien
curieux qu'en France, comme à l'étranger, on ne l'ait pas
compris.

Les royalistes en effet, les émigrés, les étrangers eux-
mêmes n'ont vu que le régicide impudent, exigeant la
faveur du frère de celui qu'il avait fait guillotiner, en un mot,
le Jacobin.

La tempête éclata aussitôt. L'interdiction et la saisie de
l'écrit, la réputation de Carnot, la violence du ton
surexcitèrent la curiosité et déchaînèrent les passions. On
s'arrachait le mémoire, on le discutait farouchement. Le
point crucial était le cas des régicides : « Monsieur Carnot
a-t-il prétendu faire l'apologie du régicide ? On croit dans le
public que c'est là l'objet et même le titre de sa brochure. »
Des ripostes violentes furent improvisées, dans les journaux,
dans les pamphlets. Mais le succès fut immense chez les
mécontents, qui étaient légion. Plus tard, on fit courir ce
mot attribué à Napoléon : « J'ai lu Carnot et j'ai cru que
je pouvais revenir. »

De Londres, le comte de La Châtre dénonçait Carnot
comme chef d'une conspiration contre les Bourbons [14].

Chateaubriand, en décembre 1814, le prit à partie dans ses
Réflexions politiques, de façon grandiloquente et injurieuse.
Carnot, écrivait-il, « joignant la théorie à la pratique, se
présente à Louis XVIII comme un homme qui a bien mérité
de lui ; il vient lui montrer le corps sanglant de Louis XVI,
et, sa tête à la main, demander son salaire ». Il évoquait la
pension reçue de la main de Napoléon : « Après avoir
égorgé l'agneau, on a caressé le tigre. »

Pourtant l'assentiment venait ensuite. Chateaubriand
approuvait les déclarations de Carnot sur la Charte :
« belles paroles auxquelles nous souscrivons de grand
cœur ». Mais celui-ci ne retint que la verte semonce ; il
retrouva sa plume des grandes polémiques et répliqua en
termes acerbes. Il trouva pourtant quelques accents émus

pour déplorer le sort des émigrés qui avaient connu la misère et le malheur : n'avait-il pas, lui-même, vécu en exil ?

Si le retour de Napoléon n'était survenu, Carnot aurait publié une deuxième réplique, évoquant les variations de Chateaubriand, favorable à la Révolution en 1797, ridiculisant le *Génie du Christianisme*, relevant l'inexactitude de toutes les citations. Carnot soulignait les contradictions : une moitié de l'écrit célébrait l'absolutisme, l'autre vantait la Charte. Enfin, exaspéré par la prétention de son contradicteur de ne trouver l'honneur que dans la monarchie, il allait jusqu'à s'étonner qu' « on n'envoie pas à Bicêtre un gentilhomme qui raisonne ainsi ». Après quoi, il faisait appel à l'union de tous les Français ! Ce qui ne l'empêchait pas de s'en prendre aux « démagogues » coupables des violences révolutionnaires, et « dirigés probablement par les étrangers »[15].

Mis en verve, Carnot publia, anonymement, quelques dialogues satiriques dans un journal, le *Véridique*. De ci-devant seigneurs, chevaliers de l'Éteignoir et de la Girouette, chanoines même, s'entretenaient de façon caricaturale des promesses du roi, des mérites de l'ignorance, des *Réflexions politiques* de Chateaubriand. Carnot s'appliquait à stigmatiser la sottise et la suffisance, l'égoïsme et la haine, qu'il trouvait chez ses adversaires.

La pensée de Carnot apparaît plus précise et moins violente dans les entretiens qu'il eut avec le célèbre homme politique et savant anglais, Lord Brougham, les 26 et 29 octobre.

Il s'agissait encore de la Révolution et de ses principaux chefs. Robespierre avait des talents, orateur, vif de pensée, mais il était méchant : « Je l'ai bien connu, nous étions ensemble dans le Comité de Salut public, mais je l'ai toujours approfondi [percé à jour ?]. » Collot et Billaud étaient « les plus détestables et méprisables de tous »…. Carnot affirmait que la nation avait voulu la mort de Louis XVI. « Il m'a parlé de Talleyrand comme de l'homme le plus fourbe et le plus lâche du monde, avec beaucoup d'esprit, mais tout à fait méprisable. » Naturellement il y eut une violente sortie contre « la poignée d'émigrés qui entourent le roi ». Mais Carnot déclare que, Directeur, il n'avait laissé rentrer que les émigrés qui n'avaient point porté les armes contre la France. Ils parlèrent aussi de Bonaparte : « C'est un tyran

que personne ne peut aimer et que les amis de la liberté ne
peuvent souffrir. » Il regretta que Bonaparte n'eût pas imité
Washington, comme lui, Carnot, le lui avait conseillé, par
écrit. Mais quand Brougham demanda si « Bonaparte avait
une correspondance en France en ce moment », Carnot lui
répondit que Bonaparte devait y dépêcher quelqu'un de
temps à autre pour savoir ce qui se passait, et Brougham
nota : « Il me paraissait parler sur le sujet avec connaissance de cause. »

On évoqua aussi les questions militaires. Carnot affirma
que toute l'armée était « contre le roi personnellement ». Il
concéda que Bonaparte avait abusé de la conscription. Il
condamna la trahison de Pichegru et celle de Moreau.

Enfin Carnot exposa qu'il était « très populaire ; le soldat
m'aime naturellement et le peuple de Paris m'est très
attaché, de manière que je ne peux pas aller en ville, dans
les rues et les boutiques, sans en recevoir les témoignages ».

Brougham fit paraître un article sur Carnot dans la *Revue
d'Édimbourg* en novembre 1814. Il commentait le *Mémoire au
Roi*, mal traduit en anglais par Goldsmith ; il présentait surtout
l'auteur que les Anglais avaient pris tour à tour pour un
buveur de sang ou pour un royaliste, avant ou après Fructidor, et dont ils faisaient un terroriste, alors qu'il était un
homme intègre et un républicain sincère. Brougham contestait cependant les idées politiques de Carnot, et même sa
géométrie de position [16].

Ainsi, à bien des égards, Carnot était-il redevenu, au printemps 1815, l'homme du jour. Il était profondément engagé
dans la lutte politique, il y déployait un réel talent d'écri-
vain, mais le combat qu'il menait contribuait à saper la
monarchie constitutionnelle qu'il voulait défendre.

Il avait pris position sur le problème central, celui du
régime. Il avait apporté l'adhésion d'un nom illustre dans
les fastes révolutionnaires. Il admettait la Charte, à défaut
d'une république modérée ; il aurait pu dire que la monarchie
serait libérale ou ne serait pas. Mais le ton et la composition
de son manifeste étaient tels qu'ils lui donnaient la portée
d'un plaidoyer personnel, d'une protestation, sinon d'une
menace. Les deux champions des thèses adverses, Chateaubriand et Carnot, étaient beaucoup moins loin qu'ils le
crurent et qu'ils ne le dirent. Réalistes tous deux, convaincus
du rôle du temps et de l'expérience, ils admettaient l'un et
l'autre le roi et la liberté selon la Charte. Il leur manquait

de distinguer entre l'adhésion à un régime et l'appartenance à un parti, de grouper et de diriger assez d'amis pour assurer un effet pratique à leurs écrits, de savoir atteindre le roi sans le heurter, de comprendre enfin qu'ils étaient, l'un et l'autre, de ces hommes à talents, de ces capacités, qui disposaient du proche avenir [17]. Derrière eux, et à leur exemple, une multitude de Français se partageaient et se combattaient pour des dissentiments dont beaucoup déjà tenaient au passé. La confusion sur ce point était telle que Carnot se tournait vers le monde rural, vers l'agriculture, et discréditait le commerce qui, en dehors des « capacités », fournissait le personnel libéral.

Comme l'a reconnu son fils, « il règne dans le *Mémoire de Carnot au Roi* une âpreté de langage et une ironie violente qui devaient le rendre parfaitement impropre à son but ». Les émigrés, les notables, la noblesse, le clergé étaient pris à partie avec une violence farouche, accusés d'avoir trahi le roi et la France, d'avoir provoqué les violences et les guerres intérieures et extérieures. Ils étaient traités d'assassins, de transfuges, de cupides, d'égoïstes et de lâches. Après leur avoir ainsi jeté à la figure le passé, Carnot leur reprochait, avec une égale violence, le présent, l'esprit de vengeance, la lutte contre ceux qui avaient pris part à la Révolution, l'action insidieuse sur le gouvernement et sur le roi pour transgresser la Charte, le réveil de l'esprit partisan et la menace de nouveaux troubles. C'était cette partie qui avait fait choisir les deux vers de Racine placés en exergue :

Bientôt ils vous diront que les plus saintes lois,
Maîtresses du vil peuple, obéissent aux rois.

CHAPITRE XIV

MINISTRE DES CENT-JOURS

L'ENTRÉE de Carnot dans le ministère formé par Napoléon à son retour de l'île d'Elbe n'était ni prévue ni désirée par l'un et l'autre de ces deux hommes. Le gouvernement de Louis XVIII était loin d'avoir rompu avec Carnot ; il continuait de lui servir la pension accordée par Napoléon ; le bruit courait même, en mars, que Carnot et Fouché allaient entrer au ministère. Carnot lui-même, à la nouvelle du retour de Napoléon, conseillait un changement de ministres et l'adoption d'une politique libérale [1].

D'autre part, Napoléon avait attribué le ministère de la Guerre, celui qui eût pu convenir à Carnot ; mais il avait, sans succès, offert l'Intérieur à Molé et à La Valette. De guerre lasse, il avait confié l'Intérieur à Maret. On a supposé que La Valette et Molé avaient proposé Carnot, peut-être fût-ce une idée de Maret ? Quoi qu'il en soit, Napoléon le fit appeler, lui dépeignit la situation, et lui proposa l'Intérieur. Carnot accorda son concours, en regrettant de le fournir dans un département qu'il ne connaissait pas [2].

La présence de Carnot — et de Fouché — donna au ministère une teinte libérale, conforme aux promesses de l'Empereur dans ses diverses proclamations au long de la route qui l'avait amené à Paris. Tel fut le commentaire général, celui de Fleury de Chaboulon, de Baudin des Ardennes, de Le Coz, l'archevêque de Besançon, et de nombre de Conventionnels ou présidents de sociétés populaires. Tous trouvaient là le gage d'une politique nouvelle, une garantie apportée à l'armée, une satisfaction fournie à l'opinion. « Croyez-vous que ce soit pour Carnot lui-même que l'Empereur l'ait rappelé au ministère ? disait une personnalité à Rousselin de Saint-Albin. Il a jugé qu'il se donnait 500 000 hommes d'un trait de plume... : ceux qui composent la classe pensante et agissante.» Déjà des républicains lui apportaient leur programme, tandis que les émigrés accusaient l'Empereur d'avoir fait alliance avec le coryphée des Jacobins [3]. C'était, pour Carnot, assumer une lourde responsabilité ; il garantissait, ou semblait garantir, la conversion de Napoléon au libéralisme.

Le titre de comte attribué au ministre ne semblait pas correspondre à ce libéralisme prétendu jacobin. La polémique se donna libre cours, dès l'époque, sur ce point. Carnot, a-t-on riposté, n'a jamais répondu à l'archichancelier, il n'a pas fait enregistrer son brevet, il n'a pas porté son titre. A l'appui de cette thèse témoignent des hommes qui touchaient de près le nouveau ministre : Ransonnet et Rousselin de Saint-Albin. Napoléon voulut-il récompenser Carnot, ou au contraire le compromettre ? On n'a pas remarqué qu'il eût été significatif que, dans le ministère, Carnot seul n'eût pas porté de titre. Il en fut pourvu au moment même de sa nomination ministérielle, et les ratures que portent les minutes soulignent l'opportunisme de cette mesure [4].

D'ailleurs tout portait les traces de la hâte. On avait prévu trois ministres pour l'Intérieur, les Cultes et le Commerce. Faute de candidats, l'ensemble fut confié au seul Carnot. Avec la même précipitation, il fallut renouveler le personnel politique en éliminant les créatures de Louis XVIII qui eussent paralysé le régime.

L'incohérence n'avait d'égale que l'impudeur. Les mêmes administrateurs avaient tour à tour prescrit de traquer Napoléon et de servir l'Empereur. Le préfet de l'Isère s'était dressé contre les « brigands de Bonaparte », puis les avait rejoints à Lyon, ce qui lui avait valu la préfecture du Rhône. Le préfet de Seine-et-Marne avait décidé, le 19 mars, d'organiser la résistance, et le 20 mars il avait félicité Napoléon de son retour. Ce furent évidemment les plus compromis qui se montrèrent les plus zélés.

Toutefois certains résistèrent réellement : on vit à Nîmes trois préfets à la fois, l'un nommé par Louis XVIII, l'autre par le comte d'Artois, le troisième par Napoléon. Le duc et la duchesse d'Angoulême tentèrent de tenir tout le Sud, de Bordeaux à Toulouse et aux Alpes. Le duc de Bourbon voulait ressusciter la Vendée.

L'urgence de l'action et les habitudes dictatoriales de Napoléon avaient provoqué la révocation d'une quarantaine de préfets avant que Carnot n'eût pris possession de ses fonctions. Elles amenèrent ensuite la nomination au ministère de l'Intérieur d'une série de directeurs, qui furent pratiquement indépendants du ministre : Bigot de Prémeneu aux Cultes, Molé aux Ponts et Chaussées, Chaptal au Commerce et à l'Industrie ; ce dernier fut même nommé ministre d'État [5].

Certes, les attributions du ministre étaient assez vastes pour laisser à ces directeurs la plus grande initiative. Il dirigeait de grands services techniques, comme les travaux de Paris, les mines, l'agriculture, l'assistance publique et la santé, sans oublier les beaux-arts, l'instruction publique, la librairie, et l'administration générale. C'était, aux dires de Beugnot, un colosse hors de toutes proportions avec ses collègues. Mais il ne fallait pas que le ministre risquât d'être isolé au milieu d'un personnel qu'il n'aurait pas choisi.

Carnot commença par faire nommer un secrétaire général, Basset de Châteaubourg, ancien préfet, gendre du sous-gouverneur à la Banque de France. Dès le 10 avril, Basset devint préfet de l'Oise, et Carnot choisit pour le remplacer Delaville Le Roulx, ancien haut fonctionnaire en Illyrie, puis en Italie. Celui-ci demanda son changement le 15 juin, car le ministre ne lui laissait à peu près aucune initiative. Ce fut pourtant lui qui exerça les fonctions pendant presque toute cette période. Le secrétaire particulier du ministre était Rousselin de Saint-Albin, qui, quoique jeune encore, avait eu une carrière très diverse et très remplie, tantôt dans l'armée auprès de Hoche, puis de Bernadotte, tantôt dans l'administration centrale ou départementale. C'était l'homme des démocrates, l'ami de Marc-Antoine Jullien, voire de Fouché, qui l'avait accrédité auprès de Carnot. Intelligent mais ambitieux, il finit par lasser Carnot qui le tint à l'écart. Dans les premiers temps, son influence s'exerça contre Napoléon qui n'était plus, à son avis, ni « un instrument national, ni même un instrument militaire » pour avoir « trop abusé de tout [6] ».

Rousselin a décrit les méthodes de travail du ministre. Il se faisait ouvrir la correspondance devant lui ; il en prenait connaissance et l'apostillait. Quand les chefs de division lui apportaient leur travail, il relisait tout, discutait, souvent longuement. « Il rassemblait toujours, et à chaque fois, toutes ses forces » sur la question qu'il traitait, se refusait aux digressions, ne menant jamais plusieurs choses à la fois. Son bureau ne portait que ce qui lui servait à l'instant même, aucun papier inutile, tout était distribué dans un ordre strict. Il professait que l'administration ne se composait que de détails [7].

Carnot réorganisa immédiatement les services ministériels, leur imposant le même ordre qu'il faisait régner autour de lui et qu'il avait apporté au ministère de la Guerre. Mais il réduisit à peu de chose les changements de personnes.

En même temps il s'appliquait à la réorganisation de l'administration et au rétablissement de l'autorité. Dès son premier « travail avec l'Empereur », le 23 mars, il était chargé d'envoyer trois commissaires extraordinaires en mission dans les régions hostiles ou incertaines : à Lille pour le Nord, à Angers pour la Vendée et l'Ouest, à Marseille pour le Midi. C'était recourir à la méthode traditionnelle et efficace, celle des représentants en mission, celle aussi de certains commissaires du Directoire, et — plus récemment — celle qui avait été usitée après le coup d'État de brumaire, et enfin en 1813 et 1814. Ces personnages étaient des informateurs qui transmettaient leurs observations et leurs propositions ; ils étaient aussi des propagandistes, chargés de réchauffer l'esprit public et donner une nouvelle impulsion aux fonctionnaires. Leur mission fut provisoirement décommandée en raison des nouvelles favorables venues des points où ils devaient se rendre [8]. Le gouvernement voulut se contenter des rouages normaux, préfets, sous-préfets et maires.

Carnot s'adressa donc aux préfets. La circulaire annonçant sa prise de fonctions était un peu fade et factice, célébrant l'Empereur, l'armée, le peuple, complimentant les préfets. Les considérations politiques vantaient le libéralisme du nouveau régime, « les magnanimes intentions de notre légitime souverain ». Elles s'adressaient aux acquéreurs de biens nationaux, aux paysans à qui l'on faisait craindre la féodalité et auprès desquels Napoléon se réclamait de la Providence. Les seules mesures prescrites étaient le rappel des membres des municipalités exclus par Louis XVIII. Quelques jours plus tard, sur l'ordre de Napoléon, le ministre invitait les préfets à suspendre provisoirement les sous-préfets et les maires des villes qui ne donnaient pas satisfaction [9].

C'était un point capital, sur lequel Fouché a porté plus d'attention que Carnot. Celui-ci était peu préparé à son rôle, celui-là avait au contraire une incomparable expérience. Carnot se tourna souvent vers Fouché, qui ne manqua pas de l'informer et de le conseiller. Ainsi le ministre de la Police signala à son collègue de l'Intérieur le grand nombre de maires des communes rurales qui étaient anciens seigneurs du lieu. Ces maires, bonapartistes en 1810, étaient devenus royalistes depuis 1814, et la nouvelle orientation politique du régime napoléonien ne pouvait que les confirmer dans leurs convictions [10]. « Il faut que les grands résultats de notre révolution ne soient plus un problème », écrivait Fouché.

Il apparut bientôt que, malgré les mutations, les préfets ne répondaient pas tous aux intentions du gouvernement. De nouvelles épurations furent donc effectuées, suivies de nominations auxquelles Carnot prit une part importante. Il se tournait volontiers, pour les postes administratifs, vers les hommes « connus par leur dévouement à la cause du peuple », patriotes de 1789, propriétaires, négociants, acquéreurs de biens nationaux, administrateurs en exercice pendant la Révolution, sages, énergiques, jouissant d'une honnête aisance. Il nomma volontiers d'anciens Conventionnels, c'était l'un de ses soucis majeurs. Mais il restait fidèle à certaines amitiés, fussent-elles nouées avec des royalistes avoués ; par exemple il maintint Vaublanc à la préfecture de la Moselle, jusqu'au jour où Napoléon s'en émut. Carnot avait servi Vaublanc après le 18 Brumaire ; en revanche celui-ci avait pris chez lui le fils aîné de Carnot exilé. La divergence des opinions n'avait pu les opposer, ils avaient l'un pour l'autre une estime réciproque, et l'expérience leur avait prouvé que les circonstances les portaient tour à tour au pouvoir ou dans l'opposition, aux honneurs ou dans la proscription. Le succès ou l'échec ne tenait pas à la justesse des principes, mais aux forces en présence [11]. Carnot voulut aussi faire appel à Robert Lindet, mais il se heurta à un refus ; en revanche il accepta de donner un poste à Cavaignac qui l'avait sollicité. Il n'oublia pas non plus Cochon de Lapparent [12].

Pourtant Carnot ne disposa pas seul des nominations ; Napoléon intervint souvent, parfois aussi Fouché et même certains commissaires extraordinaires. De sorte que le personnel préfectoral était étonnamment composite. Il était aussi instable. Au 6 avril, sur 87 préfets nommés ou conservés par Louis XVIII, 61 avaient été révoqués. Du 20 mars au 10 juin, on publia 170 nominations de préfets. Certains ne mettaient aucune hâte à rejoindre leur poste, d'autres furent révoqués le jour où l'on découvrit qu'ils s'étaient trop compromis avec le roi. Finalement le ministre ne put, à aucun moment, compter vraiment sur le Corps préfectoral [13].

Dans ces conditions, le recours aux commissaires extra-ordinaires fut méthodiquement organisé.

Le 4 avril, Napoléon avait décidé l'envoi de commissaires pour lever les gardes nationales au voisinage des régions hostiles : Rœderer se rendrait à Lyon, Thibaudeau à Dijon, Dumolard à Besançon, et les deux derniers iraient l'un à Moulins et l'autre à Grenoble. Napoléon, encore incertain de la capitale, leur faisait réserver des forces pour « appuyer Paris s'il en était besoin ». Ils étaient autorisés à faire des proclamations et à changer les autorités civiles.

Le 8 avril, Napoléon prescrivait d'envoyer un commissaire dans le Nord et le Pas-de-Calais pour changer les sous-préfets et les maires, ainsi que d'autres fonctionnaires. Il en fit partir vers Rodez, Cahors et Périgueux, sur « toute la frontière d'insurrection ». Enfin, le 20 avril, un commissaire était affecté à chaque division militaire pour accomplir une épu-ration générale et systématique. A leur arrivée, tous les sous-préfets, maires, adjoints, membres des conseils muni-cipaux, et même les officiers de la garde nationale, devaient obtenir confirmation de leurs pouvoirs ; sinon, ils ne pour-raient continuer d'exercer leurs fonctions.

Carnot avait contribué à faire prendre ces mesures et à choisir les commissaires. C'est lui qui leur donna des instruc-tions. « L'état des choses, précisait-il, n'est pas comme il y a deux ans ; il faut que les magistrats soient choisis dans l'intérêt de la population. » Confiez la direction aux hommes qui « ont la plus grande influence sur la masse de la popula-tion ». Et il expliquait aux préfets que « tous les dépositaires de l'autorité publique [devaient être] des hommes jouissant de la confiance du peuple, et animés des sentiments qui sont aujourd'hui communs au Souverain et à la grande majorité de la Nation [14] ».

Le renouvellement devait être terminé le 5 mai, à cause de la grande réunion qui devait fonder le régime en évoquant Charlemagne, et qu'on avait dénommée, pour cette raison, les Champs de Mai. Il fut donc réalisé précipitamment et médiocrement, de l'aveu même des commissaires. Ceux d'entre eux qui avaient déjà renouvelé les fonctionnaires se demandèrent quelle conduite ils devaient tenir. Il y eut du flottement, d'autant plus que la correspondance de Carnot n'était pas nette sur la politique à suivre.

Ces mesures furent encore bouleversées par le décret du 30 avril, pris à la demande de Carnot, qui en avait reçu le vœu de divers correspondants. Il prescrivait de procéder aux élections des maires dans les communes de moins de 5 000 habitants. Les commissaires s'étonnèrent qu'on remît ainsi en question une partie de leur travail, et ils signalèrent le risque de voir réélire les maires qu'ils avaient épurés. On renonça même à l'application du décret dans les régions trop hostiles, par exemple en Vendée et en Loire-Inférieure. On alla jusqu'à décider de suspendre les nouveaux élus dont on aurait à se plaindre.

Tout au long des Cent-Jours, l'incohérence régna. Sans doute tenait-elle aux circonstances, mais Carnot manquait d'expérience, et parfois aussi de pouvoirs. Il fut hésitant, flottant et, finalement, mal obéi. A la veille de Waterloo, il était encore occupé au dépouillement du travail des commissaires extraordinaires [15].

Les difficultés apparaissent assez nettement à la lecture des rapports de ces commissaires, et aussi à l'examen des grandes mesures politiques.

Dans l'ensemble du pays, la noblesse boudait ou combattait le régime. Elle s'était accommodée de l'Empire monarchique, à partir de 1810 principalement. Elle avait recouvré les fonctions politiques et administratives qui consolidaient son autorité sociale. L'Empereur avait voulu utiliser celle-ci au profit de son régime. La nouvelle politique préconisée depuis son retour de l'île d'Elbe — préconisée plutôt qu'appliquée — lui convenait d'autant moins que la Restauration lui avait permis de grandes espérances.

Le clergé regrettait Louis XVIII. Carnot représentait à ses yeux le rationalisme, la « philosophie ». Son *Mémoire au Roi* était dur contre le clergé. L'incident provoqué par le refus d'enterrer religieusement une comédienne célèbre, quelques mois plus tôt, avait donné l'occasion à Carnot de prendre position contre les autorités religieuses. Les libéraux l'en félicitaient en épîtres grandiloquentes. La crise entre le Pape et l'Empereur n'était pas dénouée, Carnot songeait à doter l'Église de France d'une organisation indépendante de Rome. Il demanda une consultation à Daunou, mais il recula devant les complications qui se fussent inévitablement produites. L'enquête qu'il dirigea sur les dispositions du clergé ne fut pas favorable. Sans doute un grand nombre d'évêques affirmaient-ils qu'il n'y avait pas à redouter de troubles, mais bien peu étaient acquis au nouveau régime ; plusieurs lui étaient hostiles, notamment dans l'Ouest et dans le Midi. Enfin l'évêque de Soissons déclarait même qu'il ne connaissait pas d'autre souverain légitime que Louis XVIII. En maints endroits, les prêtres ne faisaient pas les prières pour l'Empereur prescrites par le Concordat.

Carnot envisageait des mesures de contrainte. Il songeait à exiger que les évêques fissent lire au prône, dans leur diocèse, les actes du gouvernement, et même que les curés et desservants fussent privés de leur traitement tant que les contributions de leur paroisse n'auraient pas été acquittées. Bigot de Préameneu, plus accoutumé à traiter ces problèmes, ajourna les mesures, mais le rapport qu'il fournit pour l'*Exposé de la Situation de l'Empire* reconnaissait que le clergé dans son ensemble était royaliste. Or les commissaires n'avaient pas caché que le clergé avait conservé un pouvoir considérable, parfois prépondérant, sur les populations rurales, surtout dans les régions hostiles à l'Empire [16].

Prendre des mesures générales était difficile : favorables au clergé, elles heurtaient les libéraux ; hostiles elles renforçaient l'opposition.

De plus, la question religieuse ne se posait pas à propos des seuls catholiques. Dans les Cévennes, en particulier, se posait le problème protestant. Celui-ci était représenté par une minorité, riche et puissante, qui avait accueilli avec joie les débuts de la Révolution, et qui avait eu à souffrir pendant la Restauration. Les protestants étaient donc favorables à l'Empire, mais cela suffisait à lui rendre les catholiques hostiles [17].

Les difficultés religieuses empêchaient le régime de trouver chez les paysans l'appui qu'aurait pu lui fournir la crainte des gabelles, dîmes et droits seigneuriaux. La méfiance des paysans répugnait à soutenir trop vite un régime mal assuré et dont la chute les exposerait aux représailles. Carnot voulut pourtant exploiter les bonnes dispositions de ces paysans.

D'accord avec Fouché et Rousselin de Saint-Albin, il se proposa de publier une *Feuille villageoise*. Rousselin insistait sur la nécessité d'employer un style simple et de mêler à la propagande politique des conseils sur l'agriculture. Fouché proposait à Carnot de prendre Guinguené et Jullien de la Drôme pour rédacteurs ; Carnot leur préféra Colas, qui avait l'expérience de ces publications. C'était le prolongement, très tardif, des longs efforts multipliés au long de la Révolution, notamment sous le Directoire, pour convertir les campagnes. Le premier numéro de ce journal parut le 1er juin, ce qui ne permit pas de prolonger sa publication.

D'autre part, au Conseil d'Industrie nationale, Carnot faisait discuter les améliorations à introduire dans l'agriculture et l'élevage [18].

Entre noblesse et paysannerie, la bourgeoisie pouvait apporter un concours d'autant plus puissant que cette classe disposait de crédits, d'initiative économique, de talents et de fonctions publiques. La bourgeoisie, bénéficiaire de la Révolution, allait-elle en sauver l'héritage confié à Napoléon et à Carnot ?

Commerçants et industriels demeuraient pourtant rétifs parce que les guerres risquaient de ruiner la reprise économique provoquée par la pacification, lors de la Restauration. Les commissaires notaient ce mécontentement dans la plupart des villes manufacturières, et dans les ports de commerce et de pêche. Ainsi les morutiers de Dunkerque, les négociants de Nantes, les armateurs de Marseille, les tisserands de coton de l'Observatoire et des faubourgs Saint-Jacques et Saint-Antoine. A Brest, on reprochait à Napoléon d'avoir préféré soutenir Anvers.

Carnot, qui avait affirmé la vocation agricole de la France et l'impossibilité de battre les Anglais sur leur propre terrain, n'était pas fait pour les rassurer. Pourtant il s'intéressait vivement aux problèmes industriels et commerciaux. Peu après son arrivée au ministère, il avait formé un Conseil d'Industrie nationale où siégeaient des savants, comme dans les comités pour la défense nationale de l'an II, Berthollet, Monge, des négociants comme Gros d'Avilliers, des manufacturiers comme Ternaux. La plupart des problèmes techniques et financiers devaient y être étudiés, en particulier le développement des machines, à l'imitation des Anglais, mais en assurant une qualité supérieure aux produits.

Un prix annuel de 50 000 francs fut accordé par Napoléon, à la demande du Conseil, en faveur de celui qui aurait le plus contribué aux progrès de l'industrie nationale par l'emploi de machines. Carnot fit faire une enquête sur la situation des industries en France ; il fit aussi attribuer la Légion d'honneur à des manufacturiers.

Plus encore que le temps, la paix et les ressources financières firent défaut. Les puissances d'argent n'approuvaient pas les Cent-Jours. Une note signalait, le 23 avril, que l'exportation du métal précieux se précipitait clandestinement, en particulier par Genève, « les banquiers y prêtant la main [19] ».

Pourtant Carnot tenta de gagner les milieux d'affaires en leur attribuant un rôle administratif et politique. Déjà l'un des commissaires lui proposait de confier la municipalité de Lille aux manufacturiers, au lieu des nobles qui l'occupaient, et aussi les commandements dans la garde nationale. Carnot élargit cette politique. Il l'appliqua même — anticipation remarquable — à l'élection des députés. Il fut décidé que les commerçants et manufacturiers choisiraient des représentants spéciaux pour le Corps législatif. Cette idée fut suggérée par un Sarthois libéral, le pharmacien Pesche, figure originale, esprit novateur, qui envisageait une représentation strictement professionnelle. Si Carnot l'avait suivi jusqu'au bout, il eût divisé les électeurs — et les députés — en cinq catégories correspondant aux propriétaires, aux militaires, aux cultivateurs, aux commerçants et manufacturiers, et enfin aux savants, artistes et hommes de profession libérale. Le projet était dans l'air depuis que le Tiers avait entamé la Révolution : à Paris, à Marseille, en Dauphiné, les négociants avaient demandé que le commerce eût des députés particuliers aux États généraux ; le souhait n'était pas oublié. C'est à Carnot que se plaignit un manufacturier, Guéroult, du nombre insuffisant des représentants du commerce et de l'industrie. Ainsi ces satisfactions elles-mêmes ne suffisaient pas à rallier vraiment le monde des affaires [20].

La bourgeoisie des professions libérales attendait tout de Carnot. Lui-même voulait lui donner la première place. Rien ne l'intéressait plus que l'*intelligentsia*, les hommes à talents, les lumières. Il les préférait aux propriétaires : « On attache en général trop d'importance à la qualité de propriétaire, qui d'ailleurs est mal définie.... L'essentiel est d'obtenir des lumières.... » Plutôt que des propriétaires, mieux valait de simples locataires, mais éclairés, ainsi des fonctionnaires publics, hommes de lettres, artistes, jurisconsultes, commerçants, manufacturiers, pensionnés de l'État [21].

La confiance faite à Carnot se retourna contre lui. On lui reprocha les insuffisances de l'Acte additionnel, constitution octroyée à la façon de la Charte, laissant à l'Empereur des pouvoirs fort étendus, et créant une chambre de pairs héréditaires.

Anonymes ou signées de noms peu connus, les protestations s'en prenaient à l'homme plus encore qu'au ministre : « Carnot,... nous attendions une constitution libérale, nous voulions un gouvernement représentatif, et nous n'avons ni l'un ni l'autre. » On s'étonnait qu'il eût collaboré à un tel acte. En vain s'est-il énergiquement défendu d'avoir « beaucoup contribué à la rédaction du projet » et d'avoir fait partie d'aucune commission.

Des notes personnelles de Carnot font connaître ses vues. Il s'opposait résolument à l'hérédité des pairs, qui eût ressuscité les « familles privilégiées », favorisé des prétentions politiques excessives et heurté l'opinion publique. Le nombre des membres du Sénat devait être limité. Le Sénat aurait un pouvoir censorial sur toutes les autorités constituées. La proposition des lois appartiendrait à un comité de législation, formé de commissaires pris dans le Sénat, le Corps législatif, l'ordre judiciaire et le Conseil d'État, sous la présidence de l'Empereur. Les projets seraient soumis au Corps législatif, mais sans pouvoir jamais être modifiés. Le budget serait discuté par le Corps législatif.

Carnot prenait le contre-pied de Benjamin Constant, le grand inspirateur de l'Acte constitutionnel. Il combattait l'influence anglaise en utilisant les arguments de son *Mémoire au Roi*. L'Angleterre pouvait se permettre d'avoir un parti d'opposition, parce que sa position géographique la mettait à l'abri des invasions et la dispensait d'avoir une armée nombreuse, et aussi parce que la fortune des particuliers y était essentiellement liée à la fortune publique. « On peut dire que la constitution anglaise est fondée sur l'opposition et que la nôtre doit être au contraire fondée sur l'union. »

En présence du mécontentement provoqué par l'Acte additionnel, Carnot demanda à Napoléon de promettre des retouches et d'abolir immédiatement la dénomination de « sujets » pour désigner les Français. Il ne fut pas écouté [22].

L'acceptation de l'Acte additionnel renforça l'opposition des libéraux à Carnot. Sur l'ordre de Napoléon, on renvoya onze employés des ministères de l'Intérieur notoirement hostiles au régime, notamment le jeune Guizot, chef de bureau. Des « amis de la liberté » le reprochèrent violemment à Carnot et lui écrivirent une lettre de menaces. Delécluze lui fit remarquer que si jamais l'Empereur était

victorieux le despotisme militaire serait rétabli avec l'invo-
lontaire complicité de Carnot [23].

Ainsi le ministre n'avait pu se concilier même ceux auxquels il tenait par-dessus tout : ses pouvoirs ne le lui permettaient pas.

Restait la masse du peuple, les pauvres, les artisans, les
ouvriers, les journaliers. Napoléon songea, dit-on, à coiffer
le bonnet rouge pour déchaîner les masses. Il eût renoué
avec la révolution sociale pour mater libéraux et royalistes.
Carnot eut l'idée, passagère, de suivre cette politique :
« C'est une lutte entre les salons et la masse du peuple »,
écrivait-il, « l'intérêt du peuple est le même que celui de
l'Empereur ». Il eut même l'intention de réveiller les sociétés
populaires : « Il faut que des commissaires travaillent à
étendre et à consolider le système de la fédération des acquéreurs de biens nationaux et des amis de la liberté. » A vrai
dire il s'agissait de s'appuyer sur le peuple et de l'utiliser
comme allié, plutôt que de lui donner la parole et d'améliorer son sort; ainsi le rétablissement des sociétés populaires permettrait au gouvernement « d'avoir à sa disposition et dans sa main le plus puissant levier de l'opinion
publique [24] ». Tous ces projets restèrent en plan, car le
souvenir des violences terroristes paralysait Carnot. Il eût
frémi en lisant les conseils de Rœderer à Frochot : lever
« la canaille » en payant quelques meneurs : « Il faut que
la ménagerie soit à nous ? Je n'entends pas qu'on lui ouvre
les portes, mais que les griffes passent un peu entre les bar-
reaux.... Tenir les prolétaires, ne fût-ce bon qu'à les ôter à
l'ennemi.... Il serait nécessaire d'avoir trois ou quatre chan-
tiers de terrassiers, mais conduits et surveillés comme des
forçats par des hommes de la ligne, commandés par des
officiers retraités. » Cet avant-projet d'ateliers nationaux
était suivi d'une leçon de police dans un salon, manœuvrant
barbiers et avocats, médecins et maîtresses, curés et banquiers, pour connaître l'opinion et agir sur elle. Carnot n'était
point l'homme de telles manœuvres; pourtant Rœderer lui
fit quelques insinuations [25].

Il ne retint pas davantage les doléances qui lui vinrent
parfois du peuple. Un « ouvrier faiseur de bas à métier » lui
confia ses griefs. Il souhaitait la suppression du livret ouvrier,
ou du moins celle des frais que provoquait chaque changement d'employeur. Il demandait aussi qu'on ne donnât
aucune charge politique aux prêtres [26].

Le ministre, comme l'Empereur, se préoccupa surtout d'éviter le chômage en reprenant les travaux publics, principalement à Paris.

Sa grande idée c'était l'éducation populaire, « pour rattacher à la cause générale de la patrie des hommes condamnés jusqu'alors à un état d'ignorance et de nullité absolue », pour fournir aussi des chefs d'atelier, des maîtres ouvriers, pour éviter enfin que le cultivateur et l'ouvrier s'opposent aux perfectionnements techniques. Carnot partageait les idées de La Rochefoucauld-Liancourt et de Chaptal.

Pour assurer l'instruction élémentaire des masses, Carnot se rallia aux méthodes dites d'enseignement mutuel, qui consistaient à confier mille élèves à un seul instituteur qui les répartissait en une dizaine de classes, mais en employant les enfants comme moniteurs les uns des autres. L'établissement d'une telle école coûterait 6 000 francs à la campagne et 1 700 francs à la ville, et l'entretien annuel — malgré la gratuité — ne dépasserait guère ces sommes. Ce procédé était appliqué en Angleterre où divers Français — Laborde, Lasteyrie, Liancourt et l'abbé Gautier — l'avaient étudié. Un rapport fut fait à la Société d'encouragement pour l'industrie nationale; le 29 mars, une délégation fut envoyée au ministère de l'Intérieur. Celui-ci prépara un rapport et un décret qu'il soumit à l'Empereur.

Carnot aurait voulu couvrir la France d'un réseau de telles écoles, en commençant par les chefs-lieux de département pour aboutir aux communes. Il ne put obtenir que la création d'une école d'essai, qui servirait d'école normale. Ce fut le fameux décret du 27 avril.

L'instruction généralisée devait permettre « d'élever successivement à la dignité d'hommes tous les individus de l'espèce humaine ». Carnot ajoutait aux vues de la Société d'encouragement pour l'industrie nationale, soucieuse d'améliorer la main-d'œuvre, un mobile plus largement humain et la base même d'une démocratie. Il élargissait le champ de recrutement des élites. Il voulait compléter son projet par la création d'une école normale des arts mécaniques [27].

Des institutions d'assistance, concertées avec La Rochefoucauld-Liancourt et avec Delessert, devaient assurer la sécurité aux ouvriers, en cas de maladie, de vieillesse, de veuvage.

Ainsi l'industrialisation souhaitée de la France eût pu s'accomplir sans misère et sans crise sociale. Il s'agissait d'éviter cette prolétarisation qui avait si cruellement éprouvé une grande partie de la population anglaise. Toute la question était de savoir qui l'emporterait des vues humanitaires de Carnot ou des vues utilitaires des hommes d'affaires.

Finalement Carnot ne put assurer au régime des bases fermes et durables. Sans doute devait-il compter avec Napoléon et avec les autres ministres, dont les vues étaient plus conservatrices, mais on ne peut lui faire l'honneur d'une politique nette et fermement poursuivie. Il endossa la responsabilité de nombreuses mesures qu'il réprouvait ; il put rarement faire adopter celles qu'il souhaitait. Pourquoi, dans de telles conditions, rester au ministère ? A cause de la défense nationale.

L'appel à la garde nationale est resté la preuve la plus frappante du mouvement patriotique suscité par Carnot. A vrai dire Napoléon avait déjà fait appel à la garde nationale en 1814, et Louis XVIII avait voulu la dresser contre les partisans de l'Empire lors du débarquement de Napoléon. L'idée ne vint donc pas de Carnot. D'ailleurs, dès le 27 mars, l'Empereur lui avait prescrit la réorganisation de cette garde. Le 31, le ministre soumettait à Napoléon un projet qu'il avait préparé avec Mathieu Dumas. Une levée de 107 bataillons devait permettre de fournir les garnisons des places fortes et de libérer ainsi les troupes qui les occupaient.

La réorganisation d'ensemble fut prescrite par les décrets des 5 et 10 avril, qui devaient permettre de compter plus de 2 200 000 gardes nationaux de vingt à soixante ans. Ne seraient mis en activité que ceux des régions frontières, soit 204 bataillons, de 144 000 hommes. C'était l'application des ordres impériaux, Carnot aurait voulu « favoriser le patriotisme des classes inférieures qui ne faisaient point partie de la garde nationale et qui... voulaient payer le tribut de leurs bras... en demandant des armes ». Il ne voyait dans cet élan que « l'exercice d'un devoir civique ». Napoléon s'opposa à l'équipement et à l'armement des Fédérés et s'inquiéta de ces milliers d'artisans parisiens qui défilèrent le 14 mai. Il ne cessait des « craindre l'intervention du peuple armé dans la cause nationale [28] ».

Dans les limites assignées, Carnot voulut obtenir des résultats prompts et efficaces. Il stimula les préfets pour assurer la levée des hommes et la fabrication des armes. Les résultats correspondirent à la carte des opinions : seules les zones orientales, de Paris au Rhin, de l'Aisne à l'Isère, exécutèrent les ordres ministériels. Le reste du pays demeura inerte; en quelques endroits même l'hostilité se dessina, notamment dans le Sud-Est et dans l'Ouest. On eut à peine la moitié des effectifs prévus quand s'engagea la campagne de Waterloo [29].

Du moins Carnot avait-il réveillé le patriotisme et les espérances d'une partie des Français. Bien qu'il ne fût pas ministre de la Guerre, il reçut une multitude de propositions pour le perfectionnement des armes et de la technique militaire, accompagnées de témoignages de confiance : « Le père Carnot est là ! Nous n'avons plus rien à désirer [30]. »

Situation étrange : Carnot était comblé d'honneurs par l'Empereur et conjuré de sauver la France par de braves gens, au moment où l'Empire sombrait et où les Chambres s'apprêtaient à disposer du pouvoir. Carnot, en effet, gravissant soudain les degrés de la Légion d'honneur, avait été promu grand-officier le 15 mai et avait été nommé pair le 2 juin.

Cependant les élections avaient eu lieu. Feulint avait été élu en Saône-et-Loire. Carnot avait présenté aux pairs, le 13 juin, son *Exposé de la Situation de l'Empire;* il avait été optimiste et avait invité la Chambre à améliorer la constitution et à préparer des lois organiques. Il avait toutefois atténué l'expression de sa pensée. Un premier projet évoquait les souvenirs glorieux, 1793, l'héroïsme des troupes républicaines, 1814, l'opiniâtreté de la défense d'Anvers ; il faisait ainsi appel aux hommes attachés à la Révolution par leurs convictions, leurs sentiments et leurs intérêts. Au dernier moment, peut-être à la demande de ses collègues, il avait remplacé ces appels par une incitation à combattre la licence et l'anarchie [31].

Quelques jours plus tard, le 21 juin, Carnot se présentait de nouveau devant les pairs; c'était pour confirmer la défaite subie à Waterloo et annoncer des mesures de circonstances. Le discours était morne, les propositions vagues. Carnot avait proposé de déclarer la patrie en danger et de créer une dictature provisoire. Ni les ministres, ni les Chambres, ni même l'Empereur n'y étaient disposés. Fouché lui avait écrit, dès le 12 : « Gardons-nous de croire que les mesures qui ont réussi il y a vingt ans puissent réussir aujourd'hui. Je crains que cette allusion n'entraîne les militaires et nous perde. Tout est usé, excepté la raison [32]. »

Il est bien curieux que Napoléon ait confié à Bertrand, en 1817, ses regrets de n'avoir pas placé Carnot à la tête du Corps législatif plutôt qu'au ministère de l'Intérieur : « Il connaissait les assemblées, il était connu du parti populaire ; c'était un homme droit, accoutumé à la Révolution, et qui ne s'effrayait pas du danger ». Tout prouve au contraire que Carnot n'aurait rien pu modifier et qu'il ne savait pas retourner les sentiments d'une assemblée.

Ce fut l'abdication, où Carnot pleura. Ainsi se séparèrent à jamais deux hommes qui s'étaient tour à tour soutenus et heurtés. Leurs tempéraments les opposaient plus encore que leurs idées. Ils portèrent l'un sur l'autre des jugements sévères. Carnot avait dû subir l'autorité de ce confrère, de ce camarade militaire, qu'il avait appuyé et commandé. Il avait dû accepter d'être appelé à le servir, puis d'être secouru par lui. Finalement, il avait subi l'ascendant de ce génie, et surtout il avait pensé que l'héritage de la Révolution, déjà bien amenuisé, tenait à l'Empire. Les projets des émigrés l'avaient décidé à soutenir l'Empereur revenu. Cette fois, c'était fini. Quel espoir d'arrêter la réaction triomphante ? Ce qui tenait le plus au cœur de Carnot, ce qui lui semblait essentiel au destin de la France et de l'Europe, était perdu. Et il avait plus de soixante ans !

« Carnot ne valait rien au ministère de l'Intérieur [33] », a déclaré Napoléon à Sainte-Hélène. Jugement plus lapidaire qu'équitable. Carnot avait des vues larges et pénétrantes, il avait amorcé des réformes de grande envergure, qui eussent pu avoir des résultats très considérables, dans des domaines extrêmement variés. On serait tenté d'affirmer, au contraire, qu'il avait donné sa mesure.

Mais c'était celle d'un grand administrateur, non d'un grand politique. Il entreprenait en comptant sur l'avenir, alors que le temps était compté. Il voyait loin, mais se méprenait sur les exigences du moment présent. Il aurait pu, en période calme, accomplir une grande œuvre, mais les talents de Fouché, plutôt que ceux de Colbert, eussent répondu aux nécessités des circonstances et aux espoirs de Napoléon.

LE SUPRÊME EXIL

Par une sorte de dérision, les événements semblaient condamner Carnot à se répéter, ou plutôt à constater qu'il ne le pouvait plus. A ce moment, où la patrie en danger ne galvanisait plus la défense, il fut nommé l'un des cinq chefs suprêmes — et provisoires — de la France : membre de la Commission de gouvernement, élu avec une large majorité.

Ses collègues manquaient d'envergure, sauf un, Fouché. Ils devaient, avec le Sénat et le Corps législatif, gouverner le pays, organiser la défense, préparer l'avenir alors que le présent était désespéré. Était-ce l'heure de l'héroïsme ou celle de manœuvres de couloir ?

Le rappel du passé, les objurgations de tant d'amis, semblaient faire de Carnot l'homme de la défense nationale. « Carnot, réveille-toi ! La patrie est en danger, à ta voix des millions d'hommes s'armeront ! » Ce cri anonyme était renforcé par des invitations plus précises : « Plus de Bourbons, plus de Napoléon, la République ! Carnot ! le peuple attend de toi la liberté, il te nomme ! L'armée parle comme lui. » Telle était une lettre des troupes d'Auxonne, « l'an Ier du retour de la liberté ». Certains proposaient l'adoption de la constitution américaine. Carnot serait président. Chasles évoquait les souvenirs et les résolutions d'un ancien Conventionnel : « Je n'aurai pas, depuis 1789, tout sacrifié, tout souffert pour attendre froidement la mort des infâmes. » Il voulait, lui aussi, « sauver la patrie.... Avant quinze jours nous aurons, si on le veut, plus d'un million de braves ». Ransonnet écrivait que les soldats ne voulaient pas marcher pour Louis XVIII.

Carnot vibra à ces souvenirs ; il céda à ces invitations. Il envoyait des ordres hâtivement griffonnés : « Indiquer Paris pour le point de ralliement des troupes. Mettre la citadelle de Lille en état de défense — faire connaître le projet de défendre Paris comme moyen de sûreté pour les citoyens. » Déjà il voulait presser la fabrication des armes, proclamer l'état de siège, donner le gouvernement de Paris à Davout, lever enfin tous les Français : « Tous les citoyens en état de porter les armes se posteront sur les derrières des armées ennemies pour intercepter leurs communications et leurs subsistances [1]. »

Mais quel régime adopter ? Comme à son accoutumée, Carnot défendait la légalité : l'abdication de Napoléon avait été acceptée au profit du roi de Rome ; la question était donc tranchée en faveur de Napoléon II. C'est ce que proclama Feulint dans une circulaire aux préfets [2].

En effet Carnot porté à la Commission de gouvernement, Feulint avait été nommé ministre de l'Intérieur. C'est à ce titre qu'il saisit les autorités départementales. C'était un homme d'action, il utilisa aussitôt le pouvoir qui lui avait été confié. Coup sur coup, il expédia deux circulaires, dès le 23 juin. Par la première, il annonçait sa prise de fonctions et faisait appel à l'énergie, qui seule pouvait « garantir notre indépendance », et il prescrivait de suivre « toutes les mesures de salut public » prises ou à prendre par les Chambres et le gouvernement. La seconde ordonnait de regrouper les troupes débandées pour sauver la cause nationale à « l'avènement de Napoléon II [3] ».

Pendant que les deux frères Carnot voulaient organiser la victoire de l'Aiglon, Fouché organisait la Restauration. Après avoir pressé l'abdication de Napoléon Ier, il escamotait Napoléon II et supplantait Carnot.

Au premier scrutin, celui-ci avait obtenu 324 voix sur 511, Fouché seulement 293. Carnot en avait conclu qu'il était président de la Commission, mais, dès la première réunion, Fouché avait proposé l'élection d'un président et s'était fait élire. Dès le lendemain il appelait Vitrolles, agent de Louis XVIII ; trois jours plus tard, il avait gagné au roi le général Davout. Celui-ci fit connaître ses vues à la Commission. Fouché démasqué, on se tourna vers Carnot. « Le duc d'Otrante est désigné comme chef du parti royaliste... déjouez les complots de cet intrigant [4]. »

Déjà des députés le pressaient de les seconder. Carnot savait à quoi s'en tenir sur Fouché, mais il n'était pas plus résolu à l'action qu'il ne l'avait été à la veille du 18 fructidor : « La question politique ne nous regardait pas, puisque nous n'étions chargés que de l'exécution des lois [5]. » Fétichisme de la légalité ? Bien plutôt refus de creuser les divisions entre les Français et de recommencer la Révolution. Carnot s'en tint donc à quelques sorties violentes contre son collègue et président, et il se consacra à l'étude de la défense nationale[6].

Là encore, il dut renoncer à l'action. Cette fois pour des raisons techniques et humanitaires. Le 29 juin, il avait envoyé deux officiers du Génie auprès de Davout pour lui signaler le risque de voir l'ennemi attaquer simultanément Paris sur les deux rives de la Seine ; or la rive gauche ne pouvait résister, les officiers le confirmèrent à Carnot. Le 1er juillet, Carnot lui-même parcourut les lignes. On tint à son retour une séance de la Commission, en présence de plusieurs pairs et députés et des principaux chefs militaires, pour savoir s'il fallait livrer bataille. Thibaudeau pressa Davout de telle sorte que celui-ci se déclara en faveur du combat, pour n'être pas taxé de lâcheté. Alors Carnot, en uniforme poussiéreux, exposa qu'il venait de visiter les lieux et qu'il se prononçait sans aucun préjugé politique, car la Restauration ne pouvait lui apporter que la persécution et l'exil. Or il jugeait la défense impossible.

Cette déclaration, faite avec calme et précision, suspendit la résolution que Davout avait failli imposer. La reddition de Paris fut décidée le lendemain, et c'est Carnot qui rédigea l'exposé des motifs : « Paris... peut être enlevé de vive force.... L'idée seule des calamités que pourrait entraîner un pareil évènement est faite pour glacer d'effroi. » Ainsi Carnot capitulait ! Il songea un moment à se retirer avec une armée de réserve sur la Loire. Il avait conservé un ascendant personnel sur les troupes alors que nombre de chefs étaient discrédités. C'est à lui qu'on fit appel quand il y eut des troubles dans l'armée, le 4 juillet. Mais le temps de Wattignies était passé, emportant avec lui les espérances et les illusions : Carnot, dès le 7 juillet[7], se munit d'un passeport au nom de Rosan. Il se rendit à Presles le 9, au lendemain de l'entrée du roi à Paris[8].

Une fois de plus Carnot, placé en face d'une décision capitale, s'était laissé déborder, non sans se compromettre assez inutilement.

Ses craintes ne tardèrent pas à se réaliser. Le 24 juillet, il était placé sous la surveillance de la police, hors de Paris.

Il habitait alors son domaine de Presles, « rentré dans la retraite des philosophes », comme le dit un article de *L'Indépendant*. Il y rédigeait une justification qui ne servit qu'à irriter davantage ses ennemis. Cet *Exposé de [sa] Conduite politique* fut terminé le 12 septembre ; un mois plus tard il était sommé de s'éloigner et de résider à Blois. Il refusa et annonça qu'il allait se rendre à Paris. En fait, il s'exila [9].

***

Un peu à l'aventure, muni d'un passeport pour la Russie, obtenu par Capo d'Istria, et avec la certitude de pouvoir s'établir à Mecklembourg, Carnot, accompagné de son second fils Hippolyte, et de sa vieille bonne, Joséphine Briois, s'achemina vers le Nord. Il passa par Avesnes, montra le champ de bataille de Wattignies à son fils, gagna Bruxelles, où il arriva le 20 octobre. Il y séjourna jusqu'au 16 novembre.

Puis, faisant un vaste détour par l'Allemagne du sud et par l'Autriche, les voyageurs gagnèrent Cracovie et aboutirent à Varsovie le 6 janvier 1816 [10].

La Pologne fut pour Carnot un refuge charmant. C'était à qui l'accueillerait, le soutiendrait, l'entretiendrait. Une loge maçonnique fit une souscription qui rapporta une somme assez forte pour venir en aide au proscrit. De grands seigneurs lui proposèrent des résidences et des terres. Il fut comparé à Washington. Il y avait là tant de généraux qui avaient combattu sous les drapeaux français et qui connaissaient Carnot, les Zajaczek, les Dombrowski, les Sokolnicki. Hippolyte séjourna quelques semaines dans une résidence des Malachowski. Carnot fut reçu dans les principaux salons ; il offrit à ses hôtes quelques pièces de vers ; il se sentait presque gai et presque rajeuni, et il le reconnaissait plaisamment : « Adieu, charmante princesse, écrivait-il, vous me trouverez peut-être dans cette lettre plus jeune que je n'aurais dû être. » Les agents diplomatiques français notaient avec humeur que « Carnot est admis dans tous les cercles polonais et y reçoit bon accueil ». Lui-même tirait la conclusion dans une lettre à Feulint, « je serais parfaitement content... si j'avais un revenu de 6 000 francs ». Mais il n'avait pas même la moitié, et sa dignité lui avait fait refuser les offres qu'il avait reçues ou que des amis français — Prieur notamment — lui proposaient. Il tenta seulement, en vain, d'obtenir le versement de sa pension [11].

Les difficultés financières n'étaient rien en comparaison des polémiques soulevées par la présence et par les intentions supposées des réfugiés. Il y avait là un docteur Girardot, ancien major des chevau-légers de la garde, avec qui se lia Carnot ; un docteur Sauvé, de l'Académie de médecine de Paris ; le colonel Bontemps ; quelques autres encore comme Chovot, logeur, chez qui Carnot était descendu. C'est dans ce milieu que se produisirent les incidents qui provoquèrent non seulement à l'époque même, mais plus d'un siècle après, des polémiques assez vives [12].

L'amertume de Carnot — bien explicable — s'exhalait sans ménagements. Une note intime, de cette époque, s'exprime ainsi : « Je connais un crime qui surpasse tous les crimes, c'est celui d'un roi qui va mendier le secours des puissances étrangères pour opprimer sa propre patrie.» Ces sentiments apparaissaient dans sa conversation : «propos révoltants», «dangereux discours»! Noailles, le représentant de la France, n'était pas seul à qualifier ainsi la conversation de Carnot, «on ne se lassait pas d'entendre de sa bouche le récit de nos gloires et de nos malheurs», a écrit son fils, les Polonais en ont eux-mêmes fixé le souvenir.

L'un d'eux, Dembowski, écrivait à l'époque même que Carnot stigmatisait la réaction bourbonienne et ne croyait pas à la durée de ce régime : « Les choses ne peuvent rester dans l'état actuel, il n'y a que la présence des Alliés qui soutient les Bourbons. Le petit Napoléon a sur le trône des droits qui sont irrécusables et que l'Autriche soutiendra tôt ou tard.»

Un autre, Krasinski, nota un peu plus tard que «Carnot [était] venu à Varsovie, au nom du parti républicain, proposer au grand duc Constantin la couronne de France». Enfin le grand-duc lui-même y fit allusion, en 1817, dans une conversation avec Zajaczek : « Le général Carnot et M. de Vielcastel se sont successivement adressés à moi pour me faire part du projet des réfugiés français tendant à effectuer le renversement de la maison de Bourbon... en appelant au trône... soit un prince de la maison d'Orange, soit un prince de la maison de Russie....»

Il n'est pas douteux que le grand-duc et Carnot eurent quelques explications un peu vives ; il ne l'est pas moins que les propos qui lui sont attribués ne concordent pas entre eux, et pas davantage avec le rôle et le caractère de Carnot. Mais ses imprudences furent prodigieuses, à force de précautions inutiles....

Le grand-duc avait accueilli Carnot dès le surlendemain de son arrivée. L'entrevue se prolongea deux heures et fut bien propre à faire éclater le désaccord foncier des deux

hommes. D'ailleurs la *Gazette de Varsovie* publiait au même
moment des notes rappelant les violences de l'an II, auto-
risées par Carnot, et les mesures de Louis XVIII frappant
les régicides. Le grand-duc lui-même s'était rendu à Saint-
Pétersbourg, où il s'entretint avec le tsar. Pendant son
absence, et après son retour, la *Gazette de Varsovie* multiplia
les notes hostiles aux exilés et aux régicides. Le grand-duc
était revenu le 8 février ; une semaine plus tard, Carnot
confiait à Francœur : « Les choses ne tournent point ici
comme je l'espérais, l'empressement des particuliers n'est
point partagé par le prince... et me nuit même beaucoup
dans son esprit. C'est ce qui me décide à me rendre à Peters-
bourg.» Cette décision était dictée par Alexandre, ce qui
donna fort à penser aux exilés. Ils cherchèrent d'autres
refuges ; la Belgique était interdite, la Hollande était hostile ;
ils se tournèrent vers la Prusse [13].

Carnot s'aboucha avec le représentant de la Prusse en
Pologne. Il reçut, le 18 juin, une lettre très flatteuse de
Hardenberg, lui offrant de résider à Breslau, « où il pourrait
vivre à son choix et selon son goût, et être assuré de toute
protection». Carnot s'en fut donc à Breslau, puis même à
Berlin. Là il fut éconduit, car il n'avait reçu l'autorisation
d'y venir que de la part d'un général trop bien intentionné.

Carnot aurait voulu rentrer à Varsovie, il n'en eut pas
la possibilité. Après un bref séjour à Francfort-sur-l'Oder,
le représentant de la France, jugeant que les communications
y étaient trop faciles et la correspondance trop malaisée à
surveiller, il fut envoyé à Magdebourg [14].

L'acharnement de la Restauration à poursuivre Carnot
s'explique, croyons-nous, par le ton mystérieux de sa
correspondance : allusions obscures, personnages désignés
par des initiales, style apparemment commercial, pseudo-
nyme de Rosan. Le tout était bien vain, quand on connaissait l'écriture caractéristique de Carnot, mais attribuait
des apparences subversives aux propos les plus innocents.
Il n'était question que de *secrétaire particulier*, de *correspondants de Metz*, de *correspondants frères*, de *spéculations
dans le pays*, de *compagnies*, de *commis et associés*.... Le
cabinet noir, dont Carnot avait proscrit le fonctionnement
pendant les Cent-Jours, conclut à des complots. Des perqui-
sitions eurent lieu chez quelques correspondants de Carnot,
par exemple Ferry, ex-Conventionnel, le 12 juillet, puis chez
Feulint, les 17 et 18 juillet. Feulint fut même arrêté.

Les interrogatoires prouvèrent le caractère inoffensif de cette correspondance : « le général a répondu à toutes les objections, sans hésiter et avec l'abandon d'un homme qui n'a rien à se reprocher ». Il fut mis en liberté au bout de quelques jours [15].

* * *

En novembre 1816, Carnot s'installait à Magdebourg, où il allait passer ses sept dernières années. Il avait conscience que c'était là l'étape suprême ; il étudiait l'allemand et organisait sa vie. Le temps n'était-il pas venu d'écrire des mémoires ?

A plusieurs reprises déjà, Carnot y avait songé et même travaillé. Dans ses papiers saisis au 18 fructidor, se trouvaient des notes sur la Révolution, qui ne lui furent pas rendues. C'est vers la fin de l'Empire qu'il semble avoir rédigé ses souvenirs ; on en peut suivre la marche d'après quelques lignes curieuses inscrites successivement sur la page de garde d'un carnet :

« Ce livret est composé de 196 feuillets, cotés et paraphés de ma main le 15 mai 1813. »

« Le 18 octobre 1815, j'ai enlevé les 70 premiers feuillets.... »

« Le 1er décembre 1815, j'ai enlevé depuis la 71e page jusqu'à et y compris la page 96. »

« Le 1er juillet 1819, j'ai annulé ce journal en entier pour [en] confectionner un autre à cette date [16]. »

Cette relation était si bien attendue que les services diplomatiques et policiers s'alarmèrent quand, après la mort de son père, Hippolyte quitta Magdebourg. On écrivait à Chateaubriand, ministre des Affaires étrangères, que Carnot avait laissé des mémoires « fort importants » ; on surveillait étroitement les allées et venues du jeune homme [17]. Rien ne fut publié : Carnot n'avait rédigé que des notes fragmentaires.

Il était bien éloigné, en dépit des bruits qui couraient avec persistance, d'intriguer et de comploter. Il confiait à ses amis sa résolution de ne pas s'occuper davantage d'une révolution qui avait si mal fini, et sa préférence pour l'exil tant que la situation ne s'améliorerait pas en France [18].

Les mathématiques occupaient une partie de son temps. Il s'en entretenait avec les savants allemands et correspondait avec quelques Français. Les poésies tenaient encore une place dans ses préoccupations, il remerciait Prieur de la Côte-d'Or qui les mettait en musique, ce qui permettait à Carnot de les faire chanter par les Allemands [19]. Tout cela n'aurait pas dû l'empêcher d'écrire ses mémoires, s'il l'avait vraiment voulu.

Mais il se heurtait à une difficulté pratique : trop de documents lui manquaient à Magdebourg. Ce fut au point qu'il demanda des renseignements à ses frères restés en France. En revanche, ceux-ci fournissaient volontiers une large information à ceux qui voulaient écrire sur Carnot. Ainsi à Rioust, qui publia, dès 1817, la première biographie digne de ce nom. La qualité de ce travail fut tant appréciée par celui dont il contait la vie que ce fut là qu'il conseilla désormais de s'informer. « Cet écrit, affirmait-il, renferme peu de choses inexactes, et ces choses sont trop peu importantes pour être relevées [20]. »

Ces lignes étaient adressées au docteur Körte, un érudit, vicaire de la cathédrale de Halberstadt, qui avait entrepris d'écrire la vie de Carnot. Il avait prié celui-ci de le renseigner, ce qui nous a valu quelques lettres, un livre estimable et, probablement, l'abandon de l'autobiographie.

Carnot déclarait cependant que Rioust avait sacrifié à l'apologie, et pour Körte il s'agissait d'un ouvrage objectif. Carnot fournit donc à Körte ses divers écrits, et quelques indications sur sa carrière. C'était encore très sommaire. Carnot remercia l'auteur et le félicita, lorsque l'ouvrage fut publié, au début de l'été 1820 [21].

Les frères de Carnot jugèrent sans doute que cette nouvelle biographie était encore insuffisante ; d'autre part, elle s'adressait aux Allemands. Ils décidèrent de faire paraître un autre livre. On ne peut, en effet, attribuer l'ouvrage qu'édita Baudouin en 1824 qu'à des proches de Carnot ; eux seuls peuvent avoir fourni les « notes, écrits, papiers et correspondance » que l'auteur déclare avoir consultés, et qui figurent, pour une part, à la suite de l'ouvrage [22].

Ces trois volumes n'apportaient finalement que peu de lumière sur les pensées et sur les notes de Carnot exilé. Même après l'étude beaucoup plus vaste consacrée par Hippolyte à son père, on peut encore traiter de nouveau ce point sans trop risquer de répéter ce qui a déjà été dit.

* *

La pensée politique de Carnot se fondait toujours sur une morale. Elle s'était cependant assouplie au contact d'une

longue expérience ; assouplie au point de se détacher de
l'action. La perfectibilité humaine demeurait le principal
moteur de l'Histoire, l'éducation en était l'instrument. Mais,
si les « lumières » devaient finir par triompher, il fallait
compter avec le temps et bien se garder de rien brusquer.
Pendant cette longue attente, les préjugés devaient être
tolérés pour maintenir un équilibre vital. Il importait
aussi de tendre vers l'égalité pour éliminer l'envie, « le
plus grand fléau de l'espèce humaine », mais là encore sans
violence.

Dans la phase intermédiaire, au long de la marche vers
cette perfection grandissante, le rôle principal revenait à la
bourgeoisie. Ce Bourguignon l'exprimait par une image
du cru : « La classe intermédiaire est placée dans la société
comme le vin dans le tonneau, entre l'écume et la lie. » La
position supérieure de la noblesse n'était donc pas le signe
de sa supériorité. Toutefois Carnot nuançait sa pensée :
« Il y a noblesse et noblesse. Par exemple il y a la noblesse
des champs de bataille et la noblesse d'antichambre ; il y a
la noblesse de robe et la noblesse de garde-robe. » Évoquant
Saint-Simon, dont il connaissait les œuvres et les soucis, il
ajoutait : « Le paysan est au gentilhomme ce que le ver à
soie est à la chenille, ce que l'abeille est au frelon. » Il notait
même : « J'ai vu ces gentilshommes remplir mon antichambre et m'appeler Monseigneur. »

Noblesse de champ de bataille.... L'estime qu'il avait
pour elle tenait à l'héroïsme, non à la vertu de la guerre
elle-même. Carnot restait foncièrement pacifique : « La
guerre n'est autre chose que l'anarchie en uniforme et le
despotisme en grande tenue. »

Comment choisir celui à qui l'on confierait le pouvoir
suprême ? « S'il devient l'apanage d'une famille, cette famille
sera despotique. S'il est confié par élection, il y aura dispute
pour le choix..., à des élus du peuple, ils deviendront ambitieux et oligarques. »

Après avoir tout envisagé et tout rejeté, Carnot en venait
au procédé qui lui avait réussi dans son adolescence, qui
devait assurer le triomphe des plus qualifiés, et, par eux,
de la raison : « Les fonctions, concluait-il, ne doivent être
confiées qu'à des personnes dont l'aptitude a été constatée
par des examens. » Cet ancien élève de Mézières, ce fondateur
de Polytechnique, cet homme d'étude, aboutissait à ce
procédé qui joua un rôle si étonnant au XIXᵉ siècle. Il tenait

à maintenir la primauté de l'intelligence et s'en rapportait aux membres des jurys de concours.

Au surplus sans trop d'illusions : « les gouvernements changent de forme comme les malades de positions », la politique est l'art du moindre mal, ou plutôt le triomphe du plus fort. Finalement le plus fort, c'est le nombre, « la grande majorité des peuples », et c'est aussi la raison.

Dans cette vue de l'Histoire, l'éducation tenait une place de choix. La force n'était pas exclue, l'habitude conciliait tout, mais quel rôle incombait à la Révolution ? « C'est un orage qui dépure l'air et auquel succède un ciel plus serein. » Cet orage était-il indispensable ? Carnot en doutait, car « souvent les abus ne peuvent être détruits sans amener des crises plus funestes encore que les abus mêmes ». Ainsi, expliquait-il, un seul moyen permettait d'éviter les révolutions, c'était « de corriger les abus ».

Certes Carnot n'était pas un homme d'État. Il n'avait été révolutionnaire que par l'effet des circonstances. L'art de gouverner les hommes n'était pas le sien, et moins encore l'art de les exploiter et de les duper. Peut-on même affirmer qu'il ait eu celui de les bien choisir ?

Du moins le romantisme et les circonstances l'avaient amené à faire une place aux passions à côté de la raison. Déjà, étudiant les moyens de cultiver l'héroïsme dans une garnison assiégée, il s'était tourné vers les passions. Plus tard, cherchant un lien pour unir les Français, il l'avait trouvé dans l'amour de la patrie. Enfin, dans sa vieillesse, il admettait le rôle essentiel des passions : « éteindre les passions, c'est annuler l'homme ». Mais elles continuaient de lui faire peur, elles s'opposaient à la paix de l'âme ; aussi conseillait-il de les « détourner ».

Il semble avoir atteint lui-même à la sérénité : « Une vieillesse sans infirmités, désabusée des illusions, rassurée par la philosophie contre les terreurs de la mort, appréciant chaque chose à sa valeur, exempte des orages de la passion, environnée d'une famille aimante, est peut-être l'époque la plus heureuse de la vie. » Certes, il lui manquait une partie de sa famille ; il était aux prises avec la maladie, mais il répondait pour le reste à son idéal. Et c'est ainsi qu'il attendait une vie future, réparatrice des maux immérités.

Il s'éteignit le 2 août 1823.

CONCLUSIONS

Q UEL rôle Carnot a-t-il joué dans l'Histoire ? Telle est la question à laquelle il doit être possible d'apporter une réponse au terme de cet ouvrage.

La tradition lui attribue une place de premier plan parmi ses contemporains, qui comptaient cependant un Napoléon, un Robespierre, un Mirabeau, pour n'en pas citer d'autres. On le montre disposant du pouvoir et infléchissant le cours de l'histoire nationale et, du même coup, de l'histoire européenne. D'abord et surtout organisateur de la victoire, « il a sauvé la patrie », écrivait Stendhal, en créant une stratégie nouvelle, une armée nouvelle. Ensuite républicain, fondateur de la République, à laquelle il sacrifia tout, argent, carrière, sa vie même. Cette république, il la façonna par la dictature, par la révolution, mais sans tremper dans le sang ; il combattit les déviations de la Révolution et voulut aboutir à une démocratie pacifique, dégagée de la violence et de l'utopie, mais là il fut aux prises avec des forces supérieures. Plutôt que de fléchir, il s'exila.

C'est précisément sur ces trois points qu'il s'agit de porter quelque lumière, car les vues traditionnelles sont âprement combattues, et depuis longtemps. Examinons donc le rôle de Carnot dans l'histoire militaire, dans l'histoire politique et dans l'histoire sociale, en tenant compte de ses idées aussi bien que de ses actes. Ainsi apporterons-nous les dernières touches à son portrait, sans vouloir le reprendre et le figer, car il est mouvant, et c'est dans les pages mêmes de sa biographie qu'on doit le voir, s'affirmant et se transformant.

S'il s'agit de la puissance et de la netteté de la vision du but à atteindre — sauver la République par la victoire — et de la vigueur et de la ténacité de la volonté pour y parvenir, le surnom d' « organisateur de la victoire » est parfaitement justifié.

De même si l'on examine l'action : cette coordination des travaux, ceux des savants et des techniciens, ceux des généraux et des fabricants de guerre, ceux des armées et des représentants en mission, ceux des soldats et ceux des populations. L'unité était enfin assurée, les forces s'unissaient au lieu de s'ignorer ou de se neutraliser, leur efficacité atteignait sa plénitude. D'autant que Carnot stimulait, encourageait, menaçait, et surtout s'appuyait sur l'ardeur révolutionnaire qui animait les uns et les autres. Il a su créer la technique, l'organisation proprement dite, non pas seul assurément, mais plus que quiconque. Il incarna le patriotisme à son apogée, en l'an II; ce fut le plus beau moment de sa carrière [1].

Les plans de campagne furent aussi son œuvre à cette date, non pas sans recours à diverses sources d'inspiration — mémoires des grands capitaines, documents du dépôt de la Guerre, propositions de divers généraux ou autres officiers —, mais il les remania, les refondit, les soumit à ses préférences personnelles et les imposa aux exécutants. Dans la suite, en 1796 et 1797, il céda devant certaines exigences des chefs d'armée, qui s'éloignèrent plus ou moins des directives qu'il leur avait tracées; quant à Bonaparte, ce fut lui, au contraire, qui fournit son plan à Carnot. Enfin, en 1800 et en 1815, Carnot ne fut plus en possession de l'autorité nécessaire pour continuer ce rôle.

Même en 1793 et 1794, il ne réussit pas à faire passer dans les faits la stratégie et la tactique de masses, qu'il énonça pourtant avec clarté et à maintes reprises, mais non pas le premier. D'autre part, il ne considérait pas qu'il s'agissait là d'une transformation durable; il revint assez vite à ses idées de fortificateur pacifique, émule de Vauban. La guerre totale lui faisait horreur, comme toute manifestation de barbarie, et, s'il admit ses méthodes, ce fut en raison des circonstances impérieuses, mais aussi brièvement que possible.

En somme, il ne s'est jamais libéré de ses origines; il est demeuré ingénieur, convaincu que la première place devait revenir au talent, aux spécialistes sélectionnés par les concours. Or, et c'est là le trait curieux, il fut désavoué non seulement par les sabreurs et par les généraux sortis du rang, mais surtout par ses camarades du Génie. Les premiers n'admettaient pas ses vues sur le rôle des armes savantes, les autres condamnaient ses idées sur la fortification. S'il eut le mérite de pressentir la direction dans laquelle allait s'engager la technique de la guerre, il le fit avec une confusion telle qu'il parut, à maintes reprises, condamner les armes

22

scientifiques pour leur préférer des moyens archaïques. Tandis qu'à d'autres moments l'esprit de système le conduisait au paradoxe. Enfin la leçon de l'expérience lui fit défaut ; il ne fut pas le premier ingénieur de son temps, ni sur le terrain, ni dans les bureaux [2].

La naissance de l'armée nationale fut la transformation qui prime toutes les autres dans le domaine militaire. A vrai dire, elle devait nécessairement correspondre à l'émancipation de la nation. Carnot fut l'un des premiers à le comprendre et à le vouloir. Il détestait l'esprit de caste des officiers d'Ancien Régime, non moins que la routine et la passivité des soldats de métier, mercenaires racolés sordidement. Il ne cessa de réclamer l'obligation du service militaire pour tous sans exception, accompagnée d'un abolissement de ce service devenu un devoir civique. Ce qui devait combler l'abîme qui séparait les soldats de leurs officiers et faire disparaître l'inégalité des sanctions, les châtiments corporels, et même l'obéissance passive.

Assurément, il ne fut pas seul à vouloir faire du soldat un citoyen et, sans lui, la transformation se fût quand même accomplie. Pourtant il lui revient d'avoir saisi l'occasion de la levée en masse pour réaliser la première application du service pour des classes entières de jeunes Français. Nul, plus que lui, n'a combattu les rachats aboutissant à des remplacements aussi détestables que les racolages.

Il fut profondément déçu par les volontaires, ou pseudo-volontaires, enrôlés par contrainte ou appâtés par l'argent, et qui se montrèrent indociles, pillards, prompts à la panique et à la révolte. Il renonça, en les observant, à son idéal de discipline librement consentie. Mais il conservait l'espérance d'une amélioration future. Les chefs rapaces, suffisants et ambitieux, qui remplacèrent les officiers émigrés, suspendus ou exécutés, le révoltèrent davantage encore. Et il comptait que le recrutement par les grandes écoles permettrait de les remplacer. Lui qui détestait la jactance et la forfanterie, il fut bafoué par les Augereau et les Bernadotte.

Le césarisme, le sabre tranchant les questions politiques, était l'une de ses craintes majeures. Il tenait à subordonner les généraux aux représentants, l'armée à la nation. Il y travailla avec succès pendant longtemps, dans ses missions et au Comité. Il céda pourtant devenu Directeur, au moment où le danger était brûlant. Il soutint peu les commissaires aux armées, il nomma et favorisa Bonaparte. La clairvoyance lui fit alors défaut, et il en fut châtié le 18 Fructidor.

Ces déboires, qui furent ceux de la France entière, ne lui sont pas exclusivement imputables. Toutefois il n'avait pas compris l'ampleur des risques, quand il avait cru possible de déclarer la guerre et de lui donner des proportions gigantesques.

Et c'est par là que se rattache son grand rôle militaire à son rôle politique.

Républicain austère et invariable, fondateur de la République et aussi son ultime défenseur, tel est le second trait de la figure traditionnelle de Carnot. On entend par là non seulement l'opposition intransigeante au pouvoir personnel, mais une austérité à la Caton, le souci jaloux du bien public. Ainsi le présentait Wilhelm Doron. Les résonances de l'Histoire ont renforcé cette interprétation, sous la Seconde République, celle d'Hippolyte, et sous la Troisième, celle de Sadi Carnot.

A cette image, les adversaires ont opposé celle d'un ambitieux versatile, qui servit et combattit tour à tour tous les régimes ; celui de Louis XVI aussi bien que ceux de Robespierre et de Barras, de Napoléon et de Louis XVIII.

Si cette réplique n'est pas sans fondement, il convient de noter qu'un arriviste n'aurait pas délibérément affronté l'exil et la misère, sinon la prison ou la mort. La conduite et le rôle politiques de Carnot ne se laissent pas enfermer dans une formule simpliste.

Républicain, Carnot le fut d'abord, comme tant d'hommes de sa génération qui s'accommodaient de la royauté. Ils étaient républicains au vieux sens du mot, plus moral que politique, imprégné des souvenirs légendaires de la Rome antique. Dressé contre l'arbitraire et l'oppression, Carnot voulait conquérir la liberté pour lui, pour les « ingénieurs », pour les bourgeois et pour tous les Français. Cette liberté permettrait de mieux travailler au bien commun, au bonheur de tous, grâce au généreux dévouement des hommes libérés de toutes les servitudes, religieuses, morales, politiques.

Une telle république n'était pas, à proprement parler, un régime politique. Carnot ne devint républicain, au sens technique du terme, qu'au lendemain du 10 août, par conviction que le roi trahissait et que la nation était la véritable souveraine. L'expérience lui montrait la possibilité d'un régime politique dirigé par une assemblée, l'autorité devait donc revenir aux représentants du peuple, mandataires de la volonté générale.

Cette notion de volonté générale, empruntée à Rousseau que Carnot admira, était le principe et la justification de la République. Elle impliquait la conviction que le peuple avait effectivement une volonté *une*, c'est-à-dire que les dissidences, ou volontés particulières, procédaient du manque d'information, ou de l'hostilité au bien commun. Si elles ne s'inclinaient pas, elles devaient être matées ; ceux qui les fomentaient étaient les ennemis non seulement du régime, mais du peuple. Dans ce sens, cette république était totalitaire.

A cet aspect négatif, élimination des résistances par persuasion ou par écrasement, correspondait un aspect positif : la conviction que le peuple disposait, par sa volonté générale, de ce qui était requis pour le gouvernement de la république, savoir le but à viser pour assurer le bien commun, et les moyens d'atteindre ce but [3].

A vrai dire, les représentants seuls exprimaient cette volonté populaire, leur volonté était la loi. Pendant longtemps Carnot n'admit pas que les clubs pussent nourrir la même prétention. Il ne reconnaissait pas non plus les partis, leur existence à elle seule niait la notion fondamentale de volonté générale, une et commune à tous.

Toutefois ces questions de doctrine le touchaient moins que les exigences qui commandaient la vie du nouveau régime. Avant de souligner ce qui divisait les républicains, les fondateurs mêmes de la République, il importait de se consacrer à la lutte contre les ennemis du dehors et du dedans. La mission propre de Carnot fut d'assurer le concours de l'armée à la défense du régime. Ce fut l'objet des efforts prolongés du législateur, du représentant en mission, du membre du Comité de Salut public, voire même du Directeur.

Convertir les hommes et les chefs de l'armée d'Ancien Régime, assurer le loyalisme et la valeur des volontaires, susciter le départ de nouvelles recrues, convaincre les citoyens que la république exige l'impôt du sang, autant d'aspects d'une œuvre unique, dont les éléments sont militaires, mais dont la base et le sommet sont politiques.

La lutte à mort qui s'engagea réclamait une autorité puissamment concentrée. Carnot fut des premiers à le comprendre et à proposer les mesures nécessaires pour y parvenir. Le salut public renforçait la solidarité entre les citoyens, la déclaration des Droits de l'Homme, proposée par Carnot en 1793, surbordonnait l'individu à la collectivité.

Aucun sacrifice ne lui parut excessif pour faire triompher la république, ni l'exécution du roi, ni la Terreur, contre les ennemis de l'intérieur et de l'extérieur.

Il fut pourtant quelque peu désemparé quand il découvrit d'insidieux ennemis que la Révolution portait en elle : le goût de la violence pour elle-même, le triomphe de la brutalité et des passions sur la raison, et quand il découvrit que la volonté générale n'était plus qu'un mythe, puisque foisonnaient les divisions, les partis, les clans — exagérés ou modérés, ultras ou citras. Non seulement l'Assemblée était profondément divisée contre elle-même, mais les comités, y compris celui de Salut public, étaient aussi déchirés par des conflits internes.

Toujours empirique plus que doctrinaire, Carnot souhaitait au moins que les fondateurs de la république ne s'exterminassent pas. Il ne put s'y opposer sans risquer de périr. Alors il résolut d'abattre les terroristes pour sauver la république, sans se rendre compte du coup qu'il lui portait. Après cet événement décisif, il fut trop menacé pour prendre une part active dans l'établissement du régime constitutionnel, qui fut la Première République. Il parvint pourtant à se faire accepter et il voulut adapter le régime aux circonstances et aux variations d'opinion.

Il prôna d'abord l'organisation d'un gouvernement autoritaire qui implanterait les institutions républicaines, c'est ce que signifiaient ces nominations de fonctionnaires jacobins au début du Directoire. Puis, quand l'opinion lui parut l'exiger, il en vint à soutenir le régime parlementaire, dans lequel les représentants imposeraient leur politique au gouvernement.

Sa présence au pouvoir, Grand Comité et Directoire, attribua une portée considérable à l'évolution de sa pensée et de ses actes. Sa responsabilité n'est pas contestable dans la chute de Robespierre et dans les déchirements du Directoire. Il croyait défendre la république, et en fait il a contribué, avec beaucoup d'autres, à la ruiner.

Lui qui jugeait que trente années étaient indispensables pour agir profondément sur l'opinion, il voulut interrompre après quelques mois l'action toute puissante d'un gouvernement qui fondait un régime. Cette contradiction s'explique à la fois parce qu'il craignait d'épuiser les forces vives de la France, parce que la république qui se dessinait ne correspondait pas à son idéal de gouvernement par les hommes à talents, enfin parce qu'il ne put s'accorder avec ceux qui partagèrent avec lui, à deux reprises, le pouvoir suprême. Carnot était autoritaire, jaloux de ses prérogatives jusqu'à se montrer cassant et violent.

Pendant son premier exil, il médita sur l'ordre ; un gouvernement fort lui paraissait, comme à tant d'autres, indispensable. C'est ce qui le tourna à l'avance vers Bonaparte. Il fut vite déçu et inquiet, il se dressa contre un pouvoir qu'il avait contribué à établir.

Les contestations s'avivent, quand il s'agit d'expliquer la soumission puis la collaboration de Carnot au régime impérial.

Des contemporains et des historiens ont montré Carnot distant et réprobateur, jusqu'au jour où l'invasion menaçante le conduisit à Anvers. Il n'en est rien. Pour lui, la république parlementaire s'était révélée irréalisable ; quand l'Empire fut fortement établi, il voulut s'y rallier pour sauver ce qui restait de l'œuvre révolutionnaire — et pour lever la disgrâce qui le frappait, lui-même et sa famille [4]. Pour les mêmes raisons Carnot, ayant constaté à regret l'impossibilité de faire reconnaître Napoléon II, donna plus tard l'exemple du ralliement aux Bourbons. Dans tous les cas, il s'agissait de conserver les institutions représentatives et de conserver les gains politiques et sociaux de la Révolution. Dès qu'ils lui parurent menacés, Carnot le proclama, ce qui lui valut un nouvel et définitif exil.

En somme, il fut opportuniste sans savoir distinguer à temps ce qui était opportun. Il se trompa sur les hommes et fut trompé par eux. Il fit triompher ce qu'il abhorrait et ne sut pas maintenir ce qu'il préférait. Il fit carrière d'homme d'État sans en avoir les qualités. Cependant il avait des idées politiques et des idées sociales.

Quel sens avait donc pour Carnot la Révolution ? Si l'on entend par là, comme les contemporains, la mise en vacances de la légalité pour faire prévaloir un régime d'exception usant de la violence, Carnot n'était pas révolutionnaire. Il n'avait le tempérament ni d'un Danton, ni d'un Saint-Just, tout au contraire doux et affable dans son comportement, plus à l'aise dans un cercle que dans une assemblée, il se montrait docile à l'expérience et réticent devant les doctrines *a priori*. A tous égards, il était réformateur, disposé à s'appuyer sur les réalités, pour les amender patiemment, expérimentalement, laissant au temps et à l'habitude le soin de compléter, d'assouplir et de consolider l'œuvre. La violence était excusable dans le peuple, aveugle comme elle.

Pourtant il lui arriva de se révolter avec la fureur des pacifiques déchaînés. On « devient » révolutionnaire, a-t-il dit ; le mot est révélateur. En effet, quand il lui parut que la violence était indispensable, ainsi que les mesures d'exception pour assurer le salut public, il y recourut et s'associa à des mesures terroristes. Il espérait alors que la mêlée serait brève et le résultat conforme à ses désirs. Il était mû par le patriotisme et par les exigences de la raison d'État. Il a fortement contribué à l'établissement et au fonctionnement du gouvernement révolutionnaire.

Ce fut pour lui un épisode. Le souvenir des violences, celui surtout du sang versé sans nécessité ni méthode par des fanatiques, des ignorants, des gens tarés, lui fut toujours odieux. Dans la suite, il considéra la Révolution comme le temps des malheurs de la France, comme une période d'illusions et d'anarchie, de souffrances et de ruines. Il en vint même à contester l'importance de cette révolution dans l'histoire de l'Humanité.

C'est dans un autre sens qu'il était révolutionnaire, au sens astronomique du terme : la révolution était l'achèvement d'une stricte évolution et le cheminement d'un progrès illimité. La Révolution française, après un « siècle de lumières », devait être l'avènement des « hommes à talents », techniciens et savants. C'était un nouvel ordre social.

Pour lui, ce qui condamnait l'Ancien Régime c'était d'avoir dédaigné le mérite pour classer les hommes d'après leur naissance ; et aussi d'avoir favorisé la superstition et combattu le rationalisme. Les temps nouveaux placeraient au contraire les « lumières » au premier rang.

L'idéal de Carnot peut se comparer à celui de Saint-Simon ; son fils Hippolyte ne fut-il pas saint-simonien ?

La déception que la Révolution lui infligea fut profonde : les hommes à talents furent supplantés par les riches et par les propriétaires [5]. Carnot en vint à penser que l'élection ne valait pas beaucoup mieux que l'hérédité. Finalement le recrutement des dirigeants, des gouvernants, lui parut devoir se faire au concours, pour toutes les fonctions et pour toutes les places. Ses deux fils, Sadi le polytechnicien et Hippolyte le saint-cyrien, suivirent cette voie, mais elle ne les conduisit pas au pouvoir. Carnot, comme les techniciens en général, était plus propre à l'administration des choses qu'au gouvernement des hommes.

Son idéal technocratique ne l'amenait pourtant pas à mépriser la masse. Il n'avait pas cet impitoyable orgueil intellectuel, plus inhumain encore que la hauteur aristocratique ou la vanité naïve et cynique du riche. Car il croyait, avec la plupart de ses contemporains, à la rectitude et à la puissance de l'esprit chez tous les hommes. Il pensait que rien n'est plus répandu que le bon sens et qu'il peut se perfectionner et progresser indéfiniment. L'infériorité de la masse tenait avant tout au manque d'instruction. Toute sa vie il a réfléchi aux problèmes que pose l'enseignement, et il s'est ingénié à développer toutes les formes d'enseignement. Il a été l'un des créateurs de l'École polytechnique, comme des écoles primaires. C'était à ses yeux la condition nécessaire et suffisante de la démocratie ; si toutefois des castes héréditaires ne se rétablissaient pas.

On lui a pourtant reproché d'avoir fondé une dynastie bourgeoise, comme tant d'autres révolutionnaires. Sans examiner ici si ce fut le sort commun des révolutionnaires, notamment des plus authentiques, observons simplement le cas de Carnot. Ce qui aurait pu lui permettre de fonder une telle dynastie, c'eût été la volonté de le faire, appuyée sur des relations puissantes et sur la fortune.

Pour le premier point, l'intention, il est frappant qu'il ait si souvent voulu travailler pour les siens. Il avait un esprit de famille étonnamment développé. L'exemple le plus typique, c'est la pension octroyée par Napoléon et dont Carnot se félicite surtout à cause de ses enfants.

Le fait qu'il n'ait eu que deux héritiers, après avoir eu seulement quatre enfants, l'oppose à la génération qui l'a précédé — il avait eu dix-sept frères et sœurs — ; il peut révéler le souci de l'ascension sociale, il en facilitait la réalisation. En revanche, Carnot se fit peu de relations durables et profitables. Ses exils successifs tracèrent autour de lui une zone d'isolement, l'opposant aux anciens révolutionnaires désormais nantis qui avaient des amis dans tous les camps et amélioraient leur situation à chaque changement de régime.

Quant à la richesse, Carnot ne s'est pas donné beaucoup de peine pour l'acquérir. Ce n'était pas, à ses yeux, un but digne de lui. Toutefois son mariage lui a procuré une aisance certaine. Il a tenté de l'accroître par diverses spéculations mal connues, mais incontestables. Finalement, soit maladresse, soit malchance, il a tout perdu, ou presque, et n'a laissé qu'un modeste héritage. Ainsi on ne voit pas comment trouver dans sa carrière le point de départ de celle que fit plus tard sa famille « dans les milieux de grande bourgeoisie ».

Ce bourgeois et ce technicien s'est vivement intéressé aux questions économiques, mais surtout sur le plan de l'État. Il jugeait que c'était le souci principal d'une société et l'une des préoccupations majeures du gouvernement. La vie économique devait être favorisée, mais non dirigée par les pouvoirs publics. Une information scientifique, mathématique, était indispensable pour y parvenir.

L'abondance des hommes était l'un des facteurs les plus favorables à l'essor économique. Le rôle des machines et de l'argent ne lui échappait pas non plus et il comprit quelles profondes transformations se préparaient avec le développement de ces deux forces. Mais il hésita quand il s'agit d'en faire l'application à la France.

Après avoir voulu supplanter l'Angleterre commerciale, financière et industrielle, Carnot en était venu à prôner on ne sait quel retour à la terre.

Toutefois il affirma toujours la primauté du rôle des communications. Il observait qu'elles étaient en train de se multiplier et de devenir à la fois plus rapides et plus puissantes.

On se pose évidemment la question des relations que Carnot établissait entre les réalités économiques et les découvertes scientifiques. Il s'y employa exceptionnellement, surtout pour organiser la défense nationale, lorsqu'il groupa des équipes de savants, ou encore quand il utilisa les ballons. Avant la Révolution, il avait étudié le problème de la direction et de la propulsion de ces ballons. Il ne poursuivit pas de recherche pratique ; au contraire, ses travaux devinrent de plus en plus théoriques. Ils prirent la place laissée vacante par la poésie et remplirent les loisirs forcés que lui ménageait la politique. On ne saurait prétendre que ce mathématicien porta le goût de l'abstraction dans la vie politique. En revanche, il y conserva une méthode stricte, un goût de l'ordre et de la précision, l'amour de la clarté et le souci des résultats. Ce sont là proprement des dons d'organisateur, rarement mot historique fut aussi exact. Mais l'organisateur est administrateur plutôt qu'homme d'État. Il lui faut l'autorité et la continuité, évitant les compromis, ne composant pas avec les hommes, considérés comme administrés et non comme électeurs, ou comme puissance à ménager.

Hormis ces traits, l'activité scientifique de Carnot fut assez indépendante de sa carrière politique, même dans le domaine économique, même dans celui des communications, où il voyait pourtant l'une des causes de transformation de la vie nationale et même internationale.

Dans ce dernier domaine, il fut animé d'intentions assez contradictoires. L'idéal de l'entente internationale et de la paix universelle l'attira d'abord, et longtemps. Avec la Terreur, il en vint pourtant à attiser les haines nationales, et à justifier les annexions qui renforcent un État. Il condamna, plus tard, les humiliations des traités de Paris, œuvre des Bourbons restaurés. Il avait pourtant accepté, en 1797, le retour aux anciennes limites. Son information et ses méthodes en politique étrangère n'étaient pas meilleures que celles de la plupart de ses contemporains. Il connaissait mal l'Europe, et plus mal encore l'Amérique; pourtant sa volonté était droite et rien ne lui répugnait plus que les agissements d'un Talleyrand.

Acteur vigoureux, témoin attentif, Carnot tint une place telle qu'on connaît mal l'histoire de son temps si l'on ne tient pas compte de son action et de ses écrits. Il fournit plus encore des informations et des explications, il montre des aspects fort intéressants et encore mal connus du monde militaire et politique, plutôt qu'il ne marque une ligne de force, rectiligne et victorieuse, dans le champ des rivalités, dans le courant de l'Histoire.

Il fut l'homme du siècle des lumières, le précurseur de l'âge des polytechniciens, et il pressentit l'avènement des masses, éclairées par l'instruction et façonnées par la propagande. Ses dernières pensées furent pour s'en réjouir : « J'ai vécu dans un siècle de lumières, j'ai vu poindre l'aurore de la raison humaine et l'éternelle vérité triompher des vieux préjugés. »

BIBLIOGRAPHIE

PRINCIPAUX OUVRAGES DE L. CARNOT

Éloge de Vauban, Dijon et Paris, 1784.

Observations sur la lettre de M. Choderlos de Laclos à MM. de l'Académie française, concernant l'éloge de Vauban, par M. Carnot, Arras et Paris, 1786.

Réponse au mémoire sur la fortification perpendiculaire, par plusieurs officiers du corps royal du Génie, Paris, 1787.

Mémoire présenté au Conseil de la guerre, au sujet des places fortes qui doivent être démolies ou abandonnées, Paris, 1789.

Réclamation adressée à l'Assemblée nationale contre le régime oppressif sous lequel est gouverné le corps royal du Génie, par M. Carnot, capitaine dans le même corps, Paris, 1789.

Réponse de L.-N.-M. Carnot, citoyen français, l'un des fondateurs de la République et membre constitutionnel du Directoire exécutif, au rapport fait sur la conspiration du 18 fructidor, au Conseil des Cinq-Cents, par J.-Ch. Bailleul, au nom d'une commission spéciale, an VI.

De la Défense des places fortes, Paris, 1810.

Mémoire au Roi, 1814.

Exposé de la conduite politique de M. le lieutenant général Carnot depuis le 1er juillet 1814, Paris, 1815.

Exposé de la situation de l'Empire, présenté à la Chambre des Pairs, dans sa séance du 13 juin 1815, par S. Exc. le Ministre de l'Intérieur, Paris, 1815.

PRINCIPALES BIOGRAPHIES DE LAZARE CARNOT

Notre biographie a été entreprise en raison de l'absence d'ouvrage vraiment historique sur L. Carnot. Du moins a-t-elle été précédée par trois groupes de publications qui ont tracé les traits de la physionomie traditionnelle de l'Organisateur de la Victoire.

I. — Témoignages de contemporains favorables a Carnot.

Beffroy de Reigny, *Notice*, dans le *Dictionnaire néologique*, t. III, Paris.

Brougham, *Notice*, dans *The Edinburgh Review*, novembre 1814.

Rioust (M.-N.), *Carnot*, Paris, 1816, Gand, 1817.

Körte (W.), *Das Leben L.-N.-M. Carnot*, Leipzig, 1820.

Tissot, *Mémoires historiques et militaires sur Carnot*, Paris, 1824.

Ces trois biographies ont tiré parti d'indications fournies par la famille de Carnot et, en ce qui concerne Körte, de renseignements donnés par Carnot lui-même.

Anonyme, *Notice*, dans *Die Zeitgenossen*, Leipzig, 1824.

STENDHAL, *Notice*, dans *New Monthly Magazine*, 1ᵉʳ novembre 1824, à l'occasion de la publication du livre de Tissot.

Biographie MICHAUD, article *Carnot*, 1836, manifestant quelque esprit critique.

II. — TÉMOIGNAGE APPORTÉ PAR LE FILS DE CARNOT.

CARNOT (H.), *Mémoires sur Carnot*, par son fils, Paris, 1861-1863.

Animé par la piété filiale, par les souvenirs de l'exil de son père, qu'il avait partagé, et par ses convictions républicaines, Hippolyte a dressé un monument à la gloire de Carnot. Il a utilisé ses souvenirs personnels, des manuscrits de Carnot, les écrits de Carnot lui-même et aussi les souvenirs des contemporains de Lazare encore vivants, comme le prouve une abondante correspondance conservée dans les Archives familiales. En revanche, il n'a pu utiliser les archives officielles, ni même une partie des documents figurant aujourd'hui dans les Archives familiales, mais venus tardivement au gré des ventes d'autographes.

Cette biographie a inspiré directement les ouvrages de vulgarisation et de circonstance qui ont été publiés dans la suite jusqu'à nos jours, notamment lors de la présidence de Sadi Carnot et à l'occasion de la première guerre mondiale.

III. — OUVRAGES HISTORIQUES.

Des travaux scientifiques ont été d'abord publiés à l'étranger. En premier lieu un travail approfondi, sur un point limité, et incomplètement documenté.

WARSCHAUER (R.), *Studien zur Entwicklung der Gedanken Lazare Carnots über der Kriegsfuhrung*, Berlin, 1937.

Puis, un travail d'ensemble, le premier qui applique les méthodes historiques, mais dont l'information a beaucoup souffert du fait que l'auteur ne résidait pas en France et connaissait imparfaitement les sources de documentation françaises, et même l'ouvrage de Warschauer.

HUNTLEY-DUPRÉ, *L. Carnot, républicain patriote*, Oxford (Ohio), The Mississipi Valley Press, 1940.

Dans tout cet ensemble, non seulement l'information est demeurée très incomplète, mais les auteurs ont ignoré des réserves, des critiques et des attaques émanant des ennemis de Carnot. Celles-ci ne se trouvent pas tellement dans les pamphlets contemporains que dans des notes et mémoires, et dans des ouvrages publiés ultérieurement. Elles reposent, surtout au départ, sur des oppositions politiques, et se trouvent sous la plume d'Hébertistes ou Enragés, ou bien de monarchistes ou d'émigrés. Ainsi, dans des notes de Xavier Audouin et dans les mémoires de Théodore de Lameth. On peut les suivre jusqu'à nos jours, elles ont été renforcées par diverses publications, telles que la correspondance de Mallet du Pan ou les archives de Dropmore. Qui veut s'en faire une idée peut consulter les travaux du général Herlaut, sur Bouchotte, ou sur la mission de Saint-Just à l'armée du Nord (*Revue du Nord*, 1945).

NOTES

I. — Abréviations des références.

C. C. : Charavay, *Correspondance de Carnot*.
H. C. : Hippolyte Carnot, *Mémoires sur Carnot*.
La Sabretache (Colonel S. Carnot), Le centenaire de L. Carnot.
Arch. familiales : Archives de la famille Carnot, à Nolay.
Arch. Presles : Archives de M. François Carnot.
Coll. Carnot : Collection de M. Lazare Carnot.
Arch. nat. : Archives nationales.
Arch. adm. Guerre : Archives administratives du ministère de la Guerre.
Arch. hist. Guerre : Archives historiques du ministère de la Guerre.
Arch. Insp. Génie : Archives de l'Inspection du Génie.
Arch. Mar. : Archives du ministère de la Marine.
Arch. Aff. étr. : Archives du ministère des Affaires étrangères.
F. O. : Archives du Foreign Office.
W. O. : Archives du War Office.
B. M. : Archives du British Museum.
Œster. Nat. Bibl. Mss : Manuscrits de la Bibliothèque nationale autrichienne.
Aulard Jacobins : Aulard, *La Société des Jacobins*.
C. S. P. : Aulard, *Recueil des Actes du Comité de Salut public*.
A. P. : Archives parlementaires.
B. et R. : Buchez et Roux, *Histoire parlementaire*.
Corr. Panckoucke : Napoléon, *Correspondance*, édition Panckoucke.
B. N. : Bibliothèque nationale.
Ann. hist. Révol. : *Annales historiques de la Révolution française*.
Rév. fr. : Revue *La Révolution française*.

II. — Portraits de Lazare Carnot.

Jusqu'au Directoire, aucun portrait de Carnot ne fut fait, sinon les silhouettes dues à Feulint et le physionotrace exécuté à l'occasion de son mariage (voir le premier volume).

Personnage officiel, le Directeur figura dans la collection composée par Bonneville. Il est présenté de profil, portant le costume officiel et le chapeau empanaché. Fut-ce un portrait fait d'après nature ? Il fut gravé par J.-B. Compagnie. C'est le seul portrait publié à cette période, abstraction faite de gravures sans valeur. Carnot le fit placer en tête de sa *Réponse à Bailleul*. Il a été souvent reproduit depuis, il semble avoir inspiré Raffet, quand il voulut représenter l'Organisateur de la Victoire.

D'autre part, la famille Carnot possède un petit portrait à l'huile (18 × 22) qui est le seul montrant Carnot chauve. L'œuvre est réalisée avec soin, les traits sont fins, non sans dureté. Il en existe une bonne reproduction en couleurs *(La Sabretache)*. Il figure d'autre part sur la couverture du présent volume, au verso.

Carnot se fit portraiturer, ainsi que sa femme et que chacun de ses fils, en 1813, par Boilly. Ces portraits sont restés dans la famille ; une copie du portrait de Carnot se trouve au musée Carnavalet. C'est le seul portrait dû à un maître réputé. L'âge a boursouflé les traits, le nez est gonflé, on retrouve mal la physionomie du Directeur, d'autant que la perruque contribue à la modifier.

Ce portrait a souvent été gravé, notamment par Gaétan Dupont.

Gouverneur d'Anvers, Carnot fut représenté par Van Brée. Non seulement les traits, mais l'attitude soulignent la fatigue et l'âge. On grava ce portrait à diverses reprises.

Devenu ministre de l'Intérieur, Carnot dut se faire peindre en pied sur le désir de Napoléon. Mais il ne posa pas et le peintre reprit le portrait fait par Boilly. Son œuvre est conservée au musée de Versailles, elle a été reproduite dans *La Sabretache* (sauf la partie gauche, où l'on voit les bustes de Vauban et d'Archimède).

D'après une note manuscrite de J. Carnot (Archives familiales), les portraits les plus ressemblants sont ceux de Boilly et de Van Brée. C'est d'après ceux-ci que l'iconographie postérieure, à la mort de Carnot, fut composée. Elle connut une certaine faveur sous la présidence de Sadi Carnot.

Une excellente collection a été réalisée par M. L. Carnot, qui a bien voulu nous la présenter.

Enfin un portrait jusqu'alors inédit se trouve chez M. H. S. Carnot. Il porte la mention : « Peint après la mort par G.-G. Prost, d'Erfurt, 1823. » Il est reproduit sur la couverture du présent volume.

PREMIÈRE PARTIE

LA PATRIE EN DANGER

CHAPITRE PREMIER

LA CRÉATION D'UNE ARMÉE

1. Arch. hist. Guerre, B⁴ 1 et B¹³ 7, *Courrier des Départements*, 26 septembre, 4, 8, 9 et 12 octobre 1792.
2. Sur les marchés de Servan, voir DOMMANGET, MATHIEZ et VERMALE (*Ann. hist. révol.*, 1918, 1924, 1925 et 1937). Ces travaux demanderaient à être repris en utilisant les Arch. hist. Guerre (B¹³ 7 et 8).
3. B. et R., t. XIX, p. 56. Il était aussi question d'envoyer des gardes nationaux du Sud-Ouest pour défendre les Conventionnels Girondins à Paris (B. et R., t. XIX, p. 62 et 293 ; — *Courrier*, t. II, p. 322).
4. Sur Lacuée, voir JEAN HUMBERT, *J.-G. Lacuée, comte de Cessac*, biographie patronnée par les descendants du général.
5. B. N., Le³⁶ 4, A. P., t. LII, p. 153 et 455. Le règlement interdisait d'appartenir simultanément à deux Comités (P. V., t. I, p. 108, 143 et 352). Les Comités avaient mauvaise presse, aussi bien du côté de Gorsas que de Marat (*Courrier*, t. I, p. 233 ; *Journal de la République*, n° 47, p. 4).
6. Les manuscrits de Lomet appartiennent à M. Lazare Carnot, qui a bien voulu nous autoriser à les consulter, ce dont nous tenons à le remer-cier ici. Voir aussi Arch. hist. Guerre, B¹³ 7 et B*⁴ 29, et le dossier Lomet (Arch. hist. Guerre).
7. La plupart des documents concernant la mission ont été publiés (C. C., t. I, p. 176 à 349). Nous n'indiquons les références que pour les sources nouvelles (*Courrier*, 16 octobre 1792). Les papiers de Carnot contiennent des notes sur l'organisation d'une armée de 40 000 hommes (Arch. familiales). La liaison avec la famille Ducos est indiquée par BEFFROY (*Dictionnaire...*, t. III, p. 5).
8. Arch. Gers, L 120. Cette instruction indique la méthode suivie dans tous les départements ; nous la connaissons grâce à l'obligeance de M. Henlt, archiviste en chef du département.
9. Arch. départementales des Basses-Pyrénées, Tarn-et-Garonne, Haute-Garonne, Tarn, d'après les extraits conservés aux Arch. hist. Guerre (cartons départementaux sur les volontaires nationaux).
10. Arch. adm. Guerre, dossier Foulhiac. Le renvoi des officiers jugés tièdes eut lieu même aux armées, notamment au cours de l'été 1793, contre ceux qui paraissaient favorables au fédéralisme (affaire Dombre).
11. Brissot écrivait à Servan, le 26 novembre : « Si les Pyrénées ne séparent plus que des peuples libres, notre liberté est assise » (PERRARD, *J.-P. Brissot, Correspondance et*

Papiers, p. 312). Ce fut lui qui favorisa la création, à Bayonne, d'un Comité révolutionnaire espagnol animé par Marcheña. Carnot considérait Marcheña comme un agent provocateur, et il le combattit (H. C., t. I, p. 284 ; — MOREL-FATIO, « J. Marcheña », *Rev. hist.*, 1890). A. RICHARD, *Marcheña et les Girondins* (*Ann. révol.*, 1923). Sur la politique espagnole, voir J. CHAUMIÉ, *Lettres d'Iriarte à Aranda ;* BUNNAIN, *Bulletin de la Société d'Histoire de France*, 1944, et B. HYSLOP, *Problèmes historiques des Relations franco-espagnoles pendant la Révolution française* (*Bulletin de la Société d'histoire moderne*, mai 1949, où se trouve aussi un article de Mlle Chaumié).

12. La biographie de Laclos par Dard ne donne guère de renseignements sur cette période. Voir plutôt Arch. hist. Guerre, B^{x4} 29 et B^4 1.

13. AULARD, *C. S. P.*, t. I, p. 64, Arch. hist. Guerre B^{x4} 29, A. P., t. LIII, p. 418.

14. Merlin (de Douai) à Pache, 16 décembre (Ad., SÉE, *Le Procès de Pache*, p. 21).

15. Voir H. LIBERMANN, *La Mission de Claude-Marie Carnot-Feulint aux Armées de la Moselle et du Rhin*. L'auteur n'a pas connu les archives Feulint, où se trouve la nomination de Feulint auprès du ministre de la Guerre.

16. Arch. hist. Guerre, B^{13} 10.

17. Arch. nat. F^7 4394[1]. *Journal des Débats*, séance du 29 janvier 1793. Saint-Cyr Nugues a pensé que Servan intriguait pour être appelé à Paris (lettre à Mme Jullien de la Drôme, Toulouse, 31 janvier 1793, Arch. nat., AB[xix] 1750).

CHAPITRE II
LA RAISON D'ÉTAT

1. Carnot à Buissart, 15 février 1793 (Arch. Pas-de-Calais, coll. Barbier). Cette lettre a été publiée dans C. C. (t. I, p. 380), ainsi que le rapport de Carnot sur sa mission (*ibid.*, p. 323 et suivantes). Nous empruntons à ce rapport les citations suivantes, sauf indication contraire.

2. Lettre du 8 octobre (Arch. hist. Guerre, B^{x4} 29). L'argument de Lacuée est contredit par une lettre, demandant aussi la suppression des aumôniers, parce que les bataillons n'en avaient pas et les chefs et quartiers-maîtres touchaient les appointements de ces aumôniers absents (Arch. hist. Guerre B^{13} 20). La question mériterait d'être examinée, aucune suppression n'avait été officiellement décidée, et les titulaires réclamaient leur traitement (Arch. hist. Guerre, B^{13} 8).

3. Le fils du Conventionnel Garrau a écrit que les commissaires retardèrent leur retour, car ils auraient « voulu éviter » d'arriver avant la fin du procès. Mais ce témoignage date de 1861 (Arch. familiales). Ce qui est assuré, c'est que les commissaires aux Pyrénées ne manifestèrent pas leur opinion par correspondance, comme firent les commissaires de Nice (*Annales patriotiques*, 2 janvier 1793).

4. A. P., t. LVII, p. 99, 109, 366, 462 ; *Moniteur*, t. XV, p. 167, 184). Le baron de B... prétend que le vote fut discuté le 12 janvier, chez Dubois-Crancé, dans une réunion où se trouvait Carnot. Celui-ci aurait dit : « Si vous acquittez Louis, vous vous déclarez rebelles ; si vous le détenez seulement, ce n'est qu'une demi-mesure, un acte de pusillanimité. » Mais cet ouvrage, très hostile à Carnot, est bourré d'erreurs (Baron de B..., *Carnot*, p. 53).

5. CARNOT, *Réponse à Bailleul*, p. 71.

6. CARNOT, *Mémoire au Roi*, p. 21.

7. Arch. familiales.
8. Lettre du 15 janvier à Barère (Arch. familiales).
9. Carnot avait cessé d'appartenir au Comité de la Guerre le 22 décembre 1792 (contrairement à C. C., t. I, p. 350, note, voir Arch. nat. AF^x II 22). Il entra à une date inconnue au Comité de Défense générale (Arch. nat., AF^x II 45).
10. A. P., t. LIX, p. 24.
11. C. C., t. I, p. 401.
12. Le droit au suicide avait été défendu par nombre de philosophes au xviiie siècle (*Rev. fr.*, 1922, p. 298).
13. *Courrier des Départements*, notamment 10 janvier 1793 ; AULARD, *Jacobins*, t. IV, p. 340 ; *Révolution de Paris*, n°s 178 et 182 ; *Journal de la République*, 3 février et 5 mars 1793. Pour Grégoire, B. N., Le^{37} 2 E ; pour Clavière, B. N., 4° Lb^{41} 136^B. Et aussi GOETZ-BERNSTEIN, *La Politique extérieure de Brissot et des Girondins ;* G. GAUTHEROT, *La Révolution française dans l'ancien Évêché de Bâle*, t. I, p. 249.
14. Arch nat., AF^x II 22, H 1439 et F^7 4402. G. BOUCHARD, *Guyton - M o r v e a u*, p. 282.
15. Arch. nat., AF^x II 45.
16. Arch. nat., AF^x II 22.

nous avions eu communication de cette lettre grâce à l'obligeance de Mlle Arbelet; depuis R.-M. Brace l'a publiée (*Journal of modern History*, décembre 1949). Les dires de Carnot sur l'activité des agents de Londres, Vienne et Berlin, sont confirmés par les documents anglais (F. O. 27/42).
6. DUHEM, *Compte rendu* (Arch. hist. Guerre, B^{13} 21).
7. KÖRTE, *Carnotsleben*, p. 49, à comparer avec H. C., t. I, p. 328, 368 et 145. Le texte de Körte fut repris par Tissot, p. 226. Ni Körte ni l'auteur de la biographie publiée par Tissot ne considéraient ce passage comme émanant de Carnot. On ne saurait rien conclure du fait, tardif et polémique, que Carnot condamnait le 31 mai dans sa *Réponse à Bailleul* (p. 27 et 128).
8. Déclaration du courrier envoyé à l'armée du Nord, 29 juin 1793 (Arch. nat., W 99).
9. Levasseur, *Mémoires*. Celliez à Bouchotte, 30 juin 1793 (Arch. hist. Guerre, B^1 13).
10. Chanoine BLED, *Les Sociétés populaires à Saint-Omer* (*Mémoires de la Soc. des Antiquaires de la Morinie*, t. XXVIII, p. 386 ; C. C., t. II, p. 442).

CHAPITRE III

L'INVASION ET LA TRAHISON

1. Les A. P. (t. LX, p. 9) donnent un texte légèrement différent de celui de C. C. (t. I, p. 397), qui nous fournit ici encore la plus grande partie de la documentation.
2. Voir t. I, p. 226.
3. Arch. nat., W 16.
4. Arch. nat., F^7 3685^1. C. C. ne fournit qu'une analyse creuse (t. II, p. 9).
5. Lettre du 28 mars au soir ;

CHAPITRE IV

DÉBUTS STRATÉGIQUES

1. La mission de Carnot-Feulint dans le Nord n'a pas été étudiée. La correspondance se trouve aux Arch. hist., B^1 12 et 13 et X^E 14 et aux Arch. Insp. Génie, dossiers sur les places fortes. Plusieurs de ces dossiers ont été utilisés par Lazare, comme l'indique son apostille.
2. Rapport du 30 mai (Arch. hist. Guerre, B^1 12 et C. C., II, p. 289).
3. Décision du 1er juin (Arch. hist. Guerre, X^E 14).

4. Lettre à Bouchotte, 10 juillet (Arch. hist. Guerre, B¹ 14).

5. Correspondance du corps anglais (War Office, 1/166), FORTESCUE, *History of the British Army*, t. IV, p. 63 et suivantes. Un agent secret faisait connaître à Londres les troubles graves suscités à Paris par les défaites (F. O. 27/42).

6. Lettre de Murray à Dundas, Bruges, 19 avril 1793 (W. O. 1/166).

7. Arch. hist. Guerre, B¹ 12 et B¹³ 13. Voir aussi DUPUIS, *La Campagne de 1793 à l'Armée du Nord*. H. C., t. I, p. 321, et TISSOT, *ouvr. cité*, p. 52.

8. Lettre de Murray à Dundas, 20 mai 1793 (W. O. 1/166).

9. Voir WARSCHAUER, *Studien zur Entwicklung der Gedanken Lazare Carnots über der Kriegsfuhrung*, p. 61.

10. FORTESCUE, *ouvr. cité*, p. 113.

11. Lettre de Murray à Dundas, 1er et 4 juin (W. O. 1/166).

12. Lettre d'Henry John Spencer, La Haye, 7 juin (F. O. 37/49).

13. Lettre du 4 juin (Arch. hist. Guerre, B¹ 12).

14. Témoignage de Maribon-Montaut (Arch. nat., Dˣˡⁱⁱ 5).

15. Voir M. REINHARD, *Carnot et la Conduite de la Guerre* (*Bulletin de la Soc. d'Hist. moderne*, 1949).

16. Rapport du 19 juillet 1793 (*Wyndham Papers*, B. M. 37-855). Par son beau-frère Collignon, Carnot était en relations avec beaucoup de Hollandais.

17. Lettres de Carnot, 16 et 30 juin 1793 (C. C., t. II, p. 344 et 373). Il y est fait état de renseignements fournis par des espions. Carnot insistait volontiers sur l'importance de l'espionnage.

18. Lettres de Carnot, Defay, Delbrel, 8 juillet 1793 (B. N., Nlles acq. franc. 22736).

19. Lettre de Vincent (Arch. nat., F⁷ 4394²).

CHAPITRE V

DÉBUTS AU COMITÉ DE SALUT PUBLIC

1. Cette cooptation se fit dans des conditions mal connues. Pourquoi fit-on d'abord appel à Prieur, alors que les membres du Comité avaient étudié, dès le 12 juillet, le « système d'attaque ou de défense » de Carnot ? Dès le 4 août, Carnot proposait au Comité d'aller lui porter les « détails » que Feulint lui avait écrit qu'on lui demanderait (C. C., t. II, p. 444). Quand les fonctions des nouveaux membres commencèrent-elles ? Prieur siégeait le 4 août ; Carnot signa seulement le 11, mais une lettre était adressée, dès le 7 août, « aux citoyens Prieur et Carnot, membres du Comité de Salut public » (Arch. hist. Guerre, B¹³ 17). Les souvenirs de Barère et ceux de Prieur, qui nous informent, furent écrits longtemps après les événements et fourmillent d'erreurs. (Voir G. BOUCHARD, *Prieur de la Côte-d'Or*, p. 183 et 453.)

2. BEFFROY DE REIGNY, *Dictionnaire des Néologismes*, t. III, p. 12. — KÖRTE, *ouvr. cité*, p. 60. — TISSOT, *ouvr. cité*, p. 61. — H. C., t. I, p. 340 et 505.

3. Sur les signatures on dispose de la vaste littérature des polémiques thermidoriennes, tant à l'Assemblée que dans la presse (AULARD, *C. S. P.*, t. I, en énumère une partie). Dans le présent travail on a recouru aux minutes des arrêtés, sans pouvoir établir une statistique exhaustive — qui dépasse les moyens d'un travailleur isolé. Thompson, pour la période du 26 juillet au 23 septembre, indique — sur 306 minutes ou signatures en premier — 72 arrêtés de Carnot contre 15 de Couthon,

11 de Saint-Just et 10 de Robespierre (*Ann. hist. Rév.*, 1933, p. 454). Palmer, pour la période du 20 mai au 18 juin 1794, sur 608 minutes autographes, ou suivies d'une seule signature, en a reconnu 177 de Carnot, contre 207 de Lindet, 14 de Robespierre, 8 de Couthon et 4 de Saint-Just (PALMER, *Twelve who ruled*, p. 402). Ces relevés sont très approximatifs. Thompson s'est fié aux signatures en premier et, avec Palmer, il s'est reporté au recueil d'Aulard, qui donne les signatures avec une dangereuse fantaisie.

4. *Sur les Factions et les Partis*, p. 144.
5. *Moniteur*, t. XXII, p. 142.
6. *Feuille du Salut public*, 26 septembre 1793.
7. RICHARD, *Le Comité de Salut public et les Fabrications de Guerre*, p. 191.
8. AULARD, *C. S. P.*, t. VII, p. 270.
9. H. C., t. I, p. 518. La réponse de Duplay est citée par Mathiez (Divisions aux Comités).
10. Voir MATHIEZ, *Robespierre et l'Armée* (*Ann. hist. Rév.*, t. VIII, p. 138) et pour le rôle des places fortes, divers discours aux Jacobins (AULARD, *Jacobins*, t. V, p. 136, 208, 277, 341, 449, 549). Le rôle de la haine : « J'augmenterai autant qu'il sera en moi la haine de mes compatriotes contre le peuple anglais», est mentionné dans un autre discours aux Jacobins (*ibid.*, p. 632).
11. Voir E.-N. CURTIS, *Saint-Just*, notamment p. 58 et 146 ; — Ch. VELLAY, *Œuvres de Saint-Just*, notamment p. 32, 86 et 129. Une note de Bouchotte souligne bien l'intérêt que portait Saint-Just aux questions militaires : « Saint-Just demande pour le Comité de Salut public un tableau en masse et par arme de chaque armée, ainsi que les états-majors. Je le lui ai annoncé d'ici trois ou quatre

jours» (Arch. hist. Guerre, B¹³ 306).
12. COLLOT d'HERBOIS, *Défense...*, p. 20.
13. Arch. nat., AF II 16 (27 Germinal an II), AF II^x 22 (p. 300), 4 octobre 1793.
14. Arch. nat., AF II 23.
15. Bouchotte a fait l'objet d'une thèse de doctorat où le général Herlaut vante les qualités du ministre et montre l'inefficacité de l'action ministérielle. Pour ajouter un exemple, notons que le Comité de Salut public se plaignait à Bouchotte, le 22 juillet, de la « négligence impardonnable» de ses bureaux; ils n'avaient pas répondu depuis trois mois à ses demandes d'approvisionnement de la place de Cambrai (Arch. hist. Guerre, B¹ 15). Les mots de Robespierre furent prononcés le 26 juillet à la Convention et le 14 juin aux Jacobins. La phrase de Carnot se trouve dans une lettre à Garrau, écrite le 16 mai 1794. Plus tard Bouchotte sollicita Carnot, ministre de la Guerre puis ministre de l'Intérieur (Arch. familiales).
16. Lettres du 5 mai 1793 (Arch. hist. Guerre, B^{x12} 4), du 16 août (*ibid.*, B¹³ 306); le même jour Bouchotte suspendait le directeur de l'École de Mézières. Ordre du 17 novembre (*ibid.*, B¹³ 20).
17. Notes du 11 et du 13 août (Arch. hist. Guerre, B¹³ 306).
18. Cette correspondance figure aux Arch. hist. Guerre sous la forme de registres du Comité de Salut public (B^{x12} 4 et 5) et sous la forme des registres et des minutes de Bouchotte (B^{x12} 21, 26; B¹³ 17, 18, 19, 20; B¹³ 306), sans négliger les notes et les rapports qui se trouvent dans les séries des diverses armes (par exemple dans X^E 16).
19. HERLAUT, *Bouchotte*, t. I, p. 296 (Arch. hist. Guerre, B² 1, 19 août 1793).
20. « Je suis très sensible, ci-

toyens représentants, aux...
reproches que vous me faites
de ne pas correspondre avec
vous et de ne pas vous donner
régulièrement des nouvelles....
J'étais tranquille parce que je
savais que le ministre, qui
a toute votre confiance,
me communique toutes les
nouvelles qu'il reçoit des
armées » (Lettre de Houchard
au Comité de Salut public, le
22 août 1793, Arch. hist.
Guerre, B¹ 17). Le 6 décembre,
Hoche écrivait à Bouchotte
qu'il pensait que celui-ci com-
muniquait ses lettres au
Comité. Bouchotte lui répondit d'écrire directement pour
les choses les plus importantes
(HERLAUT, *ouvr. cité*, t. I,
p. 182).

21. Vincent, dès le 5 août, avait
affirmé que le Comité de Salut
public était un « pouvoir
monstrueux ». Il mena contre
lui une lutte résolue, servie
par des moyens puissants ; nécessairement il s'en prit surtout aux membres du Comité
qui s'occupaient des questions
militaires. La correspondance
reçue par Vincent, lors de sa
sortie de prison, montre la
multitude de ses amis, l'ardeur de leurs sentiments révolutionnaires et démocratiques,
la puissance enfin que cette
communauté de vues et cet
attachement personnel donnaient au secrétaire général.
Ce personnage mériterait une
étude, non des particularités
de l'homme, mais de son rôle
dans le mouvement hébertiste,
surtout aux armées. Le conflit
des commissaires du pouvoir
exécutif avait été très vif à
l'armée du Nord ; l'un d'eux
demandait, le 7 juillet, le
licenciement de tous les états-
majors ; un autre interdisait
à tout militaire, sous peine
d'être fusillé, de donner à
aucun soldat un congé absolu
ou limité. Ainsi le général Tour-
ville écrivait-il au ministre
de la Guerre, pour se plaindre
du « petit commissaire du

pouvoir exécutif » colportant
des « écrits incendiaires », et
utilisant comme secrétaire un
espion, tandis qu'un commissaire du pouvoir exécutif écrivait au même ministre : « mon
civisme est plus connu que
celui de ceux [les représentants en mission] qui m'ont
persécuté ». L'arrestation de
Custine avait beaucoup renforcé la position des commissaires exécutifs. Ceux-ci
étaient appuyés par quel-
ques officiers jacobins, tels que
le capitaine Calendini, qui
rapportait tous les incidents
au club parisien et lui demandait d'intervenir. Les représentants en mission, notamment Duhem, avaient saisi le
Comité de Salut public, en
stigmatisant les « aventuriers
brouillons », liés aux Ronsins
et « autres coquins » du ministre de la Guerre. Le Comité
n'intervint pas (Arch. hist.
Guerre, B¹ 14 et B¹ 15).

CHAPITRE VI

SUR LE CHAMP
DE BATAILLE DE
WATTIGNIES

1. Lettre du 16 août 1793, pu-
bliée par FINOT et FOUCARD,
*La Défense nationale dans le
Nord* (t. II, p. 7).
2. AULARD, *Jacobins*, t. V,
p. 310, 345 et 350 : Carnot et
Robespierre. — M. REINHARD,
*Carnot et la Conduite de la
Guerre.*
3. Lettre du 22 novembre 1793,
Arch. familiales.
4. Opinion de Robespierre, Arch.
nat., F⁷ 4436, pl. 3, pièce 102.
Pour Carnot, DUPUIS, *La
Campagne de 1793 à l'Armée
du Nord*, t. I, p. 272 ; GAY
DE VERNON, *Mémoires*, p. 231.
M. Gay de Vernon a eu l'amabilité de rechercher des renseignements complémentaires
dans ses archives. Nous l'en
remercions. Lettre des admi-

nistrateurs du département du Nord au Comité de Salut public (Arch. hist. Guerre, B^{x12} 4, 14 mai 1793, et C. C., t. III, p. 240).

5. Sur Grimoard, voir t. I, p. 71 ; B. et R., t. XXIV, p. 414. Sur les autres projets, M. REINHARD, *Carnot et la Conduite de la Guerre.*

6. DUPUIS, *ouvr. cité,* t. II, p. 360 et suivantes.

7. Circulaire du 2 septembre (Arch. hist. Guerre, B^{13} 18) ; notes de VINCENT (*ibid.*, B^{13} 306) ; lettre de Vincent à Renkin et Berger, 16 septembre (Arch. nat., F^7 4394^2).

8. Dossier Champmorin (Arch. adm. Guerre) ; lettre de Duvignau, 16 septembre (Arch. hist. Guerre, B^x 25 et *Ann. hist. Révol.,* 1908, p. 111). Pour l'armée révolutionnaire, voir M. Reinhard, *Carnot et l'armée révolutionnaire.* Bulletin de la société d'Histoire moderne, séance du 8 juin 1952.

9. Lettre de Vincent du 16 septembre, de Celliez et Varin le 25 juillet (Arch. hist. Guerre, X^{em} 33, X^{em} 36, B^{13} 18) ; sur les séances du 25 et du 26 septembre à la Convention, outre le *Moniteur,* on trouve des informations dans le *Courrier universel* et le *Journal des Jacobins* (HERLAUT, *Ann. hist. Révol.,* 1937, p. 400). Michon a montré le rôle de Bouchotte et des représentants en mission dans le choix des généraux (*Correspondance de Robespierre,* t. II, p. 55 et 63). Le témoignage le plus fort est celui de Carnot lui-même écrivant à son ami Garrau, le 16 mai 1794 : « Nous avons nommé sur la présentation de Bouchotte » (C. C., t. IV, p. 365).

10. H. C. affirme que Carnot « fit de vains efforts pour sauver Houchard » ; on doit noter qu'il ne rédigea pas l'ordre d'arrestation, mais il le signa.

11. Le meilleur exposé de Wattignies, d'après les sources françaises et autrichiennes,

est celui de Dupuis. On peut le compléter par la lettre de Murray à Dundas, du 18 octobre (W. O. 1/167). Elle insiste sur la défaite de l'aile gauche et affirme l'énergie de la droite. Le passage de Vaublanc se trouve dans ses *Mémoires* (p. 348). Les dispositions nouvelles de Robespierre et de Saint-Just apparaissent dans leur correspondance, notamment dans la lettre de Robespierre à Saint-Just, 2 novembre 1793 (Papiers inédits Courtois, t. II, p. 4).

12. Lettre du 2 octobre 1793 (Arch. nat., AF II 239).

13. JOURDAN, *Mémoires manuscrits,* chap. III, p. 39. (Arch. hist. Guerre, Mémoires historiques, 608^1).

CHAPITRE VII

GOUVERNEMENT RÉVOLUTIONNAIRE

1. Sur cette affaire, la source principale est la collection du *Rougyff.* La brouille entre Guffroy, Lebas et Robespierre est attestée par les mémoires de Mme Lebas (p. 124) et par ceux de Charlotte Robespierre (p. 71). Les palinodies de Guffroy apparaissent dans sa correspondance (*Arch. hist. Révol.,* 1909, p. 243, et MICHON, *Correspondance d'Augustin et de Maximilien Robespierre,* t. I, p. 122). Voir aussi JACOB, *Joseph Lebon,* t. I, p. 217. La lettre de Dupin figure aux Arch. familiales. Les biographes de Carnot ont fait une allusion à la seule affaire Duquesnoy (H. C., t. I, p. 414, TISSOT, p. 64, KÖRTE, p. 49), ils ont ignoré les séances des Jacobins. AULARD, *Jacobins,* t. V, p. 500 et suivantes.

2. AULARD, *C. S. P.,* t. VIII, p. 19 (Arch. nat., F^7 4772 et 4774^1).

3. G. BOUCHARD, *Prieur de la Côte-d'Or* p. 189 et suivantes.
4. Lettres des 18 novembre, 14 janvier et 6 février (Arch. nat., AF II 202 et 280, publiées dans C. C. et dans AULARD).
5. JUNG, *Dubois-Crancé*, t. II, p. 28. — DUBOIS-CRANCÉ, *Analyse de la Révolution française*, p. 133. — AULARD, *C. S. P.*, t. VI, p. 20.
6. AULARD, t. VIII, p. 222, 4 novembre. Clauzel affirma que Ricord possédait une lettre signée de Carnot et d'autres membres du Comité, reprochant à Fréron et à Barras « d'avoir été des modérés parce qu'ils n'avaient pas réduit Toulon en cendres». (Arch. nat., F⁷ 4435).
7. CARNOT, *Opinion sur l'Accusation contre Billaud-Varenne*, p. 6. Au début de l'hiver 1793-1794, Carnot signait souvent la correspondance adressée aux représentants en mission, dès qu'elle touchait à des questions militaires, avec Billaud-Varenne et Collot d'Herbois.
8. Lettres de Carnot (C. C., t. IV, p. 215 et 270). BARÈRE, *Mémoires*, t. II, p. 375 et 411. L'ouvrage de HADENGUE (*Les Gardes rouges de l'an II*) n'apporte rien de définitif ; il faut attendre la publication des travaux de M. Cobb. Voir bulletin de la Société d'histoire moderne, 8 juin 1952. Lettres de Carnot des 1ᵉʳ et 17 novembre (C. C., t. IV, p. 1 et 47) ; circulaire de Bouchotte, 23 novembre (Arch. hist. Guerre, B¹³ 20) ; arrêté C. S. P.
9. L'activité de la section de la Guerre se retrouve dans les registres de la correspondance (Arch. hist. Guerre, Bˣ¹² 4 et 5), d'arrêtés (Arch. nat., AFˣ II 184), du personnel (Arch. nat., F II 23) et dossier sur Chaalons (Arch. hist. Guerre). Pour le cabinet topographique (Arch. nat., AF IIˣ 170, et BERTHAUT, *Les Ingénieurs géographes*, t. I, p. 93).
10. Lettre du 4 décembre (C.

C., t. IV, p. 229) ; dans le même sens, trois lettres de Barère, contresignées par Carnot (Arch. nat., AF II 202) ; circulaire du 4 février 1794 (Arch. nat., DX LII₁).
11. Lettre de Carnot à Dumont, 27 octobre (AULARD, *C. S. P.*, t. VII, p. 58) et lettre du 16 décembre (Arch. familiales). Rapport sur la manufacture d'armes de Paris (C. C., t. III, p. 453 et suivantes). On peut remarquer, sur la vignette ornant le papier de la section de la Guerre, au pied du faisceau de licteurs, une tiare pontificale renversée (par ex. Arch. nat., AF II 202).

CHAPITRE VIII

LES ARMÉES DE LA RÉPUBLIQUE

1. Pour tout ce chapitre consulter HERLAUT (*Bouchotte*, t. I), qui aborde les mêmes problèmes. Instruction du 23 octobre (C. C., t. III, p. 384).
2. DUBOIS-CRANCÉ, *Rapport sur l'Embrigadement* (B. N., Le³⁸ 1211). De l'armée d'Italie on mandait au C. S. P., le 8 octobre 1793 : « Personne n'en connaît l'effectif, ni l'état de ses subsistances, de son artillerie, de ses munitions» (AULARD, *C. S. P.*, t. VII). Une circulaire de P. Sijas signalait l'absence des registres de contrôle et l'insuffisance des autres (Arch. hist. Guerre, B¹³ 22).
3. Arch. hist. Guerre, Bˣ² 142 f⁰ 119, 144 f⁰ 131, Reconnaissances n⁰ 1160.
4. Arch. hist. Guerre, B¹³ 20, B¹ 244. GRIMOARD, *Tableau des Campagnes de la Révolution*, t. I, tableau annexe.
5. Voir t. I, p. 223.
6. Arch. nat., F⁷ 4436 ; Arch. hist. Guerre, B¹³ 20.

7. Dupuis, *ouvr. cité*, t. I., p. 272, et t. II, p. 145. Décrets des 27 septembre et 22 novembre, circulaire d'application du 24 novembre (Cochin, t. I, p. 183 et 476).

8. Papiers du Comité de la Guerre (Arch. nat., AF II 14 et 16, AF^x II 23) et aussi AF II 198, Arch. hist. Guerre, B^{13} 23 et B. N., Le^{38} 589 et 590. Les biographes de Carnot lui ont généralement attribué une part dans l'embrigadement, alors que c'est le contraire qui est exact, comme l'ont vu les historiens de Dubois-Crancé.

9. Arch. hist. Guerre, B^1 244, B^{13} 18 et 22. Papiers du Comité de la Guerre (Arch. nat., AF II 14 et AF II^x 22). Lettre de Carnot, spécialement note inédite du 4 septembre 1793 (Arch. nat., AF II 198).

10. Arch. nat., AF II 202 ; Arch. hist. Guerre, B^{13} 21 et 23, X^d 159. Papiers du Comité de la Guerre (Arch. nat. AF II 16). Naguère Carnot était hostile à l'artillerie légère ; c'était le temps où il condamnait la guerre offensive (t. I, p. 237).

11. Arrêté du 12 février 1794 (Arch. nat., AF II 202). Mathiez, *Robespierre et l'Armée* (*Ann. hist. Révol.*, 1916, p. 138). Arch. hist. Guerre, B^{13} 23. Cependant il était prescrit de ne pas promouvoir ces officiers au-delà du grade de capitaine.

12. Arch. nat., AF II 202 ; Arch. hist. Guerre, B^{13} 21 et 24, X^E 14, 15 et 16.

13. Arch. hist. Guerre, B^{13} 17, 23 et 306 ; Arch. nat., AF II 37 ; C. C., t. IV, p. 202, 209, 269, etc. Coutenceau, *ouvr. cité*, t. I, p. 56. Lettre du volontaire Bourgeois, 8 mai 1794 (Arch. familiales).

14. C. C., t. V, p. 215, 274 et 283 (Arch. hist. Guerre, B^{13} 22 ; Arch. nat., AF^x II 182).

CHAPITRE IX

ORGANISATION DE LA VICTOIRE

1. X. Audouin, notes (Arch. hist. Guerre, 9 novembre 1792). — Th. Lameth, Mémoires manuscrits, t. I, p. 113.

2. M. Reinhard, *Carnot et la Conduite de la Guerre.*

3. Curtis, *ouvr. cité*, p. 146, 153 et suivantes (Arch. hist. Guerre, B^2 27).

4. Sur Grimoard, B. et R., t. XXIV, p. 414. Sur la réduction des garnisons, Custine, 28 mai (Arch. nat., W^a 102) ; Bouchotte, 6 août, 6 octobre, 15, 16, 23 novembre (Arch. hist. Guerre, B^1 17 ; C. C., t. III, p. 258 ; t. IV, p. 115, etc.) ; C. S. P., 25 août (Arch. hist. Guerre, B^1 17) ; Hoche (Fabre, *ouvr. cité*, p. 25, et Arch. nat., AF II 239 ; C. C., t. III, p. 373) ; Saint-Just et Lebas, 3 novembre (C. C., t. IV, p. 7). Sur la proportion des troupes actives (Arch. milit. Guerre, B^1 244).

5. Sur Berthelmy, Dupuis, *ouvr. cité*, t. I, p. 279, dossier personnel (Arch. adm. Guerre) et divers ordres et lettres (Arch. hist. Guerre, B^1 17 et Arch. nat., W^a 100). Sur l'organisation des divisions aux diverses armées, les états de situation montrent le groupement d'infanterie, légère ou de ligne, d'artillerie à pied et à cheval, de cavalerie lourde et légère (Arch. hist. Guerre, B^1 244) et aussi la correspondance des armées et des lettres de représentants (aussi Lacoste, 18 décembre 1793, Arch. nat., AF II 247).

6. Sur Grimoard, B. et R., t. XXIV, p. 414 ; sur Saint-Just, discours du 19 vendémiaire an II ; sur Hoche (Arch. nat., AF II 239) ; sur Barère, *Moniteur*, n° 248. Sur la haine de l'ennemi, C. C., t. IV, p. 447. Lettres

de Puycerda et de Kaisers-lautern (Arch. hist. Guerre, cartons Volontaires natio-naux, Lot). Sur la guerre bactériologique (Arch. hist. Guerre, Bx^{12} 5). Sur la guerre à faire en Espagne (Arch. nat., AF II 63). Sur les bri-quets phosphoriques, B^{13} 20). Sur l'évacuation des civils, lettre du 8 décembre 1793 (bibliothèque de Genève, ms. suppl. 355, f° 72).

Pour donner une idée de la persistance des souvenirs amers laissés par la dévasta-tion des pays étrangers, qu'il nous soit permis de signaler qu'un critique belge, donnant un compte rendu de notre tome I, voyait d'abord dans Carnot l'homme qui avait ravagé la Belgique.

7. Le bulletin n° 6 des *Dropmore Papers* expose, le 28 décembre, la subordination de l'armée au Comité. Le bulletin n° 10, des premiers jours de février, décrivait « la nature des ar-mées de la République », aguerries, innombrables, tou-jours attaquantes et républi-caines. Les données des *Wyn-dham Papers* (B. M. 37.855), du 25 janvier 1794, sont plus précises (pour les effectifs, lettre du 15 février). On trouve aussi des indications dans un mémoire du 15 février (F. O. 27/43). Voir également la correspondance de Mallet du Pan. Celui-ci, le 8 mars, expose le rôle personnel de Carnot (Ed. Sayous, p. 44).

8. L'information est empruntée aux archives britanniques (F. O. 27/42 à 27/47 — B. M. 37.855). Le Trosne, informa-teur de d'Antraigues, comme l'a montré Mathiez, était-il ce Letronne témoin contre Hébert, Vincent et Momoro (Arch. nat., F^2 4438) ? Je tiens à remercier ici MM. F. Crouzet et Godechot, qui m'ont aidé dans mes recherches en Angle-terre, et à signaler les publica-tions de M. Godechot sur l'in-formation que fournissent ces

archives, notamment sur la période directoriale. Sorel a signalé que Carnot réclamait l'emploi d'agents secrets pour être informé sur les intentions et les moyens des ennemis, mais il fait allusion aux agents diplomatiques (SOREL, *L'Eu-rope et la Révolution*, t. III, p. 532 et 535). Chaque décade, le Comité réclamait un rapport du service d'espionnage de chaque armée (COUTANCEAU, *ouvr. cité*, t. II, I, p. 188).

9. Rappelons que le *Système général* a été publié (C. C., t. IV, p. 279) à la date erro-née du 2 février. Plan de L.-S. Chénier, communiqué par M. Séhet.

10. Plan de Custine (Arch. nat., W^a 102), plans de Kellermann (Arch. familiales). Kellermann proposait déjà une offensive en Italie dès juillet. Plan de d'Arçon, Arch. familiales, plan de Hoche (FABRE, *ouvr. cité*, p. 29). AULARD, III, p. 215 (Arch. nat., AF II 239), plan de Grimoard (Arch. nat., F^9 1349). Plans de Sauviac. Gobert et Tardy (Arch. hist, guerre ; Arch. nat., W^o 99 et 102 ; Arch. hist. Guerre, B^1 15 et *Reconnaissances*, n° 1160). Nous avons négligé les pro-jets d'invasion de l'Espagne, conçus par Laclos, Servan, Pully, Turreau, et ceux d'expé-ditions aux Indes. Une sorte de gigantisme procédait de la conviction que les ressources de la France étaient limitées.

11. Sur l'inspiration de Lafitte Clavé, voir COUTANCEAU, *Re-vue d'Histoire*, 1905, t. I, p. 603. Le plan de Sauviac, cité plus haut, se réclame du même Lafitte.

12. Ces précisions manquent dans la correspondance de Carnot, parce qu'elles avaient été pu-bliées dans AULARD, *C. S. P.*, t. X, p. 239 et 437. On a dit depuis longtemps l'in-cohérence de ces publications.

13. *Wyndham Papers* (B. M. 37.855) et Mallet du Pan, mémoire d'avril 1796 (F. O.

27/47). Grimoard, lettre du 3 janvier 1794 (Arch. nat., F⁰ 1349). Carnot, lettre du 26 octobre 1793 (C. C., t. III, p. 407).

14. *Wyndham Papers* (même note) ; *Dropmore Papers*, p. 518 et 546 ; Mallet du Pan, lettre du 8 mars 1794 (édition Sayous, p. 44 ; Arch. adm. Guerre, dossier Mathieu Dumas) ; C. S. P. à un correspondant (AF*ᵃ* II 182), Carnot à Garrau (C. C., t. IV, p. 276). Envoi d'un plan de Turreau au Comité de la Guerre (Arch. hist. Guerre, B¹³ 21) ; envoi d'un plan à Bouchotte (Arch. hist. Guerre, B*ˣ¹²* 5). M. REINHARD, *Carnot et la Conduite de la Guerre*.

15. SAUVIAC, *Aperçu des deux dernières Campagnes de l'Armée du Nord*. Choudieu a écrit que Carnot dirigeait tous les plans de campagne et que Prieur y prit une part (*Mémoires*, p. 238).

CHAPITRE X

LA GUERRE EN L'AN II

1. Minutes de Collot d'Herbois (Arch. nat., AF II 244) ; minute de Robespierre (Arch. nat., AF II 202). Lettres échangées entre le Comité et Jourdan (C. C., t. III et IV). Louanges d'Hébert (*Moniteur*, t. XVIII, p. 382, et AULARD, *Jacobins*, t. V, p. 500). Levasseur a rapporté que Jourdan croyait Carnot hostile à sa réintégration (*Mémoires*, t. II, p. 254) ; Duquesnoy déclare avoir soutenu Jourdan, et il était en mauvais termes avec Carnot (*Réponse à Guffroy*, p. 33 et 34). Seule Mme Lebas déclare que Robespierre jugeait que l'arrestation de Jourdan était une trahison et que Saint-Just cacha le général chez l'un de ses amis (*Mémoires*, p. 145). Il est à noter que Jourdan reçut une pen-

sion sur la proposition de Bouchotte, parce « qu'il a toujours manifesté le patriotisme le plus pur » (AULARD, *C. S. P.*, t. X, p. 682). La proposition fut entérinée par le Comité, le 6 février (le visa est de Carnot, la pièce est signée Carnot, Collot d'Herbois, Billaud-Varenne et Robespierre, Arch. nat., AF II 304).

2. Voir plus haut les plans de Hoche (p. 81, 104, 106, 112 et 113). CARNOT, *Réponse à Bailleul* (p. 148, repris dans H. C.). Bouchotte s'intéressait à Hoche en août 1793 (Arch. hist. Guerre, B¹³ 306). Arrêté du 23 octobre (Arch. nat. AF II 244). Correspondance du Comité, de Pichegru et de Hoche (C. C., t. III et IV). — SAINT-JUST, *Œuvres*, édition Dellay, t. II, p. 148 et suivantes. — AULARD, *Jacobins*, t. V, p. 649. — Correspondance de Hoche à Pichegru (Arch. hist. Guerre, armée de la Moselle et du Rhin). Arrestation de Hoche, AULARD, *Études et Leçons*, 1ʳᵉ série, p. 202. — MATHIEZ, *Ann. hist. Révol.*, t. VIII, p. 139, *L'Amateur d'Autographes*, 16 août 1865 et fichier Charavay (B. N., manuscrits). Il n'est guère admissible de s'appuyer sur l'absence du nom de Robespierre au bas de l'arrêté d'arrestation, puisqu'il y a la lettre autographe du même Robespierre. Pourquoi ne pas faire valoir que Carnot ne signa pas l'ordre de mettre Hoche aux Carmes ? (Arch. nat., AF II 304).

3. Lettre du 4 décembre 1793, signée de Carnot et de Barrère (Arch. hist. Guerre, B¹³ 21).

4. Le 12 novembre 1793, le Comité de la Guerre renvoya au Comité de Salut public les dossiers de 74 militaires, suspendus ou destitués (Arch. nat., AF II 304). Carnot demanda les motifs des mesures prises concernant de nom-

breux officiers, au ministre ou aux représentants en mission (Arch. nat., AF II 304, 203).

5. Arrêté du 19 janvier, écrit par Carnot (Arch. nat., A F II 304; Arch. hist. Guerre, B¹³ 22). Le 10 février, il recevait déjà un état par armée concernant les généraux et l'état-major (Arch. hist. Guerre, B¹³ 23).

6. Arch. nat., AF II 264.

7. Arch. nat., AF II 203. Ordre du 18 septembre, réitéré le 6 janvier 1794. Nombreux exemples de l'action de Carnot dans AF II 304.

8. Bouchotte a revendiqué l'honneur d'avoir nommé d'habiles généraux (mémoires justificatifs, cités par AVENEL, *Lundis révolutionnaires*, p. 326). On peut se faire une idée de son œuvre aux Arch. hist. Guerre, dans ses cartons et dans ceux de l'état-major (X^{em} 36 et dans B¹³ 18). Le biographe de Bouchotte n'a pas traité cette question, sinon incidemment dans un article des *Ann. hist. Révol.* (1937). L'éditeur de la correspondance de Robespierre a donné des exemples probants de l'intervention des parlementaires auprès de Bouchotte (MICHON, *ouvr. cité*, p. 55 et 63).

Je n'ai pu discerner les motifs qui incitèrent Carnot à suspendre et à réintégrer le général Fabrefonds, frère de Fabre d'Églantine, en octobre 1793 (Arch. nat., AF II 304), non plus que le rôle de Fabre et de C. Desmoulins au Comité de la Guerre. Le biographe de F a b r e d'Églantine signale que celui-ci fit la fortune de Fabrefonds (L. JACOB, *Fabre d'Églantine*, p. 140). La date de la suspension de Fabrefonds coïncide avec les dénonciations contre Fabre d'Églantine.

9. Arch. nat, AF II 202.

10. La rédaction définitive se trouve aux Arch. nat. (AF II 203); elle figure dans la correspondance (C. C., t. IV, p. 300)

et avait déjà été publiée par TISSOT, *Mémoires sur Carnot*, p. 218. L'évolution des instructions correspond au changement de commandement : la première s'adressait à Ferrand, les deux autres à Pichegru. La seconde rédaction est aux Arch. hist. Guerre (armée du Nord) et aux Arch. familiales. Elle a été publiée par AULARD (*C. S. P.*, t. XI, p. 213). L'exemplaire des Arch. familiales comporte la mention : « signé sur le registre : Carnot, C.-A. Prieur, Billaud - Varenne, Jeanbon - Saint-André, Barère, Collot d'Herbois, Couthon, Robert Lindet. Pour extrait : Carnot, Billaud-Varenne ». La correspondance (C. C., t. IV) ignore ce texte.

Lettres de Carnot à Richard et Choudieu, 18 mars (C. C., t. IV, p. 306). Un exemplaire de cette lettre figure à la bibliothèque municipale de Rouen (autographes Girardin, Carnot, n⁰ 795).

Pour la critique du plan, voir COUTANCEAU et de LA JONQUIÈRE, *ouvr. cité*, t. II, I, p. 69 à 119.

11. Arch. familiales, AULARD, t. XI, p. 603 — C. C., t. IV. — CURTIS, *Saint-Just*, p. 248.

12. Arch. nat., W78, F⁷ 4394, W 434. HERLAUT, *ouvr. cité*, t. II, p. 111. — TUETEY, *Répertoire général*, t. XI, n⁰ 36. — MATHIEZ, *Les Divisions dans les Comités de gouvernement à la veille du 9 Thermidor* (*Rev. hist.*, 1915, et *Ann. hist. Révol.*, 1927) (Arch. nat., W³ 339).

13. *Journal des Débats*, n⁰ 562, C. C., t. IV, p. 324. Le 3 février, Monestier avait attaqué à Bayonne le Comité exécutif et spécialement l'entourage du ministre de la Guerre. Il en souhaitait la suppression (Arch. nat., F⁷ 4394²).

14. Arch. nat., AF II 204, I.-A. PILLE, *Réponse....* Saint-Just avait eu une altercation avec Carnot à l'occasion de l'arres-

tation du beau-frère de Sijas. La nouvelle organisation fut mise en route progressivement; les registres commencent fin avril; les dossiers furent transférés à la même époque.

15. L'action de Carnot dans les commissions a laissé de nombreuses traces (Arch. nat., AF II 23, AF^x II 170, AF^x II 65 et 241, AF^x II 182, AF II 202, 203, 305; Arch. hist. Guerre, B^{x12} 22, B^{13} 24, XD 161; C. C., t. IV, notamment p. 329 et 331).

16. Sur les opérations, outre les ouvrages spécialisés, les sources ont été consultées. La correspondance, éditée par Aulard et C. C., se consulte aisément dans les registres AF^x II 170 et 241, qu'a ignorés Aulard. On y trouve aussi bien les lettres des généraux que celle des représentants, dont les expéditions sont, au contraire, divisées entre les Archives nationales et celles de la Guerre; de plus, il y a moins de lacunes.

A remarquer une intervention de Couthon (Arch. familiales, AULARD, XIII, p. 760).

Les Arch. familiales contiennent une lettre inédite au général Moulin (21 juin 1794) et une autre, du 23 juin, aux représentants en mission à l'armée de la Moselle.

Les projets italiens amenèrent une vive entrevue entre les membres du Comité et le représentant de l'État génois, Boccardi. Celui-ci en a conservé le souvenir, rare témoignage sur l'activité intérieure du Comité. On y voit les membres discutant au milieu de la nuit: Barère exposant la situation, Saint-Just menaçant et exigeant une réponse immédiate et catégorique, Barère intervenant avec adresse. Enfin une brusque sortie de Carnot : Boccardi avait souhaité une prompte avance des Français : « Comment vouliez-vous que nous avancions dans le Piémont et la Lombardie, si nous ne sommes pas assurés de l'attitude génoise ? » (P. NURRA, *La Coalizione européa contra la Republica di Genova*, 1893, p. 92.)

17. Le premier document à consulter est le dossier de Huché (aux Arch. adm. Guerre). Il faut remarquer que de Dumouriez à Legendre, en passant par Pache et Carnot, ce Huché ne cessa d'être considéré comme un soudard. La lettre de Hentz et de Francastel, la décision du Comité de sûreté générale, la nomination par Carnot se trouvent aux Arch. nat. (D^{x}L II 6, AF II^x 254, AF II 304). Ording a donc écrit d'une façon au moins elliptique (*ouvr. cité*, p. 109). Les horreurs commises par Huché sont signalées par tous les historiens (par exemple GABORY, t. II, p. 198; t. III, p. 59), mais non pas celles qu'il perpétra en juillet 1794 (Arch. hist. Guerre, B^5 9).

18. Sur la descente en Angleterre, outre les ouvrages généraux sur cette question, correspondance de l'armée de l'Ouest (Arch. hist. Guerre, B^5 17).

CHAPITRE XI

DÉCHIREMENT DU COMITÉ

1. Bien que Hérault de Séchelles eût été sacrifié.
2. CARNOT, *Réponse à Bailleul*, p. 168. — H. C., t. I, p. 368.
3. *Moniteur*, t. XX, p. 115 et 265.
4 *bis*. C. C., t. IV (Arch. nat., AF II 37, 203, 304, 305, 348, AF II^x 182. Bibl. mun. Rouen; autographes Girardin, n° 778).
5. H. C., t. I, p. 524. D'après Prieur, l'auteur distingue deux scènes, mais l'identité des dialogues fait douter qu'il s'agisse d'événements différents. Prieur de la Côte-

d'Or, discours du 23 mars 1795 (B. N., Le [38] 1306, p. 4), *Réponse des Membres des anciens Comités aux Dénonciations de Lecointe*, p. 103.

6. DE LAUNAY, *Monge*, p. 121.

7. *Journal universel*, 28 mars 1795, p. 10017. — BERRYER, *Mémoires*. — Cf. MATHIEZ, *Ann. hist. Révol.*, 1927, p. 5.

8. Arch. nat., AF II[x] 254, f° 183.

9. La minute n'est pas signée de Carnot, mais les expéditions et les instructions (Arch. nat., F[7] 4435 et F[7] 4436).

10. GUFFROY, *Censure républicaine*, p. 43 (Arch. nat., AF II 51).

11. Arch. nat., A F II[x] 254, p. 315.

12. Arch. nat., AF II 304 (analysé dans AULARD, *C. S. P.*, t. XIII, p. 743, et mentionné par C. C., t. IV, p. 375).

13. Arch. nat., AF II 65.

14. Arch. nat., F[7] 4436.

15. FOUQUIER-TINVILLE, *Réquisitoires*, édition Fleischmann, p. 211 et 272. — BARÈRE, *Mémoires*, t. II, p. 205. — BILLAUD-VARENNE, *A ses concitoyens*, p. 3. — LECOINTRE, *Les Crimes des sept Membres...*, p. 76 ; *Réponse des Membres des deux anciens Comités*, p. 39.

16. *Dropmore Papers*, p. 588.

17. Arch. nat., F[IB] 11 Pas-de-Calais 1.

18. BAUDOT, *Notes*, p. 121, 125. — LEVASSEUR, Discours du 27 mars et 30 août 1795,

Mémoires, chap. III. — BARÈRE, *Mémoires*, t. II, p. 205.

19. Arch. nat., W 79, *Rev. hist.*, 1915, p. 80. Lettre de Florent Guiot, 2 août 1794 (AULARD, *C. S. P.*, t. XV, p. 607).

20. Arch. nat., F[7] 4437, AF II[x] 170. *Journal universel*, 27 mars 1795. A. ORDING, *ouvr. cité*, p. 99.

21. Arch. nat., AF II[x] 182, AF II[x] 254, p. 379. A. ORDING, *ouvr. cité*, p. 103.

22. Arch. familiales.

23. LEVY-SCHNEIDER, *Rev. fr.*, t. XXXVIII, p. 97. — BARÈRE, *Réponse*.

24. PILLE, Réponse à Sijas, *Journal des Hommes libres*, 5 août 1793. — A. MATHIEZ, *Ann. hist. Révol.*, 1927, p. 213.

25. Minute du discours de Ruhl (Arch. nat., F[7] 4775[5]), obligeamment communiquée par M. Cobb, à qui nous adressons nos remerciements.

26. *Moniteur*, n° XXIV, p. 572. M. REINHARD, *Carnot et l'armée révolutionnaire*. Bulletin de la Société d'histoire moderne, séance du 8 juin 1952.

27. *La Soirée des Camps ;* AULARD, *Études et Leçons ; Le Conservateur décadaire*, t. II, p. 410 et 436.

28. H. C., t. I, p. 533.

29. *Réponse des Membres des deux anciens Comités*, p. 30.

30. Arch. nat., AF II 47.

31. GOTTSCHALK, *Ann. hist. Révol.*, t. IX, p. 457 ; minute au fichier Charavay (B. N.).

DEUXIÈME PARTIE

DE THERMIDOR A L'EXIL

CHAPITRE PREMIER

LE STRATÈGE
SAUVE LE TERRORISTE

1. Intervention dans ce sens de Bourdon de l'Oise, le 11 et le 27 thermidor ; de Poultier, le 23 thermidor.
2. Arrêtés de libération (Arch. nat., AF II 203 et 305). Inquiétudes de Choderlos de Laclos qui craignait le ressentiment de Carnot (lettre du 20 septembre). Réquisitoires de Lecointre exigeant des libérations (Arch. nat., AF II 306, C. C., t. IV, p. 585); contestations sur les libérations injustifiées (séance du 13 août).
3. Arrêtés autographes de Carnot (Arch. nat., AF II 305 et 306) contre Lebon, père du Conventionnel, contre Declaye, ancien membre de l'armée révolutionnaire, spécialement brutal. Carnot les avait connus tous trois à l'amée du Nord. Répertoire (AF II 170). Circulaire du 3 septembre (Arch. nat., AF II 224 et fichier Charavay, publié dans C. C., t. IV, p. 636).
4. Discours d'Henri Larivière contre Carnot (*Moniteur*, n° 253, 13 prairial an III). Lettre de Carnot du 12 octobre, publiée par R. Schnerb (*Ann. hist. Révol.*, 1922, p. 508).
5. *L'Orateur du Peuple*, n° 27. *Moniteur*, n° 58, citation d'un article du *Morning Chronicle*.

6. *Moniteur* du 15 nivôse ; *Nouvelles politiques, nationales et étrangères*, 3 janvier 1795 ; *Journal universel*, 14 nivôse ; lettre à Garrau, 16 février 1795 (C. C., t. IV, p. 782).
7. Pour les débats, voir le *Moniteur* aux dates indiquées et aussi le *Journal universel*, qui est favorable à Carnot.
8. G. Bouchard a démontré, dans une excellente note critique, que le mot a été prononcé par Bourdon de l'Oise (BOUCHARD, *Prieur de la Côte-d'Or*, p. 464). L'attitude de celui-ci depuis les approches du 9 Thermidor confirme pleinement cette conclusion. Quant au nom de Lanjuinais, il est cité d'après H. C. (t. I, p. 485) ; celui-ci l'avait emprunté au *Précis historique* de Joseph Carnot. Mais il faut surtout remarquer que la plupart des journaux n'ont pas publié cette phrase fameuse ; elle eut donc, sur le moment, fort peu de retentissement, et l'on doit croire que Carnot fut sauvé par son plaidoyer et par sa réputation plutôt que par le cri d'un anonyme. La lettre de Merlin de Thionville a été publiée (AULARD, *C. S. P.*, t. XXIII, p. 825).
9. La documentation se trouve dans C. C., t. IV, et dans AULARD, *C. S. P.*, t. XVI et XVII. Toutefois il y manque quelques lettres, notamment celles du 16 octobre, des 3 et 8 novembre, des 11 et 12 janvier, des 12 et 16 février, et

une lettre de Garrau, du
15 octobre 1794 (Arch. familiales). En revanche, celle du
5 décembre, publiée comme
inédite (*Ann. hist. Révol.*,
1919, p. 556), figure dans C. C.,
t. IV, p. 695, à une date
erronée. La relation des sièges
se trouve dans Musset-Pathay
(deux volumes dont un de
planches, 1806). Réal rendit
compte de l'ouvrage de Sauviac dans *Le Rédacteur* du
15 février. Sur les historiographes, voir Arch. hist.
Guerre (carton spécial) ; sur
Hoche, AULARD, *C. S. P.*,
t. XV, XVI, XVIII et XIX,
et C. C., t. IV. La plupart de
ces textes sont des autographes de Carnot ; en revanche,
Hoche n'écrivait guère à Carnot. Sorel et Aulard ont posé
le problème des relations entre
les deux hommes. Mathiez l'a
repris. Chacun interprète dans
son sens les mêmes documents.
Ceux-ci ne permettent pas de
douter que Carnot a rétabli
Hoche dans un grand com-
mandement et lui a accordé
toute sa confiance, le général s'est montré très réservé.

10. Discours de Carnot sur la
frontière (*Moniteur*, t. XXVI,
p. 121).

11. Chanoine BLED, *Les Sociétés
populaires de Saint-Omer*. Nous
devons la connaissance de ce
travail à M. le chanoine
Coolen, et nous le prions de
trouver ici nos remerciements.
Les incidents de Saint-Omer
ont été rapportés inexacte-
ment par A.-J. Paris, qui
les a placés en 1795 et a mis
en cause Carnot au lieu de
Feulint (A.-J. PARIS, *Le Baron
Liborel, Mémoires de l'Académie d'Arras*, 11e série, t. XI,
1879). Cette version erronée a
été adoptée par Duteil (*Rome,
Naples et le Directoire*, p. 200).
Le texte principal figure à la
B. N. (Lb 40 1083).

12. Lettre de Carnot à Buissart,
15 septembre 1795 (Arch. Pas-
de-Calais, fonds Barbier).
Les anciens Conventionnels

avaient été élus avec 270 voix
au minimum. Carnot en avait
obtenu 111 au premier tour,
93 au second et 84 au troisième. Daunou, qui ne fut pas
élu non plus, avait eu 174
voix, puis 153 et enfin 147.
Quant à Guffroy, il était passé
de 50 à 17 et 9.

Les inscrits sur la liste
supplémentaire avaient réuni
230 voix au minimum. Dau-
nou en avait eu 172 et Carnot
135. Parmi les présidents des
sections de vote se trouvaient
d'anciens collègues de Carnot
aux Rosati et à l'Académie,
ainsi Gay et F. Dubois (Arch.
du Pas-de-Calais, assemblée
primaire de vendémiaire an
VII).

13. Plusieurs Conventionnels furent proposés par un nombre
de départements beaucoup plus
élevé : 36 pour Boissy d'Anglas et Cambacérès ; plus de 30
pour Lesage, Lanjuinais, Thibaudeau et Saladin. La répartition des départements qui
proposèrent Carnot est remarquable : Ouest vendéen et Pays
chouan. Le nom de Carnot
était accolé à celui de ses
ennemis, Larivière, Bentabole
et autres. C'est donc le pacifi-
cateur qui fut ainsi choisi. La
Sarthe, qui nomma Carnot,
comptait alors un noyau important de Jacobins (M. REI-
NHARD, *Le Régime directorial
dans le Département de la
Sarthe*).

14. Arrêté du 22 germinal et
note du 15 thermidor an III
(Arch. hist. Guerre B¹³ 37).

15. Arrêté du 14 fructidor (B¹³
37). Lettre de Bonaparte du
3 (Corr. Nap., t. I, p. 85).
Documents p u b l i é s p a r
S. Askenazi (p. 65).

16. Note du 15 vendémiaire
an IV (B¹³ 38). Le recours de
Letourneur à Carnot est mentionné par H. C. (t. I, p. 574) ;
en revanche, il est assuré qu'il
fit appel au général Rivaz
(Arch. adm. Guerre, dossier
Rivaz).

17. *Moniteur* (t. XXVI, p. 285).

CHAPITRE II

DIRECTEUR
DE LA RÉPUBLIQUE

1. H. C., t. II, p. 5. Sur le rôle des « capacités», on remarquera cette déclaration frappante de Letourneur, dans un rapport daté du 28 janvier 1795 : « Il est temps de réaliser le principe qui veut que, dans la république, les talents, les capacités, l'instruction et la moralité soient seuls appelés aux fonctions supérieures et seuls investis de l'autorité. » (B. N., 8° Le[38] 1185).

2. On s'est parfois demandé si Thibaudeau avait été véridique en affirmant qu'il avait été question de porter des généraux au Directoire (MA-THIEZ, *Le Directoire*, p. 37). Le doute est interdit, puisque cinq d'entre eux obtinrent un nombre appréciable de voix : Jourdan, Pérignon, Lacuée, Kellermann et d'Arçon, sans parler de l'amiral Bruix (*Le Censeur des Journaux*, n° 67, 2 novembre 1795).

3. « J'accepte ma nomination avec la crainte que m'inspire la faiblesse de mes moyens, mais avec la confiance qu'inspire à toute âme ardente la cause que nous défendons en commun. Je jure amour à la patrie, fidélité à la constitution, dévouement sans bornes aux principes éternels et invariables de l'humanité et de la justice» (*Le Censeur des Journaux*, n° 71, 6 novembre 1795).

4. Voir plus haut p. 23 et aussi M. REINHARD, *Le Bureau de Statistiques sous le Consulat et l'Empire* (*Population*, 1950).

5. Pour l'organisation des bureaux (Arch. nat., AF III 6 et 7, 20[a] et 20[b], 21[d], 314, F[4] 2312 et 2316). C'est Carnot qui rédigea le règlement de la tenue des séances du Directoire (AF III 340).

6. Il avait été question d'attribuer un ministère à Lacuée (Arch. familiales, lettre du 7 novembre 1795). Cochon fut nommé à la demande de Carnot, qui le contraignit à accepter (note de Rousselin de Saint-Albin, Coll. L. C. et BEFFROY DE REIGNY, *Dictionnaire*, t. III, p. 356).
Sur Mayeux, Bourotte et Bauche, Arch. nat., AF III, 195, 346, 354 et 378.
Sur le Cabinet historique et le Dépôt de la Guerre, Arch. adm. Guerre (dossiers Clarke, Dupont, Allent, Calon) ; correspondance de Clarke, Arch. hist. Guerre, notamment B[x3] 185. Sur l'historiographie, M. REINHARD, *L'Historiographie militaire sous Napoléon* (*Revue historique*, 1946).

7. CARNOT, *Réponse à Bailleul*, p. 155, 175, 185. — CARNOT-FEULINT, *Histoire du Directoire constitutionnel*, p. 9. — BARRAS, *Mémoires*, t. II, p. 28. — LA REVELLIÈRE, *Mémoires*, t. I, p. 341.

8. R. GUYOT, *Le Directoire et la Paix de l'Europe*, p. 55. Mémoires d'achats effectués pour le Directoire (Arch. nat., F[4] 2312). — STUART JONES, *An invasion that failed*, p. 66. — G. VAUTHIER, *Le Directoire et le Garde-meuble* (*Ann. révolutionnaires*, 1914, p. 511). — BEFFROY DE REIGNY, *Dictionnaire* (art. Carnot). Notes de Lomet, Coll. L. C. Pour la cave, Arch. nat., AF III 2807.

9. LOMET, *Notes* (Coll. L. C.). Voici un billet inédit adressé à Mme Carnot par Mme Tallien (Arch. familiales) : « Lorsque mon mari, madame, pria le citoyen Carnot de venir célébrer avec nous l'anniversaire du 9 Thermidor, je m'étais réservé le plaisir de vous y engager pour mon propre compte. J'en ai été privée par la nature des engagements antérieurs du citoyen La Revellière, qui vous étaient communs. Puissé-je me flatter, madame, que vous daignerez me dédommager en

venant passer la soirée du 12 et mettre le comble à votre obligeance en nous amenant le citoyen Directeur, madame votre sœur et le citoyen son mari, Thérésa Cabarrus Tallien. »

10. L'inventaire de la bibliothèque fut dressé au 18 fructidor (Arch. nat., AF III 2808). On est surpris de n'y rencontrer que deux ouvrages de BEFFROY DE REIGNY, *Les Constitutions de la Lune* et le *Testament d'un Électeur de Paris*.

Sur la Révolution il possédait l'ouvrage de Necker, *L'Histoire de la Révolution du 10 août 1792, L'Histoire des Jacobins, L'Esprit de la Constitution de 1792,* et quelques collections : les *Décades républicaines,* les *Tableaux de la Révolution,* et quelques liasses de pamphlets et de libellés.

CHAPITRE III

FAUX DÉPART JACOBIN

1. *Annales de la République française,* nº 144 ; *Journal des Hommes libres,* nº 7 ; *Dropmore Papers,* t. III, p. 86 et 160. — SCHMIDT, *Tableaux de Paris,* t. II, p. 447, 482. — CARNOT, *Réponse à Bailleul,* p. 176. — LA REVELLIÈRE, *Mémoires,* t. I, p. 405. — BEFFROY DE REIGNY, *Testament d'un Électeur de Paris,* p. 141. — FEULINT, *Histoire du Directoire constitutionnel,* p. 19 ; *Papiers de Klinglin,* t. I, p. 47. — BAILLEU, *Preussen und Frankreich,* t. I, p. 43.

2. Feulint a déjà dit que la tendance politique de chaque Directeur était définie par ses nominations. Mais personne ne les a encore étudiées (FEULINT, *Histoire du Directoire,* p. 19). Répertoire des commissaires, par départements (Arch. nat., AF III 96). Arrê-

tés de nomination accompagnés de la correspondance s'y rapportant, notamment lettres de Beffroy, Brisson, Brivel, David de l'Aube, Danjou, Dannou, Delacroix, Dasacy, Desgrouas, Deydier, Garnier de Saintes, Grégoire, Lamarque, Lindet, Loiseau, Mallarmé, Milliard, Prieur de la Côte-d'Or, Reynaud, Rougemont, Taillefer, Vaugeois, Venaille (Arch. nat., AF III 148 à 429). Parmi les officiers, il n'y a aucun des généraux commandant d'armée. Pour la Haute-Loire, Arch. nat., AF III 314 et E. DELCAMBRE, *La Période du Directoire dans la Haute-Loire.*

3. Arch. nat. AF III 325 et aussi 96 et 358. Souvent ceux qui s'adressent à Carnot se disent hostiles au nouveau Tiers, aux Thermidoriens, aux Royalistes. Mathiez a écrit que Darthé a refusé une place offerte par Carnot (*Le Directoire,* p. 151). Cela ne s'accorde pas avec les tableaux de proposition et de nomination (AF III 325). Pour le Pas-de-Calais, voir Arch. nat. F1bII, Pas-de-Calais I, et aussi BLED, *Les Sociétés populaires à Saint-Omer pendant la Révolution.* Coffin avait déjà été procureur syndic et agent national ; il était en relation avec Carnot par l'intermédiaire de Collignon (Arch. nat., AF III 325). Carnot reconnut dans la suite qu'il avait nommé des « exaltés » (*Réponse à Bailleul,* p. 184).

4. B. CONSTANT, *De la Force du Gouvernement actuel de la France,* p. 31.

5. LA REVELLIÈRE, *Mémoires,* p. 379 ; *Le Rédacteur,* nº 15, 9 nivôse an IV.

6. CARNOT, *Réponse à Bailleul,* p. 48.

7. M. REINHARD, *Le Département de la Sarthe sous le Régime directorial,* p. 102, 130, 189.

8. Feulint a condamné la faute commise en faisant contrôler les commissaires par ceux qui

leur étaient soumis (*Histoire du Directoire constitutionnel*). Correspondance de Coffin (Arch. nat., AF III 254 et F[lb] II, Pas-de-Calais I).

9. Carnot avait voulu placer Lindet : « Je vous conjure, moi personnellement, de ne pas refuser à notre patrie les services que vous pouvez lui rendre. » Il tint le plus grand compte des recommandations de commissaires faites par Lindet (Arch. nat., AF III 370 ; A. MONTIER, *R. Lindet*, p. 322). Sur E. Lepelletier, voir FEULINT, *ouvr. cité*, p. 39.

10. Carnot « força » Cochon d'accepter le ministère (BEFFROY DE REIGNY, *Dictionnaire*, t. III, p. 356). L'étroite collaboration de Carnot et de Cochon est attestée par Rousselin de Saint-Albin (coll. L. C.) et LA REVELLIÈRE (*Mémoires*, p. 416). L'arrêté nommant Cochon est de la main de Carnot (AF III 359). Sur la police, voir Arch. nat., AF III 460.

11. Arch. nat., AF III 463.

12. Lettre du 16 avril (Arch. hist. Guerre, B[13] 44).

13. *Le Tribun du Peuple*, n°s 35, 40 et 41. Les Directeurs étaient abonnés au *Tribun du Peuple*. Tout le passage sur le mouvement babouviste est emprunté aux Arch. nat. (F[7] 4276 à 4278).

14. Rousselin de Saint-Albin, notes (Coll. L. C.).

15. BAUDOT, *Notes historiques*, p. 83.

16. Lettre de Drouet à Carnot (B. N. Lb[42] 120).

17. CARNOT, *Réponse à Bailleul*, p. 183.

18. Lettre de Carnot à Garrau, 3 mai 1796 (Arch. familiales).

19. *Réponse à Bailleul*, p. 127.

20. Arch. hist. Guerre, B[13] 46.

21. Rousselin de Saint-Albin, notes (Coll. L. C.).

22. Lettre de Buissart à Carnot, 24 messidor (Arch. Pas-de-Calais, Coll. Barbier). Lettre de Hoche au Directoire, 25

août (CHUQUET, *Quatre Généraux*, t. III, p. 112).

23. *Le Rédacteur*, 27 prairial.

24. Lettre de Garrau, 14 fructidor an IV (Arch. nat., AF III 50). Voir, sur les démêlés de Garrau et des autorités militaires, G. GODECHOT, *Les Commissaires du Directoire aux Armées*.

CHAPITRE IV

FAUX DÉPART DIPLOMATIQUE ET MILITAIRE

1. R. GUYOT, *Le Directoire et la Paix de l'Europe*, source principale. La correspondance diplomatique montre Carnot à l'œuvre. Ainsi celle de Sandoz-Rollin, tout surpris de l'urbanité de Carnot : « Son maintien ne décèle en rien le jacobinisme qu'on lui connaît dans l'âme », écrivait-il le 3 janvier (BAILLEU, *Preussen und Frankreich*, von 1795 *bis* 1807, t. I, p. 43). Boccardi indique comment Carnot suggérait à Gênes de soutenir la France en paraissant céder à un coup de force des troupes françaises (COLUCCI, *La República di Genova e la Rivoluzione francese*, t. II, p. 395). Sur la frontière du Rhin, Carnot s'était expliqué à quatre reprises en 1794, les 16 et 20 juillet, 15 octobre et 14 novembre (C. C., t. IV, p. 496, 513, 688 A 709). En juillet, il renonçait au Rhin ; en octobre et novembre, poussé par le succès, il le réclamait : « La victoire nous en donne le droit. »

2. PÉTIET, *Rapport du ministre de la Guerre*.

3. Correspondance du ministre de la Guerre, octobre 1795, décembre 1796, notamment 30 et 31 décembre 1795, 16 décembre 1796 (Arch. hist. Guerre, B[13] 40, B[13] 53). Certaines lettres étaient adressées à Carnot, par exemple celles

du général Pille. On pourrait écrire un ouvrage bien curieux sur l'histoire de la désertion pendant la Révolution.

4. Lettre du commissaire de l'Isère, 22 mars 1796 (Arch. hist. Guerre, B¹³ 43) ; lettre anonyme au Directoire, 22 novembre 1795 (B¹³ 39). La correspondance des généraux et celle des commissaires du Directoire aux armées multiplient les exemples (BOURDEAU, *Les Armées du Rhin au début du Directoire.* — J. GODECHOT, *Les Commissaires du Pouvoir exécutif aux Armées,* correspondance des armées de novembre à mars (Arch. hist. Guerre).

5. L' « embauchage » ou recrutement des bandes royalistes se pratiquait surtout à l'intérieur, mais il existait aussi aux armées du front.

6. Lettres des commissaires de Seine-et-Marne, 30 décembre 1796 (Arch. hist. Guerre, B¹³ 53), des Pyrénées-Orientales et du Tarn, février 1796 (B¹³ 42).

7. *Le Rédacteur,* n° 66, 19 février 1796.

8. Petiet (Rapport). On alla jusqu'à écrire, dans *Le Rédacteur,* n° 12 ; « les jeunes gens qui sont partis gaiement... ».

9. Note de Merlin de Douai, 3 brumaire an IV (Arch. hist. Guerre, B¹³ 38). Lois des 4 frimaire et 4 nivôse, arrêté du 4 ventôse. Circulaire aux agents militaires de la République (*Le Rédacteur,* n° 46). Sur le rôle de Fréron, de Reverchon, de Turreau, de Ferry, de Fouché, du général Bonnard, commissaires chargés de poursuivre les déserteurs et les réfractaires, voir *Le Rédacteur,* n°ˢ 55, 57 et 61 ; *L'Historien,* n°ˢ 8, 86 et 95 ; Arch. hist. Guerre, B¹³ 41 à 44. Ces commissaires furent supprimés par arrêté du 13 germinal an IV. Lettre de Garrau à Carnot, 19 février 1796 (Arch. hist. Guerre, B¹³ 42). Lettres de Carnot au ministre de la Guerre, 23 juin et 6 juillet (Arch. nat., AF III 454 et 456). Lettre de Carnot à M.-J. Chénier, 26 décembre 1795 (Arch. Presles).

Les refus de départ et les retours de déserteurs sont signalés un peu partout, de l'Isère, de la Dordogne, de la Seine-et-Marne, du Tarn, de l'Aveyron, des Pyrénées-Orientales, du Rhône, de la Gironde (correspondance du ministre de la Guerre, Arch. hist. Guerre, B¹³ 40 à 53). Ainsi, à Sainte-Foi, une centaine de réquisitionnaires ont envahi la mairie, les armes à la main, déclarant qu'ils se « f... des ordres et des lois, et hacheraient ceux qui se présenteraient pour les faire partir ». Carnot nota en marge du rapport : « Il faut attaquer le mal dans son principe » (Arch. hist. Guerre, 28 décembre 1795, B¹³ 40). Le commissaire du canton d'Ablis écrivait que tous les riches cultivateurs achetaient des exemptions pour des sommes variant de 10 à 30 louis d'or (Arch. hist. Guerre, 23 juillet 1796, B¹³ 47).

10. Rapport du ministre de la Guerre au Directoire, janvier 1796 (Arch. hist. Guerre, B¹³ 41). Arrêtés et circulaires contre la vente des armes et équipements, 6 décembre 1795, 14 janvier, 8 février, 10 mars (B¹³ 40 A 43). Rapport de Milet-Mureau, 28 avril 1797 (Arch. hist. Guerre, AF III 151ᴬ). — PETIET, *Compte rendu.*

11. Réorganisation de l'armée : arrêtés des 18, 22 et 27 nivôse, 30 ventôse et 8 fructidor an IV. Tableaux de répartition des effectifs (Arch. hist. Guerre, B¹³ 39 et 41). Lettre du général Krieg, 10 juillet 1796, et de Richard à Carnot, 17 mars 1796 (B¹³ 43 et carton 20 18).

12. Les épurations accomplies dans les armées de la Révolution mériteraient un exposé que je ne puis faire ici, tant

au point de vue de l'histoire de ces armées qu'à celui de l'histoire générale. Pendant la Terreur les hommes et les sous-officiers dénoncèrent et épurèrent leurs officiers (voir note 10, p. 351). Chaque changement d'orientation politique correspondit à une épuration du personnel civil et militaire. L'examen des états indiquant les généraux et les adjudants généraux employés aux armées permet de relever un nombre assez important de destitutions après la chute des Hébertistes (voir p. 154) et un nombre plus considérable encore après celle de Robespierre. Le 3 septembre 1794, une circulaire avait prescrit aux représentants aux armées d'épurer les officiers robespierristes (Arch. hist. Guerre, X^{EM} 22). Le 23 octobre 1795, une circulaire du ministère de la Guerre ordonna aux généraux en chef et aux commissaires ordonnateurs en chef d'épurer les états-majors, en frappant surtout ceux qui avaient été nommés récemment, et en appliquant les articles XIV et XV de la loi du 3 brumaire an IV. Je n'ai trouvé qu'une réponse — incomplète — à cette circulaire (Arch. hist. Guerre, 23 octobre 1795, B^{13} 39 et 9 décembre 1795, B^{13} 40), mais les tableaux de composition des états-majors montrent de nombreux changements (X^{EM} 22). En outre, le 22 novembre 1795, Carnot avait prescrit l'épuration des cadres de l'armée du Rhin, comme punition des abus commis pendant la retraite.

13. Le 3 janvier 1796, un ordre de la Place de Paris avait interdit aux militaires le port distinctif d'un « médaillon » (B^{13} 41).

14. Rapport au ministre, 26 février 1796 (B^{13} 42). Lettre du Directoire au ministre de la Guerre (Arch. nat., AF III 345).

15. J. GODECHOT, *Les Commis-saires du Directoire aux Armées*, fournit l'étude définitive sur le sujet. La correspondance de Garrau avec Carnot est fort instructive; les Archives familiales en contiennent une partie, notamment la lettre de Carnot à Garrau, du 16 mars 1796, jusqu'alors inutilisée et dont nous citons le passage concernant les cas d'urgence.

Sur la rivalité entre civils et militaires, voir *L'Historien*, journal de DUPONT DE NEMOURS (n^{os} des 19 janvier et 13 février 1796).

16. Correspondance militaire de Hoche (Arch. hist. Guerre, armée de l'Ouest, correspondance du ministre de la Guerre, B^{13} 39 à 49. — CHUQUET, *Quatre Généraux de la Révolution*. — DÉBIDOUR, *Actes du Directoire*). Cependant, le 19 février, Hoche avait demandé à Carnot, en termes confiants, de lui donner un autre commandement (CUNEO, *Hoche*, p. 232).

CHAPITRE V

BONAPARTE, BRAVE MAIS BIEN JEUNE

1. BEFFROY DE REIGNY, *Dictionnaire néologique*, article Carnot, lettre de Bonaparte à Joseph, le 20 août 1795. (*Corr.* de Napoléon, t. I, p. 85.) Sans fournir de source, Askenazi affirme que Carnot fit donner le commandement à Bonaparte le 13 vendémiaire (ASKENAZI, *Papiers Bonaparte*, p. 21).

2. Lettre de Carnot, H. C., t. II, p. 29 (Arch. familiales); lettre du Directoire (DEBIDOUR, t. I, p. 462); lettre à Schérer, 3 février (Arch. nat., AF III 344); lettre de Ritter, 3 février (Arch. hist. Guerre, B^{13} 39).

3. MADELIN, *L'Ascension de Bonaparte*, p. 23. Le même auteur

fait remarquer encore que l'amitié de Barras pouvait être plus compromettante qu'utile.

4. SAUTEREAU DU PART, *Carnot-Feulint*, p. 31. Ritter avait dénoncé, le 3 février, « les éternels faiseurs de projets,... individus rongés par l'ambition et avides de places supérieures ». L'arrêté porte la signature de Carnot, La Revellière et Letourneur (Arch. nat., AF III 352). Vaublanc, s'autorisant des confidences de Carnot, lui attribua l'initiative (*Mémoires*, p. 318). V. Hugo, « mon père, ce général au sourire si doux », suivit cette tradition (*La France militaire*, 1835, t. II, p. 73). — Stendhal et Miot de Mélito se prononçaient pour Barras (*Vie de Napoléon*, p. 211, *Mémoires*, p. 72), ce que dément LA REVELLIÈRE (*Mémoires*, t. II, p. 23).

5. CARNOT, *Réponse à Bailleul*, p. 38.

6. Lettres du Directoire, notamment 2 mars, 12, 14 et 25 avril. *Corr.* de Panckoucke, t. I (Arch. hist. Guerre, B^{x3} 119; DEBIDOUR, t. I).

7. Lettres du ministre de la Guerre, 30 janvier, 24 février, 16 et 17 mars (Arch. nat., AF III 343, 347 et 355).

8. Directoire à Moreau (Arch. nat., AF III 357) ; Carnot à Jourdan et à Moreau (JOURDAN, *Mémoires*, p. 215 et 222). Plan de Kellermann, prévoyant la pénétration « jusqu'au cœur de l'empire » et une campagne en Piémont. Plan de Sauviac proposant une campagne jusqu'au delta du Pô et aux États pontificaux pour y trouver des ressources (Arch. familiales). Le 5 décembre 1795, Carnot avait demandé à Kellermann d'étudier s'il vaudrait mieux agir dans le Piémont ou dans le Milanais.

9. *Corr.* de Panckoucke, t. I, exemplaire de la bibliothèque du ministère de la Guerre, comportant des notes copiées par le général Pelet sur un exemplaire venant de Sainte-Hélène.

10. Carnot, 25 avril ; Bonaparte, 28 avril (*Corr.* de Panckoucke, t. I, p. 75 et 96).

11. Bonaparte, 9 mai (*Corr.* de Panckoucke, t. I, p. 138, et L. DE BROTONNE, *Lettres inédites*, n° 9). Joséphine fréquentait chez les Carnot ; les descendants de Lazare ont conservé, à Presles, un éventail donné par Joséphine.

12. Projet traité, arch. Aff. étr., Sardaigne, 272, f° 330. La date d'arrivée de la lettre directoriale est mentionnée sur l'exemplaire de la *Corr.* de Panckoucke de la bibliothèque du ministère de la Guerre.

13. Général BERTRAND, *Les Cahiers de Sainte-Hélène*, éd. Fleuriot de Langle, p. 78. Lettre de Carnot, 21 mai (Bib. de Nantes, coll. Labouchère, vol. 659, n° 148).

14. Cette lettre, du 11 juin, ne figure pas dans *Corr.* de Napoléon. L'original se trouve aux Arch. familiales ; une copie figure aux Arch. hist. Guerre (B^{x3} 123). La déclaration de Junot fut publiée dans *Le Rédacteur* du 21 floréal.

15. Lettre du 22 juin (Coll. Labouchère, vol. 659, n° 150).

16. Conversation du 5 juin (MIOT DE MÉLITO, *Mémoires*, t. I, p. 86).

17. M. REINHARD, *Avec Bonaparte en Italie*, p. 25. Sandoz-Rollin écrivait, le 2 août 1796, que les généraux français, notamment Bonaparte, étaient « pour leur patrie autant de financiers doués des p l u s grandes ressources ». Bonaparte, d'après Carnot, envoya 215 millions (BAILLEU, *ouvr. cité*, t. I, p. 80 et 83).

18. R. GUYOT, *ouvr. cité*, chap. V et VI. — J. GODECHOT, *ouvr. cité*, t. I, p. 444.

19. Cette lettre, qui figure aux Arch. familiales, complète la documentation de J. Godechot sur Garrau.

20. Arch. familiales.
21. Bailleu, *ouvr. cité*, t. I, p. 47. Lettre du Directoire à Moreau, 26 mai (Arch. nat., AF III 373) ; lettres de Jourdan, 19, 20, 21 juin (Arch. hist. Guerre, B¹ 74) ; lettres à Jourdan, 20 et 23 juin et à Moreau, le 21 juin (AF III, 380 et 381); lettre personnelle de Carnot à Jourdan (Jourdan, *Mémoires manuscrits*) ; lettres à Joubert, 23 et 28 juin, 2 juillet (AF III 381, 382 et 383).
22. Lettre du 11 juillet (*Corr. de Panckoucke*, t. I, p. 347; voir t. I, p. 211).
23. Lettres de Carnot des 17 et et 25 juillet (*ouvr. cité*, p. 351 et 356).
24. M. Reinhard, *Avec Bonaparte en Italie*, p. 109 et suivantes ; lettre de Carnot, 23 août (*Corr. de Panckoucke*, p. 457).
25. Jourdan, *Mémoires*, passim. — J. Godechot (*ouvr. cité*, p. 322 et 356) a bien montré ce que furent ces retraites, et combien celle de Moreau fut éloignée de mériter t a n t d'éloges prodigués à l'époque, voire par Carnot. Michaud d'Arçon fait ses observations en l'an VII, avec Kellermann, pour préparer la nouvelle campagne (Arch. nat., AF III 152ᴬ).
26. 17 octobre 1796 (Arch. hist. Guerre K¹ 50).
27. M. Reinhard, *Avec Bonaparte en Italie*, chap. VIII, et *L'Historiographie militaire officielle sous Napoléon Iᵉʳ* (*Revue historique*, 1946, p. 172). Les jugements de Carnot sont rapportés par Sandoz-Rollin (Bailleu, *ouvr. cité*, t. I, p. 84 et 90).
28. Guyot, *ouvr. cité*, p. 205 (Arch. Aff. étr. Naples, 124). — Dutheil, *ouvr. cité*, p. 268. — Voir aussi Stendhal, *Vie de Napoléon*, p. 207.

CHAPITRE VI

LA GUERRE
ET LA PAIX EN L'AN V

1. Lettre de Sandoz - Rollin, 2 août 1796 (Bailleu, *ouvr. cité*, t. I, p. 83). Mangourit se défie du « cousin » et de Lacuée, donc de l'entourage de Carnot (Arch. Aff. étr. Espagne, 641, fᵒˢ 281-372).
2. R. Guyot, *ouvr. cité*, p. 306 et suivantes.
3. La correspondance de Clarke est édifiante sur ce point; elle comporte deux séries : l'une adressée au Directoire, l'autre à Carnot (Arch. nat., AF III 59 et 463). Le 29 décembre 1796, Carnot avait fourni un chiffre particulier à Clarke.
4. La thèse de *L'Ami des Lois* a été reprise jusqu'à nos jours; elle ne résiste pas à l'examen attentif de la correspondance et de l'activité de Clarke ; le témoignage de Barras (invoqué par J. Godechot, *ouvr. cité*, t. I, p. 551) ne saurait prévaloir.

La minute de l'arrêté qui confiait à Carnot l'examen des armées se trouve aux Arch. hist. Guerre (B¹³ 52). Le même jour, 16 novembre, un secrétaire de légation était fourni à Clarke : c'était Camille P e r r e t, commissaire des guerres, apparenté à Carnot (Arch. nat., AF III 145).

Clarke avait été tenu au courant par Delacroix des possibilités de traiter avec les divers princes allemands (Arch. nat., AF III 59). Il emportait des instructions de Delacroix et une lettre de Carnot à l'empereur, proposant un armistice général pendant lequel on négocierait « entre les deux puissances et leurs alliés ». Clarke était pourvu d'un arrêté du Directoire ordonnant aux généraux en chef des armées d'Allemagne et d'Italie d'exécuter les conditions de l'armistice (R. Guyot, *ouvr. cité*, p. 313, textes publiés dans la *Corr.* de Panckoucke, t. II, p. 393 et suivantes, sauf l'arrêté du Directoire, dont la minute est aux Arch. hist. Guerre, 13¹³ 52).

Clarke était l'auteur d'un projet de « plan général pour nos opérations diplomatiques », dans lequel il proposait une alliance avec la Prusse et une action concertée avec les principaux princes allemands, ainsi qu'avec la Suède, le Danemark et la Turquie (Arch. familiales).

5. *L'Ami des Lois*, 6, 7 et 10 janvier 1797. Lettre des représentants de l'administration de la Lombardie à Berthier, 19 janvier (Arch. hist. Guerre, B²³ 189).

6. Carnot à Bonaparte, 30 novembre 1796 (Arch. nat., AF III 463).

7. Lettre de Carnot à Bonaparte, 29 décembre (Bibl. Nantes, Coll. Labouchère, vol. 659, n⁰ 151), lettre à Clarke, même jour (Arch. nat., AF III 463), lettre de Clarke à Carnot, 7 janvier (AF III 59).

8. GUYOT, *ouvr. cité*, p. 326. Lettres du Directoire à Bonaparte, 17 janvier, et à Clarke, 23 et 26 janvier (Arch. nat., AF III 428 et 429). Lettre de Bonaparte à Carnot (*Corr.* de Napoléon, t. II, n⁰ 1427), Carnot publia un extrait de cette lettre dans le *Journal des Défenseurs de la Patrie* du 7 février.

9. Lettres de Clarke et de Perret à Carnot, 3 février 1797 (Arch. nat., AF III 59), lettres de Carnot à Clarke, 12 février, et de Clarke à Carnot, du 5 mars (Arch. nat., AF III 463 et 59).

10. BARTHÉLEMY, *Mémoires*, p. 181. Mémoires de Demeunier sur les effets du dernier traité des États-Unis et de l'Angleterre, et les remèdes à employer ; note de Lebreton sur la Sicile, lettre de Cossigny à Truguet sur le comptoir des Indes, sur Ceylan ; état de la colonie de Cayenne, par Thé-

bault, et Réflexions sur Saint-Domingue, par le même (dossiers rassemblés par Carnot, Arch. familiales). — CARNOT, *Réponse à Bailleul*, p. 52, notamment sur l'acquisition de la Floride et de la Louisiane par la France. Comparer avec FEULINT, *Histoire du Directoire constitutionnel*, p. 126. « C'est de l'empire universel qu'il s'agit aujourd'hui », déclarait Carnot le 1ᵉʳ novembre 1796 (F. O. 27/52).

11. BAILLEU, *ouvr. cité*, t. I, p. 62. Les archives familiales contiennent une série de projets de descente en Angleterre, les uns rédigés pendant la Révolution, les autres empruntés aux collections du Dépôt de la Guerre et remontant à 1759 ou à 1777. Une note du directeur de ce dépôt, en date du 28 avril 1796, précise que quatre cartons de plans de guerre contre l'Angleterre, venant de Castries, étaient à la disposition de Carnot (Arch. hist. Guerre, B¹³ 44).

D'autres projets, adressés à Carnot, se trouvent aux Arch. nat. (AF III 57), l'un d'eux fut trouvé dans le portefeuille de Carnot, sur son bureau, le 18 fructidor (AF III 186ᵇ). Enfin un rapport de Carnot sur cette question figure au *Foreign Office* (1ᵉʳ novembre 1796, 27/52).

12. Lettre de Hoche au Comité de Salut public, 12 janvier 1795. Lettre du Directoire, 19 avril 1796 (Arch. nat., AF III 362). GUILLON, *La France et l'Irlande pendant la Révolution*, p. 86 et suivantes. Arch. Aff. étr. Angleterre, 589, fᵒ 114. — E. DESBRIÈRES, *Projets et Tentatives de Débarquement aux Iles britanniques*, t. I, p. 61 et suivantes. — STUART JONES, *ouvr. cité*, p. 85.

13. STUART-JONES, *ouvr. cité*, p. 60 et suivantes. Carnot à Hoche (Arch. nat., AF III 380). — DEBIDOUR, *ouvr. cité*, p. 688, publie cette lettre sans

préciser qu'elle est autographe ; elle marque un effort exceptionnel d'amabilité de Carnot à l'égard de Hoche. — DESBRIÈRES, *ouvr. cité*, t. I, notamment p. 107. *L'Ami des Lois*, 29 décembre 1796. Rapports de police, 28 septembre (Aulard, t. III, p. 483 et 591).

14. Les ordres de Carnot se trouvent en partie aux Arch. nat. (AF III 410, 413, 415, 423, 424, 426, 427 et en partie — souvent en expédition — aux Arch. hist. de la Guerre, B² 55 et suivants). LONGY, dans *La Campagne de 1797 sur le Rhin*, a publié une partie de cette correspondance, mais l'ouvrage lui-même doit être utilisé avec précaution, ainsi la documentation concernant la décision d'abandonner Kehl est incomplète et mal interprétée.

Carnot avait nommé Beurnonville parce que celui-ci avait, en qualité d'ancien prisonnier, une vengeance à tirer (BAILLEU, *ouvr. cité*, t. I, p. 91).

La polémique sur Kehl est exposée notamment par Bailleul et la réponse que lui fit Carnot, notamment p. 68. Voir aussi LA REVELLIÈRE, *Mémoires*, t. II, p. 13.

15. CARNOT, *Réponse à Bailleul*, p. 100. Outre les lettres mentionnées, et les ouvrages déjà cités de R. Guyot et de Godechot, voir A. FUGIER, *Napoléon et l'Italie* (p. 44 à 56) et A. LATREILLE, *L'Église catholique et la Révolution française* (p. 222 à 238). Sur la Louisiane, lettre de Carnot du 12 février (Arch. nat., AF III 463). Lettres de Clarke, 19 février et 5 mars (AF III 59).

16. PETIET, *Rapport*, p. 16 et 22. — REINHARD, *Avec Bonaparte en Italie*, chap. XII. Lettre du Directoire au ministre de la Guerre. Arrêtés rappelant les militaires absents de leur corps, et instruction sur les sanctions frappant les déserteurs, 13 février 1797 (Arch. hist. Guerre, B¹³⁵⁶).

17. LONGY, *ouvr. cité*, Lettres de Bonaparte à Carnot, 22 et 25 mars (Arch. nat. AF III 309 ; Arch. familiales), lettre de Clarke à Carnot, 24 mars (Arch. nat., AF III 309). Lettre du Directoire à Bonaparte, 15 mars (Arch. nat., AF III 438).

18. Carnot à Bonaparte, 1er avril 1797 (Arch. familiales). Cette lettre montre Carnot plus favorable à la politique de Bonaparte que ne l'indique GUYOT (*ouvr. cité*, p. 334). Comparer la lettre de Carnot à celle du Directoire (Arch. nat., AF III 441). Lettre du Directoire à Bonaparte, 17 avril, à propos de la lettre de Bonaparte au prince Charles : « Nous vous autorisons à convenir de quelques articles préliminaires... » (Arch. nat., AF III 443).

19. Lettre à Clarke (Arch. familiales, H. C., t. II, p. 149). Lettre à Bonaparte (Arch. nat., AF III 463).

20. BARTHÉLEMY, *Mémoires*, p. 240. — LA REVELLIÈRE, *Mémoires*, p. 67. — CARNOT, *Réponse à Bailleul*, p. 89.

21. Les archives anglaises prétendent que d'Arçon joua un rôle jusqu'à la fin de la campagne de 1796, à l'issue de laquelle il aurait été disgracié (F. O. 27/48, lettre à Grenville, 15 décembre 1796, et F. O. 27/44, rapport reçu le 1er février 1796). Cette assertion se concilie mal avec la critique de la campagne de 1796 faite par d'Arçon en l'an VII (Arch. nat., AF III 152 A). Une note de Venise du 10 mai 1796 affirme le rôle de Grimoard comme conseiller de Carnot, mais plutôt pour les questions diplomatiques (F. O. 27/47). Toutes ces indications manquent trop de preuves et de recoupements pour être retenues.

CHAPITRE VII

DE LA PRÉSIDENCE
A LA DÉPORTATION

1. THIBAUDEAU, *Mémoires*, t. II, p. 143. Bonaparte, au début du Consulat, s'exprimait à peu près dans les mêmes termes.
2. Arch. hist. Guerre, B¹³ 47.
3. Arch. familiales. Cette lettre n'a pas été utilisée par H. C., Les Arch. familiales contiennent un dossier de lettres de Willot, auquel nous faisons de larges emprunts.
4. Arch. hist. Guerre, B¹³ 48.
5. Lettre du 5 octobre 1796 (Arch. hist. Guerre, B¹³ 119), en réponse à la lettre de Bonaparte du 2 octobre qui traitait Willot de « royaliste enragé» (*Corr.* de Napoléon, t. II, n° 1059). Un peu plus tard, le 28 décembre, Bonaparte réclama la libération d'un chef de brigade arrêté par ordre de WILLOT (*Corr.* de Napoléon, t. II, n° 1319, et Arch. hist. Guerre, B¹³ 56, 10 février 1797).
6. Arch. hist. Guerre, notamment 7 et 14 février 1797 (B¹³ 56), pièces analogues dans B¹³ 59 et 60. La note de Carnot à Bonaparte pour lui demander d'envoyer un général remplacer Willot a été classée dans un dossier de pièces non datées (B³ 37). Les reproches de Carnot à Willot sont mentionnés dans sa *Réponse à Bailleul* et dans H. C., t. II., p. 14. Le rôle de Willot fut considérable parmi les royalistes (F. O. 27/52).
7. Hoche au Directoire, 25 août 1796 (CHUQUET, *Quatre Généraux de la Révolution*, t. III, p. 112) ; *L'Ami des Lois*, notamment 16 décembre 1796. — LA REVELLIÈRE, *Mémoires*, t. II, p. 9. — CARNOT, *Réponse à Bailleul*, p. 180.
8. MATHIEZ, *Le Directoire*, p. 264.
9. F. O. 27/52.
10. AULARD, *Rapport de Police*, t. IV, p. 43 ; *L'Ami des Lois*, 20 avril.

11. GUYOT, *Documents biographiques sur Reubell*, p. 118. — A. MEYNIER, *Le Dix-Huit fructidor*, p. 24. — CARNOT, *Réponse à Bailleul*, p. 225. — LA REVELLIÈRE, *Mémoires*, t. I, p. 380.
12. Arch. familiales. Ce texte anéantit les hypothèses de MATHIEZ (*ouvr. cité*, p. 293).
13. Lettre de Lacombe, 15 avril 1797 (*Moniteur*, t. XXVIII). Mémoire du 29 mai (Arch. nat., AF III 463). Nomination de commissaires, 21 mai (Arch. nat., AF III 456). Vaublanc à Carnot, 23 mai 1797 (AF III 463), à rapprocher des lettres de Vaublanc aux émigrés de Londres (F. O. 27/52).
14. Délibérations des 15 et 16 mai 1797 (Arch. nat., AF III 6 et AF III 463). THIBAUDEAU, *Mémoires*, t. II, p. 160 ; *Le Messager du Soir*, 19 mai.
15. Notes au bureau central de Police (Arch. Seine, série D, p. 356). AULARD, *ouvr. cité*, t. IV, p. 124. — THIBAUDEAU, *ouvr. cité*, p. 173 et 204. — B A R T H É L E M Y, *Mémoires*, p. 177. — BAILLEU, *ouvr. cité*, t. I, p. 128.
16. M. REINHARD, *Le Département de la Sarthe sous le Régime directorial*, p. 264. — GIRAULT, *Rochecotte*, passim. Rousselin de Saint-Albin (Coll. L. C.).
17. BEFFROY DE REIGNY, *Dictionnaire néologique*, article Carnot. — THIBAUDEAU, *Mémoires*. — BARTHÉLEMY, *Mémoires*, p. 209. Lettre de Mathieu Dumas à Moreau, 27 juin 1797 (Arch. hist. Guerre B¹³ 63) non publiée par V. Pierre (18 fructidor). Celui-ci a aussi négligé une lettre de M. Dumas à Moreau, du 18 juin 1797, où il vantait Latour-Maubourg et « les premiers amis de la liberté, vraie cause commune et républicaine », voir J. Godechot (*Ann. hist. Rév.*, 1932).
18. BARTHÉLEMY, *Mémoires*, p. 184 et suivantes.

19. Séances du 29 mai au 21 juin, THIBAUDEAU, *Mémoires*, t. II, p. 188.

20. Radiations d'émigrés non signées par Carnot, 24 et 26 juin ; dossier de dénonciation contre des prêtres, 21 juin ; annulation de la loi du 3 brumaire, 27 juin ; arrêtés sur les lingots d'Italie, 2 juillet, et sur la gendarmerie, 3 juillet (Arch. nat., AF III 455). Article du *Thé*, 11 juin 1797.

21. BARRAS, *Mémoires*, t. II, note du 29 juin. Lettres de Mathieu Dumas, 1er juillet, et de Carnot, 2 juillet (Coll. L. C.). Discours du 14 juillet (Arch. nat., AF III 7).

22. Compte rendu du 16 juillet (Arch. nat., AF III 7). Extraits de presse (AULARD, *ouvr. cité*, t. IV, p. 216) ; *Courrier patriotique*, 14 juillet, H. C., t. II, 117. — FEULINT, *Histoire du Directoire constitutionnel*, p. 49. — THIBAUDEAU, *ouvr. cité*, p. 208. — BARRAS, *Mémoires*, t. II, p. 429.

Il était depuis longtemps question du changement de Delacroix (Arch. Aff. étr., 641, f° 281).

23. Lettre de Mathieu Dumas, 18 juillet (Arch. hist. Guerre, B¹³ 65, publiée par V. PIERRE, *ouvr. cité*, p. 34). Sur Talleyrand, lettre de Duverne à Grenville, 18 juillet (F. O. 27/52) ; Rousselin de Saint-Albin (Coll. L. C.) et LACOUR-GAYET, *Talleyrand*, t. I, p. 223.

24. *Corr.* entre les Cinq-Cents et le Directoire (Arch. nat., AF III 7).

25. Lettre du Directoire à Hoche sur le périmètre constitutionnel, 31 mai 1796 (Arch. nat., AF III 374). Notes de l'*Historien*, journal de Dupont de Nemours, sur le périmètre constitutionnel (16 janvier et 1er avril 1796).

26. Lettres de Hoche à Truguet et au Directoire, 7 et 20 juillet (publiées par CHUQUET, *ouvr. cité*, t. II, p. 211). — CAUDRILLIER, *ouvr. cité*, p. 340.

Lettre de Carnot à Lacarrière (Arch. nat., AF III 463).

27. Séances du Directoire, du 26 et 30 juillet, 4 et 6 août (Arch. nat., AF III 7).

28. Les hésitations de Hoche apparaissent dans la correspondance militaire (Arch. hist. Guerre, B¹³ 65). Certaines pièces ont été publiées (CHUQUET, *ouvr. cité*, t. III, p. 180 et 187, t. II, p. 215. — CUNÉO, *Hoche*, p. 364. — BERGOUNIOUX, *Hoche*, p. 468). La lettre de Salme se trouve aux Arch. nat. (AF III 464). Ce général fut destitué le 21 fructidor. Hoche a connu cette lettre et ne l'a pas démenti (CHUQUET, t. II, p. 245).

Sur le gouvernement militaire, *Courrier patriotique*, 3 août.

29. Lettre du Directoire à Bonaparte (Arch. nat. AF III 257). Carnot à Sandoz : « Nous aurions bien voulu éloigner ce malheureux incident, mais les services signalés et éminents de Bonaparte nous ont subjugués » (BAILLEU, *ouvr. cité*, t. I, p. 127). Lettre de Bonaparte au Directoire, 17 juillet, publiée par DRY (*ouvr. cité*, t. II, p. 84). Clarke l'appuyait comme toujours (Arch. nat., AF III 59). Entretiens de Carnot et de l'envoyé autrichien (R. GUYOT, *ouvr. cité*, p. 516).

Lettre de Carnot à Bonaparte, 17 août [Arch. familiales et analyse dans Arch. nat. (AF III 463) parmi les lettres et minutes saisies au 18 Fructidor]. Des extraits figurent dans *Les Mémoires d'un Homme d'État* (t. IV, p. 513) et TISSOT, *ouvr. cité*, p. 255.

30. La lettre de Carnot confirme les dires de Vaublanc sur les entretiens de La Valette, contrairement aux mémoires de ce dernier, que Mathiez avait préférés (VAUBLANC, *Mémoires*, p. 319. — LA VALETTE, *Mémoires*, p. 225. — MATHIEZ, *ouvr. cité*, p. 326). Rousselin

de Saint-Albin confirme le double jeu de La Valette (notes, Coll. L. C.). Le résumé des lettres de Bonaparte figure aux Arch. familiales. La lettre de Joséphine a été publiée dans *La Sabretache*. Augereau écrivait à Bonaparte qu'il cessait de compter sur Carnot (12 août, Arch. hist. Guerre, B^{x3} 201).

31. Barras était en relations avec le prétendant (VAUBLANC, *ouvr. cité*, p. 332). Bonaparte et La Valette soutenaient Barras et les démocrates (CAUDRILLIER, p. 346). Mathieu Dumas et les modérés se flattaient, comme Carnot, de contenir les extrêmes (Arch. hist. Guerre, B^{13} 66. V. PIERRE, *ouvr. cité*, p. 37), discours du 10 août 1797 (texte et minute, Arch. nat., AF III 7). La visite de Coffin à Carnot eut lieu le 19 juillet. Coffin fut rétabli en l'an VI et fit le jeu des exclusifs (Arch. nat., AF^{18} II, Pas-de-Calais^2).

32. Pour la politique extérieure. GUYOT, *ouvr. cité*, p. 412, etc. — HUFFER, *Der Frieden von Campo Formio*, p. 146, 287, 291, 305 (Arch. nat., AF III 463).

L'altercation est indiquée dans les *Mémoires de Barras* (t. II, p. 512), mais nous ne la mentionnons que parce qu'elle est confirmée par les *Mémoires d'un Homme d'État* (t. IV, p. 502). Sur Barras et Carnot, LACOUR - GAYET, *Talleyrand*, t. I, p. 286. — BAILLEU, *ouvr. cité*, t. I, p. 143. — FEULINT, *Histoire du Directoire constitutionnel*, p. 209. Mathieu-Dumas, lettre du 14 août déjà citée. Les signatures de Carnot deviennent très rares à partir du 15 thermidor (Arch. nat., AF III 459 à 463). BARTHÉLEMY, *Mémoires*, p. 245.

Avertissements à Carnot, du 28 août (Arch. nat., F 7 7293), d'un député sur les entretiens de Sotin — ministre de la Police — et de F. Le Pelletier, d'un anonyme, et aussi de son frère de Chalon sur le danger royaliste, de Boncœur (Arch. nat., AF III 463).

Sur le rapprochement avec LA REVELLIÈRE, *Mémoires* de celui-ci (t. I, p. 357), mémorandum de WESLAY (*Dropmore Papers*, t. III, p. 340), séance du Directoire du 5 fructidor (Arch. nat., AF III 461) et BARTHÉLEMY (*Mémoires*, p. 244).

JOSEPH CARNOT, *Autobiographie* (Arch. familiales). Pigault-Montbaillarcq a écrit que Carnot songea un instant à brûler la cervelle à Barras (Arch. familiales).

33. Le récit de la fuite de Carnot est emprunté à Carnot lui-même, il est confirmé par une lettre de Carnot au capitaine du Génie Godard, le 17 ventôse an VIII (8 mars 1800). Nous prions Mlle Coyreau des Loges de recevoir nos remerciements pour la copie de cette lettre qu'elle nous a aimablement adressée. L'anecdote du ministre de la Police est rapportée par Rœderer (Arch. nat., AB^{xix} 1858).

Pour les recherches de Carnot à Salpervick (Arch. nat., F 7 7322), la lettre de Montbaillarcq est aux Arch. familiales.

Pour la révocation de Joseph Carnot, dénoncé par le commissaire de la Côte-d'Or (Arch. nat., F 7 6140).

CHAPITRE VIII

UN EXILÉ ACCUSATEUR

1. CARNOT, t. I, chap. XIX. — BARBEY, *F. Desportes*, p. 90. — CHAPUISAT, *De la Terreur à l'Annexion*, p. 199.

2. Fichier Charavay, lettres de l'an X, de l'an XII, de 1812, et lettre du 2 janvier 1800 (Arch. familiales).

3. MATHIEZ, *La Fortune de Carnot* (*Ann. hist. Révol.*, 1919). Arch. nat., AF III 463 ; Arch.

de la Seine, carton 131 et D¹²V¹ ; Arch. familiales ; Arch. de la Somme Q 259. — Feulint, *Histoire du Directoire constitutionnel*, p. 228. — H. C., t. II, p. 201. Partage du 24 octobre 1797.

4. Arch. Côte-d'Or, Q 923¹⁵. L'esprit de famille des Carnot se manifesta remarquablement en cette occasion. Les biens furent partagés en six lots de valeur égale que l'on tira au sort, l'administration des Domaines contesta le partage, mais les héritiers s'arrangèrent pour le maintenir. Le lot de Sadi comportait onze journaux de terre labourable, en plusieurs pièces, à Epertully, et cinq journaux en une seule pièce à Nolay, une rente de 500 livres, une rente de 30 livres, plus un cochon de lait et deux poulets.

5. Chapuisat, *Carnot fugitif.* — Barbey, *F. Desportes*, p. 166. — P. Grellet, *Avec Bonaparte de Genève à Bâle*, p. 40. Lettre de Bonaparte à Barras, 26 novembre 1797 (*La Sabretache*, p. 74 et Arch. familiales). Rapport de Bornes (*Dropmore Papers*, t. IV, p. 146). Des Gouttes fut récompensé, après brumaire, par le poste de préfet des Vosges (Chapuisat, *Carnot à Genève*, *Rev. fr.*, 1908, p. 334). Sur Bonstetten, la thèse de Mlle L. Herking et la correspondance de Bonstetten et Carnot (Arch. familiales).

6. H. C., t. III, p. 191. Lettre de J. Crawford à Grenville, mai 1798 (*Dropmore Papers*, t. IV, p. 184).

7. Lettre de Pichegru, 30 novembre 1798 (Welvert, *Les Régicides après la Révolution*, p. 33). Lettre de Bornes, mars 1798 (*Dropmore Papers*, t. IV, p. 144).

8. *Réponse de L.-N.-M. Carnot, citoyen français, l'un des fondateurs de la République, et membre constitutionnel du Directoire exécutif, au rapport fait sur la conjuration du 18 fruc-*

tidor au Conseil des Cinq-Cents par J.-Ch. Bailleul, au nom des commissions spéciales. Londres, 8 floréal an VI de la République.

La Bibliothèque nationale compte cinq éditions de cet ouvrage. Il fut traduit dans la plupart des langues européennes.

Les dossiers de la police contiennent un rapport sur la perquisition effectuée chez l'imprimeur Giguet et sur l'inanité des efforts faits pour arrêter la vente du livre (Arch. nat., F⁷ 6186).

L'Histoire du Directoire constitutionnel n'était pas signée par Feulint. Celui-ci faisait allusion à la démarche de Bonaparte faisant arrêter un Suisse soupçonné d'avoir facilité l'évasion de Carnot : « Le fait n'est nullement croyable... et prouverait seul, au besoin, que cet ouvrage [la réponse de Carnot à Bailleul] n'est pas de Carnot » (p. 231). Cet artifice est un peu grossier. Était-il plus habile d'écrire que « les deux hommes qui, en France, sont les plus forts de l'opinion et de la confiance publique, restent seuls à peu près les maîtres d'asseoir les fondements de la liberté ? (p. 280).

9. J. Carnot, *Précis historique* (Arch. familiales). — Lomet, *Notes manuscrites* (Coll. L. C.).

10. *Moniteur*, t. XXIX, p. 63, et *L'Ami des Lois*, 24 brumaire an VI. Ce fait fut rappelé par Körte, *ouvr. cité*, p. 136. Lettres de Feulint (*La Sabretache*, p. 79 et 80). Lettre de Carnot à Joseph, lettre de Fouché sur la suppression de la surveillance policière, lettre des amis (Arch. familiales). Restitution des objets séquestrés (Arch. nat., AF III 463).

CHAPITRE IX

MINISTRE DE BONAPARTE

1. Körte, *ouvr. cité*, p. 170. Nomination des inspecteurs

généraux aux revues (Arch. nat., AF IV 925). Les brevets de nomination et lettre de service sont adressés « au citoyen» et non au général Carnot (Arch. familiales). Arrêté sur les inspecteurs généraux (9 pluviôse an VIII, 29 janvier 1800. *Journal militaire*, an VIII, p. 162).

2. *Gazette de France*, 20 janvier 1800 (cité par Aulard, *Paris sous le Consulat*, t. I, note du 4 février 1800). Lettre de Moncey, 29 janvier (Arch. familiales). *Épître à Carnot*, Amiens, frimaire an VIII.

3. Nomination d'un premier inspecteur du Génie, réorganisation de l'armée (Arch. nat., AF IV 862 et 925).

4. Rousselin de Saint-Albin, *Notes manuscrites* (Coll. L. C.).

5. Nomination de Feulint et de Collignon (Arch. nat., AF IV 925), nomination de Carnot (Arch. adm. Guerre, dossier Carnot). Proposition pour les préfectures (Arch. nat., AF IV 8, pl. 33). — Dejean, *Beugnot*, p. 64.

6. H. C., t. II, p. 208 ; cette version se trouve dans Rioust, *ouvr. cité*, p. 119. Lacuée a laissé une autre version d'après laquelle le ministère lui aurait été proposé et n'aurait été attribué à Carnot qu'après le refus et sur l'indication de Lacuée (J. Humbert, *Lacuée*, p. 125).

7. Berthier paraît n'avoir ni donné pleine satisfaction à Bonaparte au ministère de la Guerre, ni considéré que c'était là pour lui une fonction durable (Bourrienne, *Mémoires*, t. II, p. 281). Critiques de Bonaparte à Berthier, 4 et 18 nivôse, 25 pluviôse (Arch. nat., AF IV 861) ; Berthier, circulaire lors de sa nomination (*Journal militaire*, an VIII, p. 58). Maret écrivait à Carnot que les ordres de Berthier n'étaient pas exécutés (Arch. familiales).

8. Lettres de félicitations adressées à Carnot (Arch. hits. Guerre, B^{13} 122) ; *Journal des Hommes libres*, 14 germinal an VIII.

9. Lettre au ministre de la Marine et des Colonies, 29 novembre 1799 (Arch. nat., AF IV 861).

10. Organisation du ministère (Arch. hist. Guerre : correspondance du ministère B^{12} 39 à 41, B^{13} 122 à 125). Carton sur les ingénieurs géographes. Notes de Carnot (Arch. familiales) ; notes du général Dupont (Arch. Presles) ; notes de Lomet et de Rousselin de Saint-Albin (Coll. L. C.), *Journal militaire*, an VIII, n° 29, p. 653. — Carnot, *Compte rendu sur son Ministère* (Arch. familiales). Carnot remania à plusieurs reprises l'organisation des bureaux.

11. Le travail de Carnot avec les Consuls, surtout avec Bonaparte, peut être suivi dans le détail grâce aux notes des procès-verbaux (Arch. nat., AF IV 911) et aux feuilles de travail (Arch. familiales). Le 6 mai il fut décidé par Cambacérès et Lebrun que le ministre de la Guerre serait reçu régulièrement les *primidi* et *septidi* de chaque décade, donc six fois par mois — les 1er, 7, 11, 17, 21 et 27 — mais en fait il intervient beaucoup plus souvent.

12. Les Conseils d'administration de la Guerre ont été si peu étudiés que M. Ch. Durand a cru pouvoir en placer la création en l'an X (Ch. Durand, *Études sur le Conseil d'État napoléonien*, p. 243). Pourtant les séances ont laissé des traces à la fois dans les minutes de procès-verbaux et dans les registres (Arch. nat., AF IV 1272 et AF^x IV 180). Les rapports de Carnot viennent s'ajouter à l'appui (Arch. nat., AF IV 1322, 1372 ; Arch. hist. Guerre, B^{13} 128 ; Arch. familiales).

13. Sur la section de la Guerre du Conseil d'État, Ch. Du-

RAND, *ouvr. cité*, p. 242 ; *Journal militaire*, arrêté au 5 prairial an VIII (Arch. nat., AF IV 115 et 925).

14. Oester. Nat. Bibl., Mss autographes XXXI - 1115, 27 août 1800. Pièce communiquée par M. Verpeaux que nous remercions ici.

15. Petiet à Eyssautier, 11 août 1800 (British Museum, manuscrits 15 952, F° 8). Feuille de travail du 11 prairial (Arch. familiales sur l'affaire Thuring, Arch. hist. Guerre, B^{x12} 38). Corr. sur l'armée de l'Ouest (Arch. hist. Guerre, B^{x12} 40). Lettres de Carnot à Masséna et à Moreau, 11 août et 3 juin 1800, publiées par TISSOT, *ouvr. cité*, p. 269. Notes de Lomet (Coll. L. C.) — LEGRAND, *La Révolution française en Hollande*, passim. — MIOT DE MÉLITO, *Mémoires*, t. I, p. 235 et suivantes.

16. *Le Courrier*, 23 octobre 1815, notes du ministère de la Guerre, 26 avril et 29 mai (Arch. hist. Guerre, B^{13} 122 et 124), et 2 juin (Arch. Presles).

17. *Travail des Conseils* (Arch. nat., AF IV 911). *Corr.* Carnot, Pille, Moreau (Arch. hist. Guerre, B^2 87, 88, 89 et 95). Dossiers de chacun des généraux incriminés (Arch. adm. Guerre).

18. Corr. de Bernadotte, de Carnot et des Consuls (Arch. hist. Guerre, B^{x12} 40, B^5 66, 67 et Arch. nat., AF IV 1590). La lettre de Carnot à Bernadotte, du 17 août, a été publiée dans *La Sabretache*. Les télégrammes étaient transmis par le procédé Chappe. Carnot subissait de Bernadotte les avanies qu'il avait lui-même infligées à Pache. L'attitude réservée de Bonaparte apparaît dans les feuilles de travail (Arch. familiales).

19. Bonaparte à Joseph, avant Marengo (MIOT DE MÉLITO, *Mémoires*, t. I, p. 276).

20. Rapports à Bonaparte, 28 juillet et 14 août (Arch. hist. Guerre, B^{13} 126 et 127 ;

Arch. nat., AF IV 1322). Lettre au directeur du Trésor (B. M. ms. 15.752, f° 8, et Arch. Presles). *Mémorial de Sainte-Hélène*, t. IV, p. 173). Carnot exposait qu'il avait 18 millions de dépenses mensuelles pour 5 millions de paiements (Arch. familiales).

21. Rapports au ministre, notamment du 23 septembre 1800 (Arch. hist. Guerre, B^{x12} 40) ; lettres de Dejean, 19 juillet ; de l'inspecteur aux revues Boinod, 31 juillet ; lettres de Pascal Vallongue, mai-juin 1808 (Arch. hist. Guerre, B^3 70 et 71).

22. Corr. du ministre (Arch. hist. Guerre, B^{13} 126 et 127, B^{x12} 40). Travail des Consuls, notamment 21 mai 1800 (Arch. nat., AF IV 911). Feuilles de travail, notamment le 27 mai (Arch. familiales).

23. Corr. des commandants de divisions militaires (Arch. nat., AF IV 1090). Corr. du ministre (Arch. hist. Guerre, B^{13} 124, 125 et B^{x12} 38).

24. THIBAUDEAU, *Mémoires*, p. 80. — MIOT DE MÉLITO, *Mémoires*, t. I, p. 358. Corr. sur le Midi (Arch. hist. Guerre, B^{13} 124 à 129, B^{x12} 38, et Arch. Presles). Corr. sur le Sud-Ouest, B^{13} 122 à 124.

25. Corr. du ministre (Arch. hist. Guerre, B^{13} 125 et 128). Circulaire du 3 messidor (Arch. nat. AF IV 1121). Feuilles de travail des 26 avril et 27 mai. Rapport de Carnot sur son ministère (Arch. familiales).

26. CUGNAC, *La Campagne de Marengo*, p. 18 et suivantes ; *Marengo*, t. I, p. 177 et suivantes. Corr. de Bonaparte, Augereau, Carnot et Moreau (Arch. hist. Guerre, B^2 85 à 89, B^1 94 à 97, B^{r2} 204 ; Arch. nat., AF IV 1372, 1590). Rapports de police (AULARD, *Paris sous le Consulat*, t. I, p. 310 et 312). Lettre de Carnot à son frère à Chalon - sur - Saône, 15 mai 1800 (Arch. familiales).

27. Arch. familiales.

CHAPITRE X

JE VOTERAI
CONTRE L'EMPIRE

1. Bonaparte à Carnot, 17 juin (Arch. nat., AF IV 861) ; Carnot à Bonaparte, 21 juin (copie aux Arch. familiales) ; Carnot à Dupont (TITEUX, *Dupont*, t. I, p. 87).
2. MIOT DE MÉLITO, *Mémoires*, t. I, p. 268. — Stan. DE GIRARDIN, *Mémoires*, t. I, p. 175. — RŒDERER, *Journal*, p. 13 ; *Œuvres*, t. III, p. 333. Lettre de Lucien à Joseph, 24 juin (BOURRIENNE, *Mémoires*, t. II, p. 338). — Th. JUNG, *Lucien Bonaparte*, t. I, p. 411. — FOUCHÉ, *Mémoires*, p. 184. — THIBAUDEAU, *Mémoires*, p. 29 ; *Dropmore Papers*, t. VI, p. 291.
3. TITEUX, *ouvr. cité*, t. I, p. 110 ; lettre de Maret à Carnot, 26 juin (Arch. minist. Guerre, B³ 70).
4. *Dropmore Papers*, t. VI, p. 180.
5. Lettre de Mersan, 21 octobre 1815, publiée dans *Le Courrier* du 23 octobre. Corr. de Carnot (Arch. hist. Guerre, B^{x12} 41), lettres de Carnot pour le capitaine Beffroy, 6 mars 1800 (Arch. familiales), et pour BEFFROY DE REIGNY (*Revue historique de la Révolution française*, n° 31, p. 169). Lettre de Beffroy à Collignon, 6 octobre (Arch. Presles).
6. Corr. Dugua - Bourrienne (Arch. hist. Guerre B¹³ 129) ; lettres de Bouchotte, 11 juillet 1800 (B. N. Nlles acq. p. 22734, n° 199) ; de Saint-Cyr-Nugues, 2 mai (dossier personnel, Arch. hist. Guerre). Carnot intervint en faveur de Bouchotte, mais Bonaparte « refusa de le considérer comme étant d'un grade supérieur à celui qu'il avait réellement », bien qu'il eût été ministre. (Feuille de travail du 21 messidor, Arch. familiales.)
7. Textes des démissions et des réponses, lettre de Carnot à ce sujet et lettre de Mathieu Dumas (Arch. familiales).

FOUCHÉ, *Mémoires*, p. 197. L'arrêté de nomination de Berthier indiquait : « en remplacement du citoyen Carnot démissionnaire » (Arch. nat., ADI 77).

8. Corr. sur le compte rendu (Arch. Presles). Lettres aux Arch. familiales, partiellement publiées par *La Sabretache*, notamment celle de Clarke, du 9 février 1801. Une note des Arch. familiales signale que des abus de confiance avaient été commis par un employé du ministère de la Guerre, du nom de Carnot, et qui avait été chassé. La demande présentée par Lacuée figure notamment aux Arch. hist. Guerre, B¹³ 129. Carnot était auparavant considéré comme général, c'est le titre que lui donnait volontiers Moreau (lettres des 14 juin, 12 et 16 juillet 1800. B² 87 et 88).

Lomet a écrit que la proposition de promotion fut l'œuvre de Berthier, Lomet détestait Lacuée. Cette version a été adoptée par H. C., t. 11, p. 231. *Le Précis historique* de Joseph Carnot affirme que Lacuée « insinua au Premier Consul des soupçons affreux sur notre compte à tous ».

9. Prieur à Carnot, 7 novembre 1800, et Carnot à Prieur, 14 novembre. Nous devons la connaissance de ces inédits à Mlle Arbelet, qui a eu l'amabilité de nous les communiquer à la demande de M. G. Bouchard. Nous les prions de trouver ici tous nos remerciements.
10. Lettre de Carnot à son frère de Nolay, 6 avril 1801. *Précis historique* (Arch. familiales).
11. DELISLE DE SALES, *Mémoires* (Recueil des mémoires adressé à l'Institut sur la destitution de Carnot, Paris, an VIII). La correspondance de Delisle était quelque peu emphatique lorsqu'il s'adressait à son « magnanime collègue », pour le comparer à Frédéric II, et lui-même à Voltaire, pour

affirmer que le titre de membre de l'Institut est un « véritable sacerdoce », et pour demander des secours (Arch. familiales).

12. Lettre de Carnot à Bonaparte qui l'invitait à la Malmaison, 27 mai 1801 (*La Sabretache*), lettre à son frère de Nolay, 2 février 1802 (Arch. familiales) ; lettre du 30 décembre 1801 au sénateur Lefèvre (Coll. L. C.) ; lettre du 23 mars 1802 (Arch. familiales).

13. ROUSSELIN DE SAINT-ALBIN, *Notes* (Coll. L. G.) et H. C., t. II, p. 239. Lettre de Siméon à Carnot, 21 floréal (Arch. familiales).

14. Lettre de Carnot à son frère de Nolay, 12 mai 1804 (*La Sabretache*). Malheureusement les Archives familiales ne contiennent pas les lettres de félicitations. La minute de celle de Buissard se trouve aux archives du Pas-de-Calais (Coll. Barbier) avec la lettre de Carnot annonçant l'envoi d'une demi-douzaine d'exemplaires de son discours.

15. Lettre du préfet de la Manche (Arch. nat., F⁷ 6431).

16. Rapport du premier inspecteur général de l'Artillerie au ministre de la Guerre, 17 mai 1802 (Arch. hist. Guerre, X^d 336. Cette pièce m'a été indiquée par M. le commandant Chalmin, du service historique de l'armée, à qui j'adresse ici mes remerciements). Il y avait environ 135 élèves à l'École.

17. Lettre de Carnot au Grand Chancelier de la Légion d'honneur, 18 juillet 1804 (Arch. familiales).

18. Interrogatoire de Berthois (6 juin 1804) (Arch. Murat. — dossier 97 — consultées grâce à une autorisation spéciale, pour laquelle j'adresse ici mes remerciements.)

19. Les procès-verbaux des séances de cette section du Tribunat sont des plus laconiques, et il n'y a guère d'autres sources (Arch. nat., C 634).

Les biographes sont muets sur cette période.

CHAPITRE XI
RÉCONCILIATION AVEC NAPOLÉON

1. Carnot à Buvelot-Tardent à Vevey, dont la maison lui avait servi d'asile (Bibliothèque publique et université de Genève). Lettre de Brougham à Carnot, 25 déc. 1813 (Arch. familiales). W. DORON, *Erlebtes aus den Jahren, 1790-1827*, t. III, p. 91.

2. Archives de l'Académie des Sciences. Inventaires dressés en 1813 (Arch. familiales).

3. Notes de Carnot sur un agenda correspondant aux années 1810, 1811, 1812. Notes diverses (Arch. familiales).

4. Lettre de Carnot à Tiffet, 7 novembre 1809 (Arch. familiales). Lettre de Clarke à Napoléon, 2 juillet 1809 (Arch. familiales). Carnot était en relation avec nombre d'officiers qui avaient servi aux Antilles, ou qui y avaient des intérêts. Il ne pouvait s'agir que du commerce des plantations, canne à sucre. On remarqua en effet que Carnot n'était pas partisan d'une suppression brusque du servage, qui eût ruiné les colonies (lettre du 28 janvier 1810, fichier Charavay).

5. Actes de décès (Arch. familiales). Relevé du partage de la succession (Arch. du Pas-de-Calais, enregistrement du bureau de Saint-Omer, table des partages).

6. Papiers autobiographiques de J. Carnot (Arch. familiales). Clarke, lettre à Napoléon, 2 juillet 1809 (publié dans *La Sabretache* en 1895).

7. Duchesse d'ABRANTÈS, t. XVIII, p. 63, MÉNEVAL, t. I, p. 403 et 406. Ransonnet, qui connaissait bien Carnot, fit allusion à ces dires dans une lettre à H. C. (Arch. familiales). Carnot affirma l'initiative spontanée de Napoléon,

notamment dans ses lettres à son frère de Nolay et à Prieur, c'est-à-dire à des intimes (Arch. familiales et Arch. de Mlle Arbelet).

8. Lettre de Napoléon, 17 juin 1809, Arch. nat., AF IV 880. *Corr.* de Napoléon, t. XIX, n° 15363).

9. Lettre de Clarke à Napoléon, 2 juillet 1809 (F. Masson, *La Sabretache*, 1895).

10. Arch. adm. Guerre, dossier Lajard. Lettres de Clarke et Mollien informant Carnot de sa retraite. Note de Carnot à propos de sa candidature au Sénat (Arch. familiales).

11. Lettre de Napoléon à Clarke, 31 octobre 1809 (*Corr.* de Napoléon, t. XIX, n° 15889). Sur l'audience accordée par Napoléon, il existe une source jusqu'alors inutilisée, c'est une note du conseiller Carnot (Arch. familiales, copie de Rousselin, Coll. L. C.). Voir, en sens divers, Tissot, Rioust et Körte. Lettre de Canclaux, 20 novembre (Arch. familiales).

12. Lettre de Carnot au ministre de la Guerre, 10 avril 1810 (Arch. familiales), lettre de Carnot à Napoléon, 27 février 1810 (fichier Charavay).

13. Lettre de Carnot au ministre de la Guerre, 10 avril 1810.

14. Voir t. I, p. 114. Carnot, pendant son ministère de la Guerre, avait demandé une pension pour la veuve du général de Montalembert, mais ce fut en vain. Comité des Fortifications, administration générale, p. 134 (Arch. insp. Génie). Lettres de Carnot à Favart, 3 septembre 1812, à Guyot-Duclos, 24 mai 1813. DOUGLAS, *Observation sur le But et les Erreurs des Principes de M. Carnot* (traduit de l'anglais manuscrit, Arch. insp. Génie). *Remarques sur l'Ouvrage de Carnot* (traduit de l'allemand, Arch. insp. Génie). *Rapport sur une Expérience des Bastions de Carnot, en présence de Wellington* (*Le Spec-*

tateur militaire, 1832, p. 200). AUGOYAT, *Mémoire sur l'effet des feux verticaux proposés par M. Carnot*, 1821.

15. CARNOT, *De la Défense des Places fortes*, p. 500 et suivantes.

16. Les auteurs des félicitations sont cités dans l'ordre chronologique de leurs lettres, du 11 mars 1810 au 29 janvier 1813.

17. Arch. nat., AF IV 1168. Nous remercions ici M. de Chasseloup-Laubat pour les instructions qu'il nous a aimablement fournies.

18. Lettre de Carnot à Napoléon, 21 juin 1810 (Arch. familiales).

19. Sur l'élection, voir la communication de J. Bourdon à la Société d'histoire moderne, 5 déc. 1937. La lettre est de janvier 1811 (Arch. familiales).

CHAPITRE XII

DE L'EMPEREUR AU ROI

1. Lettres de Carnot à Tiffet (Arch. familiales) et à Napoléon (H. C., t. II, p. 290).

2. Sur la publication de la lettre de Carnot à Napoléon, lettre de Francœur (Arch. familiales). Lettre de Carnot à Clarke, 27 janvier (*La Sabretache*). Lettre de Napoléon sur Anvers, 25 décembre 1813 (*Corr.* de Napoléon, t. XXVI, p. 530). Lettre du général Roguet, 8 décembre 1813 (Arch. hist. Guerre, C^{x2} 320). WAUVERMANS, *Napoléon et Carnot*, p. 149, et LANZAC DE LABORIE, *La Domination française en Belgique*, p. 306.

3. Arch. hist. Guerre, C^{x2} 322.

4. Rapport du colonel Sabatier (Arch. insp. Génie, dossier Anvers).

5. On trouve aux Arch. hist. Guerre nombre de documents non utilisés jusqu'alors. Notamment la correspondance du ministre de la Guerre avec le

gouverneur (C¹⁴ 2, 3 et 4) et les registres du siège (Cˣ² 320 et 322). Les Arch. de la Marine fournissent la correspondance du ministre de la Marine (BB³ 405, BB⁴ 376). Les Arch. de l'inspection du Génie fournissent en outre les rapports des officiers de cette arme, un extrait du Journal de l'état-major de l'escadre, le rapport du commissaire des guerres et un important mémoire du commandant de la place (dossier Défense d'Anvers). Enfin les Arch. familiales renferment les actes du gouverneur, des rapports sur le blocus, les procès-verbaux du Conseil de défense, la correspondance de Carnot et les journaux belges.

6. *Journal de l'Empire*, 13 et 19 février 1814.

7. Rapport de Paulmier fils (Arch. familiales).

8. Lettre au ministre de la Guerre (Arch. hist. Guerre, Cˣ² 322).

9. Si l'Empereur n'avait pas disséminé ses troupes dans cent places, la France aurait une armée, disait le général Decaen (mémoire de Fauconnet). L'ordre de réunir les garnisons de Flandre, du Brabant et d'Anvers pour « tenir campagne sur les derrières de l'ennemi » était du 2 mars ; il ne parvint à Carnot que le 26 mars (Arch. hist. Guerre, Cˣ² 320, 321 et 322).

10. Arch. hist. Guerre, Cˣ² 321 ; Arch. insp. Génie ; Rapport Hulot ; CARNOT, *Précis de ce qui s'est passé dans la garnison d'Anvers à l'occasion du rappel des Bourbons* (Arch. familiales).

11. Les principales lettres ont été publiées (H. C., t. II, p. 327 ; LE POITTEVIN, WAUVERMANS, *ouvr. cité*, p. 230 et suivantes).

12. La lettre personnelle de Dupont et la sanction prise contre le colonel Mahony se trouvent dans les Arch. familiales.

13. La lettre du 15 avril, jusqu'alors inédite, figure dans le registre des Arch. familiales.

14. Lettres du préfet (Arch. nat., Fⁱᶜ III Deux Nèthes 5), sur le commissaire de police, Bellemare, lettre de Ransonnet, aide de camp de Carnot (Arch. familiales). *Journal des Deux-Nèthes*, 13 et 17 avril.

15. Autographe des divers membres du Conseil (Arch. familiales).

16. Lettres de Carnot à Dupont, 17 et 19 avril (registre des Arch. familiales).

17. Lettre de Dupont à Carnot, 15 avril (Arch. familiales).

18. Lettre de Lespinasse à Carnot, 28 avril, *Le Courrier de Belgique*, 29 avril (Arch. familiales).

CHAPITRE XIII

CARNOT ET LOUIS XVIII

1. Corr. de Carnot (Arch. familiales).

2. Lettres de Prieur, 10 et 16 mai, de Des Gouttes, de Lespinasse et de la veuve Filley, 14, 11 et 25 mai, de Carnot au baron Louis et à Dupont, mai, juin (Arch. familiales).

3. Toute cette corr. figure aux Arch. familiales.

4. Lettre de Dupont à Carnot (Arch. familiales). La décoration du Lis avait été créée par ordonnance du 5 août 1814.

5. Lettre de Gouget-Deslandres (Arch. familiales). Ce personnage était considéré comme modéré, au temps du Comité du Salut public.

6. Notes du conseiller Carnot (Arch. familiales), de Rousselin de Saint-Albin (Coll. L. C.), lettre de Feulint au roi, 22 novembre (Arch. familiales).

7. Bulletins de police, juillet-octobre (Arch. nat. F⁷ 3783 et 3784). Notes de Beugnot adressées au roi à la même époque (Arch. nat. AB XIX 343, 344, 345). *Le Censeur*, nº 11, p. 507 à 520.

8. Lettres du procureur et du chancelier, 23 et 24 octobre (Arch. nat. BB³ 149). Mérilhon, qui avait établi le rapport en faveur de Carnot, eut un poste pendant les Cent-Jours et fut épuré à la seconde Restauration (Notice par Dupin).

9. « *Des Caractères d'une juste Liberté et d'un Pouvoir légitime*, par M... *L. G. M. D. L. A., Paris, chez tous les marchands de nouveautés. De l'imprimerie de C.-F. Patris, rue de la Colombe, n° 1, en la Cité; 35 pages* (Arch. familiales). C'est une épreuve corrigée par Carnot. Patris était spécialiste des publications clandestines.

10. *Mémoire adressé au Roi, en juillet 1814, par M. Carnot, lieutenant général, chevalier de l'ordre royal et militaire de Saint-Louis, membre de la Légion d'honneur, de l'Institut royal de France*, etc. Cahier de 47 pages, entièrement autographe, comportant des ratures peu nombreuses (Arch. familiales).

11. L'édition la plus correcte est celle dite de Bruxelles et comptant 47 pages (B. N. 8° LL⁴⁵ 301). Les autres éditions de 1814 en diffèrent assez peu (L L⁴⁵ 301 A et B), l'une se prétend aussi de Bruxelles, l'autre est parisienne, au nom de Plancher, qui ne figure pas parmi les libraires arrêtés par Beugnot.

12. Notes de Bazin dans *Le Lynx* jointes aux éditions de 1815.

13. Notes de l'édition de 1815. Longue lettre adressée à Carnot par un ancien négociant, grand propriétaire autrefois à Saint-Domingue (Arch. familiales).

14. *Journal des Débats*, 9 octobre 1814. *Gazette de France*, 18 octobre 1814. Lettre du comte de La Châtre, 13 novembre 1814 (Arch. nat., F⁷ 6679).

15. Manuscrit autographe des Arch. familiales.

16. Lettres et articles de Brougham (Arch. familiales).

17. B. CHENOT, *La Pensée politique de Chateaubriand* (*Mercure de France*, 1950). — M. REINHARD, *Chateaubriand et la Question constitutionnelle* (*Revue historique*, 1949).

CHAPITRE XIV

MINISTRE DES CENT-JOURS

1. Lettres de Carnot au ministre de la Guerre, 24 février 1815 (Arch. familiales) ; de Benoist à Barante, 14 mars (BARANTE, *Souvenirs*, t. II, p. 108) ; H. C., t. II, p. 402.

2. LE GALLO, *Les Cent-Jours*, p. 118. Minutes des nominations, 20 mars (Arch. nat., AF IV 859⁶).

3. LE GALLO, *ouvr. cité*, p. 193. Lettres de Le Coz, de Dumolard et de Baudin (Arch. familiales) ; de Champigny-Aubin, de François, de Vérité (Arch. nat. Fⁱᶜ 556, 1 et 2). Lettre d'un libéral anonyme (Arch. nat., Fⁱᶜ I 26). Notes de Rousselin de Saint-Albin (Coll. L. C.). Un peu plus tard, Bouchotte sollicita Carnot de lui obtenir une pension d'ancien ministre (Arch. familiales).

4. Lettre de Ransonnet (Arch. familiales) et note de Rousselin (Coll. L. C.). Le titre de *comte* a été rajouté sur le décret de nomination, et le motif *pour la défense d'Anvers* l'a été sur le brevet (Arch. nat., AF IV 859⁶).

5. Nomination de 39 préfets, 22 mars, s'ajoutant à quatre nominations antérieures (Arch. nat., AF IV 859⁶). Notes de Rousselin (Coll. L. C.). Minutes de nomination des ministres (Arch. nat., IV 589, 6 et 11).

6. Décret du 23 mars (Arch. nat., AF IV 859⁶). Le texte de la proposition infirme les dires de Welvert, d'après lequel ce secrétaire eût été imposé à C a r n o t comme surveillant (WELVERT, CARNOT, *Revue his-*

torique 1905). Décret nommant Delaville Le Roulx (Arch. nat., AF IV 859⁶). Lettre de démission du même, 15 juin (Arch. familiales). Sur Rousselin de Saint - Albin, lettre de Lacépède (Arch. nat., AF IV 1935). Lettre de Madame Jullien de la Drôme (Arch. nat., AB XIX 1750). Lettre de Rousselin à Carnot, après Waterloo (Arch. familiales). Carnot avait pris Rousselin sur la recommandation de Fouché (Arch. familiales).

7. Notes de Rousselin (Arch. familiales et Coll. L. C.).

8. Rapport et lettres sur les commissaires extraordinaires (Arch. nat., F^{ia} 553 et 555).

9. Circulaires des 20 et 27 mars (Recueil des circulaires, Arch. familiales). Lettre de Napoléon, 27 mars (Arch. nat., AF IV 907).

10. Fouché à Carnot, 30 mars et 15 avril, réponse de Carnot, corr. sur les maires (Arch. nat., F^{ici} 26).

11. Note de Carnot, 20 avril (Arch. nat., AF IV 859¹⁰). Vaublanc à Carnot, 24 et 26 mars, Carnot à Vaublanc, 28 mars (Arch. familiales), textes publiés dans *La Sabretache* et utilisés par Welvert, *ouvr. cité*, et par Cl. Bader, *Carnot et le comte de Vaublanc*. Welvert en a tiré des conclusions prouvant sa méconnaissance des autres écrits de Carnot.

12. R. Lindet à Carnot (Coll. Séhet), lettre de Cavaignac à Carnot (Arch. familiales) et nomination de Cavaignac, de Richaud et de Lapparent (Arch. nat., AF 859, 23, 18 et 17).

13. Tableau des préfets au 6 avril (Arch. nat. AF IV 859⁸). Lettre de Napoléon à Carnot, 3 avril (AF IV 907, non publiée dans la *Corr.* de Napoléon). Thiry, *Les Cent-Jours*, p. 137.

14. Minute du décret du 4 avril (Arch. nat., F^{ia} 553, texte autographe dans les Arch. familiales) ; minutes des envois successifs (Arch. nat., F^{ia} 553

et 907, corr. F^{ia} 553 à 556), circulaire aux préfets, 22 avril (Arch. familiales).

15. Lettre de Carnot à Napoléon (Arch. nat., AF IV 859²³).

16. Goudeville de Mont - Riche, *Épître à Carnot, à l'occasion de la mort de Mlle Raucourt*. Corr. de Carnot sur les questions religieuses, notamment mémoire de Daunou, du 1er avril (Arch. familiales). Compte rendu de Carnot sur l'esprit public du clergé, 25 avril, rapport du 26 mai (Arch. nat., AF IV 1935), rapport sur le Champ de Mai (Arch. nat., F¹⁹ 311). Corr. des commissaires (Arch. nat. F^{ia} 553 à 556).

17. Lettre de Dalphonse et de Pontécoulant sur le Gard, 28 avril et 17 mai (Arch. nat. F^{ia} 555).

18. Corr. sur la *Feuille villageoise* (Arch. familiales). F. Dreyfus, *La Rochefoucauld-Liancourt*, p. 435. — M. Reinhard, *Le Département de la Sarthe sous le Régime du Directoire*, p. 301.

19. Corr. des commissaires, dossier et corr. du Conseil d'Industrie nationale (Arch. familiales). Le Gallo a signalé l'attitude frondeuse de Laffitte, de la Bourse, de la Banque de France, du commerce maritime (*ouvr. cité*, p. 216).

20. Rapport de Costaz à Carnot, 21 avril 1815 (Arch. nat., F^{ia} 556¹). Pesche, lettre à Carnot, 31 mars (Arch. nat., F^{ici} 26). Docteur Delaunay, *Pesche*. Guéroult, propriétaire des mines de Fontaine-Guérard, à Carnot, 12 mai 1815 (Arch. familiales). Voir aussi Le Gallo, *ouvr. cité*, p. 219, et, en sens contraire, Radiguet (*La Rév. fr.*, 1914, p. 36).

21. Notes de Carnot (Arch. familiales). Le nom de Carnot avait été publié dans une note sur la commission de constitution (*Journal de l'Empire*, 30 mars 1815).

22. Corr. sur l'Acte additionnel

(Arch. familiales). Note remise par Carnot, avril 1815 (*Bodleian Library*, Curzon 38). Les projets comportent quelques variantes, notamment le choix de la moitié des sénateurs sur des listes de présentation, l'initiative des lois confiée exclusivement à l'Empereur.

23. Notes sur l'épuration et lettre de Delécluze (Arch. familiales) ; lettre des Amis de la Liberté (Arch. nat., F^{ici} 26).

24. Notes de Carnot et notes particulières pour le ministre (Arch. familiales) ; projet d'associations patriotiques (Arch. nat. F^{ici} 26).

25. Le plus joli fut l'attitude de Decazes lorsque des royalistes voulurent publier une pièce si défavorable aux bonapartistes. Il s'y opposa parce que les royalistes avaient utilisé le même système (Arch. nat., F^{ia} 554).

26. Lettre de François-Victor Véron, Rouen, 15 mai (Arch. familiales).

27. Reprise des travaux publiés à Paris, 21-29 mars (Arch. nat., AF IV 859^6) ; programme de la *Feuille villageoise*, n° 1 ; programme des travaux du Conseil d'industrie nationale ; corr. sur les écoles mutuelles (Arch. familiales). Rapport de Carnot à Napoléon (AF IV 859^{13}). *Journal d'Éducation populaire*, novembre 1857. — PETIET, *Souvenirs militaires*, p. 182. — FLEURY DE CHABOULON, *ouvr. cité*, t. I, p. 3. — René GIRARD, Carnot et l'éducation populaire pendant les Cent-Jours (*La Révolution française*, t. LII, p. 424).

28. Notes de Carnot, écrites dans la suite (Arch. familiales).

29. Résultats des levées (Arch. nat., AF IV 1935 ; Arch. Guerre, X^m 30).

30. Lettres reçues par Carnot, notamment en juin (Arch. familiales).

31. Projets pour l'*Exposé de la Situation de l'Empire* (Arch. familiales).

32. VILLEMAIN, *Souvenirs*, t. II, p. 286. — FLEURY DE CHABOULON, *ouvr. cité*, t. II. Lettre de Fouché à Carnot (Arch. familiales).

33. BERTRAND, *Cahiers de Sainte-Hélène*, 14 juillet et 28 octobre 1817.

CHAPITRE XV

LE SUPRÊME EXIL

1. Dossiers sur les Cent-Jours (Arch. familiales).

2. Recueil des circulaires du ministre de l'Intérieur (Arch. familiales). Il serait intéressant de savoir quels préfets ont reçu ces deux circulaires.

3. MADELIN, *Fouché*, t. II, p. 451. Un exemplaire des procès-verbaux de la commission se trouve aux Arch. familiales.

4. Lettre anonyme du 28 juin (Arch. familiales).

5. CARNOT, *Exposé de la conduite politique de M. le lieutenant général Carnot, depuis le 1er juillet*, p. 29.

6. Dossier sur les Cent-Jours (Arch. familiales). *L'Indépendant*, 1er juillet 1815.

7. Dossier sur les Cent-Jours, minute autographe du rapport de Carnot, notes de Rousselin de Saint-Albin, billet de Coulaincourt appelant Carnot (Arch. familiales).

8. Arch. de la préfecture de Police (A^a 317, n° 171), lettre de Carnot à son fils Hippolyte (Arch. familiales).

9. Lettre de Carnot, le 3 octobre, à Francœur, parlant de la « fureur » des journalistes (Arch. familiales). Lettre du ministre de la Police, 6 octobre ; lettres du préfet, 15 et 16 octobre (Arch. nat., F^{i2} 6678). Lettre de Carnot, 14 octobre, annonçant qu'il part le lendemain (Arch. familiales).

10. Lettres de Pozzo di Borgo et Capo d'Istria au duc de Richelieu (fichier Chavaray). Lettre du baron d'Œlhesy à M. Œslhing, 26 septembre 1815, auto-

risant Carnot, Merlin et Garnier à se rendre à Mecklembourg (Arch. familiales). H. C., t. II, p. 566.

11. Lettre à la princesse Giedroye, 20 août 1816 (fichier Charavay), Dépêche de Saint-Petersbourg, 28 juin (Arch. nat., F⁷ 6679). Lettre de Prieur de la Côte-d'Or à Carnot, 4 mai 1816 : « Si tu avais besoin d'argent, je pourrais sans me gêner te faire passer quelques sommes, et je serais très satisfait de cette préférence. » Lettre inédite des archives d'Aloxe, communiquée aimablement par M.-G. Bouchard.

12. Polémique entre M.-G. D'Anglade (*Revue des Questions historiques*, 1923) et M. le colonel S. Carnot (*Revue d'Histoire diplomatique*, 1924). L'article de M. d'Anglade avait été exploité à des fins politiques par des journaux locaux (*L'Éclair de Montpellier*, 6 août 1923, *La Gazette du Centre*, 11 août 1923). Contestation entre M. A. Mansuy et M. le colonel S. Carnot, à propos d'un article qui parut finalement dans la *Revue des Études napoléoniennes*, en 1934. A ces articles il faut joindre celui de M. Handelsman (*La Révolution française*, 1923).

13. Lettre de Carnot à Thibaudeau, 15 décembre 1816 (Coll. L. C.) et lettres à Francœur (*Cosmopolis*). Ces lettres ont été ignorées par les auteurs des articles ci-dessus mentionnés.

14. Lettre du marquis de Bonnay au comte d'Haussonville, 23 octobre 1826 (Arch. nat., F 6679).

15. Exemple de lettre de style pseudo-commercial : P.-A. Rosan à Jacquet, 4 juillet 1816 (Arch. nat., F⁷ 6679). Interrogatoires de Feulint (Arch. préfecture de Police, Aᵃ 327).

16. Arch. familiales.

17. Lettres à Chateaubriand, notes de police (Arch. nat., F⁷ 6679).

18. Carnot à Thibaudeau, 15 décembre 1816 (Coll. L. C.). Lettre à Francœur, 26 août 1817 (*Cosmopolis*).

19. Lettre à Prieur, 12 février 1819 : « Je ne puis guère apprécier, dans mon ignorance, que le mérite de la mélodie.... Quant à l'harmonie, je vois avec plaisir qu'elle a l'approbation de nos compositeurs allemands » (Arch. d'Aloxe, communiqué par M. Q. Bouchard).

20. Lettre de Carnot à Körte, 25 novembre 1819 (Arch. Presles). Lettre à Carnot, sans doute envoyée par Feulint, 13 novembre 1819 (Arch. familiales). Lettre de Carnot à Körte sur la biographie écrite par Rioust, 8 mars 1819 (Arch. Presles). Dans une lettre à Körte, Carnot spécifie que ses parents ont renseigné l'auteur (Kleinschmidt, *Lettres inédites du général Carnot et de son fils le sénateur, dans Deutsche Revue*, novembre 1891).

21. Lettre de Carnot à Körte, 31 juillet 1820 (Arch. Presles).

22. Ainsi on trouve un extrait d'une lettre de Carnot à Körte (p. 203) et aussi un facsimilé d'une lettre de Carnot (p. 243), une note sur les idées constitutionnelles soumises à Napoléon pendant les Cent-Jours (p. 332) ; ces pièces, ainsi que quelques autres, figuraient dans les papiers personnels de Carnot.

CONCLUSIONS

1. Stendhal a été jusqu'à écrire que Carnot avait fait surgir quatorze armées « comme par enchantement », et que Napoléon lui-même « n'avait rien fait de comparable » (*New Monthly Magazine*, 1ᵉʳ novembre 1824).

2. Napoléon confirma ces vues dans ses entretiens de Sainte-Hélène (général Bertrand, *Cahiers de Sainte-Hélène*, 8 dé-

cembre 1816 et 12 janvier 1817).

3. « Votre manière de voir, fût-elle la meilleure, ne peut être substituée à celle du peuple... autrement... nous sommes sous le régime aristocratique [substituant] la volonté de 700 individus choisis par le peuple à la volonté du peuple même. » (CARNOT, *Opinion sur l'accusation de Billaud-Varenne...*, p. 22, 3 germinal, an III.)

4. « On sait qu'en France le système républicain n'est plus qu'une théorie rejetée » (CARNOT, *Exposé de sa Conduite politique...*, p. 19). « Les républicains, désabusés par une longue expérience, et très liés par gratitude au prince qui les a délivrés [Napoléon], en sont les plus zélés défenseurs » (CARNOT, *Exposé de la Situation de l'Empire*, p. 5).

5. Des agents du gouvernement ont déclaré « que le talent est inséparable de l'aristocratie », avait noté Dubois-Crancé.

« La Révolution détruit toutes les distinctions entre les hommes. Désormais il n'y en aura plus qu'une, celle que la science et l'instruction mettront entre les ignorants et les savants », parole attribuée à son père par E.-J. Delécluze (BASCHET, *Delécluze*, p. 5).

TABLE DES MATIÈRES

LIBRAIRIE HACHETTE
Paris N° 1150
Dépôt légal : 4ᵉ trim. 1952

Imprimé
en France.

Imprimerie CRÉTÉ
Corbeil-Essonnes (S.-et-O.)

N° 2442 — 1-10-1952